SPECTRAL
ANALYSIS
and its
applications

HOLDEN-DAY SERIES IN TIME SERIES ANALYSIS

GWILYM M. JENKINS AND EMANUEL PARZEN, EDITORS

SPECTRAL ANALYSIS
and its
applications

GWILYM M. JENKINS

University of Lancaster, U.K.

and

DONALD G. WATTS

University of Wisconsin, U.S.A.

HOLDEN-DAY

San Francisco, Cambridge, London, Amsterdam

Preface

Time series analysis is now widely used in many branches of engineering, the physical sciences and economics. One important aspect of time series analysis is spectral analysis, which is concerned with the splitting up of time series into different frequency components. Applications of spectral analysis cover a wide range of problems, for example, the effect of wave oscillations on the vibration of ships and the influence of disturbances or noise on the performance of electrical guidance systems and chemical reactors.

This book has been designed primarily for post-graduate engineers, since most of the applications of spectral analysis have, in fact, been made by engineers and physicists. One of the difficulties faced by users or potential users of spectral analysis is that most of the theory has been developed by statisticians during the last fifteen years. Unfortunately, much of this literature is difficult to read. Hence it is felt that a book directed mainly toward engineers is long overdue. However, we hope this book will appeal to a much wider audience, including mathematicians, statisticians, economists, physicists and biologists.

One of the difficulties we have encountered in writing this book is that, whereas spectral analysis involves the use of sophisticated statistical techniques, many engineers lack knowledge of elementary statistics. This is true even of electrical engineers, some of whom possess considerable knowledge of probability theory. For example, the Wiener theory of prediction and control shows that an optimum filter or control system can be designed if various spectra associated with the signal and noise in the system are known. However, little attention is paid in books on control theory to the very important practical question of how to *estimate* these spectra from *finite lengths of record*. It is with such problems that we shall be concerned in this book.

To provide a gradual introduction to time series estimation problems, we have been forced in the earlier chapters to deal with elementary statistical problems. This may distract mathematical and statistical readers, but in view of our experience in expounding these ideas to engineers, we feel that

v

a self-contained introduction, which includes most of the statistical ideas needed later on in the book, is necessary. Those readers who are familiar with the material of Chapters 2, 3 and 4 can, of course, start at Chapter 5.

Chapter 1 is devoted to a brief outline of the territory covered and to a description of the kind of problems which can be solved using spectral analysis. Chapter 2 deals with the important ideas of Fourier analysis and is basic to what follows. Most of this is well known to engineers but is brought together here in a form oriented toward spectral analysis. In Chapter 3 we introduce some basic notions in probability theory which are fundamental to subsequent chapters. Chapter 4 consists of an introduction to many important ideas in statistical inference and includes a discussion of the sampling distribution approach to estimation theory, the theory of least squares and a brief reference to likelihood inference. Not all of this material is necessary for an understanding of the spectral techniques discussed later in the book, and engineering readers may wish to omit the latter part of this chapter at first reading. The most relevant parts of this chapter, as far as spectral analysis is concerned, are the sections on the sampling distribution approach to estimation theory and the theory of least squares. The latter is one of the most important weapons in the statistician's armory, and in our experience it is widely misunderstood among engineers.

Chapter 5 contains some of the simpler ideas in the theory of stochastic processes, for example, stationarity, the autocorrelation function and moving average–autoregressive processes. Methods for estimating auto-correlation functions and parameters in linear processes are described and illustrated by examples. In Chapter 6, the ideas of Fourier analysis and stochastic processes are brought together to provide a description of a stationary stochastic process by means of its spectrum. It is shown how Fourier methods need to be tailored to estimate the spectrum from finite lengths of record. The sampling properties of spectral estimators are then derived, and the important notion of smoothing of these estimators is introduced. Chapter 7 contains many simulated and practical examples of spectral estimation and gives a systematic method, called window closing, for deciding the amount of smoothing required.

In Chapter 8 the ideas of Chapters 5–7 are extended to pairs of time series, leading to the definition of the cross correlation function, the cross spectrum and the squared coherency spectrum. Chapter 9 is devoted to estimating the cross spectrum and the notion of aligning two series. Cross spectral analysis is applied in Chapter 10 to estimating the frequency response function of a linear system. Finally, we consider in Chapter 11 the spectral analysis of a vector of several time series and the estimation of the frequency response matrix of a linear system.

This book has been written at a time when there is much active work in this area and when much experience has still to be gained in the application of spectral methods. Nevertheless, it is felt that enough has been achieved already to warrant an attempt. It is hoped that the book will provide applied scientists and engineers with a comprehensive and useful handbook for the application of spectral analysis to practical time series problems, as well as proving useful as a post-graduate textbook.

We are greatly indebted to Professor K. N. Stanton of the School of Engineering, Purdue University, for making available the power-station data used in later chapters and to Professor H. J. Wertz of the University of Wisconsin for helpful suggestions regarding computer programs. We are very grateful to Mr. A. J. A. MacCormick of the Statistics Department of the University of Wisconsin and also Mr. M. J. McClellan of the U.S. Army Mathematics Research Center, University of Wisconsin, for writing and running some of the computer programs. We also thank Mr. MacCormick, and Mr. A. S. Alavi of the University of Lancaster, for checking through the manuscript.

Lancaster, U.K.   GWILYM M. JENKINS

Madison, Wis., U.S.A.   DONALD G. WATTS

Contents

Chapter 3. PROBABILITY THEORY

Chapter 4. INTRODUCTION TO STATISTICAL INFERENCE

CHAPTER 5.   INTRODUCTION TO TIME SERIES ANALYSIS

CHAPTER 6.   THE SPECTRUM

CHAPTER 7.   EXAMPLES OF UNIVARIATE SPECTRAL ANALYSIS

CHAPTER 8.   THE CROSS CORRELATION FUNCTION
          AND CROSS SPECTRUM

CHAPTER 9.   ESTIMATION OF CROSS SPECTRA

CHAPTER 10.   ESTIMATION OF FREQUENCY RESPONSE FUNCTIONS

CHAPTER 11. MULTIVARIATE SPECTRAL ANALYSIS

Notation

The notation has been chosen as carefully as possible to prevent confusion and yet to maintain explicitly the differences between estimates, estimators and theoretical quantities, as well as between time and frequency domain functions. The reader should have little trouble if he remembers that, with minor exceptions, the following conventions have been adhered to:

SYMBOLS, NOTATION AND CONVENTIONS

Item	Type	Examples
observations, time series	lc Roman	$x_1, x_2; z_t, z(t)$
random variables, stochastic processes	uc Roman	$X_1, X_2; Z_t, Z(t)$
estimates	lc Roman, lc Greek with caret	$\bar{x}, s^2; \hat{\theta}, \hat{\alpha}_1, \hat{\alpha}_2$
estimators	uc Roman, uc Greek with caret	$\bar{X}, S^2; \hat{\Theta}$
parameters	lc Greek	$\theta, \alpha_1, \alpha_2$

COVARIANCES AND CORRELATIONS (showing symbols and subscripts)

	Estimates	Estimators	Theoretical
autocovariances	$c_{xx}(u), c_{22}(k)$	$c_{XX}(u), c_{22}(k)$	$\gamma_{xx}(u), \gamma_{22}(k)$
cross covariances	$c_{xy}(u), c_{12}(k)$	$c_{XY}(u), c_{12}(k)$	$\gamma_{xy}(u), \gamma_{12}(k)$
even part	$l_{xy}(u), l_{12}(k)$	$l_{XY}(u), l_{12}(k)$	$\lambda_{xy}(u), \lambda_{12}(k)$
odd part	$q_{xy}(u), q_{12}(k)$	$q_{XY}(u), q_{12}(k)$	$\psi_{xy}(u), \psi_{12}(k)$
autocorrelations	$r_{xx}(u), r_{22}(k)$	$r_{XX}(u), r_{22}(k)$	$\rho_{xx}(u), \rho_{22}(k)$
cross correlations	$r_{xy}(u), r_{12}(k)$	$r_{XY}(u), r_{12}(k)$	$\rho_{XY}(u), \rho_{12}(k)$

SPECTRA (bar denotes smoothed, asterisk denotes complex conjugate)

	Estimates	*Estimators*	*Theoretical*
autospectra	$\overline{C}_{xx}(f), \overline{C}_{11}(f)$	$C_{XX}(f), C_{11}(f)$	$\Gamma_{xx}(f), \Gamma_{11}(f)$
cross spectra	$\overline{C}_{xy}(f), \overline{C}_{12}(f)$	$C_{XY}(f), C_{12}(f)$	$\Gamma_{XY}(f), \Gamma_{12}(f)$
cospectra	$\overline{L}_{12}(f)$	$L_{12}(f)$	$\Lambda_{12}(f)$
quadrature spectra	$\overline{Q}_{12}(f)$	$Q_{12}(f)$	$\Psi_{12}(f)$
amplitude spectra	$\overline{A}_{12}(f)$	$A_{12}(f)$	$\alpha_{12}(f)$
phase spectra	$\overline{F}_{12}(f)$	$F_{12}(f)$	$\phi_{12}(f)$
squared coherency	$\overline{K}_{12}^2(f)$	$K_{12}^2(f)$	$\kappa_{12}^2(f)$

MAJOR ABBREVIATIONS

acf	autocorrelation function
acvf	autocovariance function
ar	autoregressive
ccf	cross correlation function
ccvf	cross covariance function
cdf	cumulative distribution function
lse	least squares estimate
ma	moving average
mele	mean likelihood estimate
mle	maximum likelihood estimate
mse	mean square error
pd	probability distribution
pdf	probability density function
rv	random variable

1

Aims and Means in
Time Series Analysis

To orient and motivate the reader, this chapter gives a summary of the most useful concepts and main objectives of time series analysis.

1.1 TIME SERIES AND STOCHASTIC PROCESSES

1.1.1 Deterministic and non-deterministic functions

It is difficult to find any branch of science which does not lead to the study of data arising in the form of *time series*. A time series is a *random* or *non-deterministic* function x of an independent variable t. In most situations the function $x(t)$ will be a function of time, but in other situations it may be a function of some other physical parameter t, for example, space.

The characteristic feature of a time series is that its future behavior cannot be predicted exactly, as would be the case for a *deterministic* function of time. In many branches of applied mathematics it is convenient to assume that certain physical processes can be described by deterministic or mathematical functions of time. For example, in the majority of electrical engineering calculations it is convenient to assume that the most important features of the supply voltage can be represented by the cosine function

$$x(t) = a \cos (2\pi f_0 t + \phi), \qquad (1.1.1)$$

where f_0 is the supply frequency and a is the voltage amplitude. However, closer inspection of the amplitude reveals that it is not constant but fluctuates with time. Thus Figure 1.1 shows the voltage deviations at the terminals of a turbo-alternator as a function of time. When two records of the voltage–time curve are compared, they may not resemble each other visually. However, when their *statistical* or *average* behavior is compared, similarities begin to emerge. This observation leads to the notion of a stochastic process.

1.1.2 Stochastic processes

Since different sections of a time series resemble each other only in their average properties, it is necessary to describe these series by probability laws or models. Thus, possible values of the time series at a given time t are assumed to be described by a *random variable* $X(t)$ and its associated probability distribution. The observed value $x(t)$ of the time series at time t is then regarded as one of the infinity of values which the random variable $X(t)$ might have taken at time t.

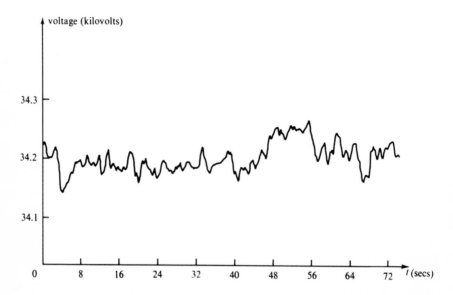

FIG. 1.1: Voltage deviations at the stator terminals of a 50-megawatt turbo-alternator

The behavior of the time series at all times can be described by a set of random variables $\{X(t)\}$ where the time variable t can take any value from $-\infty$ to $+\infty$. Thus the statistical properties of the series are described by associating probability distributions with any set of times $t_1, t_2, \ldots, t_N$. The ordered set of random variables $\{X(t)\}$ and its associated probability distributions is called a *stochastic process*. The observed time series $x(t)$ is thus regarded as one of the doubly infinite set of functions which might have been generated by the stochastic process. The set is doubly infinite because an infinite set of values is possible at any given time and there are an infinite number of time points.

Time series which occur in practice are either *discrete* or *continuous*. Examples of discrete time series are monthly figures of imports and exports or the yields of consecutive batches from a batch chemical process (Figure

5.2). Examples of continuous time series are the turbo-alternator data of Figure 1.1 or the radar return signal of Figure 5.1.

1.1.3 Experimental and non-experimental data

A more important distinction than that between discrete and continuous time series is whether the data are *non-experimental* or whether they are obtained from a planned experiment. For example, time series in economics and the social sciences are examples of non-experimental data. The economist is usually in a position where he can only *observe* the economic system and is rarely in a position to conduct planned experiments. A further difficulty associated with the analysis of economic time series is that they usually contain few observations. Therefore it is exceedingly difficult to check whether a given stochastic model provides a good fit to the data. Nevertheless, the techniques of time series analysis are of considerable importance in the analysis of economic data [1].

On the other hand, in engineering and the physical sciences, the time scale over which useful data need be collected is much smaller, so time series containing many more values can be obtained. Furthermore, it is possible to repeat experiments under similar sets of conditions so that the validity of the analysis and of different models can be checked.

1.2 TIME-DOMAIN AND FREQUENCY-DOMAIN DESCRIPTIONS OF TIME SERIES

It was stated in Section 1.1 that the stochastic process, from which the observed time series is regarded as being generated, can be described by the probability distributions associated with all possible sets of time points. To infer the nature of these probability distributions from a single or small number of series is an impossible or even meaningless exercise. In this section we discuss some of the most important simplifications which have been made in time series analysis in order to make the analysis of observed time series tractable and yet fruitful.

The most important assumptions made about a time series are that the corresponding stochastic process is *stationary*, and that a stationary stochastic process may be adequately described by the lower moments of its probability distributions. The lower moments include the *mean, variance, covariance function* and the Fourier transform of the covariance function, the power *spectrum*. An alternative approach to the above is to assume that the stochastic process can be adequately described by means of a model containing a few parameters which may be estimated from the data. These simplifying assumptions are now discussed briefly.

1.2.1 Stationarity

Examination of the output from a noise generator over a limited period of time shows that different sections of the output "look alike." In contrast, the characteristic feature of an economic time series, such as the gross national product of an industrialized country, is that its level tends to increase with time and hence different sections of the series will not be comparable. The output from the noise generator is said to be a *stationary* time series, whereas the gross national product series is said to be *non-stationary*.

Qualitatively, a stationary series is one which is in statistical equilibrium, in the sense that it contains no *trends*, whereas a non-stationary series is such that its properties change with time. Series occurring in practice are usually one of three kinds: those which exhibit stationary properties over long periods, for example, outputs from noise generators; those which are reasonably stationary over short periods, for example, measurements of atmospheric turbulence; and series which are obviously non-stationary in the sense that their visual properties are continuously changing with time.

Most methods of dealing with non-stationary time series are based on techniques for removing or filtering out the non-stationary part, leaving behind a series which can be treated as stationary. In some recent work [2], models which can describe non-stationary series have been given.

Since the statistical properties of stationary series do not change with time, these properties can be conveniently summarized by computing certain functions from the data. The function which was first used for this purpose is the autocovariance function.

1.2.2 The autocovariance function

In classical statistical work the measurements x_t ($t = 1, 2, \ldots, N$) of some physical parameter can be assumed to be independent since the experiments which generate these observations are physically independent. If the probability distribution $f_X(x)$ associated with the measurements is *Normal* or *Gaussian*, it can be completely characterized by its mean

$$\mu = E[X] = \int_{-\infty}^{\infty} x f_X(x)\, dx \tag{1.2.1}$$

and its variance

$$\sigma^2 = E[(X - \mu)^2] = \int_{-\infty}^{\infty} (x - \mu)^2 f_X(x)\, dx. \tag{1.2.2}$$

The mean measures the location or center of gravity of the distribution and the variance its variability or spread.

If the observations x_t form part of a time series, then only for a purely random series will neighboring values be independent, that is, the size of

x_t is not influenced by the size of $x_{t-1}, x_{t-2}, \ldots$. In general, neighboring values of a time series will be *correlated*. Hence, in addition to specifying the mean μ and the variance σ^2, it is necessary in the case of a stationary Normal series to specify its *autocovariance function*

$$\gamma(u) = E[(X(t) - \mu)(X(t + u) - \mu)]. \tag{1.2.3}$$

In practice $\gamma(u)$ can be estimated by

$$c(u) = \frac{1}{N} \sum_{t=1}^{N-u} (x_t - \bar{x})(x_{t+u} - \bar{x}), \tag{1.2.4}$$

where

$$\bar{x} = \frac{1}{N} \sum_{t=1}^{N} x_t$$

is the *mean* of the observed time series. The plot of $c(u)$ versus u is called the *sample autocovariance function* of the time series. It is sometimes convenient when comparing series with different scales of measurement to normalize (1.2.4) by dividing by the variance $c(0)$. Thus the *sample autocorrelation function* is defined by

$$r(u) = \frac{c(u)}{c(0)}. \tag{1.2.5}$$

The sample autocorrelation function for the turbo-alternator data of Figure 1.1 is shown in Figure 1.2. It is seen that the voltage is highly positively correlated after one lag, which corresponds to $\frac{1}{2}$ second, is still slightly positively correlated after 1 second, but over the range $1\frac{1}{2}$ to $2\frac{1}{2}$ seconds is prominently negatively correlated. This means that if a large voltage occurs which is above the mean, there is a good chance that in about 2 seconds the voltage will be less than the mean, and vice versa. The estimates $r(u)$ for lags in the range $2\frac{1}{2}$ to 10 seconds are all very small, but persistently negative, which suggests that on the average a positive deviation from the mean tends to follow a negative one after 2 to 10 seconds. However, the values of $r(u)$ in this range are extremely small and hence inferences based on them may be suspect. The tail of the sample correlation function reveals a periodicity in the voltage waveform with a period of approximately 3 seconds. This periodicity could also account for some of the negative correlation near a lag of 2 seconds.

The autocorrelation function is useful in some situations because it gives a visual picture of the way in which the dependence in the series damps out with the lag or separation u between points in the series. However, the autocorrelation function is sometimes difficult to interpret because neighboring

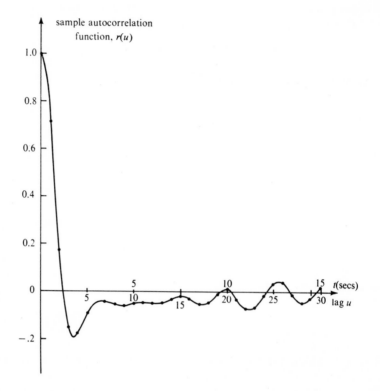

FIG. 1.2: Sample autocorrelation function for turbo-alternator data of Figure 1.1, $N = 1000$

values can be highly correlated. This means that the sample autocorrelation function may be distorted visually. A more detailed description of the properties and uses of the autocorrelation function is given in Chapter 5. Its main use in this book will be as an intermediate step in the estimation of the spectrum.

1.2.3 The spectrum

Suppose that the time series x_t consists of values of the cosine function (1.1.1) at discrete times. Then for frequencies f_0 which are multiples of the fundamental frequency $1/N$, it may be verified that the variance calculated according to (1.2.4) is $a^2/2$. If x_t is measured in volts, then this means that the average ac power or variance of the series is $a^2/2$ watts. More generally, if x_t consists of a mixture of several cosine waves with frequencies f_i and amplitudes a_i, then the variance is

$$c(0) = \sum_i \tfrac{1}{2}a_i^2. \tag{1.2.6}$$

The result (1.2.6) shows that if x_t can be regarded as being made up of mixtures of cosine waves, its variance can be decomposed into components of average power or variance $\tfrac{1}{2}a_i^2$ at the various frequencies f_i. It will be shown in Chapter 6 that if x_t is a stationary time series, the variance of the corresponding stochastic process can be decomposed into contributions at a *continuous range of frequencies* according to

$$\sigma^2 = \gamma(0) = \int_{-\infty}^{\infty} \Gamma(f)\, df,$$

where $\Gamma(f)$ is called the power *spectrum* of the stochastic process. Thus $\Gamma(f)\, \delta f$ is an approximate measure of the average power or variance in the frequency band f to $f + \delta f$.

The *spectrum estimate* of the turbo-alternator data of Figure 1.1 is shown in Figure 1.3. The main feature of this spectrum is that there is high power at low frequencies and low power at high frequencies. This is due mainly to the high positive values of the sample autocorrelation function at lags 1 and 2. Note also that the power does not drop gradually from high to low frequencies. Instead, there is a flat region over the range 0–$\tfrac{1}{2}$ cps. There is also a well-defined minor peak at frequency 0.39 cps, or period 2.54 seconds, which could explain the small periodicity in the tail of the sample correlation function of Figure 1.2.

It will also be shown in Chapter 6 that the spectrum and the autocovariance function are related according to the Fourier transform relation

$$\Gamma(f) = \int_{-\infty}^{\infty} \gamma(u) \cos 2\pi f u\, du, \tag{1.2.7}$$

and hence knowledge of the autocovariance function of the process is equivalent to knowledge of the spectrum of the process.

However, in the analysis of a finite length of record, the spectrum is often preferable to the autocovariance function. First, estimates of the spectrum at neighboring frequencies are approximately independent, and hence the interpretation of the sample spectrum is usually easier than that of the sample autocovariance function. More important, in many physical problems the spectrum is of direct physical interest. Examples of the uses of spectral analysis will be given in Section 1.3.

Digital filters. Although it is necessary to assume stationarity to describe a stochastic process by its spectrum, in practice *the stationarity assumption does*

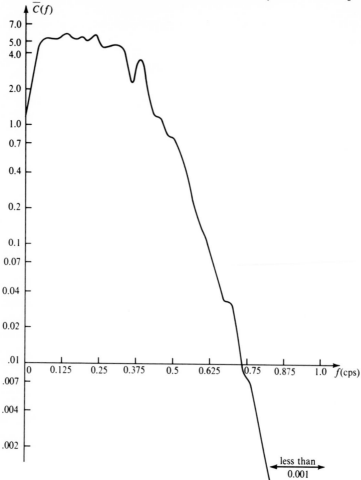

FIG. 1.3: Spectrum estimate for turbo-alternator data of Figure 1.1, $N = 1000$

not present serious problems. This is because the spectrum isolates the contributions in the series which can be attributed to different frequency bands. A non-stationary series is usually characterized by the presence of large power at low frequencies. However, in many practical applications, the information which is of interest may be at higher frequencies. In such cases, all that is necessary is to filter off the non-stationary low-frequency components and use the residual series for the spectral analysis.

A particularly simple form of digital filter for removing low-frequency components is the first difference filter

$$y_t = (x_t - x_{t-1}). \qquad (1.2.8)$$

The gain $G(f)$ of this filter is shown in Figure 1.4 and measures the extent to

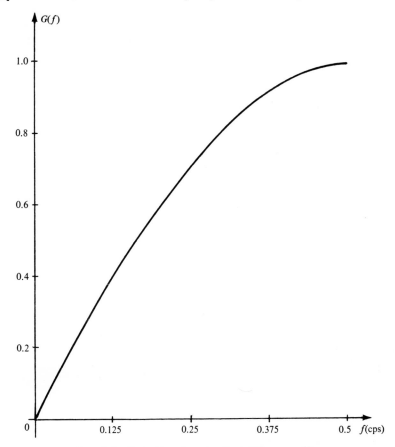

FIG. 1.4: Gain function for first difference filter

which a cosine wave of frequency f is transmitted by the filter. It is seen that low frequencies will be considerably attenuated and hence will tend not to be present in the output from the filter.

1.2.4 Parametric time series models

In many problems, such as those where it is required to *predict* future values of the series, it is necessary to construct a parametric model for the time series. To be useful, the model should be physically meaningful and involve as few parameters as possible. A powerful parametric model which has been widely used in practice for describing empirical time series is the *moving average–autoregressive process*

$$X_t - \mu = \alpha_1(X_{t-1} - \mu) + \cdots + \alpha_m(X_{t-m} - \mu) + Z_t + \beta_1 Z_{t-1} \\ + \cdots + \beta_l Z_{t-l}, \quad (1.2.9)$$

where Z_t is a purely random series, or white noise, and μ is the mean level of X_t. The model (1.2.9) is physically meaningful since it is the discrete analog of the familiar linear differential equation used to describe linear systems. The model thus represents time series as the output from a linear system whose input is white noise. By introducing a suitable number of the parameters α and β in (1.2.9) it is possible, after suitable differencing [2], to fit most empirical time series with a relatively small number of parameters.

The decision as to whether to use the autocovariance function, the spectrum or a parametric model will be dictated in practice by the needs of the situation. Different needs will require different methods of approach and hence it is important to realize that *there is no one approach which should be applied to the analysis of all time series in all situations.*

1.3 OBJECTIVES OF TIME SERIES ANALYSIS

Several different applications of spectral analysis will be described in this book. Since spectral analysis is just one tool which is available for the analysis of time series, it is useful by way of introduction to discuss the nature of time series problems in greater generality.

At the risk of oversimplification, time series problems can be classified into those which require some form of *model building* and those which lead to *frequency response studies*. These categories inevitably have a certain amount of overlap.

1.3.1 Model building

One can usually distinguish between several different kinds of models, for example, *exploratory* and *sophisticated* models; *empirical* and *physical* models; and *parametric* and *non-parametric* models.

Exploratory and sophisticated models. In the early stages of an investigation, one may know very little about a particular phenomenon. The main purpose of the time series analysis at this stage may be to look at the data in several different ways to see what hypotheses are suggested. For example, a study of the spectrum of the vertical velocity field of atmospheric turbulence [3] indicated that the peak in the spectrum moved toward lower frequencies with increased solar radiation. This suggested that there were two different causes for the fluctuations in atmospheric turbulence, a high-frequency component due to frictional forces and a low-frequency component due to heat convection caused by solar radiation. As a result of this exploratory analysis, it was possible to begin to construct a more realistic model for atmospheric turbulence.

As in the above example, it often happens that a time series model which is guessed initially may be proved inadequate subsequently. The nature of the inadequacies in the exploratory model can then be used as a basis for modifying it and constructing a more sophisticated model.

Empirical and physical models. In some situations it is possible to write down detailed models for a time series based on the physics of the situation. For example, considerable effort has gone into the construction of physical models for atmospheric turbulence [3] and hydrodynamic turbulence [4]. In other situations, so little is known about the phenomenon being investigated that it is necessary to resort to the fitting of a more empirical model, such as the moving average–autoregressive model (1.2.9). A big advantage of physical models is that they usually require fewer parameters than empirical models. The decision to spend time and effort deriving a physical model or to resort to an empirical model requires judgement and insight. In general, some compromise is necessary and one should use whatever physical knowledge is available and start building on these foundations.

Parametric and non-parametric models. The moving average–autoregressive model (1.2.9) is a *parametric* model. To fit this model it is only necessary to estimate a small set of parameters from the data. On the other hand, the description of a time series provided by the autocorrelation function or the spectrum is *non-parametric* (or *multiparametric*, since an effectively infinite number of parameters is required to specify the process).

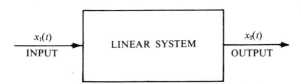

FIG. 1.5: Schematic representation of a linear system

A problem to which both of these methods may be applied is the estimation of the dynamic model of a linear system as shown in Figure 1.5. In the simplest case, where there is one input x_1 and one output x_2, it is possible to estimate the dynamic model from records $x_1(t)$, $x_2(t)$, of the input and output. For example, it may be known that a simple parametric model such as

$$T\frac{dx_2(t)}{dt} + x_2(t) = x_1(t)$$

is adequate. This model involves one parameter T, called the *time constant* of the system. In other situations it may be more convenient to describe the system by a nonparametric model requiring specification of the gain function $G(f)$ and the phase function $\phi(f)$ of the system. These are functions which describe the response of the system to cosine waves of different frequencies f.

Thus an input cosine wave $x_1(t) = a \cos 2\pi ft$ appears at the output as a cosine wave $x_2(t) = aG(f) \cos (2\pi ft + \phi(f))$, that is, the amplitude is changed from a to $aG(f)$ and the phase is changed by $\phi(f)$. It will be shown in Chapter 10 that cross spectral analysis can be used to estimate the gain and phase of a linear system.

In some situations the gain-phase description is preferable, since the model may be needed only over a limited frequency band. In other situations the overall description provided by the parametric model may be preferable.

Since spectral analysis is a non-parametric approach, its usefulness in the area of model building is limited. However, as in the turbulence example mentioned above, it is sometimes useful as an exploratory tool for suggesting models which can then be fitted parametrically.

1.3.2 Uses of time series models

Time series models are used for a variety of purposes. Some of the most common of these are (a) prediction; (b) estimation of transfer functions; (c) filtering and control; (d) simulation and optimization; and (e) generating new physical theories.

Prediction. By prediction is meant the estimation of future values $x(t + T)$ of the time series in some future range $0 \leqslant T \leqslant l$ from values of the series up to and including time t. The prediction of economic and industrial time series is a very important application of time series and is discussed in reference [2].

Estimation of transfer functions. This application has been discussed above.

Filtering and control. A more general problem than the one of prediction described above is that of linear filtering as formulated by Wiener [5]. The linear filter is a device which operates on the input $x_1(t)$ to give an output $x_2(t)$ according to

$$x_2(t) = \int_0^\infty h(u)x_1(t - u) \, du, \qquad (1.3.1)$$

where $h(u)$ is the *weighting function* or *impulse response function* of the filter. Suppose that the input $x_1(t) = s(t) + z(t)$, where $s(t)$ is the *signal* or useful information and $z(t)$ is the *noise* or unwanted information. Then, as shown in Figure 1.6, the filter is required to produce an output which is some function of the signal at a future time T. For example, the desired output might be

$$g[s(t + T)] = \frac{d}{dt} [s(t + T)].$$

The optimal filter is then defined as the weight function which minimizes the mean square of the error signal

$$\epsilon(t) = x_2(t) - g[s(t + T)]$$

between the actual and desired outputs. If models are available for the stochastic processes which describe the signal $s(t)$ and the noise $z(t)$, techniques are available [6] for calculating the gain and phase function of the optimal filter. In fact, the calculation of the optimal filter is made easier by working with the spectra of the signal $s(t)$ and the noise $z(t)$.

In control theory it is required to follow some specified signal $s(t)$ with as small an error as possible. It may be shown [6] that this reduces to a special case of the filtering problem described above.

Simulation and optimization. Many systems, for example electronic guidance systems, are much too complex to study or optimize analytically. In such a case, the system may be simulated using analog, digital or hybrid computers.

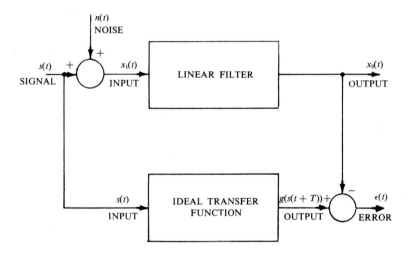

FIG. 1.6: Schematic of the general filtering problem

The disturbances entering the real system at various points can be measured, and if enough of these data are available they may be fed directly into the simulator. However, the quantity of data required for simulation studies is usually so large that it is necessary to fit models to the disturbances. The models can then be used to generate unlimited amounts of artificial data which can then be used in the simulation.

Generating new physical theories. The above applications of time series models refer to engineering problems. In applications of time series analysis in physics, the approach is somewhat different. The physicist is interested in producing theories for physical phenomena which can be used to predict as wide a range of situations as possible. Hence the time series models devised are more detailed than those required by the engineer and must be constantly modified and enlarged as greater physical insight is obtained. The use of time series analysis in building physical models for atmospheric turbulence is well illustrated in [3].

1.3.3 Frequency response studies

Although spectral analysis has an important role to play in time series model building, it is in the area of frequency response studies that it is most relevant.

It has been mentioned above that the linear system (1.3.1) transforms a cosine wave input $x_1(t) = a \cos 2\pi ft$ into a cosine wave output $x_2(t) = a\, G(f) \cos (2\pi ft + \phi(f))$. It will be shown in Chapter 6 that if $x_1(t)$ is a stationary time series, the *spectrum* of the input is changed by multiplying it by the *square* of the gain. That is, the spectrum of $x_2(t)$ is

$$\Gamma_2(f) = G^2(f)\Gamma_1(f). \tag{1.3.2}$$

Figure 7.22 shows the effect of passing an input with the spectrum shown in (a) of that figure through three systems whose squared gains are shown in (b). In the example illustrated in Figure 7.22, the input refers to the roughness of a runway, the system is the landing gear of an aircraft and the output is a typical aircraft response such as the acceleration at the center of gravity. Using the result (1.3.2), it is seen that the combination of the input spectrum with the landing gear response marked 3 produces an output spectrum with a very sharp peak, as indicated by 3 in (c) of Figure 7.22. This indicates that large accelerations will result at this resonant frequency, producing passenger discomfort and large stresses in the landing gear. Knowing the gain plots of the landing gears of typical aircraft at typical landing speeds, it is possible to lay down norms for the roughness of runways.

In the above example, it was possible to change the input spectrum by designing suitable runways, but the characteristics of the landing gear would usually have been specified from other considerations and hence would have to be regarded as fixed. The converse holds in the design of suspension units for motorcycles or cars. In recent years certain companies have based the design of suspension systems on measurements of the roughness of the roads in a particular country. Roads differ widely in their characteristics from one country to another, and hence suspension systems may be designed accordingly.

Frequency response studies may also be applied to the design of aircraft structures and to the design of experiments to optimize the performance of industrial processes. These applications are discussed more fully in Chapter 7.

1.4 SCOPE OF THE PRESENT BOOK

There is no doubt that spectral techniques have come to play an important part in the analysis of time series. However, it is important to realize that they do have limitations and should be applied judiciously. The pioneering work in the estimation of spectra from finite lengths of records is to be found in the books by Bartlett [7] and Blackman and Tukey [8]. Their books are essentially concerned with the estimation of the spectra of single time series. In the present book, these ideas are extended to the estimation of the spectra and cross spectra of several time series and their subsequent use in the estimation of gain and phase functions of linear systems.

Several topics in spectral analysis have not been included here. An important omission is the spectral analysis of stochastic processes defined in several dimensions, for example, the elevation of ocean waves as a function of earth coordinates. Another omission is that of higher-order spectra, for example, the bi-spectrum. These higher-order spectra are useful in the analysis of non-Normal processes and non-linear systems. Stochastic processes defined in several dimensions have been omitted because the book is already too long. However, non-linear spectra have been omitted mainly because we think that the extra complication introduced by these spectra will inhibit their widespread use. On the present evidence it is felt that parametric methods are preferable in these situations.

REFERENCES

[1] C. W. J. Granger, *Spectral Analysis of Economic Time Series*. Princeton University Press, Princeton, 1964.
[2] G. E. P. Box and G. M. Jenkins, *Statistical Models for Forecasting and Control*. To be published, Holden-Day, San Francisco.
[3] John L. Lumley and Hans A. Panofsky, *The Structure of Atmospheric Turbulence*. John Wiley, New York, 1964.
[4] G. K. Batchelor, *The Theory of Homogeneous Turbulence*. Cambridge University Press, Cambridge, 1953.
[5] N. Wiener, *The Extrapolation, Interpolation and Smoothing of Stationary Time Series with Engineering Applications*. John Wiley, New York, 1949.
[6] J. H. Laning and R. H. Battin, *Random Processes in Automatic Control*. McGraw-Hill, New York, 1956.
[7] M. S. Bartlett, *An Introduction to Stochastic Processes with Special Reference to Methods and Applications*. Cambridge University Press, Cambridge, 1953.
[8] R. B. Blackman and J. W. Tukey, *The Measurement of Power Spectra from the Point of View of Communications Engineering*. Dover, New York, 1958.

2

Fourier Analysis

Spectral analysis brings together two very important theoretical approaches, the statistical analysis of time series and the methods of Fourier analysis. The latter requires no detailed exposition for engineers since much of their training is deeply rooted in these methods. However, for the sake of completeness and for the benefit of other readers, this chapter describes those ideas in Fourier analysis necessary for the analysis of time series. In later chapters, it will be shown how Fourier techniques need to be modified to deal with statistical rather than deterministic functions of time.

2.1 INTRODUCTION

2.1.1 The role of Fourier analysis in applied mathematics and engineering

The analytic techniques developed by Jean-Baptiste-Joseph Fourier (1768–1830) have played an important role in the development of applied mathematics. They are particularly important in three applications: (a) for studying periodic solutions to physical problems described by differential equations, especially partial differential equations—for example, the study of wave motion of plucked strings or the transmission of electromagnetic waves in waveguides or cables; (b) as an operational device for solving differential equations—for example, ordinary differential equations with constant coefficients may be converted into algebraic equations by Fourier transformation; (c) for approximating non-periodic functions.

This book will be concerned primarily with the latter case and only incidentally with solving differential equations. It will not consider periodic solutions to physical problems. As an instance of approximating a non-periodic function, consider a deterministic function $s(t)$ of time t which will be called a *signal* and which is to be approximated by means of suitably chosen periodic functions. A deterministic signal is a function which is known exactly *for all time* and hence is a mathematical idealization. Examples of deterministic signals are

16

$$s(t) = e^{-|t|}, \quad -\infty \leqslant t \leqslant \infty,$$

or

$$s(t) = a \cos 2\pi f_1 t, \quad -\infty \leqslant t \leqslant \infty.$$

Many practical signals are usefully thought of as deterministic, for example, the supply voltage as a function of time, the output of a square-wave generator, the displacement of an object subjected to a suddenly applied constant force or the current through a resistor which is suddenly shunted across a charged capacitor. The dimensions of the first two of these signals are volts, of the third, feet, and of the fourth, amperes. However, the dimensions could be feet per second if the signal were a velocity or they could be units of temperature, pressure and so forth. For consistency it will always be assumed that t is measured in seconds and $s(t)$ in volts, since in most practical applications the physical quantity which is being studied will be converted into a voltage before recording.

The first deterministic example cited above is *non-periodic* while the second is *periodic*. Periodic means that there is a number T, called the *period* of the function, such that

$$s(t) = s(t + T) \tag{2.1.1}$$

for all t.

The function between time t and $t + T$ can be of any shape whatsoever. A particularly simple shape is the cosine function example mentioned above which has period $T = 1/f_1$, since

$$a \cos 2\pi f_1 [t + (1/f_1)] = a \cos 2\pi f_1 t.$$

It is possible to represent non-periodic functions using any class of periodic functions. In Fourier analysis, the periodic functions used are sine and cosine functions. They have the important properties that an approximation consisting of a given number of terms achieves the minimum mean square error between the signal and the approximation, and also that they are orthogonal, so the coefficients may be determined independently of one another.

2.1.2 Finite Fourier Series

Consider a signal which is specified only at discrete times, and suppose it is required to expand it in terms of periodic functions. The discrete signal can be regarded as having been derived from a continuous signal $s(t)$ of duration T by sampling the values of the signal at spacing Δ, as shown in Figure 2.1(a). This produces $N = T/\Delta$ sample values s_r, where

$$s_r = s(t = r\Delta). \tag{2.1.2}$$

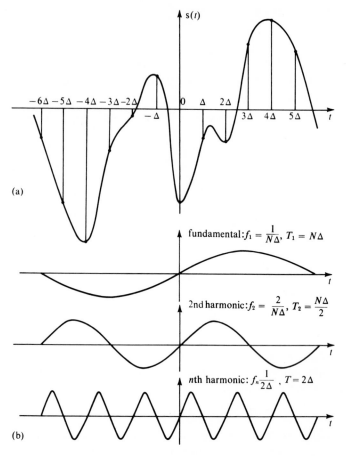

Fig. 2.1: (a) A discrete signal obtained by sampling a continuous signal
(b) The fundamental sine wave and harmonics

For convenience it is assumed that N is even and equal to $2n$ so that r may run through the integers $-n, \ldots, 0, 1, \ldots, n-1$.

Note that periodic functions which pass through the sample values may be chosen in an infinite number of ways. For example, the finite Fourier series

$$\tilde{s}(t) = A_0 + 2 \sum_{m=1}^{n-1} \{A_m \cos 2\pi m f_1 t + B_m \sin 2\pi m f_1 t\} + A_n \cos 2\pi n f_1 t \quad (2.1.3)$$

contains N constants, the A_m and B_m, which can be determined so that the discrete and continuous values coincide at the points $t = r\Delta$, that is, $\tilde{s}(t) = s_r$. It follows that the function $\tilde{s}(t)$ provides an *approximation* to the original continuous function $s(t)$ in the interval $-T/2 \leqslant t < T/2$.

On substituting $t = r\Delta$ in (2.1.3) and setting $\tilde{s}(r\Delta) = s_r$, a set of N equations for the N unknown constants is obtained. The equations are

$$s_r = A_0 + 2 \sum_{m=1}^{n-1} \{A_m \cos 2\pi m f_1 r\Delta + B_m \sin 2\pi m f_1 r\Delta\}$$

$$+ A_n \cos 2\pi n f_1 r\Delta, \qquad (r = -n, \ldots, 0, 1, \ldots, n-1). \quad (2.1.4)$$

Choosing $f_1 = 1/N\Delta$ simplifies the solution of equation (2.1.4), because then the sines and cosines are *orthogonal*, that is, they satisfy the relations

$$\sum_{r=-n}^{n-1} \sin \frac{2\pi kr}{N} \cos \frac{2\pi mr}{N} = 0, \qquad k, m \text{ integers};$$

$$\sum_{r=-n}^{n-1} \sin \frac{2\pi kr}{N} \sin \frac{2\pi mr}{N} = \begin{cases} 0, & k \neq m \\ \dfrac{N}{2}, & k = m \neq 0, n \\ 0, & k = m = 0, n; \end{cases} \quad (2.1.5)$$

$$\sum_{r=-n}^{n-1} \cos \frac{2\pi kr}{N} \cos \frac{2\pi mr}{N} = \begin{cases} 0, & k \neq m \\ \dfrac{N}{2}, & k = m \neq 0, n \\ N, & k = m = 0, n. \end{cases}$$

The frequency $f_1 = 1/N\Delta$ is called the *fundamental frequency* of the signal $\tilde{s}(t)$, and it corresponds to a period equal to the length of the record, as shown in Figure 2.1(b). The dimensions of f_1 are cycles per second (cps) when t is measured in seconds (sec).

The function $\tilde{s}(t)$ in (2.1.3) is thus composed of a sum of sine and cosine functions whose frequencies are multiples or *harmonics* of the fundamental f_1, as is illustrated in Figure 2.1(b). The highest frequency present is $n/N\Delta = 1/2\Delta$ cps, which corresponds to a period of 2 sampling intervals.

The coefficients A_m or B_m, when $f_1 = 1/N\Delta$, may be determined by multiplying both sides of (2.1.4) by $\cos(2\pi mr/N)$ or $\sin(2\pi mr/N)$ and summing over r, then making use of the orthogonality relations (2.1.5).

The final expressions for the coefficients are

$$A_m = \frac{1}{N} \sum_{r=-n}^{n-1} s_r \cos \frac{2\pi mr}{N}, \qquad (2.1.6)$$

$$B_m = \frac{1}{N} \sum_{r=-n}^{n-1} s_r \sin \frac{2\pi mr}{N}, \qquad (2.1.7)$$

for $m = 0, 1, \ldots, n$. A_0 is the *mean* or average value of s_r. Similar expressions may be derived when the number of points N is odd, say $2n - 1$, the only difference being that the A_n term vanishes.

An example. Consider the data of Table 2.1, which gives the intensity of reflected signals from one of the *E*-layers in the ionosphere. The figures given are averages, over several months, of the intensity at fixed times during the day.

TABLE 2.1: Intensity of reflected signals from ionosphere

Time	0	1	2	3	4	5	6	7	8	9	10	11
Average intensity	-6	-20	-28	-8	-1	7	-20	-6	-7	14	19	12

Table 2.2 gives the values of the coefficients A_m and B_m computed from (2.1.6) and (2.1.7) using hour 6 as the origin of time. The coefficient A_2, for example, is obtained from

$$A_2 = \frac{1}{12}\left\{(-6)\cos(-2\pi) + (-20)\cos\left(-\frac{5\pi}{3}\right) + \cdots + (12)\cos\left(\frac{5\pi}{3}\right)\right\}$$

$$= \frac{1}{12}\{-6 - 10 + \cdots + 6\} = -2.25.$$

TABLE 2.2: Fourier decomposition of mean square for ionospheric data

Source	m	A_m	B_m	R_m	$\phi_m(°)$	Contribution to mean square
mean	0	-3.667	0	3.667	180	13.44
fundamental	1	-0.475	5.584	5.604	85	62.81
2nd harmonic	2	-2.250	-7.073	7.422	-72	110.17
3rd harmonic	3	-1.250	-0.250	1.275	-11	3.25
4th harmonic	4	-0.667	0.577	0.882	41	1.56
5th harmonic	5	-1.775	-0.334	1.806	-11	6.52
6th harmonic	6	-3.500	0	3.500	0	12.25
Total						210.00

Amplitude and phase representation. It is sometimes more convenient to write (2.1.3) in the form

$$\tilde{s}(t) = R_0 + 2\sum_{m=1}^{n-1} R_m \cos(2\pi m f_1 t + \phi_m) + R_n \cos 2\pi n f_1 t, \quad (2.1.8)$$

where

$$R_m = \sqrt{A_m^2 + B_m^2}, \qquad \phi_m = \arctan -\frac{B_m}{A_m} \qquad (2.1.9)$$

and

$$A_m = R_m \cos \phi_m, \qquad B_m = -R_m \sin \phi_m. \qquad (2.1.10)$$

R_m is called the *amplitude* and ϕ_m the *phase* of the mth harmonic relative to an arbitrary origin of time. In the above formulae the origin of time has been taken at a point roughly halfway between the first and last value of s_r. If this origin were changed, the amplitude would remain unaltered but the phase would change accordingly. The amplitudes and phases for the iono-sphere data are shown in Table 2.2.

Parseval's theorem. The mean square value or average power of the signal s_r is

$$\frac{1}{N} \sum_{r=-n}^{n-1} s_r^2.$$

Using (2.1.3) and the orthogonality property (2.1.5) it may be verified that this can be written

$$\frac{1}{N} \sum_{r=-n}^{n-1} s_r^2 = R_0^2 + 2 \sum_{m=1}^{n-1} R_m^2 + R_n^2, \qquad (2.1.11)$$

which is a special case of *Parseval's theorem*. In words, it states that the mean square value of s_r, or the *average power* dissipated by s_r, can be decomposed into contributions arising from each harmonic. For the zero-th and nth harmonic the contribution is R_m^2 but for the mth harmonic the average power is $2R_m^2$.

A more convenient measure is the mean square value of s_r about the mean R_0. This is simply the *variance*

$$\sigma^2 = \frac{1}{N} \sum_{r=-n}^{n-1} (s_r - R_0)^2 = 2 \sum_{m=1}^{n-1} R_m^2 + R_n^2, \qquad (2.1.12)$$

or, in electrical terms, the *average ac power*.

The decomposition of the mean square value of s_r for the ionospheric data is shown in Table 2.1. It is seen that the mean, fundamental and first harmonic account for about 89% of the total mean square, showing that the data are very well approximated by the model

$$s_r = -3.67 + 11.2 \cos \left(\frac{\pi r}{6} + 85°\right) + 14.8 \cos \left(\frac{\pi r}{3} - 72°\right).$$

The decomposition of the mean square may be displayed by plotting the average power at the harmonic versus the frequency of the harmonic. This is called a *Fourier line spectrum* and is shown in Figure 2.2 for the ionospheric data.

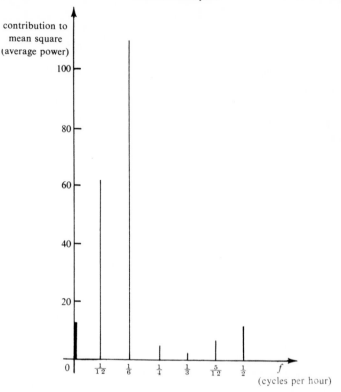

FIG. 2.2: A Fourier line spectrum (periodogram)

Complex Fourier series. The above formulae are cumbersome to manipulate, and hence for operational convenience it is preferable to express s_r in terms of *complex* amplitudes S_m, where

$$S_m = R_m\, e^{+j\phi_m} = A_m - jB_m, \quad j^2 = -1. \tag{2.1.13}$$

Thus (2.1.3) may be written

$$\tilde{s}(t) = \sum_{m=-n}^{n-1} S_m\, e^{j(2\pi mt/N\Delta)}, \tag{2.1.14}$$

where $S_{-m} = S_m^*$, the asterisk denoting a complex conjugate. Similarly, formulae (2.1.6, 7) become

$$S_m = \frac{1}{N} \sum_{r=-n}^{n-1} s_r\, e^{-j(2\pi mr/N)}, \quad -n \leqslant m \leqslant n - 1, \tag{2.1.15}$$

and Parseval's theorem (2.1.11) becomes

$$\frac{1}{N} \sum_{r=-n}^{n-1} s_r^2 = \sum_{m=-n}^{n-1} |S_m|^2. \tag{2.1.16}$$

Hence the contribution to the mean square, $2R_m^2$ in (2.1.11), is divided in (2.1.16) into two parts, each equal to $|S_m|^2 = R_m^2$, one at the frequency mf_1, the other at the frequency $-mf_1$.

Throughout this book it will be found convenient to operate with complex transforms. The resulting formulae can then be converted into real form by taking real and imaginary parts. For example, taking the real and imaginary parts of (2.1.15) gives the sine and cosine transforms (2.1.6, 7).

2.1.3 Fourier series

Suppose that a Fourier representation of a continuous signal in the interval $-T/2$ to $T/2$ is required. Note in the analysis of the previous section that if the sampling interval Δ tends to zero, then the sample points s_r will trace out the continuous signal $s(t)$. The continuous signal $\bar{s}(t)$, which is constrained to pass through the sample points s_r, must then coincide with $s(t)$, and hence in this limiting case the Fourier representation $\bar{s}(t)$ is an *exact* representation of the signal $s(t)$ over the interval $-T/2$ to $T/2$.

The Fourier coefficients S_m defined in (2.1.15) may be rewritten

$$S_m = \frac{1}{N\Delta} \sum_{r=-n}^{n-1} s_r \Delta \, e^{-j(2\pi mr\Delta/N\Delta)}, \qquad (2.1.17)$$

and if Δ tends to zero and N tends to infinity in such a way that $N\Delta = T$, then $r\Delta$ tends to t, $s_r\Delta$ tends to $s(t) \, dt$ and the sum (2.1.17) tends to the integral

$$S_m = \frac{1}{T} \int_{-T/2}^{T/2} s(t) \, e^{-j(2\pi mt/T)} \, dt. \qquad (2.1.18)$$

Similarly, (2.1.14) tends to

$$s(t) = \sum_{m=-\infty}^{\infty} S_m \, e^{j(2\pi mt/T)}. \qquad (2.1.19)$$

Parseval's theorem, (2.1.16), now becomes

$$\frac{1}{T} \int_{-T/2}^{T/2} s^2(t) \, dt = \sum_{m=-\infty}^{\infty} |S_m|^2, \qquad (2.1.20)$$

since (2.1.16) may be written

$$\frac{1}{N\Delta} \sum_{r=n}^{n-1} s_r^2 \Delta = \sum_{m=-n}^{n-1} |S_m|^2,$$

and as Δ tends to zero and N tends to infinity, $s_r^2\Delta$ tends to $s^2(t) \, dt$. Equation (2.1.20) states that the mean square of the continuous periodic signal $s(t)$

can be decomposed into an infinite number of contributions at harmonics $f_m = m/T$, $m = -\infty$ to $+\infty$, of the fundamental frequency $1/T$ cps. Equation (2.1.19) is called the *Fourier series* representation of the function $s(t)$ in the interval $-T/2 \leqslant t < T/2$. Note that although the above limiting arguments are heuristic, they can be justified rigorously.

2.1.4 *Fourier integrals*

Up to now it has been shown that two types of signal may be represented by means of trigonometric series. The first type of signal s_r consisted of a finite number (N) of equispaced ordinates, spaced Δ seconds apart. This could be represented over the given interval by a continuous signal $\bar{s}(t)$ composed of N harmonics of the fundamental frequency $1/N\Delta$ cps. The maximum frequency present is $1/2\Delta$ cps, and hence the signal $\bar{s}(t)$ is said to be *band-limited*. The second type of signal, a continuous signal $s(t)$ available over the interval $-T/2 \leqslant t \leqslant T/2$, was seen to be represented over the interval by a signal composed of an infinite number of harmonics of the fundamental frequency $1/T$ cps.

More generally, it is necessary to consider a third type of signal $s(t)$ defined over the *infinite* interval $-\infty \leqslant t \leqslant \infty$. The corresponding Fourier analysis is a limiting case of the analysis of Section 2.1.3 in which increasingly large segments T of the infinite record are analyzed. As T tends to infinity the frequency spacing $1/T$ between harmonics becomes infinitesimal, which results in a continuous amplitude distribution over frequency.

To demonstrate this limiting argument, (2.1.19) may be rewritten

$$s(t) = \sum_{m=-\infty}^{\infty} (TS_m)\, e^{j(2\pi m t/T)} \frac{1}{T}. \qquad (2.1.21)$$

In the limit, as T tends to infinity, m/T tends to f, $1/T$ tends to df, and TS_m tends to $S(f)$. Hence (2.1.21) tends to the integral

$$s(t) = \int_{-\infty}^{\infty} S(f)\, e^{j2\pi f t}\, df. \qquad (2.1.22)$$

Similarly, (2.1.18) may be written

$$TS_m = \int_{-T/2}^{T/2} s(t)\, e^{-j2\pi(m/T)t}\, dt, \qquad (2.1.23)$$

which tends to

$$S(f) = \int_{-\infty}^{\infty} s(t)\, e^{-j2\pi f t}\, dt, \qquad (2.1.24)$$

as T tends to infinity. The function $S(f)$ is called the *Fourier transform* of $s(t)$.

Parseval's relation (2.1.20) for the infinite interval case may be written

$$\int_{-T/2}^{T/2} s^2(t)\, dt = \sum_{m=-\infty}^{\infty} |TS_m|^2 \frac{1}{T}, \tag{2.1.25}$$

which tends to

$$\int_{-\infty}^{\infty} s^2(t)\, dt = \int_{-\infty}^{\infty} |S(f)|^2\, df. \tag{2.1.26}$$

The limiting operation in (2.1.25) may be thought of as first distributing the power or variance $|S_m|^2$ at frequency m/T over a band of width $1/T$, giving an average power $T|S_m|^2$ over the band. This average power then tends to a continuous distribution of power over frequency as the width of the band becomes infinitesimal.

Physically, the Fourier transform $S(f)$ represents the *distribution of signal strength with frequency*, that is, it is a density function. When s is measured in volts and t in seconds, the dimensions of $S(f)$ are "volt-seconds" or "volts per unit of f" since f has the dimensions of frequency, that is, $\sec^{-1}$.

Mathematical texts on Fourier analysis give a wide variety of sufficient conditions for the existence of the integrals (2.1.22) and (2.1.24). In this book, these conditions are avoided by using the theory of distributions conceived by Dirac and made rigorous by Schwartz. An excellent account of this theory is given in [1], and [2] may also be consulted. In this theory, every generalized function has a Fourier transform which is itself a generalized function. One consequence of the theory is that it is possible to regard a Fourier series as a special case of a Fourier integral, as will be seen later. The results of Section 2.1 are summarized in Table 2.3.

2.2 FOURIER TRANSFORMS AND THEIR PROPERTIES

2.2.1 *Well-behaved functions*

As an example of the application of (2.1.24), consider the Fourier transform of the simple function $s(t) = e^{-|t|}$. Then

$$S(f) = \int_{-\infty}^{\infty} e^{-|t|}\, e^{-j2\pi f t}\, dt$$

$$= \frac{1}{1 - j2\pi f} + \frac{1}{1 + j2\pi f} = \frac{2}{1 + (2\pi f)^2}.$$

Table 2.4 gives the Fourier transforms of some simple signals $s(t)$ which will be needed later.

These signals and their transforms are plotted in Figure 2.3. Remembering that $S(f)$ gives the distribution of signal strength with frequency, notice in Figure 2.3 that the first signal is quite smooth and hence its transform is dominated by low-frequency contributions. Also observe that sharp corners

TABLE 2.3: Summary of Fourier transforms

Description	Function	Transform	Inverse transform
Finite discrete series	$s_r,$ $r = -n, \ldots, 0, 1, \ldots, n-1$	$S_m = \dfrac{1}{N} \sum_{r=-n}^{n-1} s_r \, e^{-j(2\pi m r/N)},$ $m = -n, \ldots, 0, 1, \ldots, n-1$	$\tilde{s}(t) = \sum_{m=-n}^{n-1} S_m \, e^{j(2\pi m t/N\Delta)},$ $-\infty \leqslant t \leqslant \infty$ $\tilde{s}(t=r\Delta) = s_r, \quad \tilde{s}(t) = s(t + N\Delta)$
Continuous periodic function	$s(t) = s(t + T),$ $-\infty \leqslant t \leqslant \infty$	$S_m = \dfrac{1}{T} \displaystyle\int_{-T/2}^{T/2} s(t) \, e^{-j(2\pi m t/T)} \, dt,$ $m = 0, \pm 1, \pm 2, \ldots$	$s(t) = \sum_{m=-\infty}^{\infty} S_m \, e^{j(2\pi m t/T)},$ $-\infty \leqslant t \leqslant \infty$ $s(t) = s(t + T)$
Continuous aperiodic function	$s(t),$ $-\infty \leqslant t \leqslant \infty$	$S(f) = \displaystyle\int_{-\infty}^{\infty} s(t) \, e^{-j2\pi f t} \, dt,$ $-\infty \leqslant f \leqslant \infty$	$s(t) = \displaystyle\int_{-\infty}^{\infty} S(f) \, e^{j2\pi f t} \, df,$ $-\infty \leqslant t \leqslant \infty$

in $s(t)$, as in example (b), produce ripples or side lobes in the transform and that periodicities in $s(t)$ appear as peaks in the transform, as illustrated by example (c).

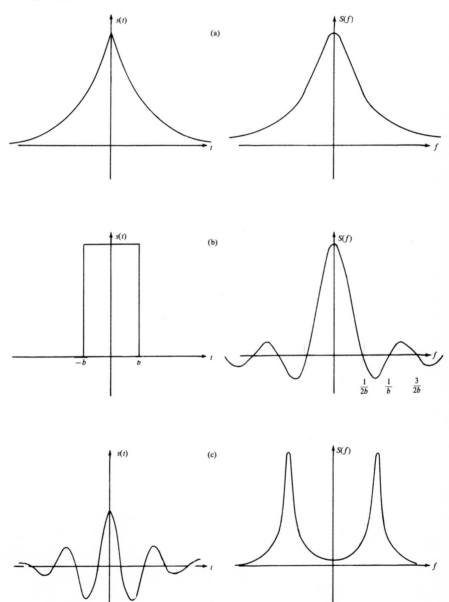

FIG. 2.3: Some simple signals and their Fourier transforms

TABLE 2.4: Some simple functions and their Fourier transforms

$s(t)$	$S(f)$
$e^{-\|t\|}$ $\quad(-\infty \leqslant t \leqslant \infty)$	$2/[1 + (2\pi f)^2]$
$\begin{cases} 0, & \|t\| > b \\ a, & \|t\| \leqslant b \end{cases}$	$2ab \, \dfrac{\sin 2\pi fb}{2\pi fb}$
$e^{-a\|t\|} \cos 2\pi f_0 t$	$\dfrac{a}{a^2 + [2\pi(f + f_0)]^2} + \dfrac{a}{a^2 + [2a(f - f_0)]^2}$

The signals in Table 2.4 are all even functions of t, and hence their Fourier transforms are real and even functions. In general this is not the case; for example, suppose $s(t)$ is the odd function

$$s(t) = \begin{cases} 0, & t < 0 \\ e^{-t}, & 0 \leqslant t \leqslant \infty. \end{cases}$$

Then, using (2.1.24),

$$S(f) = \frac{1}{1 + j2\pi f}.$$

This transform is complex and may be written as the sum of a real and imaginary part,

$$S(f) = \frac{1}{1 + (2\pi f)^2} - j \frac{2\pi f}{1 + (2\pi f)^2}.$$

Alternatively, it may be written in terms of an amplitude and phase function

$$S(f) = \frac{1}{1 + (2\pi f)^2} \exp\left(-j \arctan 2\pi f\right)$$

using (2.1.13), so that

$$R(f) = \frac{1}{\sqrt{1 + (2\pi f)^2}}, \qquad \phi(f) = \arctan -2\pi f.$$

Note that all these transforms damp out or "dissipate" as f tends to infinity. Situations will now be considered where the transform does not damp out.

2.2.2 Generalized functions

Consider two special cases of the rectangular pulse which was the second example in Table 2.4.

Unit height. If $a = 1$, then

$$S(f) = 2b \frac{\sin 2\pi fb}{2\pi fb}. \tag{2.2.1}$$

If b tends to infinity, $s(t)$ tends to a constant, equal to 1 everywhere. The behavior of $S(f)$ as b increases is illustrated in Figure 2.4, where it may be seen that $S(f)$ tends to a spike at $f = 0$. In the limit, $S(f)$ tends to a spike of infinite height at $f = 0$ and is bounded everywhere else. This is what is meant by a Dirac delta or impulse function. Hence *the Fourier transform of a constant is a delta function.*

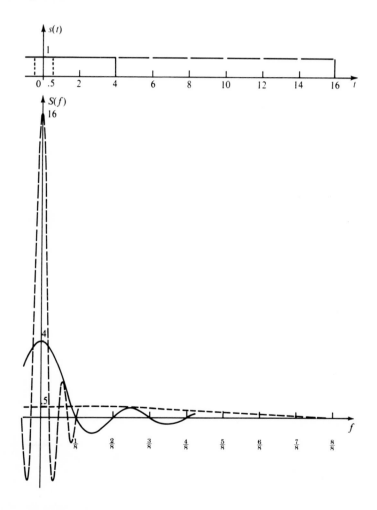

FIG. 2.4: Unit height rectangular pulses and their Fourier transforms

Unit area. If $2ab = 1$, then

$$S(f) = \frac{\sin 2\pi f b}{2\pi f b}.$$ (2.2.2)

As b tends to zero, $S(f)$ tends to unity everywhere. However, as b decreases $s(t)$ becomes taller and taller, as illustrated in Figure 2.5. It follows that $s(t)$ tends to a delta function at the origin.

These two cases show that the Fourier transform of a constant is a delta function and, conversely, that the Fourier transform of a delta function is a constant. This reciprocity is to be expected from the symmetry of the transform equations (2.1.22) and (2.1.24).

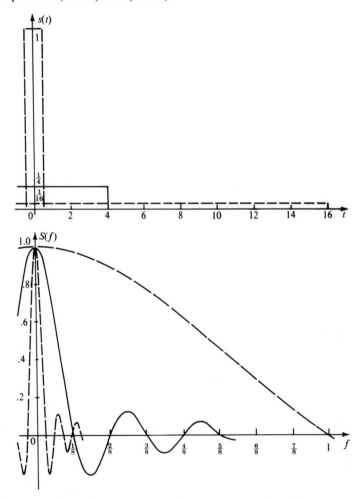

FIG. 2.5: Unit area rectangular pulses and their Fourier transforms

Delta functions. The sequence of functions (2.2.1) as b tends to infinity is not the only one which can be used to define a delta function. In general a delta function may be defined as a sequence of functions $\delta_n(t)$ such that

$$\int_{-\infty}^{\infty} \delta_n(t)\, dt = 1, \quad \text{for every } n, \tag{2.2.3}$$

and in the limit as n tends to ∞,

$$\delta(t) = \begin{cases} 0, & t \neq 0, \\ \infty, & t = 0. \end{cases} \tag{2.2.4}$$

Examples of such sequences of functions, together with their Fourier transforms, are given in Table 2.5. Note that $S_n(f)$ tends to a constant, unity, for all f as n tends to infinity.

TABLE 2.5: Sequences defining delta functions

	$\delta_n(t)$	$S_n(f)$
1.	$2n\,\dfrac{\sin 2\pi nt}{2\pi nt}$	$\begin{aligned}1,\quad &\lvert f\rvert \le n \\ 0,\quad &\lvert f\rvert > n\end{aligned}$
2.	$\sqrt{n}\,e^{-\pi nt^2}$	$e^{-\pi f^2/n}$
3.	$\dfrac{n}{2}\,e^{-n\lvert t\rvert}$	$\dfrac{n^2}{n^2 + (2\pi f)^2}$
4.	$\dfrac{1}{\pi}\,\dfrac{n}{n^2 t^2 + 1}$	$e^{-\lvert 2\pi f/n\rvert}$
5.	$\dfrac{n\sin^2(\pi nt)}{(\pi nt)^2}$	$\begin{aligned}1 - \dfrac{\lvert f\rvert}{n},\quad &\lvert f\rvert \le n \\ 0,\quad &\lvert f\rvert > n\end{aligned}$

One physical interpretation of the delta function is that of an input of energy into a system. Using an example from mechanics, suppose that a hard block is resting on a plane surface. If a very small but high-speed bullet is fired at the block, an exchange of energy occurs when the bullet rebounds. Assuming that the collision occurs so rapidly that the block does not have time to move, the bullet may be regarded as having imparted to the block an impulse of energy in the form of a change of momentum. An alternative interpretation drawn from electromagnetic theory is that of a unit point charge at the origin.

The delta function may be used as an operational device for picking out the value of a signal at a given instant of time. This is contained in the result

$$\lim_{n \to \infty} \int_{-\infty}^{\infty} \delta_n(t - t_0)s(t) \, dt = \int_{-\infty}^{\infty} \delta(t - t_0)s(t) \, dt = s(t_0). \quad (2.2.5)$$

In a similar manner, by considering the limit of the sequence of mth derivatives of $\delta_n(t)$ [1], it is possible to define the mth derivative of a delta function, namely $\delta^{(m)}(t)$. This can be used to select the mth derivative of a function at a given point. This leads to a generalization of (2.2.5), namely

$$\int_{-\infty}^{\infty} \delta^{(m)}(t - t_0)s(t) \, dt = (-1)^m s^{(m)}(t_0). \quad (2.2.6)$$

Referring to the interpretation of a delta function as a unit charge at the origin, the first derivative $\delta'(t)$ corresponds to the mathematical idealization of a unit dipole. This is because the first moment of $\delta'(t)$ is

$$\int_{-\infty}^{\infty} t \, \delta'(t) \, dt = -1,$$

using (2.2.6). Hence, the moment of $\delta'(t)$ is unity, which is the standard definition for a unit dipole.

The unit step function. A function closely related to the delta function is the *unit step function*. This corresponds physically either to the application of a unit force which is then maintained or to a change in a valve position which alters the flow in a pipe by a unit amount. Mathematically this is a signal described by

$$U(t) = \begin{cases} 0, & t < 0, \\ \frac{1}{2}, & t = 0, \\ 1, & t > 0. \end{cases} \quad (2.2.7)$$

The function $U(t)$ may be regarded as the limit of a sequence of functions $U_n(t)$, for example, the limit as n tends to infinity of

$$U_n(t) = \begin{cases} \frac{1}{2}e^{nt}, & t < 0, \\ 1 - \frac{1}{2}e^{-nt}, & t \geqslant 0. \end{cases} \quad (2.2.8)$$

As n tends to infinity, $U_n(t)$ tends to zero for t negative and to unity for t positive. Differentiating $U_n(t)$ gives

$$\frac{d}{dt}U_n(t) = \frac{n}{2} e^{-n|t|} = \delta_n(t), \quad (2.2.9)$$

which illustrates the important result that the derivative of a step function is a delta function.

The Fourier transform of the unit step function (2.2.7) is

$$S(f) = \tfrac{1}{2}\delta(f) + \frac{1}{j2\pi f}.$$

2.2.3 *Fourier series as Fourier transforms*

Consider the Fourier transform of the signal

$$s_T(t) = \begin{cases} a \cos \dfrac{2\pi t}{\Delta}, & -\dfrac{T}{2} \leqslant t \leqslant \dfrac{T}{2}, \\ 0, & |t| > \dfrac{T}{2}, \end{cases} \qquad (2.2.10)$$

which is a "periodic" signal in the interval $-T/2$ to $+T/2$. Using (2.1.24) directly, its Fourier transform is

$$S_T(f) = \frac{a}{2} \left\{ T \frac{\sin \pi T[f - (1/\Delta)]}{\pi T[f - (1/\Delta)]} + T \frac{\sin \pi T[f + (1/\Delta)]}{\pi T[f + (1/\Delta)]} \right\}. \qquad (2.2.11)$$

As T tends to infinity, the signal $s_T(t)$ becomes a truly periodic signal $s(t)$, periodic for all time, while the transform $S_T(f)$ tends to

$$S(f) = \frac{a}{2} \left\{ \delta\left(f - \frac{1}{\Delta}\right) + \delta\left(f + \frac{1}{\Delta}\right) \right\}, \qquad (2.2.12)$$

since each of the terms inside the braces is a sequence defining a delta function. Hence, the Fourier transform of a truly periodic (infinite extent) cosine wave consists of a delta function of area $a/2$ centered at $f = +(1/\Delta)$ and a delta function of area $a/2$ at $f = -(1/\Delta)$.

Similarly, the complex signal

$$s_T(t) = e^{j(2\pi m t/\Delta)}, \qquad -\frac{T}{2} \leqslant t \leqslant \frac{T}{2},$$

has the Fourier transform

$$S_T(f) = T \frac{\sin \pi T[f - (m/\Delta)]}{\pi T[f - (m/\Delta)]}.$$

Hence as T tends to infinity, $S_T(f)$ tends to $S(f) = \delta[f - (m/\Delta)]$. It follows that a periodic signal of period Δ with the Fourier series representation

$$s(t) = \sum_{m=-\infty}^{\infty} S_m e^{j(2\pi m t/\Delta)} \qquad (2.2.13)$$

has the Fourier transform

$$S(f) = \sum_{m=-\infty}^{\infty} S_m \delta\left(f - \frac{m}{\Delta}\right), \qquad (2.2.14)$$

which is a train of delta functions. Thus, by allowing generalized functions, Fourier series may be regarded as a special case of Fourier transforms.

To find the Fourier coefficients S_m corresponding to a generalized function, the classical formula (2.1.18) is no longer applicable since a generalized function cannot be integrated between finite limits. The appropriate formula to use in these circumstances is given in [1].

In particular, it may be shown that the Fourier transform of a train of delta functions

$$s(t) = \sum_{n=-\infty}^{\infty} \delta(t - n\Delta) \qquad (2.2.15)$$

is

$$S(f) = \frac{1}{\Delta} \sum_{n=-\infty}^{\infty} \delta\left(f - \frac{n}{\Delta}\right). \qquad (2.2.16)$$

Hence a train of delta functions transforms into a train of delta functions. Note that this result is symmetrical in the time and frequency domain.

The train of delta functions is not the only function which has a symmetric transformation. A much simpler function possessing this property is given by example 2 of Table 2.5 with $n = 1$. Thus, $s(t) = \exp(-\pi t^2)$ transforms to $S(f) = \exp(-\pi f^2)$.

At this point, the reader should satisfy himself that he is familiar with the various operational properties of Fourier transforms summarized in Appendix A2.1.

2.3 LINEAR SYSTEMS AND CONVOLUTION

2.3.1 Linear differential equations

One important reason for the usefulness of Fourier and spectral analysis is that they simplify the analysis of *time invariant linear systems*, that is, systems whose behavior can be described by linear integro-differential equations with constant coefficients. It may be shown in general [3] that the solution to such an equation may be written as a convolution integral

$$y(t) = \int_{-\infty}^{\infty} h(u)x(t - u)\, du, \qquad (2.3.1)$$

where $y(t)$ is the solution and $x(t)$ is the forcing function. It will be shown in Section 2.3.4 that the solution is simplified by Fourier transforms. The transform of the solution becomes

$$Y(f) = H(f)X(f),$$

where $Y(f)$, $H(f)$ and $X(f)$ are the Fourier transforms of $y(t)$, $h(t)$ and $x(t)$ respectively. Thus, convolution in the time domain transforms to multiplication in the frequency domain.

An illustration of convolution. As an example of a convolution integral, consider a simple linear system consisting of a spring and a dashpot, shown schematically in Figure 2.6. One use of such a device is to prevent screen doors from closing too violently when released. A force applied to the spring produces an *input* displacement $x(t)$ which causes an *output* displacement $y(t)$ of the dashpot wiper. The differential equation obtained by equating forces is then

$$K[x(t) - y(t)] = D\frac{dy}{dt},$$

where K is the spring constant in pounds per foot and D is the velocity constant of the dashpot (in pounds per foot per second). Rearranging this equation gives

$$T\frac{dy}{dt} + y(t) = x(t), \tag{2.3.2}$$

where $T = D/K$ is the *time constant* of the system (in seconds).

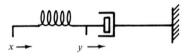

FIG. 2.6: A first-order mechanical system

Equation (2.3.2) may be used to describe the behavior of many other physical systems, for example, the temperature $y(t)$ in the outlet from a chemical reactor when the inlet temperature is $x(t)$. Equation (2.3.2) then shows that the rate of change of temperature in the outlet is directly proportional to the temperature gradient across the reactor.

The solution to equation (2.3.2) can be written as a convolution integral by introducing the integrating factor $e^{t/T}$. Thus

$$y(t) = \int_{-\infty}^{t} x(u)\frac{e^{-(t-u)/T}}{T}\,du$$

$$= \int_{-\infty}^{\infty} x(u)h(t-u)\,du, \tag{2.3.3}$$

where

$$h(u) = \begin{cases} \dfrac{1}{T}e^{-u/T}, & u \geqslant 0, \\ 0, & u < 0. \end{cases}$$

Hence the output $y(t)$ may be written as a *weighted sum* of past values of the input $x(t)$, that is, the output is a *convolution* of the input with the *weighting function* $h(u)$.

It may be shown in general [3] that the solution to any linear time-invariant differential equation may be written as in (2.3.3) or, by making a change in variable, as

$$y(t) = \int_{-\infty}^{\infty} h(u)x(t - u)\, du. \tag{2.3.4}$$

The weighting function completely characterizes the behavior of the system, just as the differential equation does.

Time-invariant linear systems. Equations (2.3.3) and (2.3.4) are general representations of what are known as *time-invariant linear systems* or filters. These are characterized by the following properties:

(a) *Linear property*: If $x_1(t)$ and $x_2(t)$ are two inputs to the system, and $y_1(t)$, $y_2(t)$ the corresponding outputs, then a linear compound $\mu_1 x_1(t) + \mu_2 x_2(t)$ of the inputs produces the *same* linear compound of the outputs, $\mu_1 y_1(t) + \mu_2 y_2(t)$.

(b) *Time-invariant property*: If the input $x(t)$ is delayed by an amount τ to give $x(t - \tau)$, the output is delayed by the same amount and is $y(t - \tau)$.

It is property (b) which ensures that the weight function $h(u)$ is independent of time. A linear system without the time-invariant property would have a weight function which depended on time t.

Systems which can be described by means of linear differential equations with constant coefficients can be shown to have the time-invariant representation (2.3.3). However, many non-linear systems can be *linearized* so that, for small perturbations in the input, (2.3.3) can be used as an approximate representation of the system.

2.3.2 Step and impulse functions

For any physical system the weight function $h(u)$ must be zero for negative values of u, which means that the system cannot respond to inputs it has not yet received. This is called the condition of physical realizability. For physically realizable systems, equations (2.3.3) and (2.3.4) may be written

$$y(t) = \int_{0}^{\infty} h(u)x(t - u)\, du, \tag{2.3.5}$$

or

$$y(t) = \int_{-\infty}^{t} x(u)h(t - u)\, du. \tag{2.3.6}$$

Impulse response functions. Suppose that the system is given a sharp impulse at time $t = 0$ so that $x(t) = \delta(t)$. Then

$$y(t) = \int_{-\infty}^{\infty} h(u)\, \delta(t - u)\, du, \tag{2.3.7}$$

which equals $h(t)$ using (2.2.5). The weight function $h(t)$ is called the *impulse response* function [4] of the system since it measures the output at time t of a system subjected to an impulse at $t = 0$.

The impulse responses for a number of simple systems are given in the first column of Table 2.6. Figure 2.7 shows the impulse responses for three of these systems. The first example (a) is a system with simple delay for which the output or impulse response is another impulse at time τ later. The second (b) is a system described by a single time-constant and represented by the differential equation (2.3.2) for which the impulse response is the exponential curve of Figure 2.7(b). The third example (c) is a second-order system represented by the differential equation

$$\frac{1}{\omega_n^2} \frac{d^2y}{dt^2} + \frac{2\zeta}{\omega_n} \frac{dy}{dt} + y = x(t), \tag{2.3.8}$$

for which the impulse response is a damped sine wave as in Figure 2.7(c).

Step response functions. It is also possible to characterize a linear system by its response to the unit step function (2.2.7). Suppose, for example, that the input is the flow rate of cold water into a heat exchanger and the output the outlet temperature. Then the step response is the variation of outlet temperature with time when a unit change is made to the input flow rate. From (2.3.5), the response at time t to a unit step at time $t = 0$ is

$$y(t) = \int_0^t h(u) \, du, \tag{2.3.9}$$

so the step response is the integral of the impulse response.

From Figure 2.7 it may be seen that the step response to a system with a pure delay τ is another step starting at time τ later, as shown in (a). For the exponential impulse response, the step response builds up exponentially to its ultimate value, as in (b). For the second-order system (c), the step response overshoots its ultimate value and then oscillates about this value with decreasing amplitude.

As t tends to infinity, the step response (2.3.9) tends to its limiting or ultimate value

$$g = \int_0^\infty h(u) \, du, \tag{2.3.10}$$

which is called the *steady state gain* of the system, since it measures the ultimate amplification of a unit step change after the system has been allowed to settle down to its new steady state value.

Stability. A system is said to be *stable* [4] if a bounded input produces a bounded output. Clearly this is desirable, since otherwise the output would

TABLE 2.6: Impulse, step, and frequen

System	Impulse response $h(t)$	Step response $y(t)$
1. gain	$g\,\delta(t)$	g
2. delay	$\delta(t - \tau)$	$\begin{matrix}0, & t < \tau \\ 1, & t \geqslant \tau\end{matrix}$
3. integration	1	t
4. single exponential	$\dfrac{1}{T}\,e^{-t/T}\cdot$	$(1 - e^{-t/T})$
5. single exponential plus delay	$\begin{matrix}0, & t < \tau \\ \dfrac{1}{T}e^{-(t-\tau)/T}, & t \geqslant \tau\end{matrix}$	$\begin{matrix}0, & t < \tau \\ (1 - e^{-(t-\tau)/T}), & t \geqslant \tau\end{matrix}$
6. two time constants	$\dfrac{e^{-t/T_1} - e^{-t/T_2}}{T_1 - T_2}$	$\left(1 - \dfrac{T_1\,e^{-t/T_1} - T_2\,e^{-t/T_2}}{T_1 - T_2}\right.$
7. quadratic lag	$\dfrac{\omega_n\,e^{-\zeta\omega_n t}\sin(\omega_n\sqrt{1 - \zeta^2}\,t)}{\sqrt{1 - \zeta^2}}$	$1 - \dfrac{e^{-\zeta\omega_n t}\sin(\omega_n\sqrt{1-\zeta^2}\,t+}{\sqrt{1 - \zeta^2}}$ $\sin\phi = \sqrt{1 - \zeta^2}$
8. differentiation	$\delta'(t)$	$-\delta(t)$
9. linear lead	$\delta(t) + T\,\delta'(t)$	$1 - T\,\delta(t)$

increase without limit. Suppose that $|x(t)| \leqslant K_1$ in (2.3.5), where K_1 is a finite constant. Then

$$|y(t)| = \left|\int_{-\infty}^{\infty} h(u)x(t - u)\,du\right| \leqslant \int_{-\infty}^{\infty} |h(u)|\,|x(t - u)|\,du$$

$$\leqslant K_1 \int_{-\infty}^{\infty} |h(u)|\,du,$$

so a sufficient condition for the system to be stable is that

$$\int_{-\infty}^{\infty} |h(u)|\,du < K_2, \qquad (2.3.11)$$

responses for some simple systems

Frequency response $H(f)$	Gain $G(f)$	Phase $\phi(f)$
g	g	0
$e^{-j2\pi f\tau}$	1	$-2\pi f\tau$
$\dfrac{1}{j2\pi f}$	$\dfrac{1}{2\pi f}$	$-\dfrac{\pi}{2}$
$\dfrac{1}{1 + j2\pi fT}$	$\dfrac{1}{\{1 + (2\pi fT)^2\}^{1/2}}$	$-\arctan 2\pi fT$
$\dfrac{e^{-j2\pi f\tau}}{(1 + j2\pi fT)}$	$\dfrac{1}{\{1 + (2\pi fT)^2\}^{1/2}}$	$-2\pi f\tau - \arctan 2\pi fT$
$\dfrac{1}{(1 + j2\pi fT_1)(1 + j2\pi fT_2)}$	$\dfrac{1}{\{[1 + (2\pi fT_1)^2][1 + (2\pi fT_2)^2]\}^{1/2}}$	$-\arctan 2\pi fT_1$ $-\arctan 2\pi fT_2$
$\dfrac{1}{1 - (f/f_n)^2 + j2\zeta(f/f_n)}$ $\omega_n = 2\pi f_n$	$\dfrac{1}{\{[1 - (f/f_n)^2]^2 + [2(\zeta f/f_n)]^2\}^{1/2}}$	$-\arctan \dfrac{2\zeta(f/f_n)}{[1 - (f/f_n)^2]}$
$j2\pi f$	$2\pi f$	$\dfrac{\pi}{2}$
$1 + j2\pi fT$	$\{1 + (2\pi fT)^2\}^{1/2}$	$\arctan 2\pi fT$

where K_2 is also a finite constant. An alternative form for the stability condition will be given in the next section.

2.3.3 Frequency response functions

For inputs more complicated than an impulse or a step, the calculation of the output by means of the convolution integral (2.3.5) is tedious. This problem is considerably simplified by making use of Fourier analysis. The approach consists of splitting up $s(t)$ into its Fourier components $S(f)$, as in (2.1.24), finding the response of the system to a periodic signal $s_1(t) = e^{j2\pi ft}$, and then adding up the responses according to (2.1.22) to give

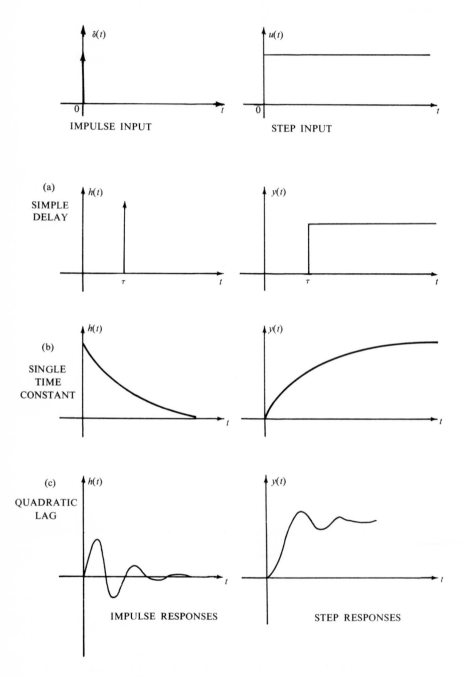

FIG. 2.7: Impulse and step responses for some simple systems

the final output. First it is necessary to know the response of the system to an input $x(t) = \cos 2\pi ft$. Substitution of this input in (2.3.5) yields

$$y(t) = \int_0^\infty h(u) \cos 2\pi f(t - u)\, du$$

$$= \int_0^\infty h(u) \left[\cos 2\pi ft \cos 2\pi fu + \sin 2\pi ft \sin 2\pi fu\right] du$$

$$= A(f) \cos 2\pi ft + B(f) \sin 2\pi ft, \qquad (2.3.12)$$

where

$$A(f) = \int_0^\infty h(u) \cos 2\pi fu\, du \qquad (2.3.13)$$

and

$$B(f) = \int_0^\infty h(u) \sin 2\pi fu\, du. \qquad (2.3.14)$$

Alternatively, (2.3.12) may be rewritten

$$y(t) = G(f) \cos [2\pi ft + \phi(f)], \qquad (2.3.15)$$

where

$$G(f) = \sqrt{A^2(f) + B^2(f)}$$

and

$$\phi(f) = \arctan - \frac{B(f)}{A(f)}.$$

Hence the response to a cosine wave of frequency f is a cosine wave at the same frequency but scaled in amplitude by a factor $G(f)$ called the *gain* and shifted in phase by an amount $\phi(f)$ called the *phase angle*.

As before, it is operationally more convenient to consider the response to a complex input

$$e^{j2\pi ft} = \cos 2\pi ft + j \sin 2\pi ft,$$

of frequency f. In this case the output is

$$y(t) = H(f)\, e^{j2\pi ft} = G(f)\, e^{j[2\pi ft + \phi(f)]}, \qquad (2.3.16)$$

where

$$H(f) = G(f)\, e^{j\phi(f)} = \int_0^\infty h(u)\, e^{-j2\pi fu}\, du \qquad (2.3.17)$$

is called the *frequency response function* of the system. Hence the frequency response function is the Fourier transform of the impulse response function.

Bode plots. The frequency response functions, gains and phases of some simple systems are given in Table 2.6 and the gains and phases are plotted in Figure 2.8. It is customary to plot the logarithm of gain against the logarithm of

SYSTEM   GAIN FUNCTION   PHASE FUNCTION

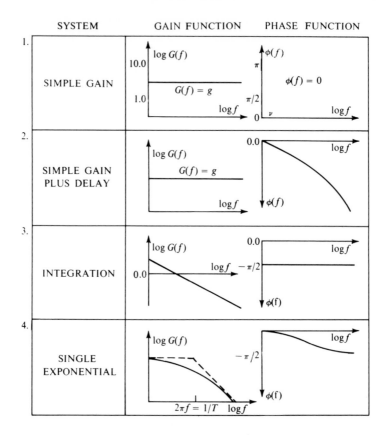

FIG. 2.8: Bode plots for some simple systems

frequency and the phase against the logarithm of frequency. These graphs
are usually called *Bode plots* [5]. The diagrams in Figure 2.8 fall naturally
into four categories:

(1) Numbers 1 and 2 have a gain which is constant with frequency and are
called *all-pass* systems.

(2) Numbers 3, 4, 5 and 6 are such that high frequencies are rejected or
attenuated by the system and low frequencies transmitted with different
gains. These systems therefore behave as low pass filters and are associated
with some form of integration or smoothing of the input.

(3) Number 7 corresponds to an oscillatory system, described by equation (2.3.8). Here the gain plot has a *resonance* or peak at a frequency
$f = f_n(1 - 2\zeta^2)^{1/2}$, where f_n is the natural resonant frequency of the system.

(4) Numbers 8 and 9 have gain plots which are such that the lower frequencies are attenuated and the higher frequencies passed. These systems act

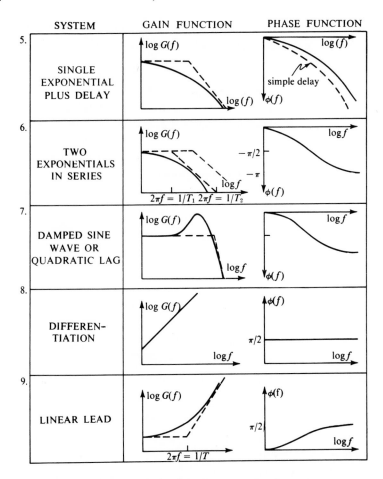

FIG. 2.8 (cont.): Bode plots for some simple systems

as *high pass filters* and involve differentiation of the input. A further difference between categories *(2)* and *(4)* is that in *(2)* integration of the input results in negative phases $\phi(f)$, that is, the output *lags* behind the input. On the other hand, in *(4)* differentiation of the input yields positive phases, so the output *leads* the input as in plot number 9.

Bandwidth. A convenient way of describing the gain function of a linear system is by its *bandwidth* [5]. Various definitions of bandwidth have been suggested, the simplest of which is the half-power bandwidth. For a system which has its maximum gain at f_0, this is defined as the frequency difference $f_2 - f_1$, where f_1 and f_2 are chosen so that

$$G^2(f_1) = G^2(f_2) = \tfrac{1}{2}G^2(f_0).$$

For example, the maximum gain occurs at $f_0 = 0$ for the single exponential system, and the half-power gain occurs at $f = 1/(2\pi T)$. Hence if T is large the bandwidth is very small, as may be seen from Figure 2.8. The impulse response will thus be very wide, and small in amplitude. On the other hand, for T small the bandwidth is large and the impulse response very tall and narrow. In the limiting case as T tends to zero, the bandwidth becomes infinite, as for the simple gain of Figure 2.8, and the impulse response tends to a delta function. Hence wide bandwidths are associated with narrow impulse response functions and, conversely, narrow bandwidths are associated with wide impulse response functions.

Stability. The systems of Table 2.6 can be represented by a differential equation of the general form

$$a_m \frac{d^m y(t)}{dt^m} + \cdots + a_1 \frac{dy(t)}{dt} + a_0 y(t) =$$

$$b_n \frac{d^n x(t - \tau)}{dt^n} + \cdots + b_1 \frac{dx(t - \tau)}{dt} + b_0 x(t - \tau). \quad (2.3.18)$$

Substituting $x(t) = e^{j2\pi ft}$, $y(t) = H(f) e^{j2\pi ft}$ in (2.3.18), it follows that the frequency response function is

$$H(f) = \frac{b_n(j2\pi f)^n + \cdots + b_1(j2\pi f) + b_0}{a_m(j2\pi f)^m + \cdots + a_1(j2\pi f) + a_0} \cdot e^{-j2\pi f\tau}. \quad (2.3.19)$$

Substituting $p = j2\pi f$ in (2.3.19) and equating the denominator to zero gives the *characteristic equation* of the system, namely

$$a_m p^m + \cdots + a_1 p + a_0 = 0. \quad (2.3.20)$$

The condition (2.3.11) that the system be stable may be shown [4] to be equivalent to the condition that the roots $\pi_1, \pi_2, \ldots, \pi_m$ of the characteristic equation (2.3.20) have negative real parts.

2.3.4 *Response to an arbitrary input*

If it is known that the response of a system to an input $x(t) = e^{j2\pi ft}$ is $y(t) = H(f) e^{j2\pi ft}$, it is possible to find the response to an arbitrary input. The first step is to Fourier transform the input to give

$$X(f) = \int_{-\infty}^{\infty} x(t) e^{-j2\pi ft} dt. \quad (2.3.21)$$

The Fourier component of the output at frequency f is

$$Y(f) = \int_{-\infty}^{\infty} e^{-j2\pi ft} \left[\int_{-\infty}^{\infty} h(u)x(t - u) du \right] dt$$

$$= \int_{-\infty}^{\infty} h(u) e^{-j2\pi fu} du \int_{-\infty}^{\infty} x(v) e^{-j2\pi fv} dv, \quad (2.3.22)$$

where $v = t - u$, that is,

$$Y(f) = H(f)X(f). \tag{2.3.23}$$

Equation (2.3.23) states that the component at frequency f in the output is obtained by multiplying the component at the *same* frequency in the input by $H(f)$, the frequency response function at that frequency. Finally, to recover $y(t)$, it is necessary to synthesize or add up the contributions from all frequencies at the same value of t, which gives

$$y(t) = \int_{-\infty}^{\infty} Y(f) e^{j2\pi ft} \, df = \int_{-\infty}^{\infty} X(f)H(f) e^{j2\pi ft} \, df. \tag{2.3.24}$$

Equations (2.3.22) to (2.3.24) show that *convolution* in the time domain is equivalent to *multiplication* in the frequency domain. Hence, if a relationship between two variables exists in the form of a differential equation (2.3.18), the solution is (2.3.24), where the frequency response function is given by (2.3.19). Hence, the Fourier transform provides an extremely useful operational method for solving linear differential equations.

The solution may be expedited by using tables of transforms. A table of transforms of generalized functions is given in [1] while Fourier transforms of more common functions are given in [6].

Several linear systems in series. Consider k non-interacting linear systems in series, as shown in Figure 2.9. Repeated use of (2.3.23) gives

$$Y(f) = H_k(f) \, H_{k-1}(f) \cdots H_1(f) \, X(f), \tag{2.3.25}$$

which shows that for linear systems in series the overall frequency response function is the product of the frequency response functions of the individual

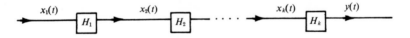

FIG. 2.9: Several linear systems in series

systems. Using (2.3.17) it follows that the overall gain is the *product* of the individual gains

$$G(f) = G_1(f) \, G_2(f) \cdots G_k(f), \tag{2.3.26}$$

and the overall phase shift is the *sum* of the individual phase shifts

$$\phi(f) = \phi_1(f) + \phi_2(f) + \cdots + \phi_k(f). \tag{2.3.27}$$

The output of the system may now be computed by adding up the contributions at all frequencies in the form

$$y(t) = \int_{-\infty}^{\infty} H_1(f) \, H_2(f) \cdots H_k(f) \, X(f) e^{j2\pi ft} \, df. \tag{2.3.28}$$

Note that only one integration is required, whereas the time-domain calcula-tion would have required the evaluation of k convolution integrals.

2.3.5 *Linear difference equations*

In the preceding sections, it was shown that a system described by a linear differential equation may also be described by means of an impulse response function $h(u)$ or a frequency response function $H(f)$, where $h(u)$ and $H(f)$ form a Fourier transform pair. The functions $h(u)$ and $H(f)$ are easily obtained from the differential equation describing the system. In this section it is shown how impulse and frequency response functions may be used to describe a system which is characterized by a linear *difference* equation.

A linear difference equation is an equation of the form

$$y_r = \alpha_1 y_{r-1} + \alpha_2 y_{r-2} + \cdots + \alpha_m y_{r-m} + \beta_0 x_r + \cdots + \beta_n x_{r-n}, \quad (2.3.29)$$

and has a general solution

$$y_r = \sum_{k=0}^{\infty} h_k x_{r-k}. \quad (2.3.30)$$

The quantities $y_r, y_{r-1}, \ldots, y_{r-m}$ and $x_r, x_{r-1}, \ldots, x_{r-n}$ could be values of continuous signals $y(t)$ and $x(t)$ at the instants $t = r\Delta,\ (r-1)\Delta, \ldots,$ $(r-m)\Delta,\ (r-n)\Delta$ respectively, that is,

$$y(t) = \alpha_1 y(t-\Delta) + \alpha_2 y(t-2\Delta)$$
$$+ \cdots + \alpha_m y(t-m\Delta) + \beta_0 x(t) + \cdots + \beta_n x(t-n\Delta). \quad (2.3.31)$$

The Fourier transform of (2.3.31) may be arranged in the form

$$Y(f) = \frac{\beta_0 + \beta_1 e^{-j2\pi f\Delta} + \cdots + \beta_n e^{-j2\pi fn\Delta}}{1 - \alpha_1 e^{-j2\pi f\Delta} - \cdots - \alpha_m e^{-j2\pi fm\Delta}} X(f),$$

so that the frequency response function $H(f)$ of the system is, from (2.3.23),

$$H(f) = \frac{\beta_0 + \beta_1 e^{-j2\pi f\Delta} + \cdots + \beta_n e^{-j2\pi fn\Delta}}{1 - \alpha_1 e^{-j2\pi f\Delta} - \cdots - \alpha_m e^{-j2\pi fm\Delta}}. \quad (2.3.32)$$

The frequency response function $H(f)$ and the discrete impulse response function h_k are related by

$$H(f) = \sum_{k=0}^{\infty} h_k e^{-j2\pi fk\Delta} \quad (2.3.33)$$

and

$$h_k = \Delta \int_{-1/(2\Delta)}^{1/(2\Delta)} H(f) e^{j2\pi fk\Delta} \, df. \quad (2.3.34)$$

$\mathcal{Z}$ *transforms.* The frequency response function (2.3.32) is best handled by making a substitution of the form $\mathcal{Z} = e^{j2\pi f\Delta}$ yielding

$$H(Z) = \frac{\beta_0 + \beta_1 Z^{-1} + \cdots + \beta_n Z^{-n}}{1 - \alpha_1 Z^{-1} - \cdots - \alpha_m Z^{-m}} = \sum_{k=0}^{\infty} h_k Z^{-k}, \qquad (2.3.35)$$

which is the Z transform [7] of the impulse response function h_k.

From an *operational* point of view, Z in (2.3.35) may be regarded as a *shift operator* with the property

$$Z^{-k} x_r = x_{r-k}. \qquad (2.3.36)$$

Hence the difference equation (2.3.29) may be written

$$(1 - \alpha_1 Z^{-1} - \alpha_2 Z^{-2} - \cdots - \alpha_m Z^{-m}) y_r =$$
$$(\beta_0 + \beta_1 Z^{-1} + \cdots + \beta_n Z^{-n}) x_r, \qquad (2.3.37)$$

that is,

$$y_r = \frac{(\beta_0 + \beta_1 Z^{-1} + \cdots + \beta_n Z^{-n})}{(1 - \alpha_1 Z^{-1} - \cdots - \alpha_m Z^{-m})} x_r = H(Z) x_r,$$

where $H(Z)$ is the *transfer function* of the discrete system. Expanding $H(Z)$ in powers of Z^{-1} gives

$$y_r = \sum_{k=0}^{\infty} h_k Z^{-k} x_r = \sum_{k=0}^{\infty} h_k x_{r-k},$$

which is the general solution (2.3.30).

Stability. Factoring Z^{-m}, substituting $p = Z$ and equating the denominator of (2.3.35) to zero gives the characteristic equation of the discrete system

$$p^m - \alpha_1 p^{m-1} - \cdots - \alpha_m = 0. \qquad (2.3.38)$$

The stability condition corresponding to (2.3.11) is

$$\sum_{k=0}^{\infty} |h_k| < K_2. \qquad (2.3.39)$$

Similarly, the stability condition corresponding to (2.3.20) is that the roots $\pi_1, \ldots, \pi_m$ of the characteristic equation (2.3.38) lie inside the unit circle.

Example. Consider the second-order difference equation

$$y_r = \alpha_1 y_{r-1} + \alpha_2 y_{r-2} + x_r. \qquad (2.3.40)$$

This has the Z transform

$$(1 - \alpha_1 Z^{-1} - \alpha_2 Z^{-2}) y_r = x_r,$$

and hence the transfer function

$$H(Z) = \frac{1}{1 - \alpha_1 Z^{-1} - \alpha_2 Z^{-2}}. \qquad (2.3.41)$$

The characteristic equation is

$$p^2 - \alpha_1 p - \alpha_2 = 0,$$

which has roots

$$\pi_1 = \frac{\alpha_1 - \sqrt{\alpha_1^2 + 4\alpha_2}}{2}, \qquad \pi_2 = \frac{\alpha_1 + \sqrt{\alpha_1^2 + 4\alpha_2}}{2}. \qquad (2.3.42)$$

The impulse response function for this system takes the form

$$h_k = \frac{1}{\pi_1 - \pi_2} \{\pi_1^{k+1} - \pi_2^{k+1}\} \qquad (2.3.43)$$

when the roots are real, that is, when $\alpha_1^2 \geqslant -4\alpha_2$. When the roots are complex, that is, $\alpha_1^2 < -4\alpha_2$,

$$h_k = R^k \frac{\sin 2\pi f_0(k+1)}{\sin 2\pi f_0}, \qquad (2.3.44)$$

where

$$\pi_1 = R\, e^{j2\pi f_0},$$
$$\pi_2 = R\, e^{-j2\pi f_0}.$$

The system is stable provided $|\pi_1| < 1$, $|\pi_2| < 1$, that is, provided α_1 and α_2 lie in the triangular region

$$\alpha_1 + \alpha_2 < 1,$$
$$\alpha_1 - \alpha_2 > -1, \qquad (2.3.45)$$
$$-1 < \alpha_2 < 1.$$

2.4 APPLICATIONS TO TIME SERIES ANALYSIS

2.4.1 Finite-length records

In practice it is only possible to obtain finite lengths of records. The statistical questions to be discussed later stem from the fact that it is necessary to estimate the accuracy of various functions obtained from finite amounts of data. Even if $s(t)$ is a deterministic function, a bias or truncation error arises if $s(t)$ is only known in a finite interval $-T/2 \leqslant t \leqslant T/2$. To see the effect of this truncation, consider the *data window* defined by

$$w(t) = \begin{cases} 1, & |t| \leqslant \dfrac{T}{2} \\[2mm] 0, & |t| > \dfrac{T}{2}. \end{cases} \qquad (2.4.1)$$

If $s(t)$ is a deterministic signal in the range $-\infty \leqslant t \leqslant \infty$, the signal actually measured in the finite interval may be written

$$s_T(t) = s(t)w(t). \qquad (2.4.2)$$

Thus, the operation of taking a finite length record is equivalent to multiplying the actual signal $s(t)$ by the data window $w(t)$. Using (A2.1.8), it follows that the finite-interval transform $S_T(f)$ is the convolution of the transforms of $s(t)$ and $w(t)$,

$$S_T(f) = \int_{-\infty}^{\infty} S(g)W(f - g)\, dg, \qquad (2.4.3)$$

where the *spectral window* $W(f)$ is the Fourier transform of the data window $w(t)$ and in this case is

$$W(f) = T\frac{\sin \pi fT}{\pi fT}. \qquad (2.4.4)$$

It is not necessary to restrict the data window to the form (2.4.1). Any reasonable data window $w(t)$ will produce a spectral window $W(f)$ which is concentrated about $f = 0$ but with side lobes or minor peaks which damp out as f gets further away from zero. For small T, $S_T(f)$ may give a very distorted picture of $S(f)$ since the window $W(f - g)$ will be wide and hence values of $S(g)$ far removed from $g = f$ will contribute to $S_T(f)$ in the integral (2.4.3). As T becomes large the distortion will be reduced. Finally, as T tends to infinity, the transform component at frequency f can be fully determined, since data windows will tend to the generalized function 1 as T tends to infinity. Hence, as T tends to infinity, $W(f - g)$ tends to a delta function centered at $g = f$ and so $S_T(f)$ tends to $S(f)$.

The effect of window shape and width on the measured transform is illustrated in Figure 2.10 for a particular input $s(t)$ whose Fourier transform consists of three delta functions centered at f_0, f_1 and f_2. Note that:

(1) Only two main peaks appear in the output transform for windows (a), (c) and (d) because the two input peaks at frequencies f_1 and f_2 are fused into one. This is the result of using a data window which is too narrow.

(2) The output transforms for windows (a) and (b) have several false peaks between the main real peaks. The false peaks are caused by the sharp edges of the data window.

(3) The ability to pick out peaks (resolvability) depends on the data window *width*, as is illustrated by the output transforms for windows (a) and (b), which are of the same shape, but have different widths.

(4) The ability to pick out peaks also depends on the data window *shape*, as is illustrated by the output transforms for data windows (b), (c) and (d), which are of the same width but have different shapes. It will be shown in Chapters 6 and 7 that the window width and shape produce similar effects in spectral analysis.

In Figure 2.10, the frequency spacing $(f_2 - f_1)$ was chosen to be $1/T$. Figure 2.10(a) shows that with a rectangular data window of length T it is not possible

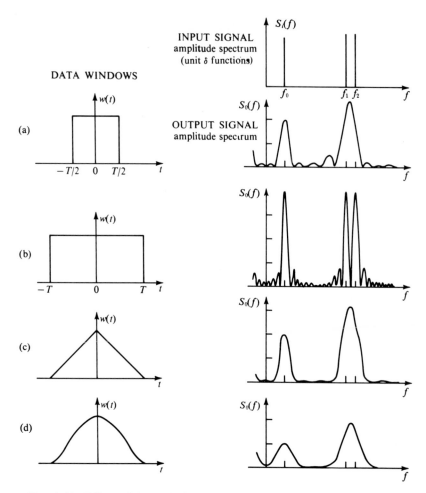

FIG. 2.10: Effect of data window shape and duration on signal spectra

to distinguish the two peaks at f_1 and f_2. However, with a rectangular window of length $2T$, the peaks are easily distinguishable. Hence, to separate two peaks at frequencies f_1 and f_2 it is necessary to use a record length T of order

$$T \geqslant \frac{1}{f_2 - f_1},$$
(2.4.5)

for the rectangular data window. Figures 2.10(c) and (d) show that for non-rectangular windows, the widths must be greater than $2/(f_2 - f_1)$ to be able to distinguish peaks. Further discussion of the record length necessary to distinguish peaks is given in Section 6.4.4.

2.4.2 *Time sampling and aliasing*

Impulse modulation. For purposes of analysis, most continuous signals $s(t)$ will be read at some fixed interval Δ and converted into *sampled* signals which can then be used for digital calculations. The sampled signal may be regarded as the result of multiplying the original continuous signal by a signal $i(t)$, which consists of a *train of impulse* or *delta functions*,

$$i(t) = \sum_{n=-\infty}^{\infty} \delta(t - n\Delta). \tag{2.4.6}$$

This produces a sampled or impulse-modulated signal $s_i(t)$ where

$$s_i(t) = s(t)i(t). \tag{2.4.7}$$

Hence, using the convolution theorem (A2.1.8),

$$S_i(f) = \int_{-\infty}^{\infty} S(f - g)I(g)\, dg, \tag{2.4.8}$$

where $I(g)$ is the transform of $i(t)$. Using the expression (2.2.16) for $I(g)$, (2.4.8) becomes

$$S_i(f) = \int_{-\infty}^{\infty} S(f - g)\frac{1}{\Delta} \sum_{n=-\infty}^{\infty} \delta\left(g - \frac{n}{\Delta}\right) dg$$

$$= \frac{1}{\Delta} \sum_{n=-\infty}^{\infty} S\left(f - \frac{n}{\Delta}\right). \tag{2.4.9}$$

Equation (2.4.9) shows that the sampled or impulse-modulated signal $s_i(t)$ has a transform with period $1/\Delta$, and that if $S(f)$ is zero when $|f| \geqslant 1/(2\Delta)$, then $S_i(f)$ is simply a periodic version of $S(f)$ as in (b) or (c) of Figure 2.11. This means that it is possible to recover $S(f)$ from $S_i(f)$ by multiplying $S_i(f)$ by $H(f)$, where

$$H(f) = \begin{cases} \Delta, & |f| \leqslant \dfrac{1}{2\Delta} \\[2mm] 0, & |f| > \dfrac{1}{2\Delta}. \end{cases} \tag{2.4.10}$$

Since multiplication in the frequency domain corresponds to convolution in the time domain, it follows that

$$s(t) = \int_{-\infty}^{\infty} \frac{\sin(\pi u/\Delta)}{(\pi u/\Delta)} s_i(t - u)\, du. \tag{2.4.11}$$

The function $\sin(\pi u/\Delta)/(\pi u/\Delta)$ is the ideal filter for recovering a continuous signal $s(t)$ from a sampled signal $s_i(t)$. Alternatively, $\sin(\pi u/\Delta)/(\pi u/\Delta)$ is the ideal interpolating function for equally spaced ordinates, and (2.4.11) is sometimes referred to as *Whittaker's interpolation formula.*

Aliasing. If the sampling interval is such that $S(f)$ falls off to zero before $|f| = 1/(2\Delta)$ as in (b) or (c) of Figure 2.11, then it is possible to recover $s(t)$ from $s_i(t)$. On the other hand, if $S(f)$ is not zero above $f_N = 1/(2\Delta)$, frequency

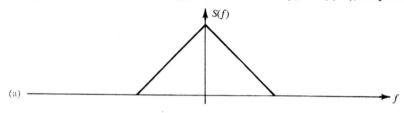

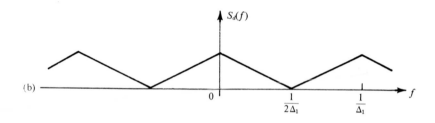

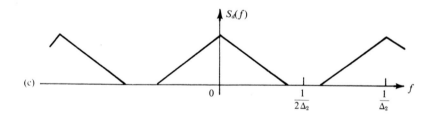

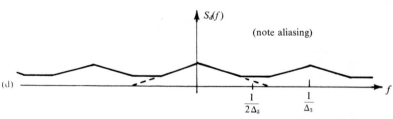

FIG. 2.11: Transforms of a signal and of the sampled signal for various sampling periods

components above $1/(2\Delta)$ in S(f) appear in $S_i(f)$, as in (d) of Figure 2.11, in the range $-1/(2\Delta) \leqslant f \leqslant 1/(2\Delta)$. The frequency $f_N = 1/(2\Delta)$ is called the *Nyquist frequency* and is the highest frequency which can be detected with data sampled at intervals Δ.

For example, if $\Delta = 0.1$ seconds, the Nyquist frequency is 5 cps. The discrete transform $S_i(f)$ at 4 cps will then be made up of contributions from S(f) at 4 cps, $10 + 4 = 14$ cps, $-10 + 4 = -6$ cps, $20 + 4 = 24$ cps, $-20 + 4 = -16$ cps and so on. These other frequencies are usually referred to as *aliases* of the frequency 4 cps, and the effect on the Fourier transform is called aliasing. It follows that in sampling continuous time series, adequate care must be taken to ensure that a high enough sampling frequency $f_N = 1/(2\Delta)$ is chosen so that misleading values of $S_i(f)$ will be avoided.

The phenomenon of aliasing arises in a number of practical contexts, such as in the use of a stroboscope or in movie films. For example, the wheels of a stage coach which is accelerating from zero appear to rotate in the correct direction with increasing speed, then they appear to be rotating in the opposite direction with decreasing speed until they stop, then they begin to rotate with increasing speed in the forward direction and so on.

An example. To illustrate the considerations discussed in this section, suppose that it is desired to calculate the length of record T and sampling interval Δ required to achieve certain objectives. Suppose it is known that the signal under study contains two sinusoidal components at frequencies of 100 cps and 99 cps. Then if it is desired to distinguish these peaks in the Fourier transform of the finite length of record, (2.4.5) shows that $1/T$ must be of the order of $100 - 99 = 1$ cps, that is, T must be of the order of 1 sec. In order to estimate a frequency as high as 100 cps, then $1/(2\Delta)$ must be at least 100 cps and hence $\Delta \leqslant 5$ millisec. Thus at least 200 data values would be needed.

If it were required to separate two frequency components at 999 and 1000 cps, then a record of 1 sec duration would still be necessary, but the sampling interval would now have to be 0.5 millisec, so 2000 data values would be required.

Hence the *length* T of the record determines the extent to which peaks in the Fourier transform may be distinguished. On the other hand, the *sampling interval* Δ determines the maximum frequency which can be distinguished.

REFERENCES

[1] M. J. Lighthill, *An Introduction to Fourier Analysis and Generalized Functions.* Cambridge University Press, Cambridge, 1959.

[2] A. Papoulis, *The Fourier Integral and its Applications.* McGraw-Hill, New York, 1962.

[3] R. Courant, *Differential and Integral Calculus*. Vol. II. Blackie and Son, London, 1952.

[4] H. M. James, N. B. Nichols and R. S. Phillips, *Theory of Servomechanisms*. McGraw-Hill, New York, 1947.

[5] H. W. Bode, *Network Analysis and Feedback Amplifier Design*. Van Nostrand, New York, 1945.

[6] G. A. Campbell and R. M. Foster, *Fourier Integrals for Practical Applications*. Van Nostrand, New York, 1942.

[7] E. I. Jury, *Theory and Application of the Z-Transform Method*. John Wiley, New York, 1964.

APPENDIX A2.1   OPERATIONAL PROPERTIES OF FOURIER TRANSFORMS

During the course of this book, it will be necessary to perform various operations with Fourier transforms. These are now summarized.

Time scaling and shift of origin. If $s(t)$ has the Fourier transform $S(f)$, then the Fourier transform of $s(\alpha t + \beta)$ is

$$\frac{1}{|\alpha|} e^{j(2\pi f \beta/\alpha)} S\left(\frac{f}{\alpha}\right). \tag{A2.1.1}$$

Example: From Table 2.5, the Fourier transform of $e^{-\pi t^2}$ is

$$S(f) = e^{-\pi f^2}.$$

Hence the transform of

$$\exp\left[-\frac{1}{2}\left(\frac{t-\mu}{\sigma}\right)^2\right] = s\left(\frac{t-\mu}{\sqrt{2\pi}\,\sigma}\right)$$

is

$$|\sqrt{2\pi}\,\sigma|\, e^{j2\pi f(-\mu)} S(\sqrt{2\pi}\,\sigma f) = \sqrt{2\pi}\,\sigma\, e^{-j2\pi f\mu}\, e^{-2\pi^2\sigma^2 f^2},$$

where

$$\alpha = 1/\sqrt{2\pi}\,\sigma, \qquad \beta = -\mu/\sqrt{2\pi}\,\sigma, \qquad \beta/\alpha = -\mu.$$

Differentiation. If $s(t)$ has the Fourier transform $S(f)$, then the mth derivative $s^{(m)}(t)$ has the Fourier transform

$$(j2\pi f)^m S(f), \tag{A2.1.2}$$

provided the derivative exists.

Example: As in the preceding example, using the transform pair

$$s(t) = e^{-\pi t^2}, \qquad S(f) = e^{-\pi f^2},$$

from Table 2.5, the Fourier transform of

$$\frac{d}{dt}\, s(t) = \frac{d}{dt}\,(e^{-\pi t^2}) = -2\pi t\, e^{-\pi t^2}$$

is

$$j2\pi f S(f) = j2\pi f\, e^{-\pi f^2}.$$

Integration. If $s(t)$ has the Fourier transform $S(f)$ then the Fourier transform of $I^m s(t)$, where

$$Is(t) = \int_{-\infty}^{t} s(u) \, du,$$

is

$$\left(\frac{1}{j2\pi f}\right)^m S(f) + K_1 \delta(f) + K_2 \delta'(f) + \cdots + K_m \delta^{m-1}(f). \qquad (A2.1.3)$$

The constants $K_1, K_2, \ldots, K_m$ in (A2.1.3) may be determined by using the values of the functions $s(t), ds/dt, \ldots, d^m s/dt^m$ evaluated at $t = 0$ since, for example,

$$s(0) = \int_{-\infty}^{\infty} S(f) \, df.$$

Example: From the preceding example, the function

$$s(t) = -2\pi t \, e^{-\pi t^2}$$

has the Fourier transform

$$S(f) = j2\pi f \, e^{-\pi f^2}.$$

Hence the Fourier transform of

$$s_1(t) = \int_{-\infty}^{t} s(u) \, du = e^{-\pi t^2}$$

is

$$S_1(f) = \frac{1}{j2\pi f} S(f) + K_1 \delta(f)$$

$$= e^{-\pi f^2} + K_1 \delta(f).$$

Integrating both sides over f gives

$$s_1(0) = \int_{-\infty}^{\infty} e^{-\pi f^2} \, df + K_1$$

$$= 1 + K_1.$$

But $s_1(0) = 1$ and hence $K_1 = 0$.

Symmetry. If $S(f)$ is the Fourier transform of $s(t)$, then $s(f)$ is the Fourier transform of $S(-t)$.

Example: The Fourier transform of

$$s(t) = \begin{cases} e^{-t}, & t \geq 0 \\ 0, & t < 0 \end{cases}$$

is $S(f) = 1/(1 + j2\pi f)$. Hence the Fourier transform of $s(t) = 1/(1 - j2\pi t)$ is

$$S(f) = \begin{cases} e^{-f}, & f \geq 0 \\ 0, & f < 0. \end{cases}$$

Similarly, the Fourier transform of $s(t) = 1/(1 + j2\pi t)$ is

$$S(f) = \begin{cases} e^{f}, & f \leq 0 \\ 0, & f > 0. \end{cases}$$

Hence the Fourier transform of

$$\frac{2}{1 + (2\pi t)^2} = \frac{1}{1 - j2\pi t} + \frac{1}{1 + j2\pi t}$$

is

$$e^{-|f|}, \quad -\infty \leqslant f \leqslant \infty.$$

Convolution and Parseval's theorem. This is a more general form of the theorem than the results (2.1.16, 20, 26) derived in Section 2.1. The generalized form states that if $s_1(t)$ and $s_2(t)$ are two complex signals with Fourier transforms $S_1(f)$ and $S_2(f)$ respectively, then

$$\int_{-\infty}^{\infty} s_1(t)s_2^*(t)\, dt = \int_{-\infty}^{\infty} S_1(f)S_2^*(f)\, df, \qquad (A2.1.4)$$

where the asterisk denotes a complex conjugate.

Three special cases of (A2.1.4) are sometimes useful:

(a) When $s_2^*(t) = h(u - t)$, (A2.1.4) reduces to

$$\int_{-\infty}^{\infty} s_1(t)h(u - t)\, dt = \int_{-\infty}^{\infty} S_1(f)H(f)\, e^{j2\pi fu}\, df. \qquad (A2.1.5)$$

(b) When $s_1(t)$ and $s_2(t)$ are real, (A2.1.4) reduces to

$$\int_{-\infty}^{\infty} s_1(t)s_2(t)\, dt = \int_{-\infty}^{\infty} S_1(f)S_2(-f)\, df. \qquad (A2.1.6)$$

(c) When $s_1(t) = s_2(t) = s(t)$, (A2.1.4) reduces to

$$\int_{-\infty}^{\infty} |s(t)|^2\, dt = \int_{-\infty}^{\infty} |S(f)|^2\, df. \qquad (A2.1.7)$$

The form (A2.1.7) of Parseval's theorem includes the form (2.1.26) which was derived in Section 2.1.

Note that because of the symmetry of the Fourier transform, the roles of the signal and its transform may be reversed. For example,

(a) $$\int_{-\infty}^{\infty} S_1(f)S_2(g - f)\, df = \int_{-\infty}^{\infty} s_1(t)s_2(t)\, e^{j2\pi gt}\, dt, \qquad (A2.1.8)$$

(b) $$\int_{-\infty}^{\infty} S_1(f)S_2(f)\, df = \int_{-\infty}^{\infty} s_1(t)s_2(-t)\, dt, \qquad (A2.1.9)$$

while the symmetry of the relation given by (c) is already evident.

It should be noted that the above operational properties apply equally well to finite and infinite Fourier series. The three forms of Parseval's theorem derived in Section 2.1 provide examples.

3

Probability Theory

This chapter contains a summary of those ideas in probability theory which are necessary for an understanding of time series problems. Section 3.1 illustrates the statistician's approach to describing physical phenomena via a sample space, a random variable and a probability distribution. Section 3.2 deals with ways of approximating a probability distribution by its lower-order moments. Finally, Section 3.3 discusses the sampling distributions of certain useful functions, such as the mean and variance, of random variables.

3.1 FREQUENCY AND PROBABILITY DISTRIBUTIONS

In Chapter 1 it was shown that deterministic models are not always adequate to describe physical systems. Thus, when a system is subject to *uncertainty* or *random variation*, it is necessary to use non-deterministic or statistical models. The mathematical theory underlying such statistical models is called probability theory.

3.1.1 Discrete random variables and distributions

As an example of a physical process which is subject to uncertainty or random variability, consider the data of Figure 3.1. This shows the fluctuation in the number of defective transistors in successive samples of 100 drawn at random from a production line. Such sampling is usually necessary to keep a check on product quality, and the plot of the number of defectives x versus the sample number is called a quality control chart.

Control charts give a clear *visual* picture of the variability in the data and are used to provide an early warning should changes of quality occur. A *quantitative* assessment of the variability may be obtained by constructing a *frequency distribution* as shown in Table 3.1 and plotted in Figure 3.2. These show n_x, the number of samples with x defective transistors, as a function of

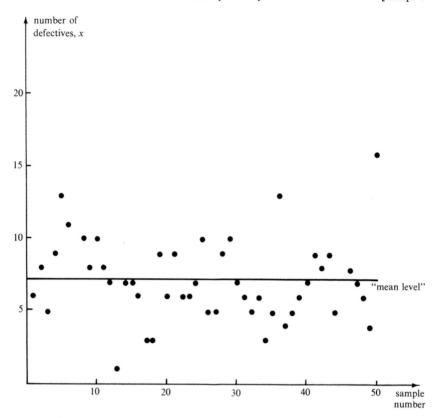

FIG. 3.1: Number of defective transistors in 50 samples of 100

x for the fifty samples shown in Figure 3.1. The frequency distribution shows that while the range of defective items per sample is 1–16, most (90%) of the samples have between 3 and 11 defectives.

TABLE 3.1: Frequency distribution of number of defectives per sample in 50 samples of size 100

x	0	1	2	3	4	5	6	7	8
n_x	0	2	0	3	2	7	9	7	5

x	9	10	11	12	13	14	15	16	TOTAL
n_x	6	4	2	0	2	0	0	1	50

Now the total number N of samples inspected is

$$\sum_{x=0}^{k} n_x = N, \qquad (3.1.1)$$

where k is the largest value which x can take and equals 100 in this example. It follows that

$$\sum_{x=0}^{k} \left(\frac{n_x}{N}\right) = 1, \qquad (3.1.2)$$

where n_x/N is the proportion of samples which have x defectives. Referring to Figure 3.2 it is seen, for example, that 5 out of 50 or 0.1 of the samples have exactly 8 defectives.

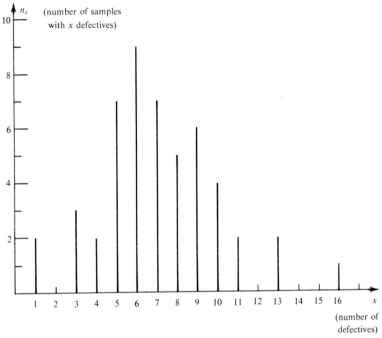

FIG. 3.2: Frequency distribution for data of Figure 3.1

Sample spaces, events, random variables and probability distributions. The quality-control data may be described by introducing four basic concepts. The first of these is the *sample space*, which is a set of points corresponding to all possible outcomes of an experiment. For example, in testing one sample of 100 transistors, there are 101 points $P_0, P_1, \ldots, P_{100}$ in the sample space, corresponding to 0, 1, 2, ..., 100 defectives.

A collection or subset of points in the sample space is called an *event* (E). For example, the sample points P_0, P_1 correspond to the event "fewer than two defectives occur." Each point in the sample space corresponds to a *simple* event.

To refer to different events in the sample space, it is necessary to introduce the concept of a *random variable* (rv). For example, the points in the sample space for the transistor data may be relabeled so that the points P_0 and P_1 correspond to the event "the rv Y takes on the value $y = 0$," and the points P_2, P_3, ..., P_{100} to the event "the rv Y takes on the value $y = 1$." Thus Y takes on a value $y = 0$ when fewer than two defectives occur, and $y = 1$ when two or more defectives occur. The rv is usually denoted in upper case, for example X or Y, and the numerical value which it takes for a particular sample in lower case, for example x or y. Note that there are many ways of attaching labels to events in the sample space. For example, an rv could be associated with the number of defectives in a sample. The rv X then takes on the values $x = 0, 1, \ldots, 100$. In general, a random variable is a function which can be used to label sets or events in the sample space.

The final concepts needed to describe the quality control example are of *probability* and *probability distribution* (pd). The probability is the proportion of times that the rv X takes on the value x, and is written $p_X(x)$. The set of numbers $p_X(x)$, $x = 0, 1, 2, \ldots, 100$ is the pd. Each of the probabilities is non-negative and they sum to unity. An estimate of $p_X(x)$ may be obtained from the observed proportions n_x/N defined in (3.1.2). As the total number N of transistors inspected increases, the proportions n_x/N provide better estimates of the probabilities $p_X(x)$.

It is sometimes possible to derive a mathematical formula for $p_X(x)$ by making reasonable physical assumptions. For example, an appropriate pd to describe the transistor problem is the *binomial* pd

$$p_X(x) = \binom{n}{x} \theta^x (1 - \theta)^{n-x}, \quad x = 0, 1, \ldots, n, \tag{3.1.3}$$

where n is the sample size and θ is the probability that a single transistor is defective.

The parameter θ may be estimated from the observed data by

$$\hat{\theta} = \frac{\text{total number of defectives observed}}{\text{total number of transistors tested}} = \frac{355}{5000} = 0.071.$$

Assuming that $\hat{\theta}$ is the correct value for θ, the probability that the rv X takes on the value x is

$$\hat{p}_X(x) = \binom{100}{x}(0.071)^x(0.929)^{100-x}, \quad x = 0, 1, \ldots, 100. \tag{3.1.4}$$

Hence the predicted number of samples with x defectives in a group of 50 samples each of size 100 is $\tilde{n}_x = 50\hat{p}_X(x)$.

TABLE 3.2: Comparison of observed and expected frequencies for binomial distribution fitted to transistor data

x	0	1	2	3	4	5	6	7	8
n_x	0	2	0	3	2	7	9	7	5
$\tilde{n}_x$	<0.1	0.3	0.9	2.3	4.2	6.2	7.5	7.6	6.8

x	9	10	11	12	13	14	15	16
n_x	6	4	2	0	2	0	0	1
$\tilde{n}_x$	5.3	3.7	2.3	1.3	0.6	0.2	0.1	<0.1

In Table 3.2 the observed frequencies n_x are compared with the expected frequencies $\tilde{n}_x$, under the assumption that the model (3.1.4) is correct. It is seen that good agreement is obtained, and hence (3.1.4) is an adequate probability model for this situation.

The question of which probability model to use in a particular problem is an important one, and should be answered carefully using all available data and background information. The answer cannot be dictated by mathematics, but must be arrived at by careful examination of the physical situation.

3.1.2 *Continuous random variables and distributions*

In many cases it is necessary to describe a situation by a *continuous rv*, that is, an rv defined over a sample space which is continuous. For example, Figure 3.3 shows the frequency distribution of collector current for a sample

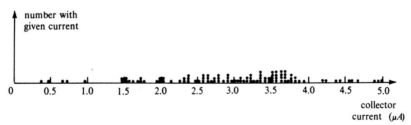

FIG. 3.3: Dot diagram for collector currents

of $N = 100$ transistors. Since the current measurement may have any non-negative value, it is necessary to introduce an rv X which takes on any value x in the continuous sample space $0 \leqslant x \leqslant \infty$.

Figure 3.3 shows that, occasionally, as many as four transistors have the same current value. However, if a more sensitive ammeter were used, it might happen that no two points coincided on the current axis and so it would be meaningless to construct a frequency distribution. Hence it is meaningless to talk of the probability of occurrence of a particular value of a continuous rv X, say $x = 2.000$ microamperes (μA).

The cumulative distribution function. Although it is not meaningful to consider the probability that a continuous rv X takes on a particular value x, it *is* possible to define the probability that the rv X will be less than some value x, that is, $\Pr\{X \leqslant x\}$. This is written $F_X(x)$ and is called the *cumulative distribution function* (cdf). A typical shape for this function is shown in Figure 3.5, and it is seen that it flattens out to a value of 1 since $F_X(\infty) = 1$.

The cdf may be estimated by the proportion of values in the sample which are less than a given value x. The *sample cdf* for the data of Figure 3.3 is shown in Figure 3.4 and consists of a series of jumps of height n_x/N at the sample values.

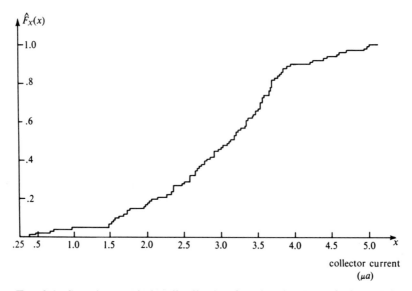

FIG. 3.4: Sample cumulative distribution function for data of Figure 3.3

The probability density function. Related to the cdf $F_X(x)$ is the *probability density function* (pdf) $f_X(x)$, given by

$$f_X(x) = \frac{dF_X(x)}{dx}, \tag{3.1.5}$$

provided the cdf is smooth enough so that the derivative exists. This will not be the case if the rv is discrete since the cdf will then have jumps or discontinuities at the discrete values of X.

The pdf is *not* a probability *distribution*, but it may be used to calculate probabilities. Thus, on integrating (3.1.5), the probability that the rv X is less than x_1 is

$$\text{Pr}\{X \leqslant x_1\} = F_X(x_1) = \int_{-\infty}^{x_1} f_X(x)\, dx, \tag{3.1.6}$$

and the probability that the rv X lies in the range x_1 to x_2 is

$$\text{Pr}\{x_1 < X \leqslant x_2\} = F_X(x_2) - F_X(x_1) = \int_{x_1}^{x_2} f_X(x)\, dx. \tag{3.1.7}$$

By definition $f_X(x)$ satisfies the properties

$$f_X(x) \geqslant 0, \quad \text{all } x; \quad \int_{-\infty}^{\infty} f_X(x)\, dx = 1. \tag{3.1.8}$$

The Normal pdf. One of the most important pdf's in statistics is the *Normal* or *Gaussian* pdf

$$f_X(x) = \frac{1}{\sqrt{2\pi}\,\sigma} \exp\left\{-\frac{1}{2}\left(\frac{x-\mu}{\sigma}\right)^2\right\}, \quad -\infty \leqslant x \leqslant \infty, \tag{3.1.9}$$

shown in Figure 3.5 together with its cdf. The Normal pdf is completely specified by the two *parameters* μ and σ^2 and will be denoted by $N(\mu, \sigma^2)$. It can be used to describe many practical situations, for example, the diameter

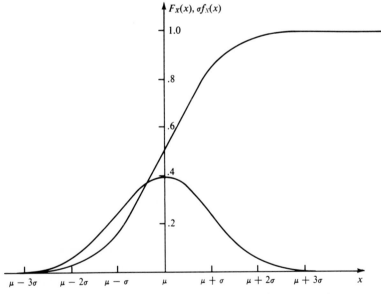

Fɪɢ. 3.5: Normal probability density function and cumulative distribution function

of machined components or the lifetime of electric bulbs. This fact can be explained by the *Central Limit Theorem*, which states that the pdf of the sum of n rv's $X = X_1 + X_2 + \cdots + X_n$ tends *very quickly* to the Normal form as n increases, whatever the pdf of the individual X_i's. Thus, if the final measurement x is a result of many small effects acting additively, it is to be expected that the Normal pdf would be appropriate. In many other situations, some suitable function $g(X)$ of the rv X may be distributed approximately in the Normal form. For example, the pdf of the logarithm of the capacitance of capacitors in a production line is well described by the Normal pdf. As in the discrete case, the relevance of a particular pdf can only be decided by careful consideration of the data and any background information.

3.1.3 Estimation of probability density functions

One way of estimating a pdf is by a *histogram*. This gives the proportion $p(n)$ of observations lying in the interval $(n - \tfrac{1}{2})\delta$ to $(n + \tfrac{1}{2})\delta$. Since

$$\Pr\{(n - \tfrac{1}{2})\delta < X \leqslant (n + \tfrac{1}{2})\delta\} \approx \delta f_X(n\delta), \quad n = 0, \pm 1, \pm 2, \ldots,$$

the estimate of the pdf is

$$\hat{f}_X(n\delta) = \frac{p(n)}{\delta}, \quad n = 0, \pm 1, \ldots,$$

and consists of rectangles of width δ. Figure 3.6 shows the histogram for the current data of Figure 3.3 for two values of interval width δ, namely 0.4 μA and 1.0 μA. The estimate based on the wide interval is relatively smooth and masks much of the fine structure of the data. By contrast, the narrow interval gives a more detailed picture but the estimate is more variable since fewer observations fall into each interval. Thus it is necessary to compromise between the conflicting requirements of fine detail and large variability. It will be shown in Chapter 6 that similar considerations apply in the estimation of spectra.

3.1.4 Bivariate distributions

Sometimes it is necessary to use more than one rv to describe a practical situation. An example occurred in the checking of a pilot's reading of an accelerometer against the more accurate measurements obtained from an automatic recorder. The data from this experiment is shown in Figure 3.7, which plots simultaneous measurements of the pilot's reading (x_1) and those of the recorder (x_2). Figure 3.7 is called a *scatter diagram* and can be used to construct a bivariate histogram by counting the number of points in rectangles in the (x_1, x_2) plane.

The data of Figure 3.7 can be described by two rv's X_1 and X_2, where X_1 is associated with the pilot's reading and X_2 is associated with the recorder

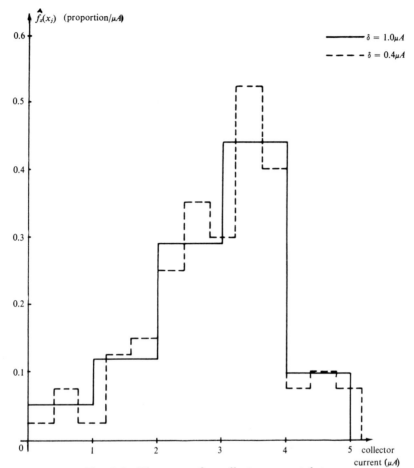

FIG. 3.6: Histograms for collector current data

reading. The sample space for this example is the region $x_1 \geq 0$, $x_2 \geq 0$, but in general it could be the whole of the (x_1, x_2) plane. With this general sample space can be associated a *bivariate cdf*

$$F_{12}(x_1, x_2) = \Pr\{X_1 \leq x_1, X_2 \leq x_2\}. \tag{3.1.10}$$

As in the univariate case, if the cdf is sufficiently smooth it may be differentiated to give the bivariate pdf

$$f_{12}(x_1, x_2) = \frac{\partial^2}{\partial x_1\, \partial x_2}\, F_{12}(x_1, x_2). \tag{3.1.11}$$

Hence the cdf may be calculated from the pdf using

$$F_{12}(x_1, x_2) = \int_{-\infty}^{x_1} \int_{-\infty}^{x_2} f_{12}(t_1, t_2)\, dt_1\, dt_2. \tag{3.1.12}$$

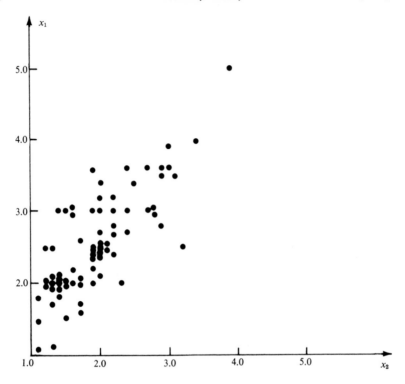

FIG. 3.7: Scatter diagram of measurements of acceleration (in units of g)

The pdf (3.1.11) may be estimated from the bivariate histogram in the same way that the pdf $f_X(x)$ was estimated from the univariate histogram.

For discrete rv's, the joint pd is written $p_{12}(x_1, x_2)$ and represents the probability that the rv X_1 takes on a value x_1 and X_2 a value x_2.

Conditional distributions and independence. For two discrete rv's, consider the function defined by the proportion of occasions on which X_1 takes on values x_1 conditional on X_2 being *fixed* at some value x_2. This function is called the *conditional pd* of X_1 given X_2 and is denoted by $p_{1|2}(x_1, x_2)$. Similarly $p_{2|1}(x_1, x_2)$ denotes the conditional pd of X_2 given X_1. The joint pd of X_1 and X_2 may then be written

$$p_{12}(x_1, x_2) = p_1(x_1)p_{2|1}(x_1, x_2) = p_2(x_2)p_{1|2}(x_1, x_2), \qquad (3.1.13)$$

where, for example, $p_1(x_1)$ is the *marginal* distribution of X_1. The marginal pd $p_1(x_1)$ may be obtained from the joint pd according to

$$p_1(x_1) = \sum_{x_2=0}^{\infty} p_{12}(x_1, x_2)$$

and represents the proportion of occasions on which X_1 equals x_1 when the value of X_2 is ignored.

When the occurrence of the value $X_1 = x_1$ is in no way influenced by the occurrence of the value $X_2 = x_2$, the conditional pd $p_{1|2}(x_1, x_2) = p_1(x_1)$ and the conditional pd $p_{2|1}(x_1, x_2) = p_2(x_2)$. The rv's X_1 and X_2 are then said to be *independent* and the expression (3.1.13) for the joint pd factors as

$$p_{12}(x_1, x_2) = p_1(x_1)p_2(x_2). \qquad (3.1.14)$$

Similarly for a continuous rv, the joint pdf factors according to

$$f_{12}(x_1, x_2) = f_1(x_1)f_{2|1}(x_1, x_2) = f_2(x_2)f_{1|2}(x_1, x_2) \qquad (3.1.15)$$

if the rv's are dependent and

$$f_{12}(x_1, x_2) = f_1(x_1)f_2(x_2) \qquad (3.1.16)$$

if the rv's are independent.

The bivariate Normal pdf. Just as the Normal pdf plays a dominant role in describing single rv's, the bivariate Normal pdf

$$f_{12}(x_1, x_2) = \frac{1}{2\pi\sigma_1\sigma_2(1 - \rho_{12}^2)^{1/2}}$$

$$\times \exp\left[-\frac{1}{2(1 - \rho_{12}^2)}\left\{\left(\frac{x_1 - \mu_1}{\sigma_1}\right)^2 + \left(\frac{x_2 - \mu_2}{\sigma_2}\right)^2 - 2\rho_{12}\left(\frac{x_1 - \mu_1}{\sigma_1}\right)\left(\frac{x_2 - \mu_2}{\sigma_2}\right)\right\}\right],$$

$$-\infty \leqslant x_1, x_2 \leqslant \infty \quad (3.1.17)$$

plays a similarly important role among bivariate pdf's. The bivariate Normal pdf depends on five parameters, μ_1, μ_2, σ_1, σ_2 and ρ_{12}. When $\rho_{12} = 0$, (3.1.17) factors into the product of two Normal pdf's showing that, when $\rho_{12} = 0$, the rv's X_1 and X_2 are independent. The parameter ρ_{12} is called the *correlation coefficient* and measures the degree of linear dependence between the two rv's.

3.1.5 Multivariate distributions

When n measurements are made on n quantities, the situation may be described by n rv's together with a joint n-dimensional cdf

$$F_{12\cdots n}(x_1, x_2, \ldots, x_n)$$

and pdf

$$f_{12\cdots n}(x_1, x_2, \ldots, x_n).$$

If the rv's are mutually independent, the joint pdf factors as

$$f_{12\cdots n}(x_1, x_2, \ldots, x_n) = f_1(x_1)f_2(x_2)\cdots f_n(x_n). \qquad (3.1.18)$$

A particularly important multivariate pdf is the *multivariate Normal pdf*, which may be written concisely in matrix notation as

$$f_{\mathbf{X}}(\mathbf{x}) = \frac{1}{(2\pi)^{n/2}|V|^{1/2}} \exp\left[-\tfrac{1}{2}(\mathbf{x} - \boldsymbol{\mu})'\mathbf{V}^{-1}(\mathbf{x} - \boldsymbol{\mu})\right], \qquad (3.1.19)$$

where $\mathbf{x}' = (x_1, x_2, \ldots, x_n)$, $\boldsymbol{\mu}' = (\mu_1, \mu_2, \ldots, \mu_n)$ are row vectors, and $\mathbf{V}^{-1}$ is the inverse of the covariance matrix $\mathbf{V}$, where

$$\mathbf{V} = \begin{pmatrix} \sigma_1^2 & \sigma_1\sigma_2\rho_{12} & \sigma_1\sigma_3\rho_{13} & \cdots & \sigma_1\sigma_n\rho_{1n} \\ \sigma_1\sigma_2\rho_{12} & \sigma_2^2 & \sigma_2\sigma_3\rho_{23} & \cdots & \sigma_2\sigma_n\rho_{2n} \\ \sigma_1\sigma_3\rho_{13} & \sigma_2\sigma_3\rho_{23} & \sigma_3^2 & \cdots & \sigma_3\sigma_n\rho_{3n} \\ \vdots & \vdots & \vdots & & \vdots \\ \sigma_1\sigma_n\rho_{1n} & \sigma_2\sigma_n\rho_{2n} & \sigma_3\sigma_n\rho_{3n} & \cdots & \sigma_n^2 \end{pmatrix}. \quad (3.1.20)$$

The multivariate Normal pdf is an $n(n + 3)/2$-parameter pdf, depending on the n means μ_i ($i = 1, 2, \ldots, n$); n variances σ_i^2 ($i = 1, 2, \ldots, n$); and the $n(n - 1)/2$ correlations ρ_{ij} ($i = 1, 2, \ldots, n, j = i + 1, \ldots, n$).

When the rv's are independent, the correlations $\rho_{ij} = 0$, the matrix $\mathbf{V}$ is diagonal and the joint pdf factors according to (3.1.18) into the product of n univariate Normal distributions.

To describe empirical data by a multivariate Normal pdf, it is necessary to estimate the above $n(n + 3)/2$ parameters. This is discussed in Chapter 4.

3.2 MOMENTS OF RANDOM VARIABLES

3.2.1 Univariate moments

Given the pd $p_X(x)$ of a discrete rv or the pdf $f_X(x)$ of a continuous rv, it is possible to calculate the probability that the rv lies between two values x_1 and x_2. Sometimes it is not possible to determine the pd or pdf exactly, and then it becomes necessary to summarize the distribution by a few numbers. The simplest of these are the *mean* and *variance*.

The mean. It is sometimes useful to know the value which the rv X takes on an average. For instance, in the quality-control example of Section 3.1.1, this value represents the average number of defectives per sample which could be expected. The average number of defectives which actually occurred in the N samples is

$$\bar{x} = \frac{1}{N} \sum_{x=0}^{k} x n_x = \sum_{x=0}^{k} x\left(\frac{n_x}{N}\right) \quad (3.2.1)$$

and is called the *sample mean* of the frequency distribution. For the data of Figure 3.1, $\bar{x} = 7.1$ and is shown as a thick horizontal line about which the values of x are clustered.

Since the proportions n_x/N estimate the probabilities $p_X(x)$, the *mean* of the pd is

$$\mu = \sum_{x=0}^{k} x p_X(x). \quad (3.2.2)$$

The mean μ is usually denoted by $E[X]$ and is called the *expected value* of the rv X. It measures the average or expected value which X will take in future experiments. Similarly, for a continuous rv,

$$E[X] = \int_{-\infty}^{\infty} xf_X(x)\,dx. \tag{3.2.3}$$

Equation (3.2.3) is identical to the expression for the center of gravity of a non-uniform rod with mass per unit area of $f_X(x)$ at a distance x from its end. Likewise, $E[X]$ is the center of gravity of the pdf of X and hence serves to *locate* the distribution.

The variance. Having located the distribution, the next obvious feature to describe is the extent to which the distribution is spread out. One measure of spread is the *variance*

$$\sigma^2 = \int_{-\infty}^{\infty} (x - \mu)^2 f_X(x)\,dx = E[(X - \mu)^2], \tag{3.2.4}$$

which measures the spread of the distribution about the mean μ. If $f_X(x)$ tends to be narrow and concentrated about μ, then σ^2 will be small. Conversely, if there are values of x remote from the mean for which $f_X(x)$ is appreciable, then σ^2 will be large.

Expanding the square in (3.2.4) gives an equivalent formula for the variance

$$\sigma^2 = E[X^2] - \mu^2. \tag{3.2.5}$$

The expression (3.2.4) is similar to the formula for the moment of inertia of a rod of non-uniform density about its center of gravity. Formula (3.2.5) then simply states that the moment of inertia about the center of gravity is equal to the moment of inertia about the origin less the moment about zero of the total mass concentrated at the center of gravity. Table 3.3 gives the mean and variance of some important discrete and continuous probability distributions.

The variance of a discrete pd may be estimated by the sample variance

$$s^2 = \frac{1}{N-1} \sum_{x=0}^{k} n_x(x - \bar{x})^2.$$

Similarly, the mean and variance of data x_i $(i = 1, 2, \ldots, n)$ corresponding to a continuous rv may be calculated from

$$\bar{x} = \frac{1}{n} \sum_{i=1}^{n} x_i;$$

$$s^2 = \frac{1}{n-1} \sum_{i=1}^{n} (x_i - \bar{x})^2. \tag{3.2.6}$$

The positive square root σ of the variance σ^2 is called the *standard deviation* and can be used to scale the distribution, as will now be shown.

TABLE 3.3: Some important distribution functions and their means and variances

Distribution	Probability distribution $p_X(x)$	Mean μ	Variance σ^2
binomial	$\binom{n}{x}p^x(1-p)^{n-x}$ $x = 0, 1, 2, \ldots, n$	np	$np(1-p)$
Poisson	$e^{-\lambda}\dfrac{\lambda^x}{x!}, \quad \lambda > 0$ $x = 0, 1, 2, \ldots, \infty$	λ	λ

	Probability density function $f_X(x)$	Mean μ	Variance σ^2
Normal	$\dfrac{1}{\sqrt{2\pi}\,\sigma}\exp\left[-\dfrac{1}{2}\left(\dfrac{x-\mu}{\sigma}\right)^2\right]$ $-\infty \leqslant x \leqslant \infty$	μ	σ^2
rectangular	$\dfrac{1}{a+b}, \quad -a \leqslant x \leqslant b$	$\frac{1}{2}(b-a)$	$\dfrac{(a+b)^2}{12}$
negative exponential	$\dfrac{1}{\mu}e^{-x/\mu}, \quad 0 \leqslant x \leqslant \infty, \quad \mu \geqslant 0$	μ	μ^2

The unit Normal distribution. The Normal pdf (3.1.9) has the important property that it is completely specified by the parameters μ and σ^2, corresponding to the mean and variance of the rv. Hence, the mean μ and standard deviation σ can be used to standardize the pdf. Thus, if X is $N(\mu, \sigma^2)$, the rv

$$Y = \frac{X - \mu}{\sigma} \qquad (3.2.7)$$

has the pdf

$$f_Y(y) = \frac{1}{\sqrt{2\pi}} e^{-y^2/2}, \quad -\infty \leqslant y \leqslant \infty. \qquad (3.2.8)$$

Hence Y is $N(0, 1)$, and (3.2.8) is called the *unit Normal* pdf.

From (3.2.7) the probability that the rv X lies inside the range $\pm \eta\sigma$ about the mean is equal to the probability that the rv Y lies inside the range $\pm \eta$. The latter probabilities $\Pr\{-\eta < Y \leqslant \eta\}$ may be obtained from standard tables [1]. Some useful values of η are given in Table 3.4.

TABLE 3.4: Probabilities associated with the unit Normal pdf

$\eta\left(1 - \dfrac{\alpha}{2}\right)$	$\Pr\{-\eta < Y \leqslant \eta\}$	α = Proportion of area *outside* $\pm\eta$
1.00	0.683	0.317
1.96	0.950	0.050
2.00	0.954	0.046
2.58	0.990	0.010
3.00	0.997	0.003

Higher moments. In general, univariate pdf's may be described by their mean μ and higher *central moments*

$$\mu_k = E[(X - \mu)^k], \quad k = 2, 3, \ldots, \tag{3.2.9}$$

and so the variance corresponds to $k = 2$. The values of μ_k for $k > 2$ are not of great practical value, since if a pdf is not adequately described by its mean and variance it is better to represent it by an appropriate non-Normal pdf and then estimate the parameters in this pdf.

Moments of functions of rv's. Sometimes it is necessary to investigate some function $Y = g(X)$ of an rv X, for example $Y = \ln X$. If so, the moments of Y may be calculated from the pdf of X by

$$E[Y] = \int_{-\infty}^{\infty} g(x) f_X(x)\, dx,$$

$$\text{Var}\,[Y] = \int_{-\infty}^{\infty} \{g(x) - E[Y]\}^2 f_X(x)\, dx \tag{3.2.10}$$

and so on.

3.2.2 Multivariate moments

The results of the previous section may be extended to higher-order distributions. For example, consider a function $g(X_1, X_2, \ldots, X_n)$ of the rv's $X_1, X_2, \ldots, X_n$ with joint pdf $f_{12\ldots n}(x_1, x_2, \ldots, x_n)$. The expected value of $g(X_1, X_2, \ldots, X_n)$ is

$$E[g(X_1, X_2, \ldots, X_n)] = \int_{-\infty}^{\infty} \int_{-\infty}^{\infty} \cdots \int_{-\infty}^{\infty} g(x_1, x_2, \ldots, x_n)$$

$$\times\, f_{12\ldots n}(x_1, x_2, \ldots, x_n)\, dx_1\, dx_2 \cdots dx_n, \tag{3.2.11}$$

which is the multivariate equivalent of (3.2.10) above.

When the function $g(X_1, X_2, \ldots, X_n)$ factors as $g(X_1, X_2, \ldots, X_n) = g_1(X_1)\, g_2(X_2) \cdots g_n(X_n)$ and, in addition, the rv's are independent so that the pdf factors, then (3.2.11) becomes

$$E[g_1(X_1)\, g_2(X_2) \cdots g_n(X_n)] = E[g_1(X_1)]\, E[g_2(X_2)] \cdots E[g_n(X_n)]. \tag{3.2.12}$$

Covariance. Functions $g(X_1, X_2, \ldots, X_n)$ which are of particular importance are products of rv's, for example,

$$g(X_1, X_2) = (X_1 - \mu_1)(X_2 - \mu_2)$$

in the bivariate case. The expected value of this product is called the *covariance* between X_1 and X_2 and is written

$$\text{Cov } [X_1, X_2] = E[(X_1 - \mu_1)(X_2 - \mu_2)]$$

$$= \int_{-\infty}^{\infty} \int_{-\infty}^{\infty} (x_1 - \mu_1)(x_2 - \mu_2) f_{12}(x_1, x_2) \, dx_1 \, dx_2. \quad (3.2.13)$$

Note from the definition (3.2.13) that $\text{Cov } [X_1, X_2] = \text{Cov } [X_2, X_1]$ and that

$$\text{Var } [X_1] = \text{Cov } [X_1, X_1].$$

If X_1 and X_2 are independent, then $f_{12}(x_1, x_2) = f_1(x_1) f_2(x_2)$ and hence $\text{Cov } [X_1, X_2] = E[X_1 - \mu_1] \, E[X_2 - \mu_2] = 0$. Thus the covariance measures the extent to which two rv's are linearly dependent.

In spectral analysis it is sometimes necessary to consider the covariance between two functions, $g(X_1, \ldots, X_n)$ and $h(X_1, \ldots, X_n)$, namely

$$\text{Cov } [g(X_1, \ldots, X_n), h(X_1, \ldots, X_n)]$$
$$= E[\{g(X_1, \ldots, X_n) - E[g(X_1, \ldots, X_n)]\}$$
$$\times \{h(X_1, \ldots, X_n) - E[h(X_1, \ldots, X_n)]\}].$$

For example, the covariance between $g(X_1, X_2) = X_1 X_2$ and $h(X_3, X_4) = X_3 X_4$ is

$$\text{Cov } [X_1 X_2, X_3 X_4] = E[(X_1 X_2 - E[X_1 X_2])(X_3 X_4 - E[X_3 X_4])].$$

3.2.3 Moments of linear functions of random variables

Consider an arbitrary linear function $\lambda_1 X_1 + \lambda_2 X_2$ of two rv's X_1 and X_2. Then using (3.2.11)

$$E[\lambda_1 X_1 + \lambda_2 X_2] = \int_{-\infty}^{\infty} \int_{-\infty}^{\infty} (\lambda_1 x_1 + \lambda_2 x_2) f_{12}(x_1, x_2) \, dx_1 \, dx_2$$

$$= \lambda_1 E[X_1] + \lambda_2 E[X_2]. \quad (3.2.14)$$

It should be noted that (3.2.14) is true even if X_1 and X_2 are not independent. In general,

$$E\left[\sum_{i=1}^{n} \lambda_i X_i\right] = \sum_{i=1}^{n} \lambda_i E[X_i]. \quad (3.2.15)$$

As an example, consider the expected value of the average $\bar{X} = (1/n) \sum_{i=1}^{n} X_i$ of a set of rv's with the *same* mean μ. Then (3.2.15) shows that

$$E[\bar{X}] = E\left[\frac{1}{n}\sum_{i=1}^{n} X_i\right] = \sum_{i=1}^{n}\frac{1}{n}\mu = \mu.$$

Hence the expected value of the average is the same as the expected value of the individual rv's.

Variance of linear functions. Using (3.2.13), the variance of the linear function $\lambda_1 X_1 + \lambda_2 X_2$ is

$$\text{Var}\,[\lambda_1 X_1 + \lambda_2 X_2] = \lambda_1^2\,\text{Var}\,[X_1] + \lambda_2^2\,\text{Var}\,[X_2] + 2\lambda_1\lambda_2\,\text{Cov}\,[X_1, X_2].$$
$$(3.2.16)$$

In general

$$\text{Var}\left[\sum_{i=1}^{n}\lambda_i X_i\right] = \sum_{i=1}^{n}\sum_{j=1}^{n}\lambda_i\lambda_j\,\text{Cov}\,[X_i, X_j], \qquad (3.2.17)$$

where $\text{Cov}\,[X_i, X_i] = \text{Var}\,[X_i]$.

When the X_i's are independent, (3.2.17) reduces to

$$\text{Var}\left[\sum_{i=1}^{n}\lambda_i X_i\right] = \sum_{i=1}^{n}\lambda_i^2\,\text{Var}\,[X_i]. \qquad (3.2.18)$$

For example, consider the rv $\bar{X} = (1/n)\sum_{i=1}^{n} X_i$ where the X_i's are independent rv's with variance σ^2. Then

$$\text{Var}\,[\bar{X}] = \sum_{i=1}^{n}\left(\frac{1}{n}\right)^2\text{Var}\,[X_i] = \frac{\sigma^2}{n}.$$

Using (3.2.15) and (3.2.18) with $n = 1$, one obtains the useful result that the *standardized* rv

$$Y = \frac{X - \mu}{\sigma}$$

has zero mean and variance unity. A further important result [2] is that if the rv's X_i are Normal, the pdf of the rv

$$Y = \sum_{i=1}^{n}\lambda_i X_i$$

is also Normal with mean given by (3.2.15) and variance given by (3.2.17).

3.2.4 *The correlation coefficient*

The expression (3.2.16) for the variance of a linear function of two random variables is necessarily positive or zero for all real values of λ_1 and λ_2. Since the right-hand side is a quadratic expression in λ_1 and λ_2, the condition for the variance to be positive is that the roots of this quadratic are imaginary. This implies

$$\text{Var}\,[X_1]\,\text{Var}\,[X_2] \geqslant (\text{Cov}\,[X_1,\,X_2])^2,$$

which may be rewritten

$$\rho_{12}^2 = \frac{(\text{Cov}\,[X_1,\,X_2])^2}{\text{Var}\,[X_1]\,\text{Var}\,[X_2]} \leqslant 1. \qquad (3.2.19)$$

The parameter ρ_{12} is called the *correlation coefficient* between X_1 and X_2, and lies in the interval $-1 \leqslant \rho_{12} \leqslant +1$.

It has been noted already that when the rv's are independent, $\text{Cov}\,[X_1,\,X_2] = 0$ and hence $\rho_{12} = 0$. In the case of a bivariate Normal pdf it has been shown conversely that if $\rho_{12} = 0$, the rv's are independent. However, if $\rho_{12} = 0$ for a non-Normal distribution, the rv's are not necessarily independent and are then said to be *uncorrelated*.

When $\rho_{12} = 0$, a scatter diagram of pairs of values (x_1, x_2) which are realizations of the rv's (X_1, X_2) would be similar to Figure 3.8(a). It is seen that knowledge of the value of one member of the pair is of no help in predicting the value of the other.

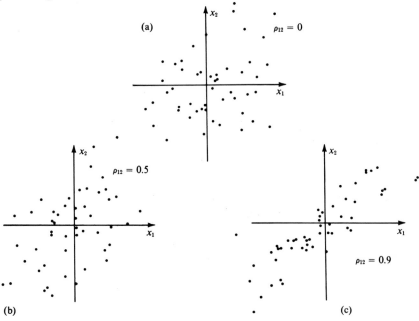

FIG. 3.8: Scatter diagrams of samples of bivariate Normal random variables

For ρ_{12} small but positive, the scatter diagram would resemble the one shown in Figure 3.8(b), which corresponds to $\rho_{12} = +0.5$. There is now a noticeable but weak tendency for the values to cluster along a straight line. Hence, high values of x_2 tend to be associated with high values of x_1 and low values of x_2 tend to be associated with low values of x_1. If the correlation coefficient had been -0.5, the slope of the straight line about which the points cluster would be negative. Hence, high values of x_2 would tend to be associated with low values of x_1 and vice versa. For values of ρ_{12} near unity, the scatter diagram tends to be more concentrated about a straight line as in Figure 3.8(c), for which $\rho_{12} = +0.9$. Hence ρ_{12} is a measure of *linear dependence* between the rv's X_1 and X_2, and in the limiting case where $\rho_{12} = 1$, there is an exact linear relationship of the form $X_2 = a + bX_1$.

Comparison of the scatter diagrams of Figure 3.8 with the scatter diagrams of the accelerometer data of Figure 3.7 shows that the accelerometer data have a correlation coefficient between 0.5 and 0.9.

A formula for the estimate $\hat{\rho}_{12}$ of the correlation coefficient will be given in Chapter 4 and this yields a value of $\hat{\rho}_{12} = 0.78$ for the accelerometer data. This value is sufficiently low to cause some anxiety about the reliability of the pilot's visual accelerometer!

Covariance of linear functions. As a final generalization of (3.2.17) consider two linear functions $\lambda_1 X_1 + \lambda_2 X_2$ and $\nu_1 X_1 + \nu_2 X_2$. The covariance between them is

$$\text{Cov}\,[(\lambda_1 X_1 + \lambda_2 X_2),\,(\nu_1 X_1 + \nu_2 X_2)]$$
$$= \lambda_1 \nu_1 \,\text{Cov}\,[X_1, X_1] + \lambda_1 \nu_2 \,\text{Cov}\,[X_1, X_2]$$
$$+ \lambda_2 \nu_1 \,\text{Cov}\,[X_2, X_1] + \lambda_2 \nu_2 \,\text{Cov}\,[X_2, X_2],\qquad(3.2.20)$$

which reduces to (3.2.16) when $\lambda_1 = \nu_1$ and $\lambda_2 = \nu_2$. In general

$$\text{Cov}\left[\sum_{i=1}^{n} \lambda_i X_i,\; \sum_{j=1}^{n} \nu_j X_j\right] = \sum_{i=1}^{n}\sum_{j=1}^{n} \lambda_i \nu_j \,\text{Cov}\,[X_i, X_j].\qquad(3.2.21)$$

Equation (3.2.21) is an important result which will be used to calculate the covariance between smoothed spectral estimators in Chapter 6.

The results of this section are given in matrix form in Appendix A3.1.

3.2.5 *Moments of non-linear functions of random variables*

In many practical statistical problems it is necessary to consider non-linear functions of rv's. For example, most problems in spectral analysis are non-linear. Except in certain special cases it is not possible to derive the exact pdf's of these non-linear functions, and hence it is necessary to describe the pdf's by their moments. In this section it is shown how to derive approximations for the mean and variance of a non-linear function of rv's.

Mean of a non-linear function. Consider a function $g(X_1, X_2, \ldots, X_n)$ of the rv's $X_1, X_2, \ldots, X_n$ which have means μ_i and covariances σ_{ij} $(i, j = 1, 2, \ldots, n)$.

Consider a Taylor series expansion of $g(X_1, X_2, \ldots, X_n)$ about the point $(a_1, a_2, \ldots, a_n)$. Then to a first-order approximation,

$$g(X_1, X_2, \ldots, X_n) \approx g(a_1, a_2, \ldots, a_n) + \sum_{i=1}^{n} \left(\frac{\partial g}{\partial X_i}\right)_a (X_i - a_i), \quad (3.2.22)$$

where $(\partial g/\partial X_i)_a$ denotes the partial derivative with respect to X_i evaluated at the point $(X_1, X_2, \ldots, X_n) = (a_1, a_2, \ldots, a_n)$.

On taking expectations in (3.2.22),

$$E[g(X_1, X_2, \ldots, X_n)] \approx g(a_1, a_2, \ldots, a_n) + \sum_{i=1}^{n} \left(\frac{\partial g}{\partial X_i}\right)_a (E[X_i] - a_i).$$
$$(3.2.23)$$

When $a_i = \mu_i$, the second term vanishes so that

$$E[g(X_1, X_2, \ldots, X_n)] \approx g(\mu_1, \mu_2, \ldots, \mu_n). \quad (3.2.24)$$

Variance of a non-linear function. From (3.2.22),

$$[g(X_1, X_2, \ldots, X_n) - g(\mu_1, \mu_2, \ldots, \mu_n)] \approx \sum_{i=1}^{n} \left(\frac{\partial g}{\partial X_i}\right)_\mu (X_i - \mu_i),$$

which is linear in the X_i, and hence on using (3.2.17),

$$\text{Var}\,[g(X_1, X_2, \ldots, X_n)] \approx \sum_{i=1}^{n} \sum_{j=1}^{n} \left(\frac{\partial g}{\partial X_i}\right)_\mu \left(\frac{\partial g}{\partial X_j}\right)_\mu \text{Cov}\,[X_i, X_j]. \quad (3.2.25)$$

Special cases of (3.2.25). If $n = 1$, then

$$\text{Var}\,[g(X)] \approx \left(\frac{dg}{dX}\right)_\mu^2 \text{Var}\,[X]. \quad (3.2.26)$$

For example, if $g(X) = X^2$, then

$$\text{Var}\,[X^2] \approx 4\mu^2 \,\text{Var}\,[X].$$

If $n = 2$,

Var $[g(X_1, X_2)]$

$$\approx \left(\frac{\partial g}{\partial X_1}\right)_\mu^2 \text{Var}\,[X_1] + \left(\frac{\partial g}{\partial X_2}\right)_\mu^2 \text{Var}\,[X_2] + 2\left(\frac{\partial g}{\partial X_1}\right)_\mu \left(\frac{\partial g}{\partial X_2}\right)_\mu \text{Cov}\,[X_1, X_2].$$
$$(3.2.27)$$

For example, if X_1 and X_2 are uncorrelated rv's and

$$g(X_1, X_2) = \sqrt{X_1^2 + X_2^2},$$

(3.2.27) reduces to

$$\text{Var}\,[g(X_1, X_2)] = \frac{\mu_1^2\,\text{Var}\,[X_1] + \mu_2^2\,\text{Var}\,[X_2]}{\mu_1^2 + \mu_2^2}.$$

Variance stabilizing transformations. It frequently happens in statistical problems that the variance of a rv is some function of its mean μ, for example $\text{Var}\,[X] = \mu^2$. It is then more logical to consider the rv $Y = X/\mu$ since $\text{Var}\,[Y] = 1$, and hence the scale of measurement of Y is independent of its mean. A more general approach is to consider a function $g(X)$ of the rv such that $\text{Var}\,[g(X)]$ is approximately independent of the mean of X and hence of the mean of $g(X)$.

Using (3.2.26), if $\text{Var}\,[g(X)]$ is to be a constant k_1,

$$k_1 \approx \left(\frac{dg}{dX}\right)_\mu^2 \phi(\mu),$$

where $\text{Var}\,[X] = \phi(\mu)$. Hence, apart from an additive constant

$$g(\mu) \propto \int \frac{d\mu}{\sqrt{\phi(\mu)}} \tag{3.2.28}$$

and the rv $g(X)$ has a variance which is approximately independent of its mean. In the above example, $\text{Var}\,[X] = \phi(\mu) = \mu^2$ so that $g(\mu) = \ln \mu$. Thus the rv $\ln X$ has a variance which is approximately independent of the mean and hence provides a more logical scale of measurement than X itself.

Variance stabilizing transformations tend to produce a pdf for the transformed rv which is closer to Normal than the pdf of X. Hence the pdf of the transformed rv is more adequately described by its mean and variance than is the pdf of X itself.

3.3 SAMPLING DISTRIBUTIONS

One of the main problems in probability theory is to find the pdf $f_X(x)$ of some function $X(X_1, X_2, \ldots, X_n)$ of n rv's $X_1, X_2, \ldots, X_n$, given their joint pdf [2]. These derived distributions are useful in statistical analysis of data in the following way.

Suppose it is intended to collect a finite sample of observations $x_1, x_2, \ldots, x_n$ from which is to be computed some function $x(x_1, x_2, \ldots, x_n)$, for example, the mean. Then, before the data is collected, one can describe all possible sets of data which might be obtained by means of random variables $X_1, X_2, \ldots, X_n$. Thus, the totality of possible experiments is described by an n-dimensional sample space with which can be associated a joint pdf $f_{12\ldots n}(x_1, x_2, \ldots, x_n)$. Using methods described, for example, in [2], it is then possible to compute the pdf $f_X(x)$ of the function $X(X_1, X_2, \ldots, X_n)$. In advance of collecting the data, this pdf can be used to predict the frequency with which different values of the function $x(x_1, x_2, \ldots, x_n)$ lie between any two limits in repeated samples of size n. Hence the pdf $f_X(x)$ is called the *sampling distribution* of the random variable $X(X_1, X_2, \ldots, X_n)$.

3.3.1 Sampling distribution of the mean, variance known

The simplest example of a sampling distribution occurs when n independent measurements are made on some variable, for example, the collector cut-off current of a transistor. In this case the joint pdf is simply

$$f_{12\ldots n}(x_1, x_2, \ldots, x_n) = f_1(x_1) f_2(x_2) \cdots f_n(x_n). \tag{3.3.1}$$

Suppose that one is interested in the variability in the sample mean of the measurements. Then if it is assumed that each X_i is distributed as $N(\mu, \sigma^2)$ it may be shown [2] that the pdf of the sample mean $\bar{X} = (1/n) \sum_{i=1}^{n} X_i$ of the rv's is $N(\mu, \sigma^2/n)$, that is,

$$f_{\bar{X}}(\bar{x}) = \frac{1}{\sqrt{2\pi}\,(\sigma/\sqrt{n})} \exp\left[-\frac{n}{2}\left(\frac{\bar{x} - \mu}{\sigma}\right)^2\right]; \tag{3.3.2}$$

(3.3.2) is called the *sampling distribution of the mean* for Normal rv's. The frequency interpretation to be placed on (3.3.2) is that if one imagined a very large number of experiments, each consisting of n independent measurements drawn from an $N(\mu, \sigma^2)$ population, the histogram of the distribution of $\bar{x}$ would tend to the Normal form (3.3.2).

The sampling distribution of the sample mean (3.3.2) is usually very close to Normal even if the individual distributions $f_1(x_1), \ldots, f_n(x_n)$ are not themselves Normal. This powerful result follows from the Central Limit Theorem [2].

A sampling distribution, like any other distribution, can be described by its moments, usually called the *sampling moments*. For example, the sampling distribution of the mean of Normal rv's (3.3.2) is completely described by the sampling moments

$$E[\bar{X}] = \mu;$$

$$\mathrm{Var}\,[\bar{X}] = \frac{\sigma^2}{n}. \tag{3.3.3}$$

The frequency interpretation to be placed on these moments is that the average of a large number of sample means will lie very close to the population or theoretical mean μ and that the variability in the means from one sample to the next can be described by the variance σ^2/n.

One of the main uses of sampling distributions is to make *probability statements* about rv's such as $\bar{X}$. For example, consider a sample of 9 values x_i, ($i = 1, 2, \ldots, 9$) of a rv X which is known to be Normally distributed with unit variance but unknown mean μ. From (3.3.2) and (3.3.3) it is known that the rv $\bar{X}$ is distributed Normally with $E[\bar{X}] = \mu$ and Var $[\bar{X}] = \frac{1}{9}$. Hence, using the probabilities associated with the Normal pdf given in Table 3.4, the probability that an observed value $\bar{x}$ of $\bar{X}$ lies in a given range may be calculated. For example,

$$\Pr\left\{\mu - \frac{1.96}{\sqrt{9}} < \bar{X} \leqslant \mu + \frac{1.96}{\sqrt{9}}\right\} = 0.95$$

or

$$\Pr\{\mu - 0.653 < \bar{X} \leqslant \mu + 0.653\} = 0.95.$$

This means that if the rv X is Normally distributed with mean μ and variance 1, the rv $\bar{X}$ has probability 0.95 of lying within ± 0.653 of μ. The frequency interpretation of this is that in a large number of samples of 9 realizations of X, approximately one out of twenty estimates $\bar{x}$ will differ from the true value μ by more than 0.653. The converse and more difficult problem of making inferences about μ from the given value of $\bar{x}$ is discussed in Chapter 4.

3.3.2 Sampling distribution of the variance

The sampling distribution of the mean involved the distribution of sums of rv's. The next simplest sampling distribution, that of the variance of Normal rv's, involves the sum of squares of rv's, $X_1^2 + X_2^2 + \cdots + X_n^2$. For example, suppose there are n independent measurements from an $N(0, 1)$ population and it is required to find the sampling distribution of the rv

$$\chi_n^2 = X_1^2 + X_2^2 + \cdots + X_n^2. \tag{3.3.4}$$

The distribution of χ_n^2 is called the *chi-squared distribution with n degrees of freedom*. The general form of the χ_ν^2 pdf with ν degrees of freedom is

$$f_{\chi_\nu^2}(x) = \frac{1}{2^{\nu/2}\Gamma(\nu/2)} x^{(\nu/2)-1} \exp\left(-\frac{x}{2}\right), \quad (0 \leqslant x \leqslant \infty), \tag{3.3.5}$$

where $\Gamma(\nu/2) = \int_0^\infty e^{-t} t^{(\nu/2)-1}\, dt$ is the gamma function with argument $\nu/2$.

Plots of $f_{\chi_\nu^2}(x)$ versus x for $\nu = 1, 2, 3$ and 10 are given in Figure 3.9. For $\nu = 1$, the pdf has an infinite ordinate at $x = 0$ and tends to zero as x tends to infinity. For $\nu = 2$ the pdf is exponential and for $\nu \geqslant 3$ the pdf settles down to a unimodal form. Note, however, that for small ν the distribution is very non-symmetrical. As n increases the pdf begins to look more like the Normal pdf, as predicted by the Central Limit Theorem.

The first two moments of the χ_ν^2 rv, obtained from the pdf (3.3.5), are

$$E[\chi_\nu^2] = \nu;$$
$$\text{Var } [\chi_\nu^2] = 2\nu. \tag{3.3.6}$$

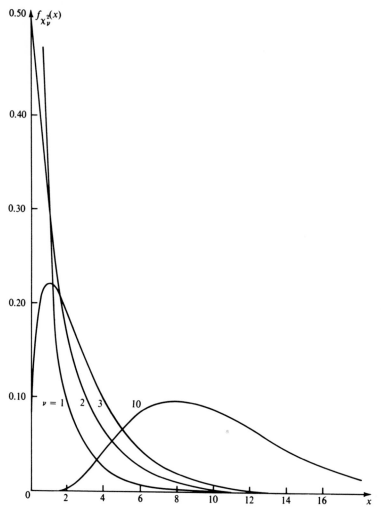

FIG. 3.9: Chi-squared probability density functions

It will be shown in Chapter 4 that one estimate of the variance from a sample of n observations is

$$s^2 = \frac{1}{n-1} \sum_{i=1}^{n} (x_i - \bar{x})^2.$$

To describe the variability in this function from one sample to the next, one introduces the corresponding rv S^2 where

$$S^2 = \frac{1}{n-1} \sum_{i=1}^{n} (X_i - \bar{X})^2. \tag{3.3.7}$$

If the X_i are independent $N(\mu, 1^2)$ rv's, it may be shown [2] that $(n - 1)S^2$ is distributed as a chi-square with $v = (n - 1)$ *degrees of freedom*. The term "degrees of freedom" is used here in the same sense as it is in statistical mechanics. Thus, for any set of n observations there will only be $(n - 1)$ independent deviations $(X_i - \bar{X})$ since their sum is zero from the definition of the mean.

Usually the observations will be assumed to be $N(\mu, \sigma^2)$. In this case, X_i/σ will be $N(\mu/\sigma, 1^2)$ and so the rv

$$(n - 1)\frac{S^2}{\sigma^2} = \frac{1}{\sigma^2} \sum_{i=1}^{n} (X_i - \bar{X})^2 \qquad (3.3.8)$$

will have a chi-squared pdf with $v = n - 1$.

Since vS^2/σ^2 is distributed as χ_v^2, probability limits of the form

$$\Pr\left\{x_v\left(\frac{\alpha}{2}\right) < \frac{vS^2}{\sigma^2} \leqslant x_v\left(1 - \frac{\alpha}{2}\right)\right\} = 1 - \alpha \qquad (3.3.9)$$

may be obtained from tables [1]. Rearranging (3.3.9) it follows that the rv σ^2/S^2 satisfies

$$\Pr\left\{\frac{v}{x_v(1 - \alpha/2)} < \frac{\sigma^2}{S^2} \leqslant \frac{v}{x_v(\alpha/2)}\right\} = 1 - \alpha. \qquad (3.3.10)$$

Plots of the lower and upper limits $v/x_v(1 - \alpha/2)$ and $v/x_v(\alpha/2)$ are given in Figure 3.10 for $\alpha = 0.01$, 0.05 and 0.2, and for $3 \leqslant v \leqslant 100$. Note that the upper and lower limits in (3.3.10) are *very* sensitive to the validity of the Normal assumption [3]. This is not the case for the probability limits for the mean, which can be based on Normal theory because of the Central Limit Theorem.

The curves of Figure 3.10 may be used to determine an interval within which the rv S^2/σ^2 may be expected to lie on $100(1 - \alpha)\%$ of occasions. For example, suppose 20 observations are to be taken from a population which is $N(\mu, \sigma^2)$. Then $v = n - 1 = 19$ and using (3.3.10) and Figure 3.10,

$$\Pr\left\{0.58 < \frac{\sigma^2}{S^2} \leqslant 2.11\right\} = 1 - 0.05 = 0.95.$$

Hence, 19 out of 20 times on average, the ratio σ^2/S^2 would be expected to lie in the range 0.58 to 2.11. Alternatively, the value of S^2 would be expected to lie in the range $0.47\sigma^2 < S^2 \leqslant 1.72\sigma^2$, or the value $vS^2/\sigma^2 = 19S^2/\sigma^2$ in the range $8.9 < 19S^2/\sigma^2 \leqslant 32.9$, with probability 0.95. The limits $8.9 = 19/2.11$ and $32.9 = 19/0.58$ for vS^2/σ^2 are the ones usually given in statistical tables.

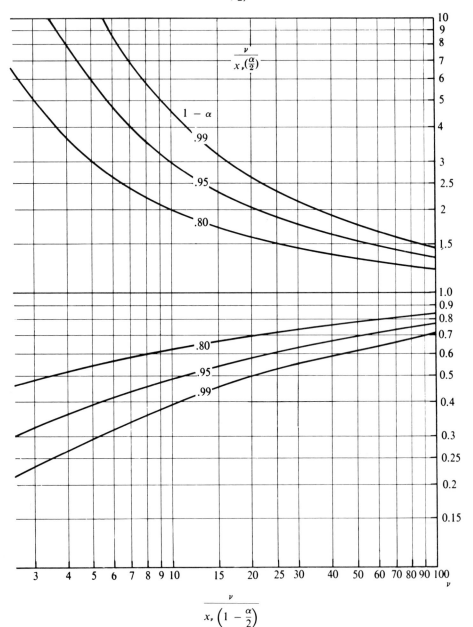

$$\dfrac{\nu}{x_\nu\left(\dfrac{\alpha}{2}\right)}$$

FIG. 3.10: Plot of $\dfrac{\nu}{x_\nu(\alpha/2)}$, $\dfrac{\nu}{x_\nu(1-\alpha/2)}$ vs. ν for $(1-\alpha) = 0.80, 0.95, 0.99$

3.3.3 Sampling distribution of the mean, variance unknown

To determine probability limits for the mean of Normal rv's, it was necessary to know σ, the population standard deviation. If σ is not known, then it is impossible to make precise probability statements using the sampling distribution of $\bar{X}$ since the probability limits will depend on the unknown value of σ. In this case σ is said to be a *nuisance parameter*.

To construct probability intervals for the mean when σ is known, it is natural to consider the rv

$$Y = \frac{\sqrt{n}\,(\bar{X} - \mu)}{\sigma}. \qquad (3.3.11)$$

This rv is $N(0, 1^2)$, and hence probability intervals may be obtained using Table 3.2.

An important advance in the theory of sampling distributions was made in 1908 by W. S. Gosset, writing under the pen name Student. He showed that if σ were replaced in (3.3.11) by the rv S where S^2 is defined by (3.3.7), the distribution of the rv

$$T_\nu = \frac{\sqrt{n}\,(\bar{X} - \mu)}{S}, \qquad \nu = n - 1, \qquad (3.3.12)$$

is independent of the nuisance parameter σ. Hence probability statements about the mean of Normal observations can be made which are independent of σ. This result is intuitively obvious, since if the observations were multiplied by some constant (for example, if the measurements were made in inches instead of feet), both numerator and denominator in (3.3.12) would be multiplied by the same factor, leaving T_ν unaltered.

The pdf of the rv T_ν is called *Student's t distribution with ν degrees of freedom* and, like the Normal pdf, it is symmetric about the origin. The effect of replacing σ in (3.3.11) by S as in (3.3.12) is to increase the variability of the rv T_ν and hence Student's t distribution is flatter than the Normal distribution. However, as ν becomes large, the distribution of S becomes more closely distributed about σ and hence the t distribution tends to the unit Normal (3.2.8), again as predicted by the Central Limit Theorem.

Student's t distribution may be used to construct intervals $t_\nu(\alpha/2)$, $t_\nu(1 - \alpha/2)$, in which the rv T_ν may be expected to lie on a proportion $1 - \alpha$ of occasions. Since the pdf is symmetric, $t_\nu(\alpha/2) = -t_\nu(1 - \alpha/2)$, and hence

$$\Pr\left\{ -t_\nu\left(1 - \frac{\alpha}{2}\right) < T_\nu \leqslant t_\nu\left(1 - \frac{\alpha}{2}\right) \right\} = 1 - \alpha.$$

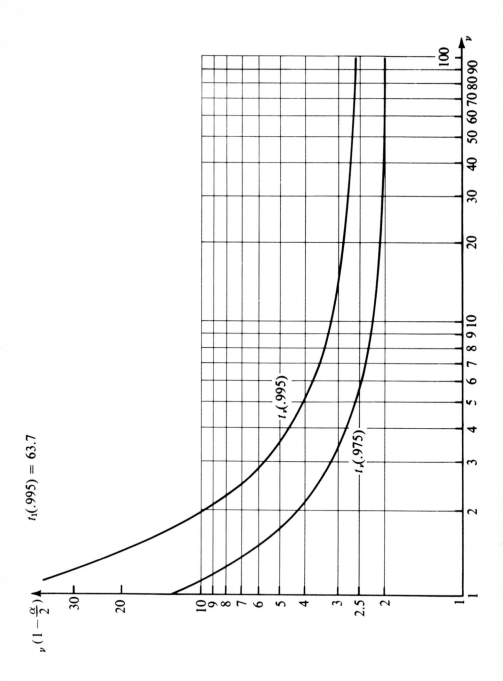

FIG. 3.11: Plot of $t_\nu(1 - \alpha/2)$ vs. ν for $(1 - \alpha) = 0.99, 0.95$

Figure 3.11 shows the curves of $t_\nu(1 - \alpha/2)$ versus ν for $\alpha = 0.05$ and $\alpha = 0.01$. Note that for ν large, the curves approach the values 1.96 and 2.58, the 0.95 and 0.99 limits for the unit Normal pdf.

To illustrate the use of Figure 3.11, suppose, as in the example of Section 3.3.1, that 9 measurements from an $N(\mu, \sigma^2)$ population are to be made. Then, from Figure 3.11, the rv $\sqrt{9}\,(\bar{X} - \mu)/S$ will be expected to lie in the interval $(-2.3, +2.3)$ on 95% of occasions. Note that the corresponding interval when σ^2 is known is, from Table 3.4, $(-1.96, +1.96)$, which is about 15% narrower.

3.3.4 Sampling distribution of the ratio of two variances

Another important sampling distribution arises when it is required to compare two estimates of variance s_1^2 and s_2^2, obtained from two independent samples of size n_1 and n_2 respectively. If the samples are from two populations distributed as $N(\mu_1, \sigma_1^2)$ and $N(\mu_2, \sigma_2^2)$, then from Section 3.3.2, the rv $\nu_1 S_1^2/\sigma_1^2$ is a $\chi_{\nu_1}^2$ rv with $\nu_1 = n_1 - 1$, and similarly the rv $\nu_2 S_2^2/\sigma_2^2$ is a $\chi_{\nu_2}^2$ rv with $\nu_2 = n_2 - 1$. When the rv's $\chi_{\nu_1}^2$ and $\chi_{\nu_2}^2$ are independent the pdf of the ratio

$$F_{\nu_1, \nu_2} = \frac{\sigma_2^2 S_1^2}{\sigma_1^2 S_2^2} = \frac{\nu_2 \chi_{\nu_1}^2}{\nu_1 \chi_{\nu_2}^2} \qquad (3.3.13)$$

is called *Fisher's F distribution with ν_1 and ν_2 degrees of freedom*.

The F distribution is a two-parameter sampling distribution, ν_1 giving the degrees of freedom of the numerator and ν_2 the degrees of freedom of the denominator. When ν_1 and ν_2 are both large, the pdf of F_{ν_1, ν_2} will tend to be concentrated about unity. However, for small values of ν_1 or ν_2, the pdf is widely distributed about unity.

In practice, the theoretical variances σ_1^2 and σ_2^2 which appear in (3.3.13) will not be known. However, if it is assumed that $\sigma_1^2 = \sigma_2^2$, it follows from (3.3.13) that S_1^2/S_2^2 is distributed as F_{ν_1, ν_2}. However, if $\sigma_1^2 \neq \sigma_2^2$, then S_1^2/S_2^2 will be distributed as $(\sigma_1^2/\sigma_2^2)F_{\nu_1, \nu_2}$ and hence the distribution will be concentrated about the value σ_1^2/σ_2^2 and not 1.

Figure 3.12 shows the 0.95 probability points for the F_{ν_1, ν_2} distribution, that is, the value $f_{\nu_1, \nu_2}(0.95)$ such that

$$\Pr\{F_{\nu_1, \nu_2} \leqslant f_{\nu_1, \nu_2}(0.95)\} = 0.95.$$

Note that since $F_{\nu_1, \nu_2} = 1/F_{\nu_2, \nu_1}$, the values f_{ν_1, ν_2} and f_{ν_2, ν_1} may be used to construct probability intervals for the rv F_{ν_1, ν_2}. Thus,

$$\Pr\left\{\frac{1}{f_{\nu_2, \nu_1}(0.95)} < F_{\nu_1, \nu_2} \leqslant f_{\nu_1, \nu_2}(0.95)\right\} = 0.90.$$

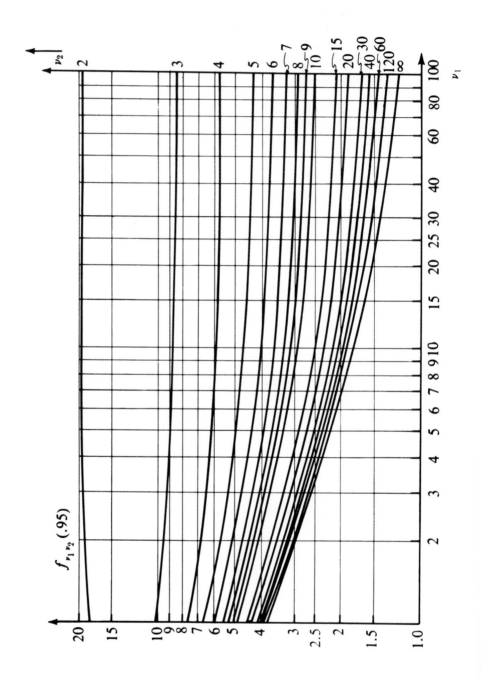

FIG. 3.12: Plot of $f_{\nu_1\nu_2}$ (0.95) vs. (ν_1, ν_2)

For example, if $v_1 = 4$, $v_2 = 20$, then from Figure 3.12,

$$\Pr \{F_{4,20} \leqslant 2.9\} = 0.95;$$

$$\Pr \{F_{20,4} \leqslant 5.9\} = \Pr \{F_{4,20} > 0.17\} = 0.95.$$

Hence

$$\Pr \{0.17 < F_{4,20} \leqslant 2.9\} = 0.90.$$

3.3.5 Two properties of the chi-squared distribution

Approximation by a chi-squared distribution. The chi-squared distribution occupies a central position in the approximation to the distribution of smoothed estimators of the spectral density function. In general, the chi-squared rv is useful for approximating a positive valued rv, say Y. For example, suppose that it is required to approximate the pdf of a positive rv Y by the pdf of a rv $a\chi_v^2$, where a and v are as yet unspecified. It is assumed that the first two moments of Y are given. Then if they are equated to the first two moments of the rv $a\chi_v^2$, as deduced from (3.3.6),

$$E[Y] = av;$$

$$\text{Var }[Y] = 2a^2v.$$

Solving for a and v gives

$$v = \frac{2(E[Y])^2}{\text{Var }[Y]}; \qquad (3.3.14)$$

$$a = \frac{E[Y]}{v}, \qquad (3.3.15)$$

which gives the parameters of the approximating χ^2 distribution in terms of the first two moments of Y.

The decomposition theorem for chi-squared random variables. Suppose that an rv χ_v^2 is decomposed into k rv's $\chi_{v_i}^2$ according to

$$\chi_v^2 = \chi_{v_1}^2 + \chi_{v_2}^2 + \cdots + \chi_{v_k}^2.$$

Then it may be shown [4] that if

$$v_1 + v_2 + \cdots + v_k = v, \qquad (3.3.16)$$

the rv's $\chi_{v_i}^2$ are mutually independent. Conversely, if the χ_v^2 are independent, then (3.3.16) follows.

A simple application of this very important property is the following. Suppose that $X_1, X_2, \ldots, X_n$ are n independent $N(0, 1^2)$ rv's. Then

$$\sum_{i=1}^{n} X_i^2 = (\sqrt{n}\,\bar{X})^2 + \sum_{i=1}^{n} (X_i - \bar{X})^2.$$

The left-hand side is a χ_n^2 rv and the first term on the right-hand side, being the square of an $N(0, 1^2)$ is a χ_1^2 variable. Now it may be verified that the rv's $\bar{X}$ and $X_i - \bar{X}$ are independent and hence the two χ^2 rv's on the right-hand side are independent. The result (3.3.16) then states that the second term has $n - 1$ degrees of freedom.

REFERENCES

[1] R. A. Fisher and F. Yates, *Statistical Tables*. Oliver and Boyd, London, 1938.
[2] E. Parzen, *Modern Probability Theory and its Applications*. John Wiley, New York, 1960.
[3] S. L. Anderson and G. E. P. Box, "Permutation theory in the derivation of robust criteria and the study of departures from assumption." *Jour. Royal Stat. Soc.* **B 17**, 1 (1955).
[4] A. Hald, *Statistical Theory with Engineering Applications*. John Wiley, New York, 1952.

APPENDIX A3.1: MOMENTS OF LINEAR FUNCTIONS OF RANDOM VARIABLES

The results derived in Section 3.2.3 for linear functions of random variables may be written more elegantly in matrix notation. Thus, if

$$\boldsymbol{\lambda}' = (\lambda_1, \lambda_2, \ldots, \lambda_n), \qquad \mathbf{X}' = (X_1, X_2, \ldots, X_n)$$

are row vectors, and a prime denotes a transposed matrix, then the result (3.2.15)

$$E\left[\sum_{i=1}^{n} \lambda_i X_i\right] = \sum_{i=1}^{n} \lambda_i E[X_i] \tag{A3.1.1}$$

may be written in matrix form as

$$E[\boldsymbol{\lambda}'\mathbf{X}] = \boldsymbol{\lambda}' E[\mathbf{X}] = \boldsymbol{\lambda}'\boldsymbol{\mu}, \tag{A3.1.2}$$

where $\boldsymbol{\mu}' = E[\mathbf{X}'] = (E[X_1], E[X_2], \ldots, E[X_n])$. Similarly, the result (3.2.17)

$$\text{Var}\left[\sum_{i=1}^{n} \lambda_i X_i\right] = \sum_{i=1}^{n}\sum_{j=1}^{n} \lambda_i \lambda_j \, \text{Cov}\,[X_i, X_j] \tag{A3.1.3}$$

may be written in matrix form as

$$\text{Var}\,[\boldsymbol{\lambda}'\mathbf{X}] = E[\boldsymbol{\lambda}'(\mathbf{X} - \boldsymbol{\mu})(\mathbf{X} - \boldsymbol{\mu})'\boldsymbol{\lambda}] = \boldsymbol{\lambda}'\mathbf{V}\boldsymbol{\lambda}, \tag{A3.1.4}$$

where $\mathbf{V} = E[(\mathbf{X} - \boldsymbol{\mu})(\mathbf{X} - \boldsymbol{\mu})']$ is called the *covariance matrix* of the rv's X_i and is given by

$$\mathbf{V} = \begin{pmatrix} \text{Var}\,[X_1] & \text{Cov}\,[X_1, X_2] & . & . & . & \text{Cov}\,[X_1, X_n] \\ \text{Cov}\,[X_2, X_1] & \text{Var}\,[X_2] & & . & . & . & \text{Cov}\,[X_2, X_n] \\ \vdots & \vdots & & & & \vdots \\ \text{Cov}\,[X_n, X_1] & \text{Cov}\,[X_n, X_2] & . & . & . & \text{Var}\,[X_n] \end{pmatrix}. \quad (A3.1.5)$$

The covariance matrix has the following properties:

(1) Since $\text{Cov}\,[X_i, X_j] = \text{Cov}\,[X_j, X_i]$, the matrix $\mathbf{V}$ is symmetric, that is, $\mathbf{V} = \mathbf{V}'$.

(2) Since the variance of an rv is always non-negative, the expression (A3.1.4) will always be non-negative for any choice of λ. This implies that the matrix $\mathbf{V}$ is positive semi-definite, that is, the determinant of $\mathbf{V}$ and all its principal minors are non-negative.

Finally, the result (3.2.21) for the covariance between two different linear functions of the rv's X_i may be written

$$\text{Cov}\,[\lambda'\mathbf{X}, \nu'\mathbf{X}] = \lambda'\mathbf{V}\nu. \quad (A3.1.6)$$

4

Introduction to
Statistical Inference

Statistics is the science of handling data—how to collect the right kind of data, how to analyze it and how to use the results of the analysis in making sensible practical recommendations. The branch of statistics which is concerned with developing general methods of approach to the analysis of data is called the theory of *statistical inference*.

In turn, the theory of statistical inference consists of two parts, tests of significance and estimation theory.

In a test of significance, a given set of data is examined to see whether it is consistent or not consistent with a specific hypothesis about a random variable, for example, whether it is Normally distributed with given mean μ and given standard deviation σ. In the theory of estimation, the data is used to estimate the values of the parameters in some assumed pdf for the rv and to determine the accuracy of the estimates. In this chapter it is maintained that tests of significance are used far too frequently in situations where the practical problem demands that one should estimate parameters. The latter approach is usually more relevant in practice than the restricted yes–no type of answer permitted by the test of significance.

Two approaches to the theory of inference will be distinguished in this chapter, namely the *sampling distribution* approach and the *likelihood* approach. A special case of likelihood methods, which is of fundamental importance in the estimation of power spectra, is the *theory of least squares* discussed in Section 4.3. Likelihood methods are ideally suited to situations where a small set of parameters is to be estimated from the data. As such they are not of direct relevance to the estimation of power spectra which contain effectively an infinite number of parameters. The only approach which is possible in this situation is via the sampling distribution. However, likelihood methods are included in this chapter because of their importance in estimating parameters in parametric models.

4.1 HISTORICAL DEVELOPMENT OF STATISTICAL INFERENCE

The theory of probability was developed to predict, in *advance* of performing an experiment, the probability that a random variable X lies between two limits x_1 and x_2. As the theory developed, it was inevitable that certain modes of statistical inference began to develop as well. Statistical inference is concerned with the converse problem to that of probability theory, namely how to use the data $x_1, x_2, \ldots, x_n$ *after* the experiment to make inferences about the properties of the rv X. For example, suppose that a sequence of 15 throws of a coin resulted in 12 heads, and that it is required to know whether the result is compatible with the assumption of a fair coin. The classical solution to this problem is an example of an early mode of inference which is now called a *test of significance*. The solution makes use of probability concepts exclusively and consists of calculating the probability that 12 or more heads would be observed under the hypothesis that the coin is fair. If this probability is small, then it can be regarded as weighty evidence that the assumption of a fair coin is false; if the probability is large, the hypothesis that the coin is fair is not contradicted. In the above example, the probability of 12 or more heads in 15 throws, assuming a fair coin, is 0.018, which suggests that the coin is not fair.

Another early mode of inference was the method of least squares discovered by Karl Friedrich Gauss (1777–1855) while he was trying to determine the orbits of comets from observational data. In this problem, the orbital position has an assumed functional form involving certain measured *variables* and certain fixed orbital constants or *parameters*. The estimation problem considered by Gauss was to determine the best estimates of the parameters from the data and to give some measure of the accuracy of these estimates.

Apart from the pioneering work of Gauss, most of the theory of statistical inference has been developed since the beginning of the twentieth century. Much of the motivation for this development has come from what are usually called the nonphysical sciences, such as biology, genetics and agriculture. In these subjects, the experimental units are extremely variable, for example, the animals on which drugs or foodstocks are tested or the land on which varieties of wheat are to be compared. Because of these large variations, very little progress in experimentation was possible without the development of sophisticated methods of *statistical analysis* and *experimental designs* for collecting informative data. On the other hand, the introduction of statistical methods has been slow in the physical sciences. For example, in experimental physics it is possible, with considerable expense and sophisticated techniques, to reduce variability from one experiment to the next so that statistical questions can be neglected.

By contrast, the scale of experimentation in industrial work is much wider, ranging from development work in the laboratory, through the pilot plant stage to large-scale industrial experimentation. In these situations, adequate control of conditions is either impossible or uneconomic, and so statistical techniques are vital.

The problems encountered in these experimental areas have stimulated the development of theories of statistical inference. In this chapter two important approaches to the theory will be discussed. The first has its origins in probability theory and is called the *sampling distribution approach*. The second has origins in least squares theory and is called the *likelihood approach*.

4.2 THE SAMPLING DISTRIBUTION APPROACH TO STATISTICAL INFERENCE

In this section it is shown how the sampling distribution approach can be applied, first to estimation problems, and then to tests of significance.

4.2.1 The basic method

It was shown in Chapter 3 that *before* collecting a sample of observations $x_1, x_2, \ldots, x_n$, it is useful to regard them as realizations of random variables $X_1, X_2, \ldots, X_n$, defined on an n-dimensional sample space. With this sample space is associated a pdf called the *sampling distribution* which, in general, will depend on a set of unknown parameters $\theta_1, \theta_2, \ldots, \theta_k$. For example, if the random variables are independent and Normally distributed, with mean θ_1 and variance θ_2, the sampling distribution associated with the data is

$$f_{12\ldots n}(x_1, x_2, \ldots, x_n; \theta_1, \theta_2) = \frac{1}{(\sqrt{2\pi\theta_2})^n} \exp\left[-\frac{1}{2\theta_2} \sum_{t=1}^{n} (x_t - \theta_1)^2\right], \quad (4.2.1)$$

where $\theta_1 = \mu$ and $\theta_2 = \sigma^2$ in the previous notation. The parameters have been included in the left-hand side of the expression (4.2.1) for the sampling pdf to show that it is a function not only of the x's, but also of the unknown parameters θ_1 and θ_2.

Suppose now that the observations $x_1, x_2, \ldots, x_n$ are given and that it is required to estimate the parameters θ_i in the joint pdf of the rv's $X_1, X_2, \ldots, X_n$. The sampling distribution approach to the estimation problem may be summarized under three headings.

Choice of the sampling pdf. First a guess is made of a reasonable form for the joint pdf of the observations. This pdf will depend on various assumptions, such as the independence of the rv's X_i and the form of $f_i(x_i)$. Clearly this stage will depend critically on prior knowledge of the situation being investigated. For example, if the independence assumption is not justified, then some of the parameters in the joint pdf may describe the dependence between the rv's X_i. In some cases, the inference does not depend very critically on the assumptions made concerning the mathematical form of the joint pdf. However, in other situations the inference may be very sensitive to assumptions and hence some statistical skill and insight is required in setting up the exact form of the model.

Choice of estimator. Functions $\hat{\Theta}(X_1, X_2, \ldots, X_n)$ of the rv's are considered as possible *estimators* of the parameter θ. Each such function, being itself an rv, will have a sampling distribution $f_{\hat{\Theta}}(\hat{\theta}; \theta)$ which depends on the unknown value θ and which can be derived from the joint pdf of the data by the methods described in [1]. The *estimate* $\hat{\theta}(x_1, x_2, \ldots, x_n)$ which is obtained from a particular experiment is then regarded as a realization of the rv $\hat{\Theta}(X_1, X_2, \ldots, X_n)$.

To choose between different estimators, it is necessary to define an optimality criterion. For example, of two estimators $\hat{\Theta}_1$ and $\hat{\Theta}_2$ with sampling distributions as shown in Figure 4.1, $\hat{\Theta}_1$ would be selected without any doubt

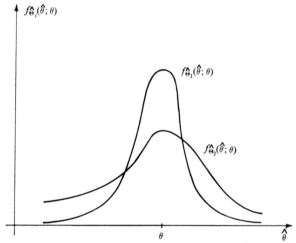

FIG. 4.1: Sampling distributions for two estimators

since $f_{\hat{\Theta}_1}(\hat{\theta}; \theta)$ is more concentrated about the true value θ than is $f_{\hat{\Theta}_2}(\hat{\theta}; \theta)$. Hence in any given sample there is a greater probability that $\hat{\Theta}_1$ will be closer than $\hat{\Theta}_2$ to θ. Hence, if the sampling distributions of two estimators were known exactly, a choice between them could be made by comparing the probabilities of being close to the true value θ. However, in the majority of applications it is not possible to calculate sampling distributions exactly. In such situations it is necessary to accept a less detailed description of the estimator in terms of its lower-order moments.

Various criteria based on moments have been proposed and may be used to compare given estimators. The most important of these is the mean square error criterion discussed in Section 4.2.3. A class of estimators which have smallest mean square error for large sample size are the *maximum likelihood estimators* discussed in Section 4.2.4.

Confidence intervals. From the sampling distribution of the chosen estimator $\hat{\Theta}$ or from an approximation to its sampling distribution based on lower-order moments, probability statements may be made about $\hat{\Theta}$ such as

$$\Pr\{-l_1 < \hat{\Theta} - \theta \leqslant l_2\} = 1 - \alpha$$

or, equivalently,

$$\Pr\{(\hat{\Theta} - l_2 \leqslant \theta) \text{ and } (\hat{\Theta} + l_1 > \theta)\} = 1 - \alpha.$$

Hence, the probability that the random variable representing the interval between $\hat{\Theta} - l_2$ and $\hat{\Theta} + l_1$ encloses the true parameter θ is $1 - \alpha$. The corresponding interval based on the estimate, namely $(\hat{\theta} - l_2, \hat{\theta} + l_1)$, is then said to be a *confidence interval* with confidence coefficient $1 - \alpha$ for θ. By this is meant that the interval will enclose the true value on $100(1 - \alpha)\%$ of occasions on average.

The construction of confidence intervals is one of the most important aspects of the estimation procedure and is discussed in Section 4.2.2. In cases where it is not possible to construct exact confidence intervals, it is nevertheless valuable to provide approximate ones, thus giving a rough indication of the accuracy of the estimate. A method for deriving approximate confidence intervals is given in Section 4.2.4.

Discussion. The logic of the sampling distribution approach should be carefully noted. The sampling distribution $f_{\hat{\Theta}}(\hat{\theta};\theta)$ can be used to calculate the probability that a value $\hat{\theta}$ of the rv $\hat{\Theta}$ lies between two limits in all possible samples of size n, *assuming the parameter θ is known.* Hence, as discussed in Chapter 3, the probability distribution enables us to argue from the general *model* to the particular *sample*. However, the object in estimation theory is to use the estimate $\hat{\theta}$ to make statements about θ, that is, to argue from the sample to the correct model. From this point of view, the sampling distribution approach to estimation theory is artificial in the sense that it is necessary to consider not only the particular sample available, but all other samples that *might* have been obtained. Nevertheless, the sampling distribution approach is important because of its historical significance and also because of the following:

(1) In many situations it leads to conclusions which are very similar to those arrived at by other modes of inference, such as the likelihood method to be described later.

(2) In situations where repeated sampling is involved, for example, in inspecting industrial components, an approach which involves consideration of all possible samples is logical. However, this is the domain of *statistical decision theory* and not *statistical inference.*

(3) In situations where the problem cannot be reduced to one of estimating a small set of parameters, as in spectral analysis which involves the estimation of a large number of parameters, it seems to be the only approach possible.

4.2.2 Confidence intervals

Confidence interval for the mean. To illustrate the sampling distribution approach and to demonstrate how confidence intervals are constructed, suppose it is required to estimate the mean μ for the transistor current data of Figure 3.3 using only nine observations. Proceeding by the three steps given in Section 4.2.1, the first step is to assume a form for the pdf to be associated with the observations. From the histograms of Figure 3.6, it is reasonable to assume that the observations can be described by a Normal pdf. In addition, since the transistors were selected at random times from the production line, it is reasonable to assume that the rv's are independent. Hence the sampling distribution associated with the observations was assumed to be (4.2.1) with $\mu = \theta_1$, $\sigma^2 = \theta_2$ both unknown.

The second step is to choose estimators for the mean μ. Possible choices include the sample mean

$$\bar{X} = \frac{1}{n}(X_1 + X_2 + \cdots + X_n) \tag{4.2.2}$$

and the median, which is the "middle" observation in the sample. For example, the median of the transistor data below is 3.12. For the sampling pdf (4.2.1), it may be shown [5] that the "best" estimator, both by virtue of having the smallest mean square error and also by having the largest probability of lying within a prescribed range about μ, is the sample mean $\bar{X}$.

The third step is to determine a confidence interval for μ based on the chosen estimator $\bar{X}$. As shown in Section 3.3.3, when σ is not known the sampling distribution of

$$T_\nu = \frac{\sqrt{n}\,(\bar{X} - \mu)}{S}$$

is Student's t distribution with $\nu = n - 1$ degrees of freedom. Hence

$$\Pr\left\{-t_\nu\left(1 - \frac{\alpha}{2}\right) < \frac{\sqrt{n}\,(\bar{X} - \mu)}{S} \leqslant t_\nu\left(1 - \frac{\alpha}{2}\right)\right\} = 1 - \alpha$$

or

$$\Pr\left\{\bar{X} - t_\nu\left(1 - \frac{\alpha}{2}\right)\frac{S}{\sqrt{n}} \leqslant \mu \text{ and } \bar{X} + t_\nu\left(1 - \frac{\alpha}{2}\right)\frac{S}{\sqrt{n}} > \mu\right\} = 1 - \alpha.$$

Thus there is a probability of $1 - \alpha$ that the interval $\bar{X} \pm t_\nu(1 - \alpha/2)(S/\sqrt{n})$ encloses the true value μ. Hence a $100(1 - \alpha)\%$ confidence interval for μ based on the estimates $\bar{x}$ and s obtained from a given sample is

$$\bar{x} \pm t_\nu\left(1 - \frac{\alpha}{2}\right)\frac{S}{\sqrt{n}}. \tag{4.2.3}$$

Returning to the example, the current values in μA for the nine transistors selected at random from the production line were

$$
\begin{array}{ccc}
1.73 & 3.81 & 3.12 \\
3.00 & 3.48 & 1.68 \\
3.64 & 4.91 & 0.39,
\end{array}
$$

so that

$$\sum x = 1.73 + 3.00 + \cdots + 0.39 = 25.76$$

and

$$\sum x^2 = (1.73)^2 + (3.00)^2 + \cdots + (0.39)^2 = 88.6860.$$

Thus

$$\bar{x} = \frac{25.76}{9} = 2.86$$

and

$$s^2 = \frac{88.686 - 9(2.86)^2}{8} = \frac{6.89}{8} = 0.86, \qquad s = 0.93.$$

Hence using (4.2.3), with $\bar{x} = 2.86$, $s = 0.93$, $n = 9$ and the value $t_8(0.975) = 2.31$ from Figure 3.11, the 95% confidence interval for μ is

$$[2.86 - (0.77)(0.93), \quad 2.86 + (0.77)(0.93)],$$

that is, (2.15, 3.57).

The interpretation of this 95% confidence interval is that, having constructed a random interval which has probability 0.95 of enclosing the true mean, we have 95% confidence on this particular occasion that the interval obtained happens to include μ.

Note that an infinite number of confidence intervals with confidence coefficient $1 - \alpha$ can be constructed for this example. In this case, by choosing an interval which is symmetric about the sample mean, the interval of smallest length is obtained.

Confidence intervals for the variance. To construct a confidence interval for the variance σ^2 of a Normal pdf, use is made of the result that the sampling distribution of $(n - 1)S^2/\sigma^2$ is the same as that of a χ_ν^2 rv. Hence, using Figure 3.10, limits l_1 and l_2 may be read off such that

$$\Pr\{l_1 < \frac{\sigma^2}{S^2} \leqslant l_2\} = 1 - \alpha$$

or

$$\Pr\{(l_2 S^2 \geqslant \sigma^2) \text{ and } (l_1 S^2 < \sigma^2)\} = 1 - \alpha.$$

Hence, the $100(1 - \alpha)$% confidence interval based on the estimate s^2 is

$$(l_1 s^2, \ l_2 s^2). \tag{4.2.4}$$

For the collector current data, $s^2 = 0.86$ and, using Figure 3.10, $l_1 = 0.36$, $l_2 = 5.95$ when $\alpha = 0.05$. Hence, a 95% confidence interval for σ^2 is $[(0.36)(0.86), (5.95)(0.86)]$, that is, $(0.31, 5.11)$. This implies that the 95% confidence interval for σ is $(0.56, 2.26)$.

Confidence intervals for the ratio of two variances. If S_1^2 is an estimator of σ_1^2 with v_1 degrees of freedom and S_2^2 is an independent estimator of σ_2^2 with v_2 degrees of freedom, then as shown in Section 3.3.4, the sampling distribution of

$$\frac{S_1^2/\sigma_1^2}{S_2^2/\sigma_2^2}$$

is Fisher's F_{v_1, v_2} distribution. Hence, as shown in Section 3.3.4,

$$\Pr\left\{\frac{1}{f_{v_2, v_1}(1 - \alpha/2)} < F_{v_1, v_2} \leqslant f_{v_1, v_2}\left(1 - \frac{\alpha}{2}\right)\right\} = 1 - \alpha. \qquad (4.2.5)$$

On substituting $F_{v_1, v_2} = \sigma_2^2 S_1^2/\sigma_1^2 S_2^2$ into (4.2.5) and rearranging,

$$\Pr\left\{\left(\frac{S_2^2}{S_1^2}\frac{1}{f_{v_2, v_1}(1 - \alpha/2)} < \frac{\sigma_2^2}{\sigma_1^2}\right) \text{ and } \left(\frac{S_2^2}{S_1^2} f_{v_1, v_2}\left(1 - \frac{\alpha}{2}\right) \geqslant \frac{\sigma_2^2}{\sigma_1^2}\right)\right\} = 1 - \alpha.$$

Hence, a $100(1 - \alpha)\%$ confidence interval based on estimates s_1^2 and s_2^2 obtained from two independent samples is

$$\left\{\frac{s_2^2}{s_1^2}\frac{1}{f_{v_2, v_1}(1 - \alpha/2)}, \frac{s_2^2}{s_1^2} f_{v_1, v_2}\left(1 - \frac{\alpha}{2}\right)\right\}. \qquad (4.2.6)$$

For example, for the transistor current data, $s_1^2 = 0.86$, based on $v_1 = 8$ degrees of freedom. The sample variance for another sample of 100 transistors was found to be $s_2^2 = 1.025$, based on $v_2 = 99$ degrees of freedom. From Figure 3.12, $f_{8, 99}(0.95) = 2.05$, $f_{99, 8}(0.95) = 3.01$, and hence substituting these values and the ratio $s_2^2/s_1^2 = 1.025/0.86 = 1.16$ in (4.2.6) gives a 90% confidence interval for σ_2^2/σ_1^2,

$$\left[(1.16)\left(\frac{1}{3.01}\right), (1.16)(2.05)\right],$$

or $(0.39, 2.38)$. Since this confidence interval includes the ratio $\sigma_2^2/\sigma_1^2 = 1$, the possibility that $\sigma_1^2 = \sigma_2^2$ is not ruled out.

4.2.3 Properties of estimators

It was shown in Section 4.2.1 that a good estimator of a parameter could be obtained by comparing the sampling distributions of different estimators. Sometimes it is not possible to derive the exact sampling distribution, and then it is necessary to resort to approximate methods for choosing estimators. These make use of properties based on the lower-order moments of the estimators. The most important of these properties are bias, variance and mean square error.

Bias. The bias of an estimator $\hat{\Theta}$ of θ is defined by

$$B = E[\hat{\Theta}] - \theta. \qquad (4.2.7)$$

When $B = 0$, the pdf of the estimator is centered exactly at the true value θ and the estimator is *unbiased*. It is natural to choose an estimator with small or zero bias but, as will be seen shortly, it is not always wise to insist that an estimator be unbiased.

Variance. The variance of the estimator,

$$\text{Var} [\hat{\Theta}] = E[(\hat{\Theta} - E[\hat{\Theta}])^2], \qquad (4.2.8)$$

measures the spread of the pdf of $\hat{\Theta}$ about its expected value, and hence in general the variance should be small. However, the requirements of small bias and small variance are not necessarily compatible, since often reducing one inflates the other. For example, consider estimators

$$S_k^2 = \frac{1}{k} \sum_{i=1}^{n} (X_i - \bar{X})^2 \qquad (4.2.9)$$

for the variance σ^2 of a Normal rv. Since $(1/\sigma^2) \sum_{i=1}^{n} (X_i - \bar{X})^2$ is a χ_v^2 rv with $v = n - 1$, using (4.2.7) and (3.3.6), the bias of this estimator is

$$B_k = \left(\frac{n - 1 - k}{k} \right) \sigma^2, \qquad (4.2.10)$$

and from (3.3.6)

$$\text{Var} [S_k^2] = \frac{2(n - 1)}{k^2} \sigma^4. \qquad (4.2.11)$$

Thus an unbiased estimator for σ^2 is obtained when $k = n - 1$, in which case

$$\text{Var} [S_{n-1}^2] = \frac{2\sigma^4}{n - 1}.$$

On the other hand, the variance of the estimator (4.2.9) may be reduced by making k large. However, increasing k inflates the bias, which tends to $-\sigma^2$ as k tends to infinity. Clearly, a compromise is necessary between variance and bias.

Mean square error. One compromise between variance and bias is obtained by minimizing the *mean square error* (mse) of the estimator, namely

$$E[(\hat{\Theta} - \theta)^2] = \text{Var} [\hat{\Theta}] + B^2. \qquad (4.2.12)$$

For the above example, the mse is

$$\frac{2(n - 1)}{k^2} \sigma^4 + \frac{(n - 1 - k)^2}{k^2} \sigma^4.$$

This has a minimum value of $2\sigma^4/(n + 1)$ at $k = n + 1$, as compared with an mse of $2\sigma^4/(n - 1)$ for the unbiased $(k = n - 1)$ estimator.

In some cases the mse is minimized when the bias is zero so that the mse is a minimum when the variance is a minimum. Such estimators are called *minimum variance–unbiased* estimators.

One difficulty associated with using the mse criterion is that it only enables us to compare a given class of estimators. It does not tell us how these estimators should be chosen in the first place. However, one class of estimators which satisfies the minimum mse property for large sample sizes is based on the likelihood function introduced by R. A. Fisher. These estimators are discussed in Section 4.2.4 and have played an important part in statistical estimation since they become unbiased in large sample sizes and also have minimum variance among all possible estimators. Hence, for large sample sizes the maximum likelihood estimators are minimum mse estimators.

Consistency. Another property of estimators which is based on the sampling distribution is *consistency*. Suppose that the bias and variance of an estimator tend to zero as the sample size n becomes large. This means that the sampling distribution will tend to be centered about θ and that the precision of the estimator increases without limit. An estimator possessing this property is called a *consistent estimator*.

For example, if the sampling distribution tends to Normal, as it usually does under a wide range of conditions, the sampling distribution for large n will be close to

$$f_{\hat{\theta}}(\hat{\theta}; \theta) = \frac{\sqrt{n}}{\sqrt{2\pi}\,c} \exp\left[-\frac{n}{2c^2}(\hat{\theta} - \theta)^2 \right].$$

As n tends to infinity, this behaves like a delta function centered about θ.

4.2.4 Maximum likelihood estimators

Univariate likelihood functions. The problem of finding a good estimator for a statistical parameter was solved for many cases by R. A. Fisher [2, 3], who introduced the class of *maximum likelihood estimators*. To illustrate this approach, consider the problem of estimating the mean life of a batch of light bulbs. It is assumed that the lifetime of a bulb is well described by an rv X with pdf

$$f_X(x; \lambda) = \lambda \exp(-\lambda x), \quad 0 \leqslant x \leqslant \infty.$$

Hence the sampling pdf for a sample of n bulbs chosen at random is

$$f_{12\ldots n}(x_1, x_2, \ldots, x_n) = \lambda^n \exp\left(-\lambda \sum_{i=1}^{n} x_i \right). \tag{4.2.13}$$

Before the experiment is performed, the pdf (4.2.13) gives the frequency of occurrence of different samples when λ is specified. *After* the experiment has been performed, it has a different interpretation. In this case the sample values $x_1, x_2, \ldots, x_n$ are known and the parameter λ is unknown. The function of λ obtained by substituting the sample values in the pdf (4.2.13) is called the *likelihood function* $L(\lambda)$ for the parameter λ. It is a function which ranks one's preferences for different values of λ.

For example, suppose that three bulbs taken at random from a batch were tested and found to have lifetimes of 2.6, 1.9, and 1.5 hours respectively. Since $\sum x_i = 6$, the likelihood function is

$$L(\lambda) = \lambda^3 \exp(-6\lambda). \qquad (4.2.14)$$

The function (4.2.14) is plotted in Figure 4.2 and is a unimodal curve with a maximum at $\lambda = 0.5$. The value $\hat{\lambda}$ of λ which maximizes $L(\lambda)$ is called the

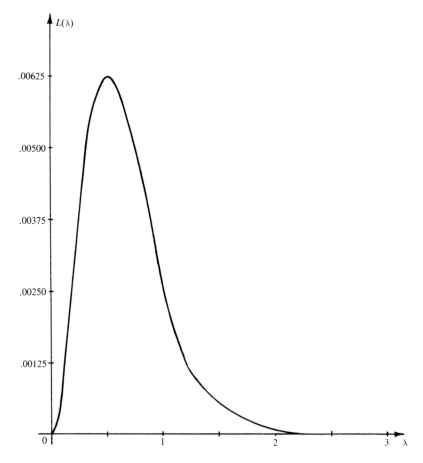

FIG. 4.2: Likelihood function for a sample of three from an exponential distribution

maximum likelihood estimate (mle) of λ. It is the preferred value of λ since it is the value which maximizes the probability of obtaining the given sample.

Provided the likelihood function is well-behaved, the maximum likelihood estimate can be obtained by solving the equation

$$\frac{dL(\lambda)}{d\lambda} = 0.$$

For the likelihood based on the pdf (4.2.13), this gives an mle $\hat{\lambda} = 1/\bar{x}$. In the above example, $\bar{x} = 2$, and hence $\hat{\lambda} = 0.5$.

When the likelihood function is not well-behaved, for example, when the maximum occurs at a boundary of the permissible parameter values, it is not possible to locate the maximum by differentiation. Meaningless results can only be avoided by plotting the likelihood function.

Multivariate likelihood functions. When the likelihood function is a function of k parameters $\theta_1, \theta_2, \ldots, \theta_k$, the mle's maximize $L(\theta_1, \theta_2, \ldots, \theta_k)$ simultaneously. If the maximum can be located by differentiation, the mle's are the solutions of the k equations

$$\frac{\partial L(\theta_1, \theta_2, \ldots, \theta_k)}{\partial \theta_j} = 0, \quad (j = 1, 2, \ldots, k). \tag{4.2.15}$$

It is sometimes more convenient to maximize the log likelihood function $l(\theta_1, \theta_2, \ldots, \theta_k) = \ln L(\theta_1, \theta_2, \ldots, \theta_k)$. The maximum likelihood equations are then

$$\frac{\partial l}{\partial \theta_j} = \frac{\partial (\ln L)}{\partial \theta_j} = \frac{1}{L} \frac{\partial L}{\partial \theta_j} = 0, \quad (j = 1, 2, \ldots, k). \tag{4.2.16}$$

Example 1: Consider the likelihood function of the mean and variance for a sample of n observations which are assumed to have a Normal pdf, namely

$$L(\mu, \sigma^2) = \frac{1}{(\sqrt{2\pi}\sigma)^n} \exp\left[-\frac{1}{2\sigma^2} \sum_{t=1}^{n} (x_t - \mu)^2\right], \tag{4.2.17}$$

so that the log likelihood function is

$$l(\mu, \sigma^2) = -\frac{n}{2} \ln 2\pi - n \ln \sigma - \frac{1}{2\sigma^2} \sum_{t=1}^{n} (x_t - \mu)^2. \tag{4.2.18}$$

The mle's based on (4.2.18) are the solutions of

$$\frac{1}{\hat{\sigma}^2} \sum_{t=1}^{n} (x_t - \hat{\mu}) = 0;$$

$$-\frac{n}{\hat{\sigma}} + \frac{1}{\hat{\sigma}^3} \sum_{t=1}^{n} (x_t - \hat{\mu})^2 = 0, \tag{4.2.19}$$

that is,

$$\hat{\mu} = \frac{1}{n} \sum_{t=1}^{n} x_t = \bar{x};$$

$$\hat{\sigma}^2 = \frac{1}{n} \sum_{t=1}^{n} (x_t - \bar{x})^2.$$

(4.2.20)

Example 2: Suppose that n pairs of measurements (x_{1i}, x_{2i}), $i = 1, 2, \ldots, n$, are available, as for the accelerometer data of Figure 3.7. If it is assumed that they can be described by two rv's whose joint pdf is the bivariate Normal, then the log likelihood function based on n pairs of observations is

$$l(\mu_1, \mu_2, \sigma_1^2, \sigma_2^2, \rho_{12}) = -n \ln 2\pi - n \ln \sigma_1 - n \ln \sigma_2 - \frac{n}{2} \ln (1 - \rho_{12}^2)$$

$$- \frac{1}{2(1 - \rho_{12}^2)} \sum_{i=1}^{n} \left\{ \left(\frac{x_{1i} - \mu_1}{\sigma_1} \right)^2 \right.$$

$$\left. - 2\rho_{12} \left(\frac{x_{1i} - \mu_1}{\sigma_1} \right) \left(\frac{x_{2i} - \mu_2}{\sigma_2} \right) + \left(\frac{x_{2i} - \mu_2}{\sigma_2} \right)^2 \right\}.$$

(4.2.21)

The likelihood function (4.2.21) is five-dimensional in the parameters, and the mle's may be obtained by differentiating it, in turn, with respect to all five parameters and solving the resulting equations. It may be verified that the estimates of the means and variances are the same as those obtained from the likelihood (4.2.17) and that the mle of the correlation coefficient ρ_{12} is

$$\hat{\rho}_{12} = \frac{\sum_{i=1}^{n} (x_{1i} - \bar{x}_1)(x_{2i} - \bar{x}_2)}{\{\sum_{i=1}^{n} (x_{1i} - \bar{x}_1)^2 \sum_{i=1}^{n} (x_{2i} - \bar{x}_2)^2\}^{1/2}} = r_{12}.$$

(4.2.22)

Note that (4.2.22) may be written

$$r_{12} = \frac{c_{12}}{\sqrt{c_{11}c_{22}}},$$

(4.2.23)

where

$$c_{12} = \frac{1}{n} \sum_{i=1}^{n} (x_{1i} - \bar{x}_1)(x_{2i} - \bar{x}_2)$$

(4.2.24)

is the mle of the covariance γ_{12} between the two rv's, and c_{11} and c_{22} are the mle's of the variances σ_1^2 and σ_2^2 respectively.

Since the likelihood function is only a function of θ when the observations are known, the mle $\hat{\theta}$ is obtained directly as a function of the observations. It has been customary in statistical work to disregard the likelihood function at this point and revert to the sampling distribution approach, which involves associating with the estimate $\hat{\theta}$ an estimator $\hat{\Theta}$ and finding its sampling properties. This is compatible with the sampling distribution approach to estimation, but is not what is meant by the likelihood approach to inference, which is discussed in Section 4.4.

The sampling properties of maximum likelihood estimators are summarized in [5]. The most important of these is that for large n, mle's are approximately unbiased and Normally distributed with variance

$$\text{Var } [\hat{\Theta}] \approx \frac{-1}{E[\partial^2 l(\theta)/\partial \theta^2]_{\hat{\theta}}}, \tag{4.2.25}$$

which is the minimum variance that can be achieved by any unbiased estimator. Hence approximate confidence intervals may be constructed using the mle, the variance (4.2.25) and Table 3.4.

The result (4.2.25) shows that the variance of the maximum likelihood estimator is inversely proportional to the second derivative, and hence to the curvature, of the likelihood function at its maximum. The expression

$$E\left[-\frac{\partial^2 l(\theta)}{\partial \theta^2}\right]_{\hat{\theta}}$$

is called the *Fisher information measure* and will be reinterpreted in Section 4.4.

4.2.5 Tests of significance

Another mode of inference included within the framework of the sampling distribution approach is the *test of significance*. This is concerned with deciding whether or not a hypothesis concerning statistical parameters is true. For example, it may be required to test whether a sample $x_1, x_2, \ldots, x_n$ of observations is compatible with the hypothesis that they have come from a Normal pdf with specified values μ_0, σ_0^2 for the mean and the variance.

In many situations where tests of significance are applied, the problem would be better answered by estimating the parameters and quoting confidence intervals. In this section a simple example of a test of significance is given and it is then shown how more information could be obtained by treating it as an estimation problem.

The notion of a significance test goes back to the early developments in the theory of probability. A systematic theory of significance tests was developed on somewhat independent lines by R. A. Fisher on the one hand and jointly by J. Neyman and E. S. Pearson on the other. The latter two embedded the idea of a significance test in what they called the *theory of testing hypotheses*, an account of which is given in [4].

Stages in a significance test. The stages in setting up a significance test are illustrated for the transistor example of Section 4.2.2.

(1) Set up a null hypothesis, H_0, for example, that the collector current for a batch of transistors is distributed Normally with mean μ_0 but unknown variance.

(2) Decide on a set of alternative hypotheses. In this example, it would be natural to take these to be $\mu > \mu_0$ since one would only be interested in rejecting a batch if the mean collector current were too high.

(3) Decide on the best function of the observations or *statistic* to test the null hypothesis. If the variance is known, it is possible to show [4] that the best statistic is the mean $\bar{X}$. When the variance is unknown, as in this example, the best statistic is

$$T_\nu = \frac{\sqrt{n}\,(\bar{X} - \mu_0)}{S}.$$

(4) Derive the sampling distribution of the statistic under the null hypothesis. In the above example this will be a Student's t distribution with $\nu = n - 1$ degrees of freedom.

(5) Using (4) and (2), the sample space $\mathscr{S}$ can then be divided into a *critical region* $\mathscr{C}$ and an *acceptable region* $\mathscr{S} - \mathscr{C}$ which consists of all points in the sample space lying outside the critical region $\mathscr{C}$. The critical region is chosen so that the probability $\Pr\{x_1, x_2, \ldots, x_n$ lies in $\mathscr{C} \mid H_0$ is true$\} = \alpha$, where α is small, say 0.05 or 0.01. The probability α is called the *significance level* of the test.

(6) The significance test then consists of rejecting the null hypothesis if the observed sample $x_1, x_2, \ldots, x_n$ falls in $\mathscr{C}$ and not rejecting it if it falls in $\mathscr{S} - \mathscr{C}$. Since there is a small probability that the sample point falls in $\mathscr{C}$ when H_0 is true, any occasion when this happens is regarded as evidence against the null hypothesis.

In the above example, since $\Pr\{T_\nu > t_\nu(1 - \alpha)\} = \alpha$, the critical region is defined by

$$t = \frac{\sqrt{n}\,(\bar{x} - \mu_0)}{s} > t_{n-1}(1 - \alpha)$$

or

$$\bar{x} > \mu_0 + \frac{s t_{n-1}(1 - \alpha)}{\sqrt{n}}.$$

An example. Suppose, for example, that $n = 4$, $\bar{x} = 10$ and $s = 2$ and that it is desired to test the null hypothesis that $\mu_0 = 8$ with significance level $\alpha = 0.025$. From Figure 3.11, $t_3(0.975) = 3.18$, and hence the critical region is

$$\bar{x} > 8 + \frac{2(3.18)}{2} = 11.18.$$

Since the actual $\bar{x}$ does not lie in the critical region, the null hypothesis is not rejected at the 2.5% significance level.

Suppose that alternative hypotheses $\mu > \mu_0$ and $\mu < \mu_0$ were of equal importance. For example, if the weight of some packed commodity had to conform to a specified mean μ_0, one might be equally interested if a particular sample were under or over weight. It would now be reasonable to choose as the critical region

$$t > t_{n-1}\left(1 - \frac{\alpha}{2}\right), \qquad t < -t_{n-1}\left(1 - \frac{\alpha}{2}\right),$$

that is,

$$\bar{x} > \mu_0 + \frac{st_{n-1}(1 - \alpha/2)}{\sqrt{n}}, \qquad \bar{x} < \mu_0 - \frac{st_{n-1}(1 - \alpha/2)}{\sqrt{n}}. \quad (4.2.27)$$

For the above example with $\mu_0 = 8$, the critical region is

$$\bar{x} > 11.18, \qquad \bar{x} < 4.72.$$

Since the observed value $\bar{x} = 10$ does not lie in the critical region, the null hypothesis would not be rejected at the 5% significance level. This is called a two-sided significance test as opposed to the one-sided test given above.

Confidence intervals and tests of significance. To demonstrate the relation between a significance test and a confidence interval, note that the confidence interval (4.2.3) for μ is

$$\bar{x} \pm \frac{st_{n-1}(1 - \alpha/2)}{\sqrt{n}}.$$

Hence from (4.2.27), if μ_0 lies inside the confidence interval the null hypothesis is not rejected, while if μ_0 lies outside the confidence interval the null hypothesis is rejected.

In the above example, the 95% confidence interval is

$$10 \pm \frac{2(3.18)}{\sqrt{4}} = (6.82, 13.18).$$

Since $\mu_0 = 8$ is included in this interval the null hypothesis is not rejected at the 5% significance level. In fact, any null hypothesis in the range 6.82 to 13.18 would not have been rejected at this significance level. The extra information contained in the confidence interval now becomes apparent. It shows that this experiment was so imprecise that values of μ as large as 13 are plausible. In this case the only sensible conclusion is that more data is required in order to estimate μ more precisely.

4.3 LEAST SQUARES ESTIMATION

4.3.1 The principle of least squares

The principle of least squares was discovered by the German mathematician, Carl Friedrich Gauss, who first worked on this topic in 1821 and returned to it many times during his life. His principle of least squares represents one of the first major advances in statistics, and even to this day it is one of the most powerful techniques available to statisticians.

Suppose that the output η of a system can be predicted from k input variables $x_1, x_2, \ldots, x_k$ using an assumed linear model

$$\eta = \theta_1 x_1 + \theta_2 x_2 + \cdots + \theta_k x_k. \tag{4.3.1}$$

For example, η might be the yield of a chemical process, the x's process variables such as temperatures, pressures and flow rates, and the θ's *unknown* physical parameters such as kinetic constants.

The theory of *linear* least squares is concerned with estimating the parameters θ_r from data consisting of simultaneous measurements of the output and input variables. The estimated parameters may be substituted in (4.3.1), which can then be used to predict the output for future values of the input variables.

Note that the prediction equation (4.3.1) need not be linear in the x's, only in the parameters θ. For example, if $x_1 = 1$, $x_2 = x, \ldots, x_k = x^{k-1}$, then η is a polynomial in x of degree $k - 1$. When the output is a non-linear function of the parameters, the methods described in this section are easily modified [6] to estimate the parameters by applying linear least squares iteratively.

In practice the response η can only be observed subject to an error z. This is inevitable because of measurement error and variability not under one's control. If the model is not adequate, the error will also contain systematic effects due to the inadequacy of the model. Therefore the final form of the model is

$$Y_i = \eta_i + Z_i$$
$$= \theta_1 x_{i1} + \theta_2 x_{i2} + \cdots + \theta_k x_{ik} + Z_i, \tag{4.3.2}$$

where

(a) Y_i $(i = 1, 2, \ldots, N)$ is an rv corresponding to the measured response y_i in the ith experiment.

(b) $x_{i1}, x_{i2}, \ldots, x_{ik}$ are the values which the input variables $x_1, x_2, \ldots, x_k$ take in the ith experiment.

(c) Z_i is a rv representing the error term and $E[Z_i] = 0$.

Note that if the errors have a non-zero mean θ_1, this can be allowed for by setting $x_{i1} = 1$ in (4.3.2).

Gauss' theorem. The least squares approach to the problem of estimating the θ's is contained in Gauss' fundamental theorem. This states that if the errors Z_i are uncorrelated, that is, Cov $[Z_i, Z_j] = 0$ when $i \neq j$, and have the same mean $E[Z_i] = 0$ and the same variance $E[Z_i^2] = \sigma^2$, then the optimum estimates of the parameters θ_r are those values $\hat{\theta}_r$ which minimize the sum of squares of the discrepancies between the observed values and fitted model, that is, the sum of squares

$$S(\theta_1, \theta_2, \ldots, \theta_k) = \sum_{i=1}^{N} (y_i - \theta_1 x_{i1} - \theta_2 x_{i2} - \cdots - \theta_k x_{ik})^2. \quad (4.3.3)$$

As shown in Appendix A4.1, the estimates $\hat{\theta}_r$ are optimum in the sense that any arbitrary linear function

$$L = \lambda_1 \theta_1 + \lambda_2 \theta_2 + \cdots + \lambda_k \theta_k$$

of the θ's is estimated with minimum mse by the estimator

$$\hat{L} = \lambda_1 \hat{\theta}_1 + \lambda_2 \hat{\theta}_2 + \cdots + \lambda_k \hat{\theta}_k.$$

The *least squares estimates* (lse's) $\hat{\theta}_r$, $(r = 1, 2, \ldots, k)$ may be obtained by differentiating $S(\theta_1, \theta_2, \ldots, \theta_r, \ldots, \theta_k)$ with respect to the θ_r and solving the resulting set of k equations

$$\sum_{i=1}^{N} x_{ir} \{ y_i - \hat{\theta}_1 x_{i1} - \cdots - \hat{\theta}_k x_{ik} \} = 0, \quad r = 1, 2, \ldots, k, \quad (4.3.4)$$

which are usually called the *normal equations*.

An example. To illustrate Gauss's method of least squares, consider the estimation of the acceleration θ of a body moving from rest under a constant applied force. The model is

$$\eta = \theta x,$$

where η is the velocity of the body after time x. An experiment was performed in which the velocities y_i $(i = 1, 2, \ldots, N)$ of the body were measured at different times x_i. The time measurements x_i were very accurate, whereas the velocity measurements were subject to error. Hence the probability model for the experiment is

$$Y_i = \theta x_i + Z_i. \quad (4.3.5)$$

Figure 4.3 and Table 4.1 show the data (x_i, y_i) obtained from an actual experiment.

TABLE 4.1: Velocity–time data for estimating acceleration

x_i (seconds)	1	2	3	4	5	6	7	8	9
y_i (ft/sec)	35	58	94	121	147	175	212	247	264
Residuals $y_i - \hat{\theta} x_i$	5.0	−1.9	4.1	1.2	−2.8	−4.7	2.3	7.3	−5.6

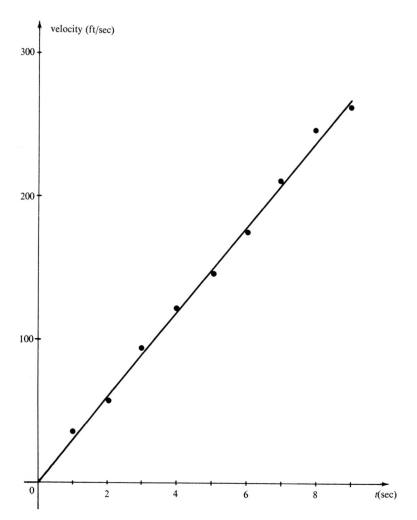

FIG. 4.3: Velocity–time data and least squares regression line

For this example the sum-of-squares function (4.3.3) is

$$S(\theta) = \sum_{i=1}^{N} (y_i - \theta x_i)^2, \qquad (4.3.6)$$

which, when differentiated with respect to θ and set equal to zero, yields the single normal equation

$$\sum_{i=1}^{N} x_i(y_i - \hat{\theta} x_i) = 0.$$

Hence the lse is

$$\hat{\theta} = \frac{\sum_{i=1}^{N} x_i y_i}{\sum_{i=1}^{N} x_i^2}. \tag{4.3.7}$$

For the data of Table 4.1, $\sum x_i y_i = 8538$, $\sum x_i^2 = 285$, and hence

$$\hat{\theta} = \frac{8538}{285} = 29.96 \text{ ft/sec}^2.$$

The fitted line $y = \hat{\theta}x$ is shown in Figure 4.3 and is called the regression line of y on x. It can now be used to predict the velocity y at a specified time x in any future experiments conducted under the same conditions.

4.3.2 Confidence intervals for one parameter

Mean and variance of the least squares estimator. As noted earlier, it is essential to have an estimate of the accuracy of an estimated parameter, for example, in the form of a confidence interval. This in turn can be used to construct a confidence interval for a prediction made from the fitted model.

In the above example, confidence intervals for θ may be derived by considering the sampling properties of the estimator $\hat{\Theta}$ corresponding to the lse (4.3.7).

Since the x's are fixed constants, the mean of $\hat{\Theta}$ is

$$E[\hat{\Theta}] = \frac{\sum_{i=1}^{N} x_i E[Y_i]}{\sum_{i=1}^{N} x_i^2} = \frac{\sum_{i=1}^{N} x_i^2 \theta}{\sum_{i=1}^{N} x_i^2} = \theta,$$

so that the estimator is unbiased. Similarly, from (3.2.18), its variance is

$$\text{Var}[\hat{\Theta}] = \frac{\sigma^2 \sum_{i=1}^{N} x_i^2}{(\sum_{i=1}^{N} x_i^2)^2} = \frac{\sigma^2}{\sum_{i=1}^{N} x_i^2}, \tag{4.3.8}$$

since $\text{Var}[Y_i] = \text{Var}[Z_i] = \sigma^2$. Hence if σ^2 were known, (4.3.8) could be used to set confidence limits on θ, noting that if the Y_i are Normally distributed, $\hat{\Theta}$ will also be Normally distributed. Furthermore, even if the Z_i are not Normally distributed, $\hat{\Theta}$ will be close to Normal by the Central Limit Theorem and so the analysis will be robust with respect to the distribution assumptions made about the Z_i.

Estimating the residual variance. In general it will be necessary to estimate σ^2 from the data. To see how this is done, consider

$$\sum Z_i^2 = \sum (Y_i - \theta x_i)^2$$
$$= \sum \{Y_i - \hat{\Theta}x_i + x_i(\hat{\Theta} - \theta)\}^2, \tag{4.3.9}$$

where the summation limits have been omitted temporarily. Expanding (4.3.9) gives

$$\sum Z_i^2 = \sum (Y_i - \hat{\Theta}x_i)^2 + 2(\hat{\Theta} - \theta) \sum x_i(Y_i - \hat{\Theta}x_i) + (\hat{\Theta} - \theta)^2 \sum x_i^2,$$

and since $\hat{\Theta}$ is the least squares estimator, the middle term vanishes yielding

$$\sum (Y_i - \theta x_i)^2 = \sum (Y_i - \hat{\Theta} x_i)^2 + (\hat{\Theta} - \theta)^2 \sum x_i^2. \qquad (4.3.10)$$

Taking expectations throughout (4.3.10) gives

$$N\sigma^2 = E\left[\sum (Y_i - \hat{\Theta} x_i)^2\right] + \mathrm{Var}\,[\hat{\Theta}] \sum x_i^2,$$

and on using (4.3.8)

$$E\left[\sum_{i=1}^{N} (Y_i - \hat{\Theta} x_i)^2\right] = (N - 1)\sigma^2.$$

Thus the rv

$$S^2 = \frac{1}{N - 1} \sum_{i=1}^{N} (Y_i - \hat{\Theta} x_i)^2$$

is an unbiased estimator of σ^2. Since $(N - 1)S^2$ is a quadratic form in Normal rv's and $E[(N - 1)S^2] = (N - 1)\sigma^2$, it follows that it is distributed as $\sigma^2 \chi^2_{N-1}$.

The result (4.3.10) is a special case of the partition theorem (3.3.16) for χ^2. Thus, since the rv's Y_i are $N(\theta x_i, \sigma^2)$, the left-hand side of (4.3.10) is distributed as $\sigma^2 \chi^2_N$. Furthermore, the rv $(\hat{\Theta} - \theta)$ is $N(0, \sigma^2/\sum x_i^2)$ and hence the rv $(\hat{\Theta} - \theta)^2 \sum x_i^2$ is distributed as $\sigma^2 \chi^2_1$. It may also be shown that the two chi-squared rv's on the right-hand side of (4.3.10) are independent. Hence the chi-squared rv with N degrees of freedom on the left-hand side of (4.3.10) may be partitioned into two independent chi-squared rv's, one with $N - 1$ and the other with 1 degree of freedom.

Confidence intervals for θ. Since $\hat{\Theta} - \theta$ is independent of S, it follows that the rv

$$\frac{\sqrt{\sum x_i^2}\,(\hat{\Theta} - \theta)}{S}$$

has a t_ν distribution with $\nu = N - 1$ degrees of freedom. Hence a $100(1 - \alpha)\%$ confidence interval for θ is

$$\hat{\theta} \pm t_{N-1}\left(1 - \frac{\alpha}{2}\right) \frac{s}{\sqrt{\sum x_i^2}}, \qquad (4.3.11)$$

where $\hat{\theta}$ is given by (4.3.7), and

$$s^2 = \frac{1}{N - 1} \sum (y_i - \hat{\theta} x_i)^2$$

is the variance estimate. Note that

$$\sum (y_i - \hat{\theta} x_i)^2 = \sum y_i^2 - \hat{\theta}^2 \sum x_i^2, \qquad (4.3.12)$$

and hence once $\hat{\theta}$ is known, only $\sum y_i^2$ need be calculated in order to evaluate the residual sum of squares and the variance estimate.

For the data of Table 4.1, $\sum y^2 = 255{,}949$. Hence

$$s^2 = \tfrac{1}{8}\{255{,}949 - (29.96)^2(285)\} = 21.06,$$

so the 95% confidence interval for θ is

$$29.96 \pm \frac{(2.306)\sqrt{21.06}}{\sqrt{285}} = (29.33,\ 30.58).$$

It is also useful to examine the individual residuals from a fitted regression equation to see whether any observation is anomalous or whether the residuals follow a pattern. For this example, the individual residuals $y - \hat{\theta}x$ are shown in the third row of Table 4.1 and it is seen that they contain no obvious patterns which would lead one to doubt the model.

The residual sum of squares (4.3.12) may also be written

$$\sum (y_i - \hat{\theta}x_i)^2 = (1 - r^2)\sum y_i^2, \tag{4.3.13}$$

where

$$r = \frac{\sum x_i y_i}{(\sum x_i^2 \sum y_i^2)^{1/2}}$$

is the estimate of the correlation coefficient between x_i and y_i, knowing that the regression line passes through the origin. Hence (4.3.12) may be written

$$\sum y_i^2 = (1 - r^2)\sum y_i^2 + r^2 \sum y_i^2. \tag{4.3.14}$$

The result (4.3.14) shows that in this example the sum of squares of the y's about zero can be partitioned into a component $r^2 \sum y_i^2$ which is due to the sum of squares of the fitted values about zero plus the sum of squares of the residuals between the observed and fitted values.

The result (4.3.14) has many analogs in spectral analysis as will be shown in later chapters.

Forecast variance. If the model (4.3.5) is used to forecast a future velocity y corresponding to a given time x, the best estimate of y is

$$\hat{y} = \hat{\theta}x + \hat{z},$$

where $\hat{z} = 0$ is the best estimate of the error. The corresponding rv has variance

$$\text{Var}\,[\hat{Y}] = x^2\,\text{Var}\,[\hat{\theta}] + \text{Var}\,[\hat{Z}]$$

$$= \sigma^2\left(\frac{x^2}{\sum x_i^2} + 1\right).$$

Hence a $100(1 - \alpha)\%$ confidence interval for the forecast value is

$$\hat{y} \pm t_{n-1}\left(1 - \frac{\alpha}{2}\right)s\sqrt{1 + \frac{x^2}{\sum x_i^2}}. \tag{4.3.15}$$

The interval (4.3.15) increases with x and also brings out the general point that the accuracy of the forecasts depends on the design of the experiment, that is, on the choice of the x's.

4.3.3 Confidence regions for many parameters

The extension of the results of Section 4.3.2 to the estimation of several parameters is most readily achieved using matrix theory. These results are derived in Appendix A4.1 and are only summarized in this section. It is shown in Appendix A4.1 that the confidence interval is replaced in the multi-parameter case by a confidence region in the k-dimensional space of the θ's. It is also shown that an alternative way of looking at the lse's is that they minimize the volume of the confidence region for the parameters. For any given parameter this implies that the lse minimizes the length of the confidence interval in the dimension of the parameter.

For N observations and k parameters, the results derived in Appendix A4.1 may be summarized as follows.

The normal equations:

$$(\mathbf{X'X})\hat{\boldsymbol{\theta}} = \mathbf{X'y}, \qquad (A4.1.7)$$

or in scalar form

$$p_{x_r y} = \hat{\theta}_1 p_{x_r x_1} + \hat{\theta}_2 p_{x_r x_2} + \cdots + \hat{\theta}_k p_{x_r x_k}, \quad (r = 1, 2, \ldots, k),$$

where, for example,

$$p_{x_r y} = \sum_{i=1}^{N} x_{ir} y_i.$$

Estimated covariance matrix between estimates:

$$\mathbf{C} = (\mathbf{X'X})^{-1}\sigma^2, \qquad (A4.1.9)$$

or in scalar form

$$\mathbf{C} = \begin{pmatrix} p_{x_1 x_1} & p_{x_1 x_2} & \cdots & p_{x_1 x_k} \\ p_{x_2 x_1} & p_{x_2 x_2} & \cdots & p_{x_2 x_k} \\ \vdots & \vdots & & \vdots \\ p_{x_k x_1} & p_{x_k x_2} & \cdots & p_{x_k x_k} \end{pmatrix}^{-1} \sigma^2.$$

Estimate of residual variance:

$$\left. \begin{aligned} s^2 &= \frac{1}{N-k} (\mathbf{y'y} - \mathbf{y'X}\hat{\boldsymbol{\theta}}) \\ &= \frac{1}{N-k} (\mathbf{y'y} - \hat{\boldsymbol{\theta}}'\mathbf{X'X}\hat{\boldsymbol{\theta}}) \end{aligned} \right\}, \qquad (A4.1.12)$$

or in scalar form

$$s^2 = \frac{1}{N-k} (p_{yy} - p_{x_1 y}\hat{\theta}_1 - \cdots - p_{x_k y}\hat{\theta}_k).$$

100(1 − α)% *confidence region:*

$$(\boldsymbol{\theta} - \hat{\boldsymbol{\theta}})'\mathbf{X}'\mathbf{X}(\boldsymbol{\theta} - \hat{\boldsymbol{\theta}}) \leqslant ks^2 f_{k,N-k}(1 - \alpha), \tag{A4.1.15}$$

or in scalar form

$$\sum_{r=1}^{N}\sum_{s=1}^{N}(\theta_r - \hat{\theta}_r)(\theta_s - \hat{\theta}_s)p_{rs} \leqslant ks^2 f_{k,N-k}(1 - \alpha),$$

where

$$\Pr\{F_{k,N-k} \leqslant f_{k,N-k}(1 - \alpha)\} = 1 - \alpha.$$

Forecast variance:

$$\mathrm{Var}\,[\hat{Y}] = \sigma^2 + \mathbf{x}'\mathbf{C}\mathbf{x}, \tag{A4.1.18}$$

or in scalar form

$$\mathrm{Var}\,[\hat{Y}] = \sigma^2 + \sum_{j=1}^{k}\sum_{l=1}^{k} x_j x_l \, \mathrm{Cov}\,(\hat{\Theta}_j, \hat{\Theta}_l).$$

An example. As an illustration of the above results consider the special case of a two-parameter model

$$Y_i = \theta_1 + \theta_2 x_i + Z_i. \tag{4.3.16}$$

The lse's $\hat{\theta}_1$ and $\hat{\theta}_2$ obtained from (A4.1.7) are derived in Appendix A4.1.2 and are

$$\hat{\theta}_1 = \frac{\sum x^2 \sum y - \sum xy \sum x}{N \sum x^2 - (\sum x)^2};$$

$$\tag{4.3.17}$$

$$\hat{\theta}_2 = \frac{N \sum xy - \sum x \sum y}{N \sum x^2 - (\sum x)^2}.$$

From (A4.1.9) the estimated covariances between the estimators are

$$\widehat{\mathrm{Var}}\,[\hat{\Theta}_1] = \frac{s^2 \sum x^2}{N \sum (x - \bar{x})^2},$$

$$\widehat{\mathrm{Var}}\,[\hat{\Theta}_2] = \frac{s^2}{\sum (x - \bar{x})^2}, \tag{4.3.18}$$

$$\widehat{\mathrm{Cov}}\,[\hat{\Theta}_1, \hat{\Theta}_2] = -\frac{s^2 \sum x}{N \sum (x - \bar{x})^2},$$

where the estimated variance s^2 is, from (A4.1.12),

$$s^2 = \frac{1}{N-2}\left\{\sum y_i^2 - \hat{\theta}_1 \sum y_i - \hat{\theta}_2 \sum y_i x_i\right\}. \tag{4.3.19}$$

Finally, using (A4.1.15), the 100(1 − α)% confidence region for θ_1, θ_2 is

$$N(\theta_1 - \hat{\theta}_1)^2 + (\theta_2 - \hat{\theta}_2)^2 \sum x_i^2 + 2(\theta_1 - \hat{\theta}_1)(\theta_2 - \hat{\theta}_2)\sum x_i$$
$$\leqslant 2s^2 f_{2,N-2}(1 - \alpha). \tag{4.3.20}$$

4.3.4 Orthogonality

In the above example, the least squares estimators for the parameters in the model (4.3.16) were seen to have a non-zero covariance, and the confidence ellipse for (θ_1, θ_2) was seen to involve cross-product terms of the form $(\theta_1 - \hat{\theta}_1)(\theta_2 - \hat{\theta}_2)$. A typical confidence region for the model (4.3.16) is shown in Figure 4.4(a), where it is seen that the axes of the ellipse are skew to the (θ_1, θ_2) axes. Hence it is not possible to specify a confidence interval for θ_1 and θ_2 separately. In an extreme case it might happen that the estimators were so highly correlated that a wide range of estimates $(\hat{\theta}_1, \hat{\theta}_2)$ could explain the data.

However, it is possible to reparameterize this problem to obtain estimators which have zero covariance, that is, estimators which are *orthogonal*. For the two-parameter model, the orthogonal parameterization is

$$Y_i = \theta_1^* + \theta_2^*(x_i - \bar{x}) + Z_i. \qquad (4.3.21)$$

From (A4.1.7), the lse's are

$$\hat{\theta}_1^* = \bar{y} = \frac{1}{N} \sum y_i;$$

$$\hat{\theta}_2^* = \frac{\sum (x_i - \bar{x})(y_i - \bar{y})}{\sum (x - \bar{x})^2}, \qquad (4.3.22)$$

and from (A4.1.9)

$$\widehat{\mathrm{Var}}\, [\hat{\theta}_1^*] = \frac{s^2}{N};$$

$$\widehat{\mathrm{Var}}\, [\hat{\theta}_2^*] = \frac{s^2}{\sum (x_i - \bar{x})^2}; \qquad (4.3.23)$$

$$\widehat{\mathrm{Cov}}\, [\hat{\theta}_1^*, \hat{\theta}_2^*] = 0,$$

where

$$s^2 = \frac{1}{N-2} \left\{ \sum (y_i - \bar{y})^2 - (\hat{\theta}_2^*)^2 \sum (x_i - \bar{x})^2 \right\}. \qquad (4.3.24)$$

The $100(1 - \alpha)\%$ confidence region for θ_1, θ_2 is the ellipse

$$N(\theta_1^* - \hat{\theta}_1^*)^2 + (\theta_2^* - \hat{\theta}_2^*)^2 \sum (x_i - \bar{x})^2 \leqslant 2s^2 f_{2,N-2}(1 - \alpha), \qquad (4.3.25)$$

which has no cross-product terms because of the zero covariance between the estimators. A typical confidence region of this form is shown in Figure 4.4(b). Since the axes of the ellipse are now parallel to the parameter axes, separate confidence intervals for the two parameters can be specified.

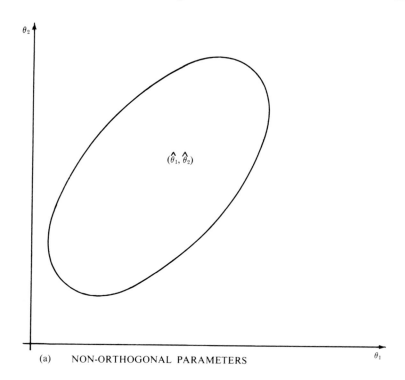

(a)   NON-ORTHOGONAL PARAMETERS

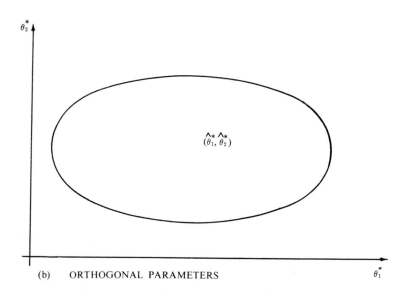

(b)   ORTHOGONAL PARAMETERS

Fig. 4.4: Confidence regions for two parameters

When $k > 2$ the device of subtracting the mean of the x's as in (4.3.21) does not lead to orthogonal parameterization. However, the estimators are more nearly orthogonal than they were before subtracting the means and, in particular, they will all be orthogonal to the constant term in the model. Hence it is advisable to fit the model

$$Y_i = \theta_1 + \theta_2(x_{i2} - \bar{x}_2) + \theta_3(x_{i3} - \bar{x}_3) + \cdots + \theta_k(x_{ik} - \bar{x}_k) + Z_i,$$
$$(4.3.25)$$

rather than the model

$$Y_i = \theta_1 + \theta_2 x_{i2} + \theta_3 x_{i3} + \cdots + \theta_k x_{ik} + Z_i.$$

It is shown in Appendix A4.1 that the results of this section are easily generalized to allow the error rv's Z_i to have an arbitrary covariance matrix.

4.4 LIKELIHOOD INFERENCE

4.4.1 The basic method

The likelihood function was introduced into statistics by R. A. Fisher but, as indicated in Section 4.2, Fisher's main use of it was in deriving maximum likelihood estimators which could then be used in the sampling distribution approach to estimation. However, the likelihood approach to inference stems from the work of G. A. Barnard [7, 8] and represents a completely different approach to statistical inference. Barnard's approach may be summed up in the statement that probability distributions are useful in describing data *before* they have been collected, whereas likelihoods are useful in describing parameters *after* the data have been collected.

One of the important features of likelihood inference is that it brings out very clearly the fact that in estimating a parameter, the sample space is irrelevant. This is logical, since the properties of the estimate must surely depend on the data available, not on the data which *might* have been obtained.

The likelihood mode of inference may be summarized by the following steps:

(1) The sampling pdf for the observations is assumed, apart from some unknown values of the parameters.

(2) The likelihood function is obtained by substituting the actual values of the observations into the pdf.

(3) The likelihood function is plotted as a function of the unknown parameters.

(4) Suitable means of summarizing the likelihood function are found.

As a simple example of the likelihood approach, consider the somewhat artificial problem of estimating the mean μ of a Normal pdf whose variance

σ^2 is known. The sampling pdf (4.2.1) of the sample before the data are collected is

$$f_{12\ldots n}(x_1, x_2, \ldots, x_n) = \left(\frac{1}{\sqrt{2\pi}\,\sigma}\right)^n \exp -\frac{1}{2\sigma^2} \sum_{i=1}^{n} (x_i - \mu)^2$$

$$= \left(\frac{1}{\sqrt{2\pi}\,\sigma}\right)^n \exp -\frac{1}{2\sigma^2}\left\{ \sum_{i=1}^{n} (x_i - \bar{x})^2 + n(\bar{x} - \mu)^2 \right\}.$$

After the data are available, the likelihood function for μ is proportional to

$$L(\mu) = K \exp -\frac{n}{2\sigma^2} (\bar{x} - \mu)^2. \tag{4.4.1}$$

Hence, apart from a multiplicative constant, the likelihood function, regarded as a function of μ, is a Normal pdf with mean $\bar{x}$ and variance σ^2/n. By contrast, in the sampling distribution approach, $\bar{X}$ is Normally distributed about μ with variance σ^2/n.

The likelihood function (4.4.1) is summarized by its mean $\bar{x}$ (the mle) and its variance σ^2/n. Thus the precision with which a parameter is estimated is easily seen by plotting the likelihood function. If the likelihood function is flat, the parameter is imprecisely estimated because values of the parameter remote from the mle have a likelihood which is not much smaller than that associated with the mle. Conversely, if the likelihood function is concentrated about the mle, the parameter is precisely estimated.

4.4.2 Properties of likelihood functions

This section deals with the interpretation of likelihood functions and with rules for combining them.

The likelihood principle. The likelihood principle states that if two experiments lead to likelihood functions which are proportional, then the inferences to be made are the same in both experiments.

For example, suppose that 8 transistors are inspected for defects. Before the experiment has been carried out, the number of defectives can be described by a random variable R, a sample space $r = 0, 1, 2, \ldots, 8$ and the binomial probability distribution

$$p_R(r) = \binom{8}{r} p^r (1 - p)^{8-r}. \tag{4.4.2}$$

After an experiment consisting of inspecting 8 transistors, three of which are found defective, the likelihood function is

$$L(p) = 56p^3(1 - p)^5. \tag{4.4.3}$$

Now suppose that a different experiment was performed in which transistors were tested until r were found defective. Before such an experiment is performed, the number of transistors tested can be described by a random variable N, a sample space $n = r, r + 1, \ldots, \infty$ and the Pascal probability distribution

$$p_N(n) = \binom{n-1}{r-1} p^r (1-p)^{n-r}, \qquad (4.4.4)$$

which gives the probability of having to test n transistors to get exactly r defectives.

If $n = 8$ tests were required to produce $r = 3$ defectives, the likelihood function after this experiment is

$$L(p) = 21 p^3 (1-p)^5. \qquad (4.4.5)$$

Equation (4.4.5) is proportional to (4.4.3) and hence according to the likelihood principle, the information about the parameter p is the same in both experiments. If a sampling distribution approach is adopted, the inference to be made from these two experiments would be different since the sample spaces and the probability distributions are different. Consequently, the confidence interval for p in the first experiment should be different from that in the second.

Note that the likelihood principle is a formal expression of the fact that the sample space is irrelevant to the estimation of p. For a further discussion of the likelihood principle, the reader is referred to [8] and [9].

Multiplication of likelihoods. If the likelihood function of a parameter θ with respect to data D_1 is denoted by $L(\theta|D_1)$ and if independent data D_2 yields a likelihood function $L(\theta|D_2)$, then the overall likelihood based on data D_1 and D_2 is

$$L(\theta|D_1, D_2) = L(\theta|D_1)L(\theta|D_2).$$

This result follows immediately from the fact that if the two sets of data are independent, the sampling pdf will be the product of the two sampling pdf's.

In this sense the likelihood function obeys the same multiplicative rule as the pdf of independent rv's. The likelihood also satisfies the same condition as a probability distribution in that it is a non-negative quantity. However, the correspondence ends here. Thus there is no rule for combining likelihoods which is analogous to the addition rule for the probability of the union of two mutually exclusive events.

Likelihood odds. Consider the likelihood function (4.4.3) for the parameter p. The maximum likelihood estimate is $\hat{p} = \frac{3}{8}$ which gives a likelihood of $L(\frac{3}{8}) = 0.282$. For another value of p, say $p = \frac{1}{8}$, the likelihood is $L(\frac{1}{8}) = 0.0104$. Hence the *likelihood odds* of $p = \frac{3}{8}$ versus $p = \frac{1}{8}$ are 27:1.

This statement may be interpreted as follows:

(1) The likelihood odds measure the relative evidence provided by the data that $p = \frac{3}{8}$ as opposed to $p = \frac{1}{8}$. Contrary evidence obtained multiplicatively from another independent experiment in which the likelihood odds were

$$\frac{L(\frac{1}{8})}{L(\frac{3}{8})} = 27$$

would be required before the two hypotheses were deemed equally likely.

(2) A person without any further information would be prepared to lay betting odds of 27:1 that the value $p = \frac{3}{8}$ was correct as compared with $p = \frac{1}{8}$.

4.4.3 Examples of likelihood functions

Estimating an exponential parameter. Consider the problem discussed in Section 4.2.4 concerning the estimation of the mean life of light bulbs. The first step in the likelihood approach is to write down the sampling pdf for the observations. In this case, an appropriate sampling pdf is

$$f_{123}(x_1, x_2, x_3 \mid \lambda) = \lambda^3 \exp\left(-\lambda \sum_{i=1}^{3} x_i\right). \tag{4.4.6}$$

The next step is to substitute the observed values $x_1 = 2.6$, $x_2 = 1.9$ and $x_3 = 1.5$ in (4.4.6), which gives the likelihood function

$$L(\lambda) = \lambda^3 \exp(-6\lambda). \tag{4.4.7}$$

The third step is to plot the likelihood function which is shown in Figure 4.2. The fourth step is to summarize the likelihood function. More elaborate methods of describing likelihood functions will be given in Section 4.4.5. For the present a very simple approach is adopted.

Unlike the likelihood function (4.4.1), the likelihood function (4.4.6) is skew. Figure 4.2 shows that it rises steeply from $\lambda = 0$ to a maximum at $\lambda = 0.5$ and then tends to zero relatively slowly as λ tends to infinity. The value $\lambda = 0.5$ is the most *likely* or *plausible* value of λ given these three observations, and is called the *maximum likelihood estimate* $\hat{\lambda}$ of λ. The values $\lambda = 0.1$ and $\lambda = 1.4$ both yield likelihood odds of 10:1 relative to $\hat{\lambda}$. Thus the odds are at least 10:1 against values of λ less than 0.1 and greater than 1.4. Hence the region $\lambda = 0.1$ to $\lambda = 1.4$ is said to be a *credible region* with odds less than 10:1 against any value in this region.

Estimating a binomial parameter. Consider the problem of estimating a binomial parameter discussed in Section 4.4.2. Using (4.4.2) or (4.4.4) the likelihood function for r successes in n trials is

$$L(p) = K p^r (1 - p)^{n-r}. \tag{4.4.8}$$

The likelihood functions for two cases $r = 1$, $n = 8$ and $r = 3$, $n = 8$ are shown in Figure 4.5, both curves having been normalized to have a maximum of unity. On differentiating (4.4.8) the mle is found to be $\hat{p} = r/n$.

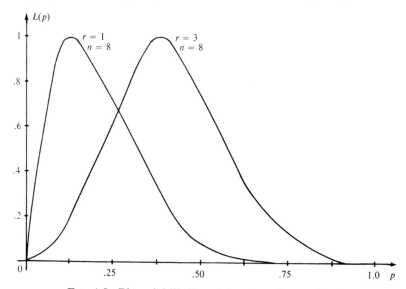

FIG. 4.5: Binomial likelihood functions (normalized)

For the $r = 1$ case, the likelihood curve is similar to the curve of Figure 4.2, that is, it rises sharply to a maximum at $p = \hat{p}$, and then falls off slowly for p greater than $\hat{p}$. The 10:1 credible region extends from 0.006 to 0.49 with the mle at 0.125.

For the $r = 3$ case, the likelihood curve is quite symmetric about the mle $\hat{p} = 0.375$, and the 10:1 credible region extends from 0.095 to 0.71.

4.4.4 *Least squares and likelihood estimation*

Least squares estimation is equivalent to maximum likelihood estimation, provided the errors are Normally distributed. To show this, consider the simple one-parameter model

$$Y_i = \theta x_i + Z_i$$

discussed in Section 4.3. If it is assumed that the errors Z_i are independent with mean zero and variance σ^2, then the least squares estimate is obtained by minimizing the sum of squares

$$S(\theta) = \sum_{i=1}^{N} (y_i - \theta x_i)^2. \tag{4.4.9}$$

If the errors are assumed independent with mean zero and variance σ^2 *and* Normally distributed, then the pdf for the data before the experiment is performed is

$$f_{12\ldots N}(y_1, y_2, \ldots, y_N) = \frac{1}{(\sqrt{2\pi}\,\sigma)^N} \exp -\frac{1}{2\sigma^2} \sum_{i=1}^{N} (y_i - \theta x_i)^2.$$

After the data are collected, the log-likelihood function is

$$l(\theta) = -\frac{N}{2} \ln 2\pi - N \ln \sigma - \frac{1}{2\sigma^2} \sum_{i=1}^{N} (y_i - \theta x_i)^2. \qquad (4.4.10)$$

Thus the estimate $\hat{\theta}$ which maximizes the log-likelihood function (4.4.10) is the same as that which minimizes the sum of squares (4.4.9). *Hence the* lse *is the same as the* mle *for Normally distributed errors.*

The lse's have been advocated in Section 4.3.1 on the basis of the mean square error criterion. However, the mse criterion has no place in likelihood theory since it involves averaging over the sample space. Hence it is necessary to reinterpret the theory of least squares in terms of the likelihood approach.

The log-likelihood function (4.4.10) may be rewritten

$$l(\theta) = \log K - \frac{1}{2\sigma^2} \sum x_i^2(\theta - \hat{\theta})^2, \qquad (4.4.11)$$

where $\hat{\theta} = \sum x_i y_i / \sum x_i^2$ is the lse or mle. Hence the likelihood function is proportional to a Normal pdf with mean $\hat{\theta}$ and variance

$$\frac{\sigma^2}{\sum x_i^2}. \qquad (4.4.12)$$

Note that (4.4.12) is exactly the same as the sampling variance (4.3.8) of the least squares estimator. Since the variance (4.4.12) is

$$\frac{-1}{[\partial^2 l(\theta)/\partial \theta^2]} = \frac{\sigma^2}{\sum x_i^2},$$

it follows that the Fisher information measure $E[\partial^2 l/\partial \theta^2]_{\hat{\theta}}$ is replaced in the likelihood approach by the *actual* second derivative of the log-likelihood function at its maximum.

Credible regions. It was shown in Section 4.4.3 that the notion of likelihood odds can be used to define a credible region for a parameter such that, for any value of the parameter within this region, the likelihood odds are less than a given amount against this value. However, if the function is Normal, a credible region based on likelihood odds is equivalent to a region based on enclosing a certain proportion of the area under the likelihood function. For example, a 7.5:1 Normal credible region is equivalent to enclosing 95% of the area. The 95% credible region for the parameter θ in the above example is

$$\hat{\theta} \pm 1.96\left(\frac{\sigma^2}{\sum x_i^2}\right)^{1/2},$$

and this is also a 7.5:1 credible region. In basing the interval on the area, one is implicitly treating the likelihood function as a probability distribution. This is made explicit in the Bayesian approach to inference [10, 11].

Least squares when the independent variables are subject to error. In the treatment of least squares in Section 4.3, it was assumed that the x's were not subject to error. However, it will be impossible to exert any control over the independent variables in many situations, such as the time series problems of later chapters. In such situations the x_i may be regarded as realizations of random variables. For the one-parameter case, the joint sampling pdf of the observations before they are made may be written

$$f_{12\ldots N}(y_1, y_2, \ldots, y_N) = f_{12\ldots N}(y_1, y_2, \ldots, y_N \mid \theta, x_1, \ldots, x_N) f'_{12\ldots N}(x_1, \ldots, x_N).$$

The joint pdf $f_{12\ldots N}$ represents the conditional distribution of the y's given that the x's are fixed and the density $f'_{12\ldots N}$ describes the pdf of the x's.

After the data are available, the likelihood function may be written

$$L(\theta) = L(\theta \mid x_1, \ldots, x_N) L'(x_1, \ldots, x_N).$$

Since $L'(x_1, \ldots, x_N)$ does not involve θ, the likelihood function for θ will be the same, apart from a multiplicative constant, as the likelihood function $L(\theta \mid x_1, \ldots, x_N)$ obtained by regarding the x's as fixed or not subject to error. The only way in which the variation in the x's can influence the estimation of θ is to make the likelihood function wider and hence increase the variance of the estimator. Thus, knowledge of the distribution of the x's cannot help in the estimation of θ. Note again that the sampling distribution approach gives a different answer to this problem since the variance of $\hat{\Theta}$ is

$$\text{Var}\,[\hat{\Theta}] = E\left[\frac{\sigma^2}{\sum_{i=1}^{N} X_i^2}\right],$$

where the expectation is taken over the sample space of the X's. In the likelihood approach, the sample space of the X's is irrelevant and the "variance" of the likelihood function is still given by (4.4.12) and hence depends only on the particular x values which occurred in the data.

4.4.5 Methods of summarizing likelihood functions

Quadratic likelihoods. The log-likelihood function (4.4.11) is quadratic in the parameter θ. More generally, if the model is linear in the parameters and the errors are Normal, the log-likelihood function is a quadratic form in the

θ's. Hence the likelihood function itself is a multivariate Normal distribution and may be described by its means, the mle's of the parameters, and its co-variance matrix. From (3.1.19), it is seen that the matrix of second derivatives

$$\frac{-\partial^2 l}{\partial \theta_i \, \partial \theta_j}$$

is the inverse of the covariance matrix associated with this multivariate Normal distribution.

Non-quadratic likelihoods. When the model is non-linear in the parameters or the sampling distribution is non-Normal, the likelihood function cannot be simply described in terms of its first two derivatives. As a general rule, when the log-likelihood function is not quadratic, it is best to *plot the whole of the likelihood function.* The problem of inference about θ can then be summarized as one of describing or *approximating* the likelihood function in as simple a way as possible. In some situations it is possible to have likelihood functions which have multiple maxima, and summarizing the likelihood function is difficult. However, if the plot of the likelihood function shows a single maximum, the methods described below may be used.

The first involves approximating the likelihood function by a Normal likelihood function, while the second involves transforming the parameters so that the likelihood function of the transformed variables is closer to Normal than the untransformed likelihood function.

Method 1: Approximation by a Normal distribution. Suppose that although the likelihood function is not Normal, it is reasonable to approximate it by a Normal pdf in θ. Since the likelihood function is undetermined to a constant multiplier, the approximation will be

$$L(\theta) \approx K \exp -\frac{1}{2\sigma^2} (\theta - \bar{\theta})^2, \tag{4.4.13}$$

where $\bar{\theta}$ is the mean of the approximating distribution and σ^2 its variance. If the "moments" of the likelihood function are defined by

$$I_k = \int_{-\infty}^{\infty} \theta^k L(\theta) \, d\theta,$$

then using the properties of the Normal pdf, the constants K, $\bar{\theta}$ and σ^2 in (4.4.13) are

$$K = \frac{I_0}{\sqrt{2\pi} \, \sigma} = \frac{I_0^2}{\sqrt{2\pi} \, \sqrt{I_2 I_0 - I_1^2}};$$

$$\bar{\theta} = \frac{I_1}{I_0}; \tag{4.4.14}$$

$$\sigma^2 = \frac{I_2}{I_0} - \bar{\theta}^2 = \frac{I_2 I_0 - I_1^2}{I_0^2}.$$

Mean likelihood estimates. Barnard [7] has called

$$\bar{\theta} = \int_{-\infty}^{\infty} \theta L(\theta)\, d\theta \Big/ \int_{-\infty}^{\infty} L(\theta)\, d\theta \qquad (4.4.15)$$

the *mean likelihood estimate* (mele). When $L(\theta)$ is Normal, the mele is the same as the mle, but in general they will be different.

The advantage of the mele over the mle is that the former takes account of the *whole* of the likelihood function whereas the mle represents just one point on the curve. The mle can therefore be quite misleading for small samples when the likelihood function is non-Normal. For large samples, most likelihood functions tend to become Normal in shape and so the mle together with its variance is adequate to describe the whole of the likelihood function.

It is possible to show [4] that if there is no reason to assume *a priori* that any value of θ is more likely than any other, the estimator corresponding to the mele (4.4.15) is the estimator with smallest mse for any sample size. This does not mean that, for all values of θ, the mse of this estimator is uniformly smaller than that of any other estimator. It means that when averaged over all values of θ the composite mean square error is smallest.

From the likelihood point of view, the mse is not a relevant criterion and hence the mele is best regarded as a convenient way of describing the centre of location of the likelihood function.

An example. To illustrate this method of summarizing the likelihood function, consider the binomial parameter example of Section 4.4.2. The likelihood function (4.4.8) yields the mle

$$\hat{p} = \frac{r}{n},$$

whereas the mele is

$$\bar{p} = \frac{r+1}{n+2},$$

with variance

$$\sigma^2 = \frac{r+1}{n+2} \frac{(n-r+1)}{(n+3)(n+2)}.$$

Hence for $r = 3$, $n = 8$, the likelihood function (4.4.8) can be approximated by a Normal pdf with mean $\bar{p} = 0.4$ and variance $\sigma^2 = 0.022$. Hence a 95% or 7.5:1 credible region for p is 0.11 to 0.69. For $r = 1$, $n = 8$, the approximating Normal pdf will have mean $\bar{p} = 0.2$ and variance $\sigma^2 = 0.015$. As can be seen from Figure 4.5, the Normal approximation for $r = 3$ will be much better than that for $r = 1$, owing to the skewness of the latter likelihood function. In fact the 95% credible region for $r = 1$ has a negative lower limit showing that the Normal approximation cannot be justified. In this case a better method of approach is the following.

Method 2: Transformation of parameters. If the log-likelihood function is not quadratic, a useful approach is to find transformations $\phi_i(\theta_1, \theta_2, \ldots, \theta_k)$ of the parameters such that the likelihood function is approximately multivariate Normal when plotted against the ϕ_i.

As noted previously, if the likelihood function is Normal, the second derivative of the log-likelihood is constant, that is, the Fisher information measure is constant. If the likelihood function is non-Normal, then $-d^2l/d\theta^2$ will be a function of θ. This is undesirable since now there is different information about θ at different points on the θ scale. Hence it is desirable to find a transformation $\phi = \phi(\theta)$ such that, on the ϕ scale, $-d^2l/d\phi^2$ is constant in the neighborhood of the mle $\hat{\phi} = \phi(\hat{\theta})$ of ϕ.

Making the transformation $\phi = \phi(\theta)$,

$$\frac{dl}{d\phi} = \frac{dl}{d\theta}\frac{d\theta}{d\phi}$$

and

$$\frac{d^2l}{d\phi^2} = \left(\frac{d^2l}{d\theta^2}\right)\left(\frac{d\theta}{d\phi}\right)^2 + \left(\frac{dl}{d\theta}\right)\left(\frac{d^2\theta}{d\phi^2}\right).$$

At the mle, $dl/d\phi = 0$ since $dl/d\theta = 0$, and so

$$\frac{d^2l}{d\phi^2} = \left(\frac{d^2l}{d\theta^2}\right)_{\hat{\theta}}\left(\frac{d\theta}{d\phi}\right)^2.$$

If $-d^2l/d\phi^2$ is to be a positive constant k,

$$\left(\frac{d\theta}{d\phi}\right)^2 = \frac{k}{-\left(\dfrac{d^2l}{d\theta^2}\right)_{\hat{\theta}}},$$

and hence, apart from a constant multiplier, the desired transformation $\phi(\theta)$ is

$$\phi(\theta) = \int\left(-\frac{d^2l}{d\theta^2}\right)^{1/2} d\theta. \tag{4.4.16}$$

An example. Consider the binomial likelihood (4.4.8) discussed above. This has

$$\frac{d^2l}{dp^2} = -\frac{r}{p^2} - \frac{n-r}{(1-p)^2}$$

$$= -\frac{n}{\hat{p}(1-\hat{p})},$$

when evaluated at the mle $\hat{p} = r/n$. Hence, using (4.4.16),

$$\phi(p) = \int\frac{dp}{\sqrt{p(1-p)}} = \arcsin\sqrt{p}.$$

Thus the likelihood function plotted against $\arcsin\sqrt{p}$ will be better approximated by a Normal pdf with mean $\hat{\phi}$ and variance σ^2 obtained using (4.4.14).

Figure 4.6 shows the transformed likelihoods for the cases $r = 1$, $n = 8$ and $r = 3$, $n = 8$. In both cases the likelihood functions are similar in shape to the Normal curve, whereas before transformation the curve for $r = 1$ was very non-Normal, as shown in Figure 4.5.

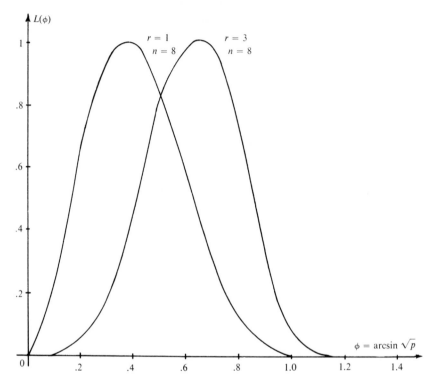

FIG. 4.6: Transformed binomial likelihood functions (normalized)

Table 4.2 shows the mean and variance of the approximating Normal distribution and the 95% or 7.5:1 credible region for p before and after transformation.

TABLE 4.2: Mean likelihood estimates and credible regions for binomial parameters based on untransformed and transformed likelihoods

	mle	Before transformation			After transformation			
	$\hat{p}$	$\bar{p}$	$\sigma_{\bar{p}}^2$	95% region	$\bar{p}$	$\bar{\phi}$	$\sigma_{\bar{\phi}}^2$	95% region
$n = 8, r = 3$	0.375	0.4	0.0217	(0.11, 0.69)	0.374	0.655	0.0256	(0.10, 0.68)
$n = 8, r = 1$	0.125	0.2	0.0145	$(-0.04, 0.44)$	0.148	0.394	0.0265	(0.05, 0.43)

It is seen that the transformation changes the mele more for the skew likeli-hood ($r = 1$) than for the more symmetrical likelihood ($r = 3$).

4.4.6 *Estimation of a Normal mean and variance*

To illustrate the methods of likelihood inference described in previous sec-tions, consider the problem of estimating the mean and variance from a sample of observations which are assumed to have a Normal pdf. Using (4.2.1) the likelihood function for μ and σ^2 is

$$L(\mu, \sigma^2) = \frac{1}{(\sqrt{2\pi}\,\sigma)^n} \exp -\frac{1}{2\sigma^2} \left[\sum_{i=1}^{n} (x_i - \bar{x})^2 + n(\bar{x} - \mu)^2 \right]. \qquad (4.4.17)$$

A convenient way of describing two-dimensional likelihoods is to plot contours on which the likelihood is constant in the (μ, σ^2) plane. If the likeli-hood function is a bivariate Normal distribution, these contours will be ellipses; if it is not, then it may be possible to transform the parameters so that it becomes approximately bivariate Normal.

Since the likelihood function (4.4.17) is Normal with respect to μ, it is not necessary to find a transformation for this parameter. Furthermore, since the estimators of μ and σ^2 are independent, it is only necessary to find a transformation for σ^2. From (4.4.17)

$$\frac{\partial l}{\partial \sigma^2} = -\frac{n}{2\sigma^2} + \frac{1}{2\sigma^4} \sum_{i=1}^{n} (x_i - \mu)^2$$

and

$$\frac{\partial^2 l}{\partial^2 \sigma^2} = \frac{n}{2\sigma^4} - \frac{1}{\sigma^6} \sum_{i=1}^{n} (x_i - \mu)^2. \qquad (4.4.18)$$

Hence the mle's are

$$\hat{\mu} = \bar{x}, \qquad \hat{\sigma}^2 = \frac{1}{n} \sum_{i=1}^{n} (x_i - \bar{x})^2,$$

and near the mle's, (4.4.18) becomes

$$\frac{\partial^2 l}{\partial^2 \sigma^2} = -\frac{n}{2\hat{\sigma}^4}.$$

Hence using (4.4.16), the Normalizing transformation is $\phi = \ln \sigma^2$. The likelihood function of the transistor data of Figure 3.3 is shown as a function of μ and $\ln \sigma^2$ in Figure 4.7, and it is seen that the likelihood contours approximate ellipses very closely in the region where the likelihood function is of importance.

Marginal likelihoods. The bivariate likelihood function (4.4.17), when plotted as a function of μ and $\ln \sigma^2$, behaves virtually like the product of two Normal

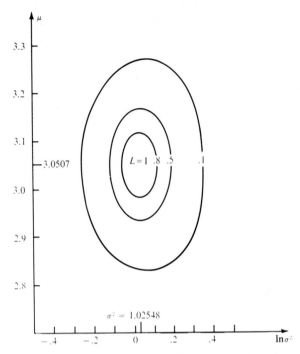

FIG. 4.7: Contours of constant likelihood for mean and variance of Normal observations when $n = 100$

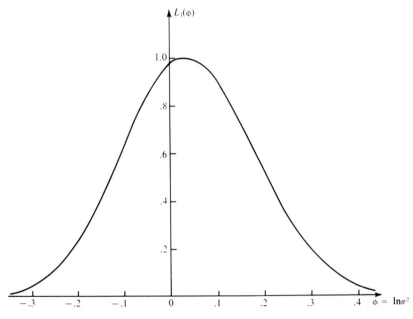

FIG. 4.8: Marginal likelihood function for σ^2 when $n = 100$

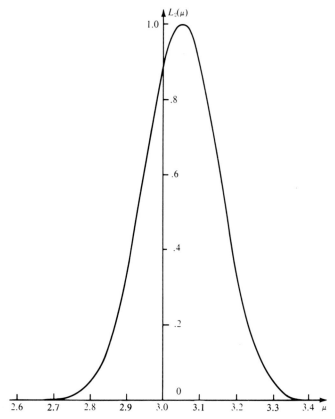

FIG. 4.9: Marginal likelihood function for μ when $n = 100$

distributions. Integrating $L(\mu, \sigma^2)$ with respect to μ gives the *marginal likeli-hood* for σ^2, namely

$$L_1(\sigma^2) = \int_{-\infty}^{\infty} L(\mu,\sigma^2)d\mu = \frac{1}{(\sqrt{2\pi}\,\sigma)^{n-1}} \exp{-\frac{1}{2\sigma^2}} \sum_{i=1}^{n} (x_i - \bar{x})^2. \quad (4.4.19)$$

Now the bivariate likelihood function is approximately Normal when plotted against μ and $\phi = \ln \sigma^2$ and so the marginal likelihood for μ may be obtained by integrating $L(\mu, \phi)$ with respect to ϕ, that is,

$$L_2(\mu) = \int_1^{\infty} L(\mu, \sigma^2 = e^{\phi})\, d\phi$$

$$= \int_0^{\infty} L(\mu, \sigma^2) \frac{d\sigma^2}{\sigma^2}$$

$$= K\left[\sum_{i=1}^{n} (x_i - \mu)^2 \right]^{-n/2} \quad (4.4.20)$$

The marginal likelihoods (4.4.19) and (4.4.20) are shown in Figure 4.8 and Figure 4.9 for the transistor data of Figure 3.3. The marginal likelihood for

μ is plotted against μ while the marginal likelihood of σ^2 is plotted against $\ln \sigma^2$. Note that the marginal likelihood for σ^2 is proportional to a χ^2 distribution while the marginal likelihood for μ is proportional to a t distribution. Hence in this example, the credible regions for μ and σ^2 would be exactly the same as those given in Section 4.2 based on the sampling distribution approach.

4.5 SUMMARY

In this chapter three aspects of the theory of statistical inference have been discussed with special reference to problems of parameter estimation. These are: the sampling distribution approach, the least squares approach and the likelihood approach. A fourth method, the Bayesian approach, has been omitted, but it is very similar in outlook to the likelihood approach.

These three modes of statistical inference are not disconnected but represent a gradual historic development. Furthermore, the answers to practical problems obtained using the various approaches will not differ greatly and in many cases will not differ at all. For example, the sampling distribution approach results in a t_{n-1} distribution for the sampling distribution of the mean, whereas the likelihood approach gives the same distribution for the marginal likelihood. In the sampling distribution approach, the t_{n-1} distribution represents the distribution of possible values of $\bar{x}$ about μ in repeated samples, whereas in the likelihood approach it represents the distribution of plausible values of μ about $\bar{x}$.

Historically it is natural that the sampling distribution approach should have come first, since it only required the direct application of existing probability theory to problems of statistical inference. For example, the sampling distribution of an estimator is a probability distribution which gives the relative frequency of occurrence of values of the estimator in repeated samples of size n. From the pdf of the estimator a region can be calculated which has a given probability $1 - \alpha$ of enclosing the correct values of the parameters. By replacing the estimators with the estimates from a given sample, a $100(1 - \alpha)\%$ confidence region for the parameters is obtained.

The theory of least squares was also developed within the sampling distribution framework. Thus the lse's have the property that they have minimum mean square error, or equivalently that they minimize the expected volume of the confidence region for the parameters.

The likelihood approach, although giving answers which are often similar to those obtained from the sampling distribution approach, represents a complete change of emphasis. Whereas the sampling distribution describes all possible values of the observations for given values of the parameters, the likelihood function describes all possible values of the parameters for given values of the observations.

The likelihood approach also enables the theory of least squares to be reinterpreted. For example, the likelihood function is effectively the sum-of-squares surface $S(\theta_1, \theta_2, \ldots, \theta_k)$, when the errors Z are Normal and independent. Since this is a quadratic form in the θ's, the likelihood function is simply described in terms of the lse's $(\hat{\theta}_1, \hat{\theta}_2, \ldots, \hat{\theta}_k)$ and the second derivatives of S. These derivatives can be interpreted as the covariances of the estimators in the sampling distribution approach or as measures of spread of the likelihood function in the likelihood approach. The most important aspect of the likelihood approach is to plot the likelihood function on scales for which there is approximately equal information about all parameters. Then the likelihood function may be summarized by its mele and credible region.

There are differences as well as similarities between these approaches. The likelihood approach correctly focuses attention on the one set of observations available, not on other sets of observations which might have been obtained. In some situations the likelihood approach leads to answers which are more sensible than those obtained from the sampling distribution approach. An example was given in Section 4.4.4, where it was shown that knowledge of the distribution of the errors in the independent variables conveys no information about the estimation of the parameters in least squares models. Other instances where the sampling distribution approach fails occur when estimators chosen because they are good on average are quite absurd when used with reference to a given sample. Plotting of the likelihood function in such cases will indicate that the particular sample contains little information. As a general rule, the likelihood function never lies.

REFERENCES

[1] E. Parzen, *Modern Probability Theory and its Applications.* John Wiley, New York, 1960.
[2] R. A. Fisher, "On the mathematical foundation of theoretical statistics." *Phil. Trans.* A **222**, 309 (1922).
[3] R. A. Fisher, "Theory of statistical estimation." *Proc. Cambridge Phil. Soc.* **22**, 700 (1925).
[4] E. L. Lehman, *Testing Statistical Hypotheses.* John Wiley, New York, 1959.
[5] A. Hald, *Statistical Theory with Engineering Applications.* John Wiley, New York, 1952.
[6] G. E. P. Box, "Fitting empirical data." *Ann. N. Y. Acad. Sci.* **86**, 3 (1960).
[7] G. A. Barnard, "Statistical inference." *Jour. Royal Stat. Soc.* B **11**, 116 (1949).
[8] G. A. Barnard et al., "Likelihood inference and time series." *Jour. Royal Stat. Soc.* A **125**, 321 (1962).
[9] A. Birnbaum, "On the foundations of statistical inference." *Jour. Amer. Stat. Assoc.* **57**, 269 (1962).

[10] H. Jeffreys, *Theory of Probability*. 3rd Ed. Clarendon Press, Oxford, 1961.
[11] L. J. Savage et al., *The Foundations of Statistical Inference*. Methuen, London, 1962.

APPENDIX A4.1   LINEAR LEAST SQUARES THEORY

Minimum mean square error estimates. This section contains proofs of some general results in the theory of linear least squares. The results quoted in Section 4.3 are special cases of these.

It is assumed that the model for the experiment is

$$Y_i = \theta_1 x_{i1} + \theta_2 x_{i2} + \cdots + \theta_k x_{ik} + Z_i, \quad (i = 1, 2, \ldots, N), \quad \text{(A4.1.1)}$$

or in matrix form

$$\mathbf{Y} = \mathbf{X\theta} + \mathbf{Z}, \quad \text{(A4.1.2)}$$

where the column vectors $\mathbf{Y}$, $\mathbf{\theta}$ and $\mathbf{Z}$ are transposes of the row vectors

$$\mathbf{Y}' = (Y_1, Y_2, \ldots, Y_N),$$
$$\mathbf{\theta}' = (\theta_1, \theta_2, \ldots, \theta_k),$$
$$\mathbf{Z}' = (Z_1, Z_2, \ldots, Z_N),$$

respectively, and

$$\mathbf{X} = \begin{pmatrix} x_{11} & x_{12} & \cdots & x_{1k} \\ x_{21} & x_{22} & \cdots & x_{2k} \\ \vdots & \vdots & & \vdots \\ x_{N1} & x_{N2} & \cdots & x_{Nk} \end{pmatrix}$$

is the matrix of set points of the k input variables $x_1, x_2, \ldots, x_k$ during the N experiments. It is assumed also that the errors $\mathbf{Z}$ have zero means and covariance matrix $\mathbf{V}$ with elements $V_{ij} = \text{Cov}\,[Z_i, Z_j]$. Otherwise the joint pdf of the errors is unspecified.

Given the observed responses $\mathbf{y}$ from the N experiments, the *generalized least squares estimates* (glse's) $\hat{\mathbf{\theta}}$ are those which minimize the quadratic form

$$(\mathbf{y} - \mathbf{X\theta})'\mathbf{V}^{-1}(\mathbf{y} - \mathbf{X\theta}) \quad \text{(A4.1.3)}$$

with respect to $\mathbf{\theta}$. Differentiating (A4.1.3) with respect to $\mathbf{\theta}$ and equating to zero gives the following linear equation for the glse's:

$$(\mathbf{X}'\mathbf{V}^{-1}\mathbf{X})\hat{\mathbf{\theta}} = \mathbf{X}'\mathbf{V}^{-1}\mathbf{y}. \quad \text{(A4.1.4)}$$

The criterion (A4.1.3) may be justified from two points of view:

(a) Using (3.1.19) and (A4.1.2) and assuming that the errors are distributed as a multivariate Normal pdf with covariance matrix $\mathbf{V}$, the log-likelihood function of the parameters $\mathbf{\theta}$ is equal to (A4.1.3), apart from an additive constant. Hence the glse's are mle's under the extra assumption that the errors are multivariate Normal.

(b) Suppose that the estimates $\hat{\theta}$ in (A4.1.4) are replaced by their corresponding estimators $\hat{\Theta}$. Then the generalized principle of least squares states that the estimators $\hat{\Theta}$ are such that the mean square error between

$$L = \lambda_1 \theta_1 + \lambda_2 \theta_2 + \cdots + \lambda_k \theta_k = \lambda' \theta$$

and

$$\hat{L} = \lambda_1 \hat{\Theta}_1 + \lambda_2 \hat{\Theta}_2 + \cdots + \lambda_k \hat{\Theta}_k = \lambda' \hat{\Theta}$$

is minimized. Hence an arbitrary linear function of the parameters is estimated with minimum mean square error.

Proof of the generalized least squares principle. To prove that the least squares estimators obtained from (A4.1.4) minimize the mse between L and $\hat{L}$, consider an estimator $\hat{L}$ of L which is a general linear function of the rv's Y_i, that is,

$$\hat{L} = l_0 + l_1 Y_1 + l_2 Y_2 + \cdots + l_N Y_N = l_0 + \mathbf{l'Y}.$$

From (A4.1.2), $E[\mathbf{Y}] = \mathbf{X\theta}$, since $E[\mathbf{Z}] = 0$ and hence

$$E[\hat{L}] = l_0 + \mathbf{l'X\theta}.$$

Further, since the Y_i have the same covariance matrix as the Z_i,

$$\text{Var}\,[\hat{L}] = \mathbf{l'Vl}.$$

Hence the mse of the estimator $\hat{L}$ is

$$\text{Var}\,[\hat{L}] + (E[\hat{L}] - L)^2 = \mathbf{l'Vl} + (l_0 + \mathbf{l'X\theta} - \lambda'\theta)^2.$$

Now if $L = \lambda'\theta$ can take on unbounded values, the mse will be unbounded unless $\mathbf{l'X} = \lambda'$. Hence the mse is minimized by setting $l_0 = 0$ and minimizing $\mathbf{l'Vl}$ subject to the constraint

$$\mathbf{l'X} = \lambda'. \tag{A4.1.5}$$

This is equivalent to finding the unconditional minimum of

$$\mathbf{l'Vl} - (\mathbf{l'X} - \lambda')\mu,$$

where $\mu' = (\mu_1, \mu_2, \ldots, \mu_k)$ is a vector of Lagrange multipliers. Equating the derivatives with respect to $\mathbf{l'}$ to zero gives

$$\mathbf{Vl} = \mathbf{X\mu}. \tag{A4.1.6}$$

Solving (A4.1.5) and (A4.1.6) for μ' and $\mathbf{l'}$ yields

$$\mu' = (\mathbf{X'V^{-1}X})^{-1}$$

and

$$\mathbf{l'} = \lambda'(\mathbf{X'V^{-1}X})^{-1}\mathbf{X'V^{-1}}.$$

Hence the minimum mse estimator of L is

$$\hat{L} = \mathbf{l'y} = \lambda'(\mathbf{X'V^{-1}X})^{-1}(\mathbf{X'V^{-1}Y}).$$

But, from (A4.1.4), this is just

$$\hat{L} = \lambda' \hat{\Theta},$$

where $\hat{\boldsymbol{\theta}}$ is the estimator corresponding to the estimate (A4.1.4). The proof given above is a generalization of one given by Barnard [1] when the errors Z_i are uncorrelated. If the errors are uncorrelated and have the same variance σ^2, then $\mathbf{V} = \sigma^2\mathbf{I}$, where $\mathbf{I}$ is the identity matrix. (A4.1.4) then becomes

$$(\mathbf{X}'\mathbf{X})\hat{\boldsymbol{\theta}} = \mathbf{X}'\mathbf{y}. \qquad (A4.1.7)$$

An example: To illustrate the use of (A4.1.7), consider the simple two-parameter case of (A4.1.1),

$$Y_i = \theta_1 + \theta_2 x_i + Z_i, \quad i = 1, 2, \ldots, N,$$

assuming that the errors Z_i are uncorrelated with mean zero and variance σ^2. Then (A4.1.7) reduces to

$$\begin{pmatrix} 1 & 1 & \cdots & 1 \\ x_1 & x_2 & \cdots & x_N \end{pmatrix} \begin{pmatrix} 1 & x_1 \\ 1 & x_2 \\ \vdots & \vdots \\ 1 & x_N \end{pmatrix} \begin{pmatrix} \hat{\theta}_1 \\ \hat{\theta}_2 \end{pmatrix} = \begin{pmatrix} 1 & 1 & \cdots & 1 \\ x_1 & x_2 & \cdots & x_N \end{pmatrix} \begin{pmatrix} y_1 \\ y_2 \\ \vdots \\ y_N \end{pmatrix},$$

that is,

$$\begin{pmatrix} N & \sum x \\ \sum x & \sum x^2 \end{pmatrix} \begin{pmatrix} \hat{\theta}_1 \\ \hat{\theta}_2 \end{pmatrix} = \begin{pmatrix} \sum y \\ \sum xy \end{pmatrix},$$

where all the summations run from $i = 1$ to N.

Hence the lse's are

$$\hat{\theta}_1 = \frac{\sum x^2 \sum y - \sum xy \sum x}{N \sum x^2 - (\sum x)^2}; \qquad \hat{\theta}_2 = \frac{N \sum xy - \sum x \sum y}{N \sum x^2 - (\sum x)^2}.$$

For the orthogonal parameterization of Section 4.3.4, namely

$$Y_i = \theta_1^* + \theta_2^*(x_i - \bar{x}) + Z_i,$$

the matrix equation (A4.1.7) reduces to

$$\begin{pmatrix} N & 0 \\ 0 & \sum (x - \bar{x})^2 \end{pmatrix} \begin{pmatrix} \hat{\theta}_1^* \\ \hat{\theta}_2^* \end{pmatrix} = \begin{pmatrix} \sum y \\ \sum y(x - \bar{x}) \end{pmatrix}.$$

Hence the lse's are

$$\hat{\theta}_1^* = \bar{y} = \frac{1}{N} \sum y; \qquad \hat{\theta}_2^* = \frac{\sum y(x - \bar{x})}{\sum (x - \bar{x})^2} = \frac{\sum (y - \bar{y})(x - \bar{x})}{\sum (x - \bar{x})^2}.$$

Covariance matrix of the estimators. To estimate the accuracy of the estimates of the parameters it is necessary to calculate the covariance matrix of the corresponding estimators. The diagonal elements of this matrix give the variances of each estimator and the off-diagonal elements give the covariances between each pair of estimators.

Now

$$\hat{\boldsymbol{\theta}} = (\mathbf{X}'\mathbf{V}^{-1}\mathbf{X})^{-1}\mathbf{X}'\mathbf{V}^{-1}\mathbf{Y},$$

and using (A3.1.2)

$$E[\hat{\boldsymbol{\theta}}] = (\mathbf{X}'\mathbf{V}^{-1}\mathbf{X})^{-1}\mathbf{X}'\mathbf{V}^{-1}E[\mathbf{Y}].$$

Hence the covariance matrix of the estimators is

$$C = E[(\hat{\Theta} - E[\hat{\Theta}])(\hat{\Theta} - E[\hat{\Theta}])']$$
$$= E[(X'V^{-1}X)^{-1}X'V^{-1}(Y - E[Y])(Y - E[Y])'V^{-1}X(XV^{-1}X')^{-1}]$$
$$= (X'V^{-1}X)^{-1}. \qquad (A4.1.8)$$

When $V = \sigma^2 I$, (A4.1.8) reduces to

$$C = (X'X)^{-1}\sigma^2. \qquad (A4.1.9)$$

For the above two-parameter example

$$(X'X) = \begin{pmatrix} N & \sum x \\ \sum x & \sum x^2 \end{pmatrix},$$

and so

$$C = (X'X)^{-1}\sigma^2 = \frac{\sigma^2}{N\sum(x - \bar{x})^2}\begin{pmatrix} \sum x^2 & -\sum x \\ -\sum x & N \end{pmatrix}.$$

Hence

$$\text{Var}\,[\hat{\Theta}_1] = \frac{\sigma^2 \sum x^2}{N\sum(x - \bar{x})^2};$$

$$\text{Var}\,[\hat{\Theta}_2] = \frac{\sigma^2}{\sum(x - \bar{x})^2};$$

$$\text{Cov}\,[\hat{\Theta}_1, \hat{\Theta}_2] = -\frac{\sigma^2 \sum x}{N\sum(x - \bar{x})^2}.$$

For the orthogonal parameterization,

$$(X'X) = \begin{pmatrix} N & 0 \\ 0 & \sum(x - \bar{x})^2 \end{pmatrix}$$

and so

$$C = \frac{\sigma^2}{N\sum(x - \bar{x})^2}\begin{pmatrix} \sum(x - \bar{x})^2 & 0 \\ 0 & N \end{pmatrix}.$$

Hence

$$\text{Var}\,[\hat{\Theta}_1^*] = \frac{\sigma^2}{N};$$

$$\text{Var}\,[\hat{\Theta}_2^*] = \frac{\sigma^2}{\sum(x - \bar{x})^2};$$

$$\text{Cov}\,[\hat{\Theta}_1^*, \hat{\Theta}_2^*] = 0.$$

It has been shown above that the least squares estimators minimize the mean square error (or variance, since the estimators are unbiased) of a linear function $\lambda'\theta$ of the θ's. Since

$$\text{Var}\,[\lambda'\hat{\Theta}] = \lambda'C\lambda, \qquad (A4.1.10)$$

it follows that the least squares estimators minimize the determinant $|C|$ of the covariance matrix of the $\hat{\Theta}$'s.

Estimation of the residual variance. This problem in its greatest generality would involve the estimation of all the elements of the covariance matrix $\mathbf{V}$ of the errors. In this section only the special case $\mathbf{V} = \sigma^2 \mathbf{I}$ is considered, and so the estimation of $\mathbf{V}$ reduces to that of estimating the common variance σ^2 of the Z_i.

Let $S(\boldsymbol{\theta})$ denote the quadratic form

$$S(\boldsymbol{\theta}) = \sigma^2 \mathbf{z}' \mathbf{V}^{-1} \mathbf{z} = \sigma^2 (\mathbf{y} - \mathbf{X}\boldsymbol{\theta})' \mathbf{V}^{-1} (\mathbf{y} - \mathbf{X}\boldsymbol{\theta})$$

which, when $\mathbf{V} = \mathbf{I}\sigma^2$, reduces to a sum of squares

$$S(\boldsymbol{\theta}) = (\mathbf{y} - \mathbf{X}\boldsymbol{\theta})'(\mathbf{y} - \mathbf{X}\boldsymbol{\theta}).$$

At the estimates $\theta = \hat{\theta}$,

$$S(\hat{\boldsymbol{\theta}}) = \mathbf{y}'\mathbf{y} - \hat{\boldsymbol{\theta}}'\mathbf{X}'\mathbf{y} - \mathbf{y}'\mathbf{X}\hat{\boldsymbol{\theta}} + \hat{\boldsymbol{\theta}}'\mathbf{X}'\mathbf{X}\hat{\boldsymbol{\theta}},$$

but since $\hat{\boldsymbol{\theta}}'\mathbf{X}'\mathbf{y} = \hat{\boldsymbol{\theta}}'\mathbf{X}'\mathbf{X}\hat{\boldsymbol{\theta}}$ from (A4.1.7),

$$S(\hat{\boldsymbol{\theta}}) = \mathbf{y}'\mathbf{y} - \mathbf{y}'\mathbf{X}\hat{\boldsymbol{\theta}}$$

and, substituting for $\mathbf{y}'\mathbf{X} = \hat{\boldsymbol{\theta}}'\mathbf{X}'\mathbf{X}$,

$$S(\hat{\boldsymbol{\theta}}) = \mathbf{y}'\mathbf{y} - \hat{\boldsymbol{\theta}}'(\mathbf{X}'\mathbf{X})\hat{\boldsymbol{\theta}}. \tag{A4.1.11}$$

Replacing estimates by estimators in (A4.1.11) and taking expectations [2] gives

$$E[S(\hat{\boldsymbol{\theta}})] = N\sigma^2 - k\sigma^2 = (N - k)\sigma^2,$$

and so

$$s^2 = \frac{\mathbf{y}'\mathbf{y} - \hat{\boldsymbol{\theta}}'(\mathbf{X}'\mathbf{X})\hat{\boldsymbol{\theta}}}{N - k} \tag{A4.1.12}$$

is an unbiased estimate of σ^2. For the one-parameter case, (A4.1.12) reduces to

$$s^2 = \frac{1}{N - 1} \sum_{i=1}^{N} (y_i - \hat{\theta}_1 x_i)^2,$$

as derived in Section 4.3.2. For the two-parameter case, (A4.1.12) becomes

$$s^2 = \frac{1}{N - 2} \sum_{i=1}^{N} (y_i - \hat{\theta}_1 - \hat{\theta}_2 x_i)^2$$

$$= \frac{1}{N - 2} \left\{ \sum_{i=1}^{N} y_i^2 - N\hat{\theta}_1^2 - 2\hat{\theta}_1\hat{\theta}_2 \sum_{i=1}^{N} x_i - \hat{\theta}_2^2 \sum_{i=1}^{N} x_i^2 \right\},$$

and for the orthogonal two-parameter case,

$$s^2 = \frac{1}{N - 2} \sum_{i=1}^{N} \{y_i - \hat{\theta}_1^* - \hat{\theta}_2^*(x_i - \bar{x})\}^2$$

$$= \frac{1}{N - 2} \left\{ \sum_{i=1}^{N} (y_i - \bar{y})^2 - (\hat{\theta}_2^*)^2 \sum_{i=1}^{N} (x_i - \bar{x})^2 \right\}.$$

By an argument similar to that used in Section 4.2.3, the estimator based on a divisor $N + 2 - k$ has the smallest mse and hence is preferable to (A4.1.12). However, (A4.1.12) is the estimate which is generally used in practice.

Confidence regions. To derive confidence regions for θ consider the identity

$$\mathbf{y} - \mathbf{X}\theta = (\mathbf{y} - \mathbf{X}\hat{\theta}) - \mathbf{X}(\theta - \hat{\theta}).$$

Hence

$$\frac{S(\theta)}{\sigma^2} = (\mathbf{y} - \mathbf{X}\theta)'\mathbf{V}^{-1}(\mathbf{y} - \mathbf{X}\theta)$$

$$= (\mathbf{y} - \mathbf{X}\hat{\theta})'\mathbf{V}^{-1}(\mathbf{y} - \mathbf{X}\hat{\theta}) + (\theta - \hat{\theta})'\mathbf{X}'\mathbf{V}^{-1}\mathbf{X}(\theta - \hat{\theta})$$

$$- (\mathbf{y} - \mathbf{X}\hat{\theta})'\mathbf{V}^{-1}\mathbf{X}(\theta - \hat{\theta}) - (\theta - \hat{\theta})'\mathbf{X}'\mathbf{V}^{-1}(\mathbf{y} - \mathbf{X}\hat{\theta}).$$

The last two terms are identically zero in view of the normal equations (A4.1.4). The vanishing of these cross-product terms stems from the fact that the vectors $\mathbf{y} - \mathbf{X}\hat{\theta}$ and $\mathbf{X}(\theta - \hat{\theta})$ are orthogonal in the N-dimensional sample space. Omitting these vanishing terms and substituting $\mathbf{Y}$ for $\mathbf{y}$ and $\hat{\Theta}$ for $\hat{\theta}$,

$$S(\theta) = S(\hat{\Theta}) + (\theta - \hat{\Theta})'\mathbf{X}'\mathbf{V}^{-1}\mathbf{X}(\theta - \hat{\Theta})\sigma^2. \qquad (A4.1.13)$$

Assuming that the errors Z_t are Normally distributed, it follows that $S(\theta)$ is a quadratic form in N Normal variables and hence is a χ_N^2 rv. This rv is decomposed according to (A4.1.13) into a χ_{N-k}^2 and a χ_k^2. Hence

$$\sigma^2 \frac{(\theta - \hat{\Theta})'\mathbf{X}'\mathbf{V}^{-1}\mathbf{X}(\theta - \hat{\Theta})}{S(\hat{\Theta})} \frac{N - k}{k}$$

is distributed as an $F_{k,N-k}$ rv. It follows that a $(1 - \alpha)$ probability region is

$$\sigma^2(\theta - \hat{\Theta})'\mathbf{X}'\mathbf{V}^{-1}\mathbf{X}(\theta - \hat{\Theta}) \leqslant \frac{k}{N - k} f_{k,N-k}(1 - \alpha)S(\hat{\Theta}). \qquad (A4.1.14)$$

Substituting $\hat{\theta}$ for $\hat{\Theta}$ in (A4.1.14) gives the $100(1 - \alpha)\%$ confidence region for the parameters θ. The region (A4.1.14) is an ellipsoid in the k-dimensional space of the θ's and it is readily verified that its volume is inversely proportional to the determinant $|\mathbf{X}\,\mathbf{V}^{-1}\mathbf{X}|$. But $\mathbf{C} = (\mathbf{X}'\mathbf{V}^{-1}\mathbf{X})^{-1}$, and hence it follows that since the lse's minimize $|\mathbf{C}|$, they also minimize the volume of the confidence ellipsoid for the parameters.

Substituting $\mathbf{V} = \mathbf{I}\sigma^2$ in (A4.1.14) and noting from (A4.1.12) that $s^2 = S(\hat{\Theta})/(N - k)$ is the estimate of σ^2, a $100(1 - \alpha)\%$ confidence region for θ is

$$(\theta - \hat{\theta})'\mathbf{X}'\mathbf{X}(\theta - \hat{\theta}) \leqslant ks^2 f_{k,N-k}(1 - \alpha) \qquad (A4.1.15)$$

when $\mathbf{V} = \mathbf{I}\sigma^2$.

For one parameter, (A4.1.15) is

$$(\theta - \hat{\theta})^2 \leqslant \frac{s^2}{\sum x^2} f_{1,N-1}(1 - \alpha), \qquad (A4.1.16)$$

which is another form for the confidence interval (4.3.11) since $t_{N-1}^2(1 - \alpha/2) = f_{1,N-1}(1 - \alpha)$.

For the two-parameter example, (A4.1.15) becomes

$$((\theta_1 - \hat{\theta}_1), (\theta_2 - \hat{\theta}_2)) \begin{pmatrix} 1 & 1 & \cdots & 1 \\ x_1 & x_2 & \cdots & x_N \end{pmatrix} \begin{pmatrix} 1 & x_1 \\ 1 & x_2 \\ \vdots & \vdots \\ 1 & x_N \end{pmatrix} \begin{pmatrix} \theta_1 - \hat{\theta}_1 \\ \theta_2 - \hat{\theta}_2 \end{pmatrix} \leqslant 2s^2 f_{2,N-2}(1 - \alpha).$$

This reduces to

$$N(\theta_1 - \hat{\theta}_1)^2 + 2(\theta_1 - \hat{\theta}_1)(\theta_2 - \hat{\theta}_2) \sum_{i=1}^{N} x_i + (\theta_2 - \hat{\theta}_2)^2 \sum_{i=1}^{N} x_i^2$$
$$\leqslant 2s^2 f_{2,N-2}(1 - \alpha),$$

which is the equation for an ellipse in the (θ_1, θ_2) plane.

For the orthogonal two-parameter model, (A4.1.15) reduces to

$$N(\theta_1^* - \hat{\theta}_1^*)^2 + (\theta_2^* - \hat{\theta}_2^*)^2 \sum_{i=1}^{N} (x_i - \bar{x})^2 \leqslant 2s^2 f_{2,N-2}(1 - \alpha),$$

which is also the equation of an ellipse in the (θ_1^*, θ_2^*) plane, but in this case the axes of the ellipse are parallel to the coordinate axes.

Derivation of confidence regions directly from sum-of-squares contours. In non-linear problems it is not possible to derive explicit expressions for the lse's and the matrix $X'V^{-1}X$. Examples of these are given in Section 5.4.4. Then the decomposition (A4.1.13) may be written

$$S(\theta) = S(\hat{\theta}) + S(\theta - \hat{\theta}).$$

Using the same argument as in the derivation of (A4.1.14), it follows that

$$\frac{S(\theta) - S(\hat{\theta})}{S(\hat{\theta})} \frac{N - k}{k}$$

is distributed as an $F_{k,N-k}$ rv. Hence the region

$$S(\theta) \leqslant S(\hat{\theta}) \left[1 + \frac{k}{N - k} f_{k,N-k}(1 - \alpha)\right] \qquad \text{(A4.1.17)}$$

is a $100(1 - \alpha)\%$ confidence region for the parameters. When contours of $S(\theta)$ are available, the $100(1 - \alpha)\%$ contour is then located by multiplying the residual sum of squares at the lse's by the constant on the right-hand side of (A4.1.17).

Forecast variance. If the model (A4.1.1) is used to forecast the response in a future experiment, the forecast value will be

$$\hat{y} = \hat{\theta}_1 x_1 + \hat{\theta}_2 x_2 + \cdots + \hat{\theta}_k x_k + \hat{z}$$
$$= \hat{\theta}'x + \hat{z}$$
$$= \hat{\theta}'x,$$

since $\hat{z} = 0$. The variance of the corresponding estimator is

$$\text{Var}[\hat{Y}] = \text{Var}[\hat{\theta}'x] + \text{Var}[\hat{Z}]$$
$$= x'Cx + \sigma^2, \qquad \text{(A4.1.18)}$$

using (A3.1.4). When $V = \sigma^2 I$, (A4.1.18) reduces to

$$\text{Var}[\hat{Y}] = (x'(X'X)^{-1}x + 1)\sigma^2. \qquad \text{(A4.1.19)}$$

Hence a $100(1 - \alpha)\%$ confidence interval based on the forecast value $\hat{y}$ and the estimate s^2 of σ^2 is

$$\hat{y} \pm t_{N-k}\left(1 - \frac{\alpha}{2}\right) s\sqrt{1 + \mathbf{x}'(\mathbf{X}'\mathbf{X})^{-1}\mathbf{x}}. \qquad (A4.1.20)$$

APPENDIX REFERENCES

[1] G. A. Barnard, "The logic of least squares." *Jour. Royal Stat. Soc.* **B 25**, 124 (1963).
[2] R. L. Plackett, *Principles of Regression Analysis*. Clarendon Press, Oxford, 1960.

5

Introduction to
Time Series Analysis

This chapter is concerned with basic concepts in the theory of time series. Most important among these are the notion of a stochastic process, a stationary process, a linear stationary process and the autocovariance function of a stationary process. It is shown in Section 5.1 that, to describe the statistical nature of an observed time series, it is necessary to regard it as a member of an abstract ensemble of functions called a stochastic process. The simplest type of stochastic process is a linear process which can be generated by a linear operation on a purely random process. Two special cases of the linear process which are of considerable practical importance are the autoregressive and moving average processes. In Section 5.2 it is shown that a general stationary stochastic process can be conveniently described by its autocovariance function, while the linear stationary process is best described by its parameters. Section 5.3 deals with the estimation of the autocovariance function from an observed time series, and Section 5.4 deals with the estimation of the parameters of autoregressive and moving average processes.

5.1 STATIONARY AND NON-STATIONARY STOCHASTIC PROCESSES

5.1.1 Definition and classification of time series

By a statistical time series is meant a signal, or function of time, $x(t)$, which exhibits *random* or *fluctuating* properties. Given a record of such a series, it is not possible to predict future values of the series exactly as would be the case if it were a deterministic signal as described in Chapter 2. It follows that time series can only be described by statistical laws or models which could be used, for example, to forecast future values of the series. Examples of such statistical time series are:

(a) The fluctuating voltage in a wire due to the random motion of the electrons, usually called *thermal noise* by electrical engineers.

(b) The fluctuating yield from a chemical reactor as measured on a continuous basis by an infra-red spectrometer.

(c) The voltage output from a radar receiver. A typical radar return signal is shown in Figure 5.1.

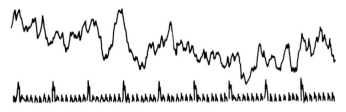

FIG. 5.1: A radar return signal

Discrete and continuous series. The time series of examples (a), (b) and (c) are continuous measurements and are called *continuous time series.* Another type of series is a *discrete time series,* for which the values are given only at specific instants of time. One way in which a discrete time series may be obtained is by sampling a continuous time series at equal intervals of time, say Δ. Writing $x(t=r\Delta) = x_r$, the sequence $\{x_r\}$, $r = \ldots, -2, -1, 0, 1, 2, \ldots$, constitutes a discrete time series.

The continuous time series of examples (a), (b) and (c) have to be recorded by a physical instrument possessing inertia. Hence such series are *band-limited,* that is, they contain no frequencies higher than a certain maximum frequency determined by the frequency response function of the instrument. Thus, using the theory of Chapter 2, it is possible to determine a sampling interval Δ such that the discrete time series $\{x_t\}$ obtained by sampling the continuous time series $x(t)$ contains all the information in the original series $x(t)$. Hence a continuous time series may be analyzed in either analog (continuous) or digital (discrete) form.

A discrete time series may also arise when a physical quantity does not have an instantaneous value but has meaning only when *accumulated* or integrated over a suitable time interval. Examples of such accumulated series are the daily rainfall figures from a meteorological station or the yields from consecutive batches in an industrial process. An example of a discrete time series is given in Figure 5.2, which shows the accumulated yields from 70 consecutive batches of a distillation column plotted against the batch number. The data on which this figure are based is given in Table 5.1. Note that although there is a definite high–low pattern in the data, it is impossible to predict exactly the value of the next batch.

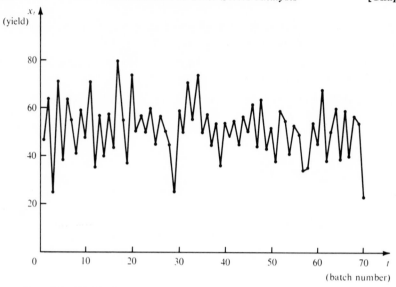

FIG. 5.2: Yields from 70 consecutive batches of an industrial process

TABLE 5.1: Yields from 70 consecutive batches
of an industrial process

1–18	19–36	37–54	55–70
47	37	45	53
64	74	54	49
23	51	36	34
71	58	54	35
38	50	48	54
65	60	55	45
55	44	45	68
41	57	57	38
59	50	50	50
48	45	62	60
71	25	44	39
35	59	64	59
56	50	43	40
40	71	52	57
58	56	38	54
44	74	60	23
80	50	55	
55	58	41	

Multivariate time series. In many situations one is interested in a vector

$$\mathbf{x}'(t) = \{x_1(t), x_2(t), \ldots, x_q(t)\}$$

of time series, in which case $\mathbf{x}(t)$ is said to be a *multivariate time series*. An example of a bivariate time series occurs when $x_1(t)$ is the "angle-off" of a radar detector in azimuth and $x_2(t)$ is the "angle-off" in elevation. Note that these two time series arise on an equal footing since they characterize different aspects of the performance of the radar dish.

Sometimes $x_1(t), \ldots, x_l(t)$ are the inputs to a physical system and $x_{l+1}(t), \ldots, x_q(t)$ the corresponding outputs from the same system. For example, $x_1(t)$ might be the inlet flow rate of cold water to a water heater and $x_2(t)$ the temperature of the outlet flow. From a knowledge of the behavior of the water heater it is possible to make reasonable predictions of the series $x_2(t)$ from $x_1(t)$. In this case the time series do not arise on an equal footing, because changes in $x_1(t)$ can cause changes in $x_2(t)$, but not conversely.

It should now be clear that the word "series" in time series is used rather loosely to mean continuous functions of time $x(t)$ or discrete sequences $\{x_t\}$ ordered in time. The word "time" is also used rather loosely in that t may refer to some other physical parameter, such as *space*. For example, in the study of aircraft vibration, experiments are sometimes performed in which strain gauges are attached to the wing or some other part of the aircraft and the fluctuating stresses on the structure measured at different aircraft heights. Although the aircraft is flown for a certain period of time, the record obtained is more a function of the region in space traversed by the aircraft than a function of time.

Multidimensional time series. In some situations, the series is a function $x(t_1, t_2, \ldots, t_k)$ of several physical parameters $t_1, t_2, \ldots, t_k$, in which case it is said to be a *multidimensional series*. For example, $x(t_1, t_2)$ may represent measurements of the local fluctuations in the earth's magnetic field at a point with coordinates t_1, t_2. In other situations, the process being studied may be both multivariate and multidimensional. For example, geophysicists are interested in investigating the relationship between the earth's magnetic field $x_1(t_1, t_2)$ and the depth of the ocean $x_2(t_1, t_2)$.

5.1.2 Description of a stochastic process

Definition of a stochastic process. When time series data are analyzed it is necessary to perform various operations on the actual numbers obtained from an experiment. *Before* the data are collected it is convenient, as in all statistical work, to regard them as being one of the many sets of data which might have arisen. This is achieved by associating with each point of time t in the range $(-\infty \leqslant t \leqslant \infty)$ an rv $X(t)$ which has a sample space $\{-\infty \leqslant X(t) \leqslant \infty\}$ and an associated pdf $f_{X(t)}(x)$. In addition, it is necessary to specify the joint pdf's associated with any arbitrary set of times $(t_1, t_2, \ldots, t_n)$. Thus a time series can be described by an ordered set of rv's $X(t)$, $(-\infty \leqslant t \leqslant \infty)$ for continuous time series and an ordered set of rv's $\{X_t\}$, $t = 0, \pm 1, \pm 2, \ldots$, for a discrete time series.

An ordered set of rv's is called a *stochastic process*. It provides a probabilistic description of a physical phenomenon which evolves in time according to well-defined probability laws. Note that the sample space associated with a univariate stochastic process is doubly infinite, extending from $-\infty$ to $+\infty$ at each point of time and time itself extending from $-\infty$ to $+\infty$. The doubly infinite set of time functions which can be defined on this sample space is called an *ensemble*.

The ensemble. An observed time series $x(t)$ is regarded as one realization of an infinite ensemble of functions which might have been observed. The one or few time series to be analyzed are regarded as having been drawn at random from such an ensemble of functions in much the same way that a sample of people is drawn at random from a population to conduct a survey. In the same way that the sample has to be representative of the population which is to be described, it usually serves as an aid to clear thinking in time series work to write down at the start of an investigation the exact nature of the ensemble or population from which the observed time series is regarded as being a typical member. For example, suppose it was desired to measure wave heights by means of a transmitter attached to a buoy. If the buoy is dropped at random into the sea, the observed time series could be regarded as being one of the many series which might have been observed had the location of the buoy been slightly different. More careful examination might show that this time series would be typical only if attention were confined to a particular time of day or part of the year or particular region of the ocean. The more factors brought into the experiment, the wider becomes the ensemble of time series being described, and hence the more care required in the interpretation of the results.

In many practical problems, one will be interested in the way the properties of the time series vary when certain external conditions are varied deliberately in an experimental design. In other situations it will not be possible to exercise control over external factors, for example, the influence of solar radiation on the statistical properties of atmospheric turbulence is not under control. Nevertheless, the correlation of the statistical properties of the time series with these uncontrollable factors may well be the most important conclusion which emerges from the analysis. The main purpose of this discussion is to show that what constitutes the ensemble of possible time series in any given situation is dictated by good scientific judgment and not by purely statistical matters.

Probability distributions associated with a stochastic process. If the ensemble is clearly defined, then in advance of collecting the data the behavior of a time series at a given instant in time may be described by the rv $X(t)$ and its pdf $f_{X(t)}(x)$.* As emphasized in Chapter 3, the choice of $f_{X(t)}(x)$ is a matter for good judgment or experience.

Similarly, the random variables $X(t_1)$ and $X(t_2)$ at two times t_1 and t_2 can be described by their joint pdf $f_{X(t_1)X(t_2)}(x_1, x_2)$, which is abbreviated to $f_{12}(x_1, x_2)$. One way of regarding these pdf's is that a proportion $f_1(x_1)\,\delta x_1$ of the members of the ensemble passes through a gap of width δx_1 about the point x_1 at time t_1, as shown in Figure 5.3. Similarly, a proportion $f_{12}(x_1, x_2)\,\delta x_1\,\delta x_2$ of the ensemble of functions passes through the gap x_1 to $x_1 + \delta x_1$ at t_1 *and* the gap x_2 to $x_2 + \delta x_2$ at time t_2.

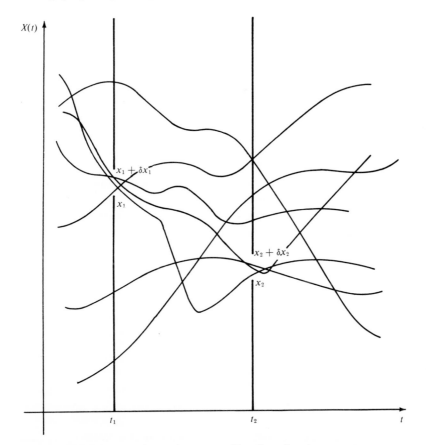

FIG. 5.3: Members of an ensemble of stochastic processes

* Strictly speaking, the rv's $X(t)$ should be described by their cumulative distribution functions since the pdf's may not exist, but we disregard this point since it is not relevant from a practical point of view.

Another pdf which will be useful is the *conditional pdf*

$$f_{2|1}(x_1, x_2) = \frac{f_{12}(x_1, x_2)}{f_1(x_1)}, \tag{5.1.1}$$

which is read as "the pdf of X_2 given X_1". Thus, of the proportion $f_1(x_1)\,\delta x_1$ of the ensemble which passes through the gap x_1 to $x_1 + \delta x_1$ at t_1, only the fraction $f_{2|1}(x_1, x_2)$ passes through the gap x_2 to $x_2 + \delta x_2$ at time t_2.

In general, a univariate stochastic process can be described by the joint pdf's

$$f_{X(t_1)X(t_2)\ldots X(t_n)}(x_1, x_2, \ldots, x_n),$$

for an arbitrarily chosen set of times $t_1, t_2, \ldots, t_n$, but such a description might be rather complicated. In practice a simpler approach, based on the lower-order moments of these distributions, is necessary.

Simple moments of a stochastic process. At any single point in time, univariate moments of the form

$$E[(X(t))^k] = \int_{-\infty}^{\infty} x^k f_{X(t)}(x)\, dx \tag{5.1.2}$$

can be defined. Hence a very simple description of a stochastic process would be to plot its *mean function* $\mu(t)$ and its *variance function* $\sigma^2(t)$ as a function of t. Similarly, the bivariate moments

$$E[(X(t_1))^k (X(t_2))^l] = \int_{-\infty}^{\infty} \int_{-\infty}^{\infty} x_1^k x_2^l f_{X(t_1)X(t_2)}(x_1, x_2)\, dx_1\, dx_2 \tag{5.1.3}$$

could be used to describe the dependence between the values of the time series at two neighboring points t_1 and t_2. The simplest of the moments (5.1.3) and the most important in practice is the *autocovariance function* (acvf)

$$\gamma_{XX}(t_1, t_2) = E[(X(t_1) - \mu(t_1))(X(t_2) - \mu(t_2))]. \tag{5.1.4}$$

Note that $\gamma_{XX}(t_1, t_1) = \sigma^2(t_1)$. Note also that the autocovariance function of a time series has the same properties as the covariance between two rv's X_1 and X_2 given in Section 3.2.2.

Since $\gamma_{XX}(t_1, t_2)$ depends on the scale of measurement of X, it is convenient, in comparing two series with possibly different scales of measurement, to define a normalized quantity called the *autocorrelation function* (acf)

$$\rho_{XX}(t_1, t_2) = \frac{\gamma_{XX}(t_1, t_2)}{\sigma(t_1)\sigma(t_2)}.$$

Like the ordinary cross correlation coefficient (3.2.19), $\rho_{XX}(t_1, t_2)$ lies between limits -1 and $+1$, corresponding to complete negative and positive linear dependence.

More generally, the stochastic process could be described by its higher moments

$$E[(X(t_1))^{k_1} (X(t_2))^{k_2} \cdots (X(t_n))^{k_n}], \tag{5.1.5}$$

but these are not very useful in practice.

5.1.3 Stationarity and the autocovariance function

Stationarity. In general the properties of a stochastic process will be time dependent, that is, the current value $x(t)$ will depend on the time which has elapsed since the process was started. A simplifying assumption which is often made is that the series has reached some form of *steady state* or *equilibrium*, in the sense that the statistical properties of the series are independent *valid in DSP.* of absolute time. For example, it would be reasonable to assume for the batch data of Figure 5.2 that, if process control were adequate, the statistical properties of the series would remain fairly stable with time. A minimum requirement for this to hold is that the pdf $f_{X(t)}(x)$ is *independent of time* and hence a *stationary time series* has a constant mean μ and a constant variance σ^2. Therefore, the common pdf $f_X(x)$ can be estimated by forming the histogram of the data as described in Chapter 3. For example, the histogram of the data of Table 5.1 is shown in Figure 5.4, from which it may be seen that the empirical distribution is unimodal and does not contradict the hypothesis

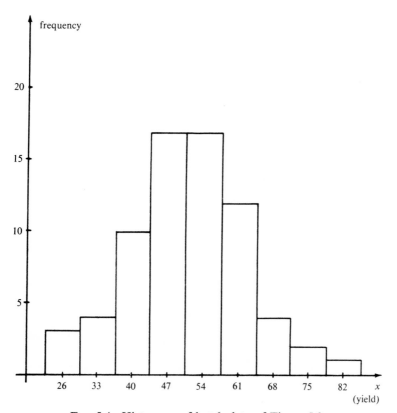

FIG. 5.4: Histogram of batch data of Figure 5.2

that the data may be described by a Normal rv. If the data extends over a considerable period of time, the reasonableness of the stability assumption could be checked, for example, by constructing a separate histogram for each half of the series. If the two histograms are consistent, the assumption of a constant pdf is probably justified.

Another consequence of assuming that the process is in a state of equilibrium is that the joint pdf $f_{12}(x_1, x_2)$ depends only on the time difference $t_2 - t_1$ and not on the absolute values of t_1 and t_2. Suppose that the time series is discrete and that the observed values are $x_1, x_2, \ldots, x_n$. Then the pairs of points (x_1, x_{k+1}), (x_2, x_{k+2}), ..., (x_{n-k}, x_n) can be regarded as $(n - k)$ observations from the joint pdf $f_{12}(x_1, x_2)$, which is now the same for all times $k\Delta$ apart.

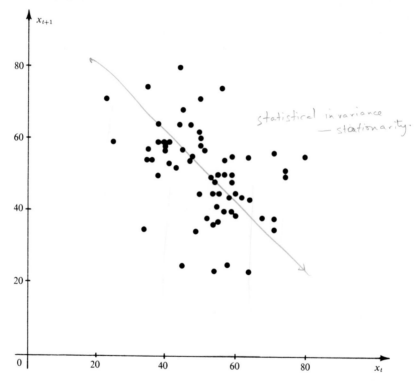

FIG. 5.5: Scatter diagram for pairs of consecutive batches from data of Figure 5.2

Figure 5.5 shows the scatter diagram for consecutive batches (x_t, x_{t+1}) for the data of Table 5.1. It is seen that the points fall mainly in the northwest and southeast corners of the diagram, bringing out the negative dependence between neighboring batches evident in Figure 5.2.

More generally still, the equilibrium condition implies that the properties of the multivariate pdf associated with any set of times $t_1, t_2, \ldots, t_n$ depend only on the time differences $|t_i - t_j|$. Another way of saying this is that the pdf associated with any set of times $t_1, t_2, \ldots, t_n$ is the same as that associated with any other set of times obtained by translating $t_1, t_2, \ldots, t_n$ ahead or backward by an amount k. In mathematical terms,

$$f_{X(t_1) X(t_2)\ldots X(t_n)}(x_1, x_2, \ldots, x_n) = f_{X(t_1+k)\ldots X(t_n+k)}(x_1, x_2, \ldots, x_n), \quad (5.1.6)$$

for all sets of times and for all displacements k. A stochastic process which satisfies the conditions (5.1.6) is said to be *completely stationary.*

The autocovariance function. An immediate consequence of the stationarity assumption is that the acvf $\gamma_{XX}(t_1, t_2)$ is a function of $u = t_2 - t_1$ only, and hence may be written

$$\gamma_{XX}(u) = E[(X(t) - \mu)(X(t + u) - \mu)] = \text{Cov}\,[X(t), X(t + u)]. \quad (5.1.7)$$

The displacement u is called the *lag.* The acvf shows how the dependence between adjacent values in the stochastic process changes with lag u. If the $X(t)$ have a multivariate Normal pdf, then the acvf and the mean completely characterize the process, as stated in Section 3.1.5.

The autocorrelation function. For stationary processes the acf

$$\rho_{XX}(u) = \frac{\gamma_{XX}(u)}{\gamma_{XX}(0)} \quad (5.1.8)$$

is a function only of the lag u. Methods for estimating the acvf and acf are postponed until Section 5.3, but Figure 5.6 illustrates the sample acf of the batch data of Figure 5.2. It is seen that the autocorrelations damp out very quickly and that there is virtually no correlation after about 10 lags. Further-more, the autocorrelations alternate in sign, showing that a high yield in one batch tends, on average, to produce a low yield in the following batch and vice versa.

Weak stationarity. A weaker assumption than (5.1.6) which is sometimes made is that multivariate moments of the form (5.1.5) up to order

$$k_1 + k_2 + \cdots + k_n = K$$

depend only on time differences $|t_i - t_j|$. A stochastic process with this property is said to be stationary up to order K. For example, if $K = 2$, only the mean, variance and acvf (5.1.7) depend on time differences and the process is stationary to second order. However, if the multivariate pdf in (5.1.6) is Normal, so that it is completely specified by its means and covari-ances, it follows that second-order stationarity implies complete stationarity.

A purely random process. The simplest example of a stationary process is the discrete process Z_t with the rv's Z_t mutually independent. In this case (5.1.7) implies that $\gamma_{ZZ}(k) = 0$ for all $k \neq 0$. This process is called a *purely random process* by statisticians and *band-limited white noise* by engineers.

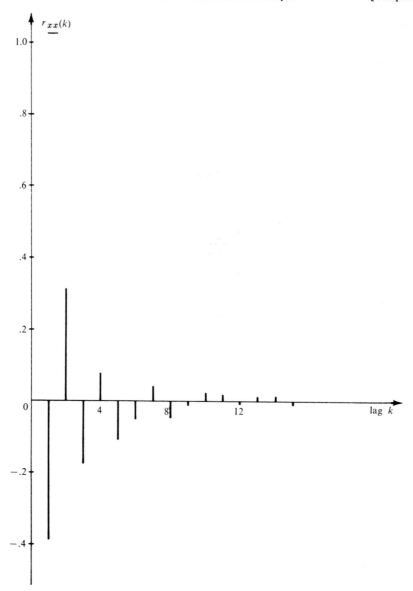

FIG. 5.6: Sample autocorrelation function for data of Figure 5.2

5.1.4 Classification of time series occurring in practice

Most research work in time series analysis has been concerned with the properties of stationary time series. If an empirical series is not stationary, then various devices can be used to remove obvious trends, leaving behind a residual series for which it is reasonable to assume stationarity. For example, some definite mathematical function, such as exponentials, Fourier series or polynomials, may be fitted to the data. Another device used extensively in later chapters is to filter or remove low-frequency trends by a suitably designed filter.

Time series normally encountered in practice may be classified into three broad categories:

(a) Those which are stationary over relatively long periods of time because of some form of control over external conditions. Examples are series obtained from random noise generators, such as thermionic valves kept under constant temperature conditions, and the Wolfer series of sunspot numbers recorded over a period of several centuries. From a practical point of view, no series is likely to remain stationary indefinitely and so the important question is how long a record can be analyzed before the assumption breaks down. In dealing with geophysical series such as the sunspot numbers, conditions may remain stable over periods of centuries. In other situations, however, conditions may remain stable only over periods of hours or minutes, or perhaps not at all.

(b) Those series which may be treated as stationary provided a sufficiently short length of series is examined. The tracking errors of an operator are considered stationary when the characteristics of the tracking signal are kept stable and measurements are made over a sufficiently short period so that the operator does not become fatigued. When measuring the stress on some part of an aircraft flying through turbulence, it is well known that over short time periods, say up to half an hour, the series may be regarded as stationary. For periods longer than this, the variance of the series can change markedly, owing to changes in the level or intensity of turbulence.

(c) Series which are quite obviously non-stationary, both from their visual appearance, and also from *a priori* knowledge of the phenomenon being studied.

Time series may be non-stationary in a variety of ways. Some examples of the simpler forms of non-stationarity follow.

Non-stationarity in the mean. Many series exhibit trends in the mean without visibly showing any more complicated form of non-stationarity. For example, most economic time series contain broad trends which reflect the gradual growth of the economy. On top of these are superimposed higher-frequency fluctuations due to shorter term economic factors, for example, the use of economic regulators, and much higher frequency oscillations due to speculation. It is usually assumed (arbitrarily) that, when measured on a logarithmic scale, economic time series such as gross national product, prices, and investments can be split up into a trend series (non-stationarity in the mean) and a residual series which is stationary.

Non-stationarity in mean and variance. An instance of a series which may be non-stationary in variance is the turbulence example given above. Another case is in the control of an industrial series. These series tend to wander away from their target values in a non-stationary manner, due to the effect of random disturbances, unless adjustments are applied to compensate for these disturbances. Non-stationary models which describe the behavior of such series and which can be used to design optimal control systems have recently been given in [1, 2]. These non-stationary models may also be extended to describe the "trends" and "periodicities" found in economic series [3] and hence provide a basis for forecasting these series. The important feature of these models is that the "trend" is not regarded as a deterministic function of time but is stochastic and changes as the process evolves.

A simple non-stationary process. A simple non-stationary process X_t can be derived from the stationary purely random process Z_t according to

$$X_1 = Z_1$$
$$X_2 = Z_1 + Z_2 = X_1 + Z_2$$
$$\cdot \qquad \cdot \qquad \cdot \qquad \cdot$$
$$X_t = Z_1 + Z_2 + \cdots + Z_t = X_{t-1} + Z_t. \qquad (5.1.9)$$

If $E[Z_t] = \mu$, it follows from (3.2.15) that $E[X_t] = t\mu$. Similarly, if Var $[Z_t] = \sigma_Z^2$, it follows from (3.2.18) that

$$\text{Var } [X_t] = \sigma^2(t) = t\sigma_Z^2.$$

The stochastic process (5.1.9) is usually called a *random walk* and has the property that as time advances the rv X_t tends to oscillate about the line $X = t\mu$ with an ever-increasing amplitude. The random walk process is thus non-stationary in the mean and non-stationary in the variance.

Using (5.1.4), the acvf of the X_t process is

$$\gamma_{XX}(t_1, t_2) = \min (t_1, t_2)\sigma_Z^2.$$

Equation (5.1.9) is also called a process with *uncorrelated* or *orthogonal* increments, since

$$Z_t = X_t - X_{t-1}$$

is a purely random process and hence is uncorrelated (has no covariance) with other increments such as $Z_{t-1} = X_{t-1} - X_{t-2}$.

5.1.5 Minimum mean square error system analysis

In the previous sections simple ways of describing time series by their lower-order moments have been discussed. The most important of these moments is the acf. One of the many uses of the acf is as an initial guide in constructing a probability model for the mechanism which has generated the time series. In the next chapter it is shown that a time series can be described in equivalent terms by means of its spectral density function, which is the Fourier transform of the acf.

An important use of the acf or spectral density function in engineering problems is based on the fact that knowledge of either of these functions is sufficient for the minimum mean square error design of linear filters or linear control systems when the signals involved are corrupted by noise. The minimum mean square error design theory was first developed by Wiener [4] and has played an important role in the development of modern control and communication theory.

Servomechanism design. One of the first uses of minimum mean square error analysis by engineers was in the design of servomechanisms for anti-aircraft guns and radar tracking systems [5]. For example, a radar tracking system is expected to track an aircraft in spite of distortion of the radar echo due to the variation in the overall reflection coefficient of the aircraft caused by propeller rotation, engine vibration and changes in the aircraft's aspect due to yaw, roll and pitch. It was realized that the tracking system could not be expected to follow an aircraft perfectly under such adverse conditions, and hence that its average performance and the likely spread in the performance would have to be investigated rather than its exact performance. One way of describing these properties uses the mean square error between the desired and the actual outputs of the system. The mean square error, in turn, can be expressed in terms of the covariance functions of the input and desired output signals. Hence, knowledge of the covariance functions is sufficient for minimum mean square error system design.

Estimation of the impulse response of a linear system. A second use of the minimum mean square error criterion is in the problem of "system identification." Here one is given the input to and corresponding output from a system and is required to derive a linear approximation for the system to use in control or modeling. For example, suppose that the system is represented by the black box of Figure 5.7. If the input is a realization of a stochastic process $X(t)$, the output may be regarded as a realization of a stochastic process $Y(t)$ where

$$Y(t) - \mu_Y = \int_0^\infty h(u)(X(t - u) - \mu_X)\, du + Z(t). \qquad (5.1.10)$$

Equation (5.1.10) states that the output may be calculated by taking a weighted average of the input with weighting function $h(u)$. In (5.1.10), $Z(t)$ is a noise or error term which contains a systematic component, due to the inadequacy of the linear system approximation, and a random component, due to measurement errors and lack of control over other variables influencing the output.

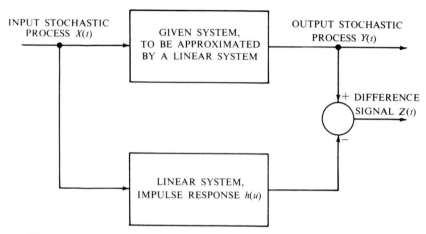

FIG. 5.7: Minimum mean square error impulse response determination

If the correlation function of the processes $X(t)$ and $Y(t)$ are known exactly, Wiener's minimum mean square error criterion states that the function $h(u)$ should be chosen so as to minimize the mean square error of the noise component, that is,

$$E[Z^2(t)] = E\left[\{(Y(t) - \mu_Y) - \int_0^\infty h(u)(X(t - u) - \mu_X)\,du\}^2\right]. \quad (5.1.11)$$

The rationale behind (5.1.11) is discussed more carefully in Section 5.3.1, when the system identification problem is considered for finite lengths of record.

If the stochastic processes $X(t)$ and $Y(t)$ are assumed to be stationary, (5.1.11) may be written

$$E[Z^2(t)] = E[(Y(t) - \mu_Y)^2] - 2E\left[(Y(t) - \mu_Y)\int_0^\infty h(u)(X(t - u) - \mu_X)\,du\right]$$

$$+ E\left[\int_0^\infty \int_0^\infty h(u)h(v)(X(t - u) - \mu_X)(X(t - v) - \mu_X)\,du\,dv\right]$$

$$= \gamma_{YY}(0) - 2\int_0^\infty h(u)\gamma_{XY}(u)\,du + \int_0^\infty \int_0^\infty h(u)h(v)\gamma_{XX}(u - v)\,du\,dv,$$

$$(5.1.12)$$

where $\gamma_{YY}(0) = \sigma_Y^2$ is the mean square value of $Y(t)$,

$$\gamma_{XY}(u) = E[(X(t) - \mu_X)(Y(t + u) - \mu_Y)]$$

is the cross covariance function between $X(t)$ and $Y(t + u)$ and

$$\gamma_{XX}(u) = E[(X(t) - \mu_X)(X(t + u) - \mu_X)]$$

is the autocovariance function of $X(t)$.

Hence the mean square error is completely specified by the covariance functions $\gamma_{YY}(0)$, $\gamma_{XY}(u)$, $\gamma_{XX}(u)$ and the impulse response $h(u)$.

The function $h(u)$ which produces the minimum mse is obtained using the calculus of variations as shown in Appendix A5.1. It is shown there that $h(u)$ must satisfy the Wiener–Hopf integral equation

$$\gamma_{XY}(u) = \int_{-\infty}^{\infty} h(v)\gamma_{XX}(u - v) \, dv, \quad u \geqslant 0. \tag{5.1.13}$$

Note that $h(v)$ has to be identically zero for negative v in order that the approximating system be physically realizable.

The main point here is that the linear system which best approximates the given process is completely specified by the process covariance functions $\gamma_{XX}(u)$ and $\gamma_{XY}(u)$. This is one reason that these functions have been so widely used by engineers.

5.2 THE AUTOCORRELATION AND AUTOCOVARIANCE FUNCTIONS

5.2.1 Basic properties

In this section the properties of the acvf and the acf are derived. The cross covariance function $\gamma_{XY}(u)$ introduced in Section 5.1.5 will be discussed more fully in Chapter 8.

In general, a stochastic process $X(t)$ has an acvf

$$\text{Cov} \, [X(t), X(t + u)] = \gamma_{XX}(t, t + u) \tag{5.2.1}$$

and an acf

$$\rho_{XX}(t, t + u) = \frac{\text{Cov} \, [X(t), X(t + u)]}{\{\text{Var} \, [X(t)] \, \text{Var} \, [X(t + u)]\}^{1/2}}$$

$$= \frac{\gamma_{XX}(t, t + u)}{\{\gamma_{XX}(t, t)\gamma_{XX}(t + u, t + u)\}^{1/2}}$$

$$= \frac{\gamma_{XX}(t, t + u)}{\sigma_X(t)\sigma_X(t + u)}. \tag{5.2.2}$$

When $X(t)$ is stationary, (5.2.1) and (5.2.2) reduce to

$$\text{Cov} \, [X(t), X(t + u)] = \gamma_{XX}(u) \tag{5.2.3}$$

and

$$\rho_{XX}(u) = \frac{\gamma_{XX}(u)}{\gamma_{XX}(0)} = \frac{\gamma_{XX}(u)}{\sigma_X^2} \tag{5.2.4}$$

respectively. Hence

$$\gamma_{XX}(u) = \sigma_X^2 \rho_{XX}(u).$$

The function $\rho_{XX}(u)$ plotted against the lag u is called the *autocorrelation function* of the stationary process $X(t)$. If the process is continuous, u can take on any value from $-\infty$ to $+\infty$, but for a discrete process $\rho_{XX}(u)$ will be defined only for integer values of u.

The properties of the acf (5.2.4) are summarized below.

Property 1. $\rho_{XX}(0) = 1.$

This follows immediately from the definition (5.2.4) by setting $u = 0$.

Property 2. $\rho_{XX}(u) = \rho_{XX}(-u).$

Because of the stationarity assumption,

$$\begin{aligned}
\gamma_{XX}(u) &= \text{Cov}\,[X(t), X(t + u)] \\
&= \text{Cov}\,[X(t - u), X(t)] \\
&= \text{Cov}\,[X(t), X(t - u)] \\
&= \gamma_{XX}(-u).
\end{aligned}$$

It follows from (5.2.4) that $\rho_{XX}(u) = \rho_{XX}(-u)$. Hence both the acvf and the acf are even functions of the lag u. Thus they need only be calculated for positive u.

Property 3. $|\rho_{XX}(u)| \leqslant 1$ for all u.

This follows from the fact that the variance of the rv

$$Y = \lambda_1 X(t) + \lambda_2 X(t + u)$$

is positive, as described in Section 3.2.4.

Property 4. The autocorrelation matrix is positive semi-definite, that is, the determinant

$$\begin{vmatrix}
1 & \rho_{XX}(t_2 - t_1) & \rho_{XX}(t_3 - t_1) & \cdots & \rho_{XX}(t_n - t_1) \\
\rho_{XX}(t_2 - t_1) & 1 & \rho_{XX}(t_3 - t_2) & \cdots & \rho_{XX}(t_n - t_2) \\
\vdots & \vdots & \vdots & & \vdots \\
\rho_{XX}(t_n - t_1) & \rho_{XX}(t_n - t_2) & \rho_{XX}(t_n - t_3) & \cdots & 1
\end{vmatrix}$$

and all its principal minors are positive or zero. This is a more general result than Property 3, and follows from the fact that the variance of the rv

$$Y = \lambda_1 X(t_1) + \cdots + \lambda_n X(t_n)$$

is positive or zero. Property 4 implies that the autocorrelations of a stationary process cannot be chosen arbitrarily but must satisfy relations among themselves. Note that when $n = 2$, Property 4 reduces to Property 3. The above positive semidefinite property leads to the concept of the power spectrum of the process and is discussed more fully in Chapters 6 and 11.

Property 5. If the stochastic process is continuous, then $\rho_{XX}(u)$ must be a continuous function of the lag u. This continuity condition is required in order to develop a sensible mathematical theory in continuous time. It is enough, in fact, for $\rho_{XX}(u)$ to be continuous at $u = 0$, since this implies continuity everywhere else.

White noise. One of the consequences of Property 5 is that it is not possible to define a continuous-time stochastic process which is the analog of the purely random process in discrete time introduced in Section 5.1.3. Such a continuous random process would require that $\rho_{ZZ}(0) = 1$ and $\rho_{ZZ}(u) = 0$ when $u \neq 0$, but this acf would be discontinuous at $u = 0$.

One way out of this difficulty is to define a purely random process in continuous time, or *white noise*, as a process which consists entirely of uncorrelated contiguous impulses. Its acvf is thus

$$\gamma_{ZZ}(u) = \sigma_Z^2 \, \delta(u), \tag{5.2.5}$$

where $\delta(u)$ is the Dirac delta function. Since $\delta(u)$ may be regarded as a function which is zero when $u \neq 0$ and infinite when $u = 0$, the covariance between neighboring points is zero but at the expense of making the variance $\gamma_{ZZ}(0)$ of the process infinite. It will be shown later that the infinite variance is a necessary consequence.

5.2.2 The linear process and its autocovariance function

An important class of stochastic processes may be generated by passing a purely random process or white noise through a linear system, or filter. In continuous time the relation between the output process $X(t)$ and the input $Z(t)$ may be written

$$X(t) - \mu = \int_0^\infty h(v)Z(t - v) \, dv, \tag{5.2.6}$$

and in discrete time,

$$X_t - \mu = \sum_{k=0}^{\infty} h_k Z_{t-k}, \tag{5.2.7}$$

where $E[Z(t)] = 0$ and $E[Z_t] = 0$. The stochastic process which is derived from white noise using (5.2.6) or (5.2.7) is called a *linear process*.

Taking expectations in (5.2.6),

$$E[X(t) - \mu] = \int_0^\infty h(v)E[Z(t - v)] \, dv = 0,$$

that is,

$$E[X(t)] = \mu.$$

Hence the acvf of the output is

$$\gamma_{XX}(u) = E[(X(t) - \mu)(X(t + u) - \mu)]$$

$$= \int_0^\infty \int_0^\infty h(v)h(v')E[Z(t - v)Z(t + u - v')]\, dv\, dv'. \quad (5.2.8)$$

If the $Z(t)$ process is stationary with acvf $\gamma_{ZZ}(u)$, then (5.2.8) reduces to

$$\gamma_{XX}(u) = \int_0^\infty \int_0^\infty h(v)h(v')\gamma_{ZZ}(u + v - v')\, dv\, dv'. \quad (5.2.9)$$

Substituting the result (5.2.5) for the acvf $\gamma_{ZZ}(u)$ of white noise in (5.2.9) yields

$$\gamma_{XX}(u) = \sigma_Z^2 \int_0^\infty h(v)h(v + u)\, dv. \quad (5.2.10)$$

Hence the acf of a linear process $X(t)$ is

$$\rho_{XX}(u) = \frac{\displaystyle\int_0^\infty h(v)h(v + u)\, dv}{\displaystyle\int_0^\infty h^2(v)\, dv}. \quad (5.2.11)$$

It will be shown in Chapter 6 that the $X(t)$ process is stationary if

$$\int_0^\infty |h(v)|\, dv < M, \quad (5.2.12)$$

where M is finite. Note that (5.2.12) is identical to the condition (2.3.11) that the linear system is stable. The result (5.2.10) is extended in Appendix A5.2 to give the following expressions for the third and fourth moments and the fourth cumulant:

$$E[(X(t) - \mu)(X(t + u_1) - \mu)(X(t + u_2) - \mu)]$$

$$= E[Z^3] \int_0^\infty h(v)h(v + u_1)h(v + u_2)\, dv, \quad (5.2.13)$$

$$E[(X(t) - \mu)(X(t + u_1) - \mu)(X(t + u_2) - \mu)(X(t + u_3) - \mu)]$$

$$= E[Z^4] \int_0^\infty h(v)h(v + u_1)h(v + u_2)h(v + u_3)\, dv, \quad (5.2.14)$$

and

$$K_X(u_1, u_2, u_3) = K_4(Z) \int_0^\infty h(v)h(v + u_1)h(v + u_2)h(v + u_3)\, dv, \quad (5.2.15)$$

where

$$K_X(u_1, u_2, u_3)$$
$$= E[(X(t) - \mu)(X(t + u_1) - \mu)(X(t + u_2) - \mu)(X(t + u_3) - \mu)]$$
$$- \gamma_{XX}(u_1)\gamma_{XX}(u_3 - u_2) - \gamma_{XX}(u_2)\gamma_{XX}(u_3 - u_1) - \gamma_{XX}(u_3)\gamma_{XX}(u_2 - u_1), \quad (5.2.16)$$

and

$$K_4(Z) = E[Z^4(t)] - 3\sigma_Z^4.$$

Corresponding formulae for the discrete linear random process (5.2.7) may be obtained by replacing integrals with sums. For example, (5.2.10) becomes

$$\gamma_{XX}(k) = \sigma_Z^2 \sum_{j=0}^{\infty} h_j h_{j+k}, \tag{5.2.17}$$

and the stationarity or stability condition corresponding to (5.2.12) is

$$\sum_{j=0}^{\infty} |h_j| < M, \tag{5.2.18}$$

where M is finite. Equation (5.2.18) is identical to the stability condition (2.3.39) for discrete systems.

An example of a linear process. As a special case of the linear process, suppose that the sample mean of $Z(t)$ is calculated over an interval T, that is,

$$X(t) = \frac{1}{T} \int_{t-T}^{t} Z(v) \, dv.$$

Hence

$$h(v) = \begin{cases} 0, & v < 0 \\ \dfrac{1}{T}, & 0 \leqslant v \leqslant T \\ 0, & v > T. \end{cases}$$

The expected value of $X(t)$ is

$$E[X(t)] = \frac{1}{T} \int_{t-T}^{t} E[Z(v)] \, dv = 0,$$

if $E[Z(t)] = 0$. Using (5.2.9), if the $Z(t)$ process is an arbitrary stationary process, the autovariance of $X(t)$ is

$$\gamma_{XX}(u) = \frac{1}{T^2} \int_0^T \int_0^T \gamma_{ZZ}(u + v - v') \, dv \, dv'.$$

On making the transformation $y = v - v'$ and setting $u = 0$,

$$\text{Var}\,[X(t)] = \frac{1}{T} \int_{-T}^{+T} \left(1 - \frac{|y|}{T}\right) \gamma_{ZZ}(y) \, dy. \tag{5.2.19}$$

When $Z(t)$ is white noise, (5.2.19) reduces to

$$\text{Var}\,[X(t)] = \sigma_X^2 = \frac{\sigma_Z^2}{T}. \tag{5.2.20}$$

Note that (5.2.20) is identical to the expression for the variance of the sample mean of T independent rv's in the discrete case, namely,

$$\text{Var}\,[\bar{Z}] = \text{Var}\left[\frac{1}{T} \sum_{k=1}^{T} Z_k\right] = \frac{\sigma_Z^2}{T}.$$

Thus for discrete white noise, the variance of the sample mean is equal to the variance of the signal Z divided by the number of observations, but for continuous white noise the finite quotient σ_Z^2/T is obtained by dividing the *infinite* variance by the *infinite* number of independent observations. This example is sufficient to show that the interpretation and derivation of results using white noise must be done carefully.

It should be noted also that the delta function in the expression (5.2.5) for the covariance function of white noise is an essential part of the expression and does not simply serve as a "locating" parameter. This means that the variance is truly infinite and that the covariance between arbitrarily close-spaced values is truly zero. Physically, the process must have infinite variance in order that the arbitrarily close-spaced values of the process will be uncorrelated, that is, so the process can fluctuate widely from instant to instant.

The Bachelier–Wiener process. Related to white noise in continuous time is the analog of the discrete process (5.1.9) which has uncorrelated increments. Formally, the continuous analog to the random walk may be written

$$X(t) = \int_{-\infty}^{t} Z(v)\, dv \qquad (5.2.21)$$

or

$$X(t_2) - X(t_1) = \int_{t_1}^{t_2} Z(v)\, dv.$$

If $X(t)$ is a continuous process with uncorrelated increments, then $E[(X(t_2) - X(t_1))(X(t_4) - X(t_3))]$ will be zero if the intervals (t_1, t_2) and (t_3, t_4) do not overlap. If they do overlap as follows

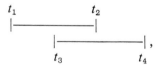

then on writing

$$X(t_2) - X(t_1) = X(t_2) - X(t_3) + X(t_3) - X(t_1)$$

and

$$X(t_4) - X(t_3) = X(t_4) - X(t_2) + X(t_2) - X(t_3),$$

$$E[\{X(t_2) - X(t_1)\}\{X(t_4) - X(t_3)\}] = E[\{X(t_2) - X(t_3)\}^2].$$

It can be shown further [6] that this expectation must be of the form $\sigma_Z^2 |t_2 - t_3|$ for any sensible process with uncorrelated increments.

Now consider the derived process

$$Y(t) = \frac{X(t + \tau) - X(t)}{\tau}.$$

From (5.2.11), the acvf of $Y(t)$, for fixed τ, is

$$\gamma_{YY}(u) = \begin{cases} 0, & |u| > \tau \\ \dfrac{\sigma_Z^2}{\tau^2}(\tau - |u|), & |u| \leqslant \tau. \end{cases} \tag{5.2.22}$$

Hence as τ tends to zero, $\gamma_{XX}(u)$ tends to $\sigma_Z^2\,\delta(u)$, the acvf of white noise, which may therefore be thought of as the improper stochastic process which is the derivative $\dot{X}(t)$ of a process with uncorrelated increments.

If, in addition, $X(t + \tau) - X(t)$ is Normal with expectation $\tau\mu$ and variance $\tau^2\sigma_Z^2$, then $Y(t)$ is Normal or Gaussian white noise consisting of uncorrelated impulses whose areas have mean μ and variance σ_Z^2. This is the process used by Wiener and others to describe the Brownian motion of a particle under the random bombardment of the particles of fluid in which it is suspended.

5.2.3 Finite moving average processes

Suppose the weights h_k in the linear process (5.2.7) are zero for $k > l$, that is,

$$X_t - \mu = h_0 Z_t + h_1 Z_{t-1} + \cdots + h_l Z_{t-l}. \tag{5.2.23}$$

Then if Z_t is a purely random process, X_t is called a finite *moving average* (ma) process of order l.

Finite ma processes are useful in many areas, for example, in predicting the behavior of econometric and control systems. However, they are most useful when considered jointly with the autoregressive processes to be introduced in the next section. From (5.2.17) it follows that the acvf of the finite ma process (5.2.23) is zero for $k > l$. For example, consider the second-order ma process

$$X_t - \mu = Z_t + 0.5 Z_{t-1} + 0.5 Z_{t-2}.$$

Using (5.2.17) it follows that the acvf of the X_t process is

$$\gamma_{XX}(0) = \sigma_Z^2\{1 + (0.5)^2 + (0.5)^2\} = 1.50\sigma_Z^2$$
$$\gamma_{XX}(1) = \sigma_Z^2\{1(0.5) + (0.5)^2\} = 0.75\sigma_Z^2$$
$$\gamma_{XX}(2) = \sigma_Z^2\{1(0.5)\} = 0.5\sigma_Z^2$$
$$\gamma_{XX}(k) = 0, \quad k \geqslant 3.$$

Hence the acf is

$$\rho_{XX}(k) = \begin{cases} 1, & k = 0 \\ 0.5, & k = 1 \\ 0.333, & k = 2 \\ 0, & k \geqslant 3. \end{cases}$$

An example of a continuous finite ma process is the process $Y(t)$ used in the derivation of the Bachelier–Wiener process for which the acvf (5.2.22) is zero for $|u| > \tau$.

5.2.4 Autoregressive processes

Continuous first-order process. Consider a first-order linear system described by the differential equation of the form (2.3.2), namely,

$$T\frac{dx}{dt} + x(t) = z(t),$$

where $z(t)$ is the input to the system and $x(t)$ is the output. If white noise $Z(t)$ is fed into this system, the output $X(t)$ will be a linear process (5.2.6) with $h(v) = (1/T)\exp - v/T$. The process $X(t)$ defined by

$$T\frac{dX(t)}{dt} + (X(t) - \mu) = Z(t) \tag{5.2.24}$$

is called a first-order *autoregressive* (ar) *process*. It follows from (5.2.11) that the acf of the output is

$$\rho_{XX}(u) = e^{-|u|/T}. \tag{5.2.25}$$

The stability condition (5.2.12) requires that the time constant T be positive, which is also the condition that the $X(t)$ process be stationary with finite variance.

Discrete first-order process. A discrete first-order ar process is derived from a purely random process Z_t according to

$$X_t - \mu = \alpha_1(X_{t-1} - \mu) + Z_t. \tag{5.2.26}$$

This follows from the fact that (5.2.26) may be written in $\mathcal{Z}$ transform notation as

$$(1 - \alpha_1 \mathcal{Z}^{-1})(X_t - \mu) = Z_t.$$

Hence,

$$(X_t - \mu) = \left(\frac{1}{1 - \alpha_1 \mathcal{Z}^{-1}}\right) Z_t = Z_t + \alpha_1 \mathcal{Z}^{-1} Z_t + \alpha_1^2 \mathcal{Z}^{-2} Z_t + \cdots$$

$$= Z_t + \alpha_1 Z_{t-1} + \alpha_1^2 Z_{t-2} + \cdots.$$

Using (5.2.17) it follows that the acf of the ar process X_t is

$$\rho_{XX}(k) = \alpha_1^{|k|}, \quad k = 0, \pm 1, \pm 2, \ldots. \tag{5.2.27}$$

The stability or stationarity condition (5.2.18) now leads to the condition $|\alpha_1| < 1$, since $\sum_{k=0}^{\infty} |h_k| = 1/(1 - |\alpha_1|)$.

An example. Figure 5.8(a) shows a series of 40 terms generated according to
(5.2.26) with $\alpha_1 = 0.9$. Values for the purely random process Z_t were taken
from tables of independent Normal deviates [7]. With $\alpha_1 = 0.9$, the acf is
$\rho_{XX}(k) = (0.9)^{|k|}$, which takes a long time to decay to zero. Thus neighboring
points in the process have large positive correlation, for example, $\rho_{XX}(1) =$
0.9, and the smooth nature of the series is reflected in a smooth acf. The series
shown in Figure 5.8(b) corresponds to the case $\alpha_1 = -0.9$. Adjacent points
are now highly negatively correlated since $\rho_{XX}(k) = (-0.9)^{|k|}$ and the acf
oscillates from positive to negative values, reflecting the oscillatory nature
of the series. Note that the continuous first-order ar process (5.2.24) can give
rise only to positive correlations and therefore corresponds to the discrete
case $\alpha_1 \geqslant 0$.

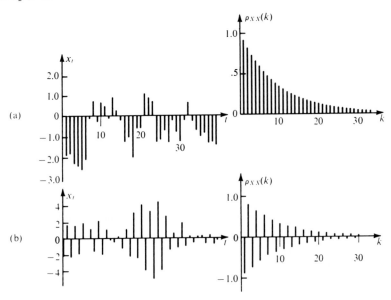

FIG. 5.8: Samples from first-order autoregressive processes and their theoretical
autocorrelation functions; (a) $\alpha_1 = +0.9$, (b) $\alpha_1 = -0.9$

The first-order ar process is sometimes referred to as a first-order Markov
process. This is because the pdf of X_t is completely characterized by a
knowledge of X_{t-1} and is independent of the rv's preceding X_{t-1}. From
(5.2.26) it is seen that if Z_t is Normal with mean 0 and variance σ_Z^2, the
conditional pdf $f_{X(t)|X(t-1)}(x_t, x_{t-1})$ is Normal with mean $\alpha_1 x_{t-1}$ and variance σ_Z^2.

Continuous second-order processes. The continuous second-order ar process
may be written

$$a_2 \frac{d^2 X}{dt^2} + a_1 \frac{dX}{dt} + (X(t) - \mu) = Z(t). \qquad (5.2.28)$$

Two types of second-order processes may be distinguished. Thus if the characteristic equation $a_2 p^2 + a_1 p + 1 = 0$ has real roots $\pi_1 = 1/T_1$, $\pi_2 = 1/T_2$, (5.2.28) may be written

$$T_1 T_2 \frac{d^2 X}{dt^2} - (T_1 + T_2) \frac{dX}{dt} + (X(t) - \mu) = Z(t). \qquad (5.2.29)$$

If the roots of the characteristic equation are complex, $\pi_1 = \omega_n e^{j\theta}, \pi_2 = \omega_n e^{-j\theta}$, then the second-order process may be written

$$\frac{1}{\omega_n^2} \frac{d^2 X}{dt^2} - \frac{2\zeta}{\omega_n} \frac{dX}{dt} + (X(t) - \mu) = Z(t), \qquad (5.2.30)$$

where $\zeta = \cos\theta$. The processes (5.2.29, 30) may be regarded as outputs from a second-order linear system when the inputs are white noise. For example, (5.2.30) corresponds to the second-order system (2.3.8) of Chapter 2 when the input is a continuous sequence of random impulses. Hence the output $X(t)$ is a continuous disturbed periodic function. For (5.2.30) to have meaning, it is necessary to assume that the changes in $Z(t)$ produce discontinuous changes in the velocity $\dot{X}(t)$ of the output.

Discrete second-order processes. In discrete time the second-order ar process is

$$X_t - \mu = \alpha_1 (X_{t-1} - \mu) + \alpha_2 (X_{t-2} - \mu) + Z_t. \qquad (5.2.31)$$

The model (5.2.31) was used by the statistician G. U. Yule in 1921. With $Z_t = 0$ in (5.2.31), Yule argued that this model would describe the behavior of a simple pendulum damped by air resistance proportional to its velocity. If Z_t is a purely random process, then the pendulum is subjected to random shocks in displacement at equidistant times. Instead of damping out, the pendulum now oscillates with a disturbed periodic motion.

Figure 5.9 shows a series of 40 terms from a discrete second-order ar process (5.2.31) with $\alpha_1 = 1.0$, $\alpha_2 = -0.5$. It is seen that there is a definite periodic tendency in the series. However, the period and phases are constantly changing due to the influence of the random component Z_t.

The process (5.2.31) may be regarded as the output from a discrete linear system when the input is a purely random process Z_t. The impulse response function of this sytem has been derived in Section 2.3.5 and is

$$h_k = \frac{\pi_1^{k+1} - \pi_2^{k+1}}{\pi_1 - \pi_2}, \qquad (5.2.32)$$

when $\alpha_1^2 \geqslant -4\alpha_2$. When $\alpha_1^2 < -4\alpha_2$,

$$h_k = \frac{R^k \{\sin 2\pi f_0 (k+1)\}}{\sin 2\pi f_0}, \qquad (5.2.33)$$

where $\pi_1 = R\,e^{j2\pi f_0}$, $\pi_2 = R\,e^{-j2\pi f_0}$. It has also been shown in Chapter 2 that for stationarity, the parameters α_1 and α_2 in (5.2.31) must lie in the triangular region

$$\alpha_1 + \alpha_2 < 1$$
$$\alpha_1 - \alpha_2 > -1$$
$$-1 < \alpha_2 < 1. \qquad\qquad (5.2.34)$$

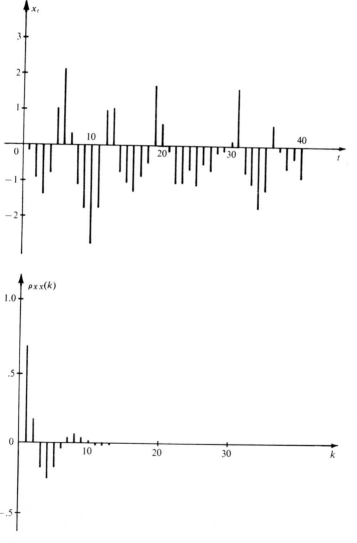

FIG. 5.9: Sample from a second-order autoregressive process and the theoretical autocorrelation function

Autocorrelation functions. Using (5.2.10) and the impulse responses given in Table 2.6, the acf for the continuous process (5.2.29) is

$$\rho_{xx}(u) = \frac{T_1\, e^{-|u|/T_1} - T_2\, e^{-|u|/T_2}}{T_1 - T_2}. \tag{5.2.35}$$

Similarly, for the continuous process (5.2.30),

$$\rho_{xx}(u) = \frac{e^{-\zeta\omega_n|u|}\, \sin(\omega_n\sqrt{1-\zeta^2}\,|u| + \phi)}{\sqrt{1-\zeta^2}}, \tag{5.2.36}$$

where $\phi = \arcsin\sqrt{1-\zeta^2}$.

The acf of the discrete process (5.2.31) may be obtained from (5.2.32) and (5.2.17) and is

$$\rho_{xx}(k) = \frac{\pi_1(1 - \pi_2^2)\pi_1^{|k|} - \pi_2(1 - \pi_1^2)\pi_2^{|k|}}{(\pi_1 - \pi_2)(1 + \pi_1\pi_2)} \tag{5.2.37}$$

when the roots are real and

$$\rho_{xx}(k) = \frac{R^{|k|}\cos(2\pi f_0 k - \phi_0)}{\cos\phi_0} \tag{5.2.38}$$

when the roots are complex. The damping factor R, the frequency f_0 and the phase ϕ_0 in (5.2.38) are given by

$$R = \sqrt{-\alpha_2},$$

$$\cos 2\pi f_0 = \alpha_1/(2\sqrt{-\alpha_2})$$

and

$$\tan\phi_0 = \frac{1 - R^2}{1 + R^2}\tan 2\pi f_0.$$

For the series shown in Figure 5.9, in which $\alpha_1 = 1.0$, $\alpha_2 = -0.5$, the damping factor R is 0.71, the frequency f_0 is 0.125 and the phase ϕ_0 is 18°30′. The acf of this series is plotted below the series itself in Figure 5.9 and is seen to damp out very rapidly.

Because of the wide variety of acf's which ar processes can produce, they have been widely used as models for analyzing stationary time series. The problem of estimating the parameters of autoregressive processes will be discussed in Section 5.4.

5.2.5 General autoregressive–moving average processes

This section contains a summary of the most important properties of ar and ma processes. The general ar process of order m in discrete time is generated from the purely random process Z_t according to the difference equation

$$(X_t - \mu) = \alpha_1(X_{t-1} - \mu) + \alpha_2(X_{t-2} - \mu) + \cdots + \alpha_m(X_{t-m} - \mu) + Z_t. \tag{5.2.39}$$

In continuous time the general ar process is defined as the output from a linear filter whose input is white noise and for which the relation between input and output is defined by the differential equation

$$a_m \frac{d^m X}{dt^m} + a_{m-1} \frac{d^{m-1} X}{dt^{m-1}} + \cdots + a_0(X(t) - \mu) = Z(t), \qquad (5.2.40)$$

where, as discussed previously, $Z(t)$ changes dx/dt discontinuously.

Stability or stationarity.

(1) *Discrete process.* The discrete ar process X_t is stationary if the roots of the characteristic equation

$$p^m - \alpha_1 p^{m-1} - \cdots - \alpha_m = 0 \qquad (5.2.41)$$

lie inside the unit circle $p^2 = 1$.

(2) *Continuous process.* The continuous ar process $X(t)$ is stationary if the roots of the characteristic equation

$$a_m p^m + a_{m-1} p^{m-1} + \cdots + a_0 = 0 \qquad (5.2.42)$$

have negative real parts.

It has been noted in Section 5.2.2 that the stationarity condition is the same as the stability condition for the corresponding linear system. The above conditions then follow from (2.3.38) and (2.3.20).

The autocorrelation function.

(1) *Discrete process.* The discrete process X_t has an acf which satisfies the difference equation

$$\rho_{XX}(k) = \alpha_1 \rho_{XX}(k-1) + \alpha_2 \rho_{XX}(k-2) + \cdots + \alpha_m \rho_{XX}(k-m), \quad k \geq 1$$

$$1 = \alpha_1 \rho_{XX}(1) + \cdots + \alpha_m \rho_{XX}(m-1) + \frac{\sigma_Z^2}{\gamma_{XX}(0)}, \qquad k = 0.$$

$$(5.2.43)$$

The general solution to this difference equation is

$$\rho_{XX}(k) = A_1 \pi_1^{|k|} + A_2 \pi_2^{|k|} + \cdots + A_m \pi_m^{|k|}, \qquad (5.2.44)$$

where the π_i are the roots (possibly complex) of (5.2.41). When complex roots occur, they combine to give factors of the form $R_i^{|k|} \cos(f_i k + \phi_i)$ in (5.2.44). Hence, in general, the acf $\rho_{XX}(k)$ will be a mixture of geometric terms and damped sine waves. The constants A_i in (5.2.44) may be obtained by solving the first m of the equations (5.2.43) for the ρ's in terms of the α's, as illustrated below.

(2) *Continuous process.* The continuous process $X(t)$ has an acf which satisfies the differential equation

$$a_m \frac{d^m \rho_{XX}(u)}{du^m} + a_{m-1} \frac{d^{m-1} \rho_{XX}(u)}{du^{m-1}} + \cdots + a_0 \rho_{XX}(u) = 0, \quad (u > 0). \quad (5.2.45)$$

This has a general solution

$$\rho_{XX}(u) = A_1 e^{-\pi_1|u|} + A_2 e^{-\pi_2|u|} + \cdots + A_m e^{-\pi_m|u|}, \qquad (5.2.46)$$

where the π_i are the roots of (5.2.42). If complex roots occur, then they combine to give terms of the form $e^{-k_1|u|} \cos(k_2u + \phi)$.

Proof. The above results are proved for the discrete case only. If the process

$$(X_t - \mu) = \alpha_1(X_{t-1} - \mu) + \cdots + \alpha_m(X_{t-m} - \mu) + Z_t$$

is multiplied throughout by $(X_{t-k} - \mu)$, then

$$(X_t - \mu)(X_{t-k} - \mu) = \alpha_1(X_{t-1} - \mu)(X_{t-k} - \mu) + \cdots$$
$$+ \alpha_m(X_{t-m} - \mu)(X_{t-k} - \mu) + Z_t(X_{t-k} - \mu).$$

Hence, taking expectations on both sides,

$$\sigma_X^2 \rho_{XX}(k) = \alpha_1 \sigma_X^2 \rho_{XX}(k-1) + \cdots + \alpha_m \sigma_X^2 \rho_{XX}(k-m) + E[Z_t(X_{t-k} - \mu)].$$

Now the random variable X_{t-k} may be expressed as

$$(X_{t-k} - \mu) = \sum_{i=0}^{\infty} h_i Z_{t-k-i},$$

and since this does not involve Z_t, it follows that $E[Z_t(X_{t-k} - \mu)] = 0$. The result (5.2.43) then follows.

Example. The acf of a discrete second-order ar process satisfies the recurrence equation

$$\rho_{XX}(k) = \alpha_1 \rho_{XX}(k-1) + \alpha_2 \rho_{XX}(k-2), \quad k > 0. \qquad (5.2.47)$$

This has a solution

$$\rho_{XX}(k) = A_1 \pi_1^{|k|} + A_2 \pi_2^{|k|}, \qquad (5.2.48)$$

where π_1, π_2 are roots of the characteristic equation $p^2 - \alpha_1 p - \alpha_2 = 0$. Hence

$$\pi_1 + \pi_2 = \alpha_1, \qquad \pi_1 \pi_2 = -\alpha_2.$$

Now the first equation in (5.2.47) is

$$\rho_{XX}(1) = \alpha_1 \rho_{XX}(0) + \alpha_2 \rho_{XX}(-1).$$

Hence

$$\rho_{XX}(1) = \frac{\alpha_1}{1 - \alpha_2} = \frac{\pi_1 + \pi_2}{1 + \pi_1 \pi_2},$$

since $\rho_{XX}(0) = 1$, $\rho_{XX}(-1) = \rho_{XX}(1)$.

From (5.2.48),

$$\rho_{XX}(0) = 1 = A_1 + A_2,$$

$$\rho_{XX}(1) = \frac{\pi_1 + \pi_2}{1 + \pi_1\pi_2} = A_1\pi_1 + A_2\pi_2.$$

Hence

$$A_1 = \frac{\pi_1(1 - \pi_2^2)}{(1 + \pi_1\pi_2)(\pi_1 - \pi_2)}, \qquad A_2 = \frac{-\pi_2(1 - \pi_1^2)}{(1 + \pi_1\pi_2)(\pi_1 - \pi_2)},$$

and so

$$\rho_{XX}(k) = \frac{(1 - \pi_2^2)\pi_1^{k+1} - (1 - \pi_1^2)\pi_2^{k+1}}{(1 + \pi_1\pi_2)(\pi_1 - \pi_2)},$$

agreeing with the result (5.2.37) for $k > 0$.

The sampling property. If the continuous autoregressive process (5.2.40) is sampled at equal time intervals Δ, then the resulting discrete process is

$$(X_t - \mu) = \alpha_1(X_{t-1} - \mu) + \cdots + \alpha_m(X_{t-m} - \mu)$$
$$+ Z_t + \beta_1 Z_{t-1} + \cdots + \beta_{m-1} Z_{t-m+1}, \quad (5.2.49)$$

where Z_t is a purely random process. Equation (5.2.49) is a mixture of the discrete ma (5.2.23) and the discrete ar process (5.2.39). The interesting feature of (5.2.49) is that, whereas the original continuous process has an input which is white noise, the discrete sampled ar process has an input which is an ma process of order one less than the order of the differential equation describing the system. Hence this input will have non-zero correlations for the first $(m - 1)$ lags. The result (5.2.49) is given in [8].

General mixed autoregressive–moving average processes. More generally it is possible to define a mixed ar–ma process in discrete time,

$$(X_t - \mu) = \alpha_1(X_{t-1} - \mu) + \cdots + \alpha_m(X_{t-m} - \mu)$$
$$+ Z_t + \beta_1 Z_{t-1} + \cdots + \beta_l Z_{t-l}, \quad (5.2.50)$$

where l is independent of the value of m. For stationarity the characteristic equation of the ar component must have roots lying inside the unit circle.

In continuous time the mixed process takes the form

$$a_m \frac{d^m X}{dt^m} + a_{m-1} \frac{d^{m-1} X}{dt^{m-1}} + \cdots + a_0(X(t) - \mu)$$
$$= b_l \frac{d^l Z}{dt^l} + b_{l-1} \frac{d^{l-1} Z}{dt^{l-1}} + \cdots + b_0 Z(t). \quad (5.2.51)$$

It follows from (2.3.19) that the stationarity or stability conditions for the continuous process (5.2.51) are that $l \leqslant m - 1$ and that the roots of the characteristic equation of the ar component have negative real parts.

The importance of the model (5.2.50) is that, whereas a model based on a purely autoregressive process (5.2.39) or a purely moving average process

(5.2.23) may require a large number of parameters, the mixed model (5.2.50) may only require a relatively small number of parameters.

5.2.6 *Interpretation of the autocorrelation function*

A stochastic process is said to be Gaussian or Normal if the multivariate distribution associated with an arbitrarily chosen set of points is multivariate Normal. Then the process is completely characterized by its mean, variance and acf. However, there will be a very wide class of non-Normal processes which have the same acf as a given Normal process but which differ markedly from it in other respects. For example, it has been shown in Section 5.2.4 that the model (5.2.24) leads to an exponential acf $\rho_{XX}(u) = e^{-|u|/T}$. If the input to the first-order system (5.2.24) is Normal, then by a suitable extension of the Central Limit Theorem it may be shown that the output is also Normal and so is completely specified by its acf.

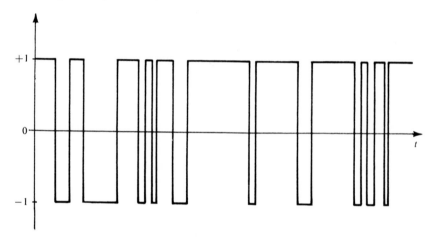

FIG. 5.10: A realization of a random telegraph signal

Another process will now be constructed which has an exponential acf but which is otherwise markedly different from the Normal process. This process is called the *random telegraph signal* and is described in [9]. Alpha-particles from a radioactive source are used to trigger a flip-flop device which takes the states $+1$ and -1 alternately. The times t_i at which changes occur constitute a Poisson process with parameter λ so that a typical realization of the process might be as shown in Figure 5.10. Assuming that the process was started up at time $t = -\infty$,

$$\Pr\{X(t) = 1\} = \Pr\{X(t) = -1\} = \tfrac{1}{2}$$

and so $E[X(t)] = 0$. Hence the acvf is

$$\gamma_{xx}(u) = E[X(t)X(t + u)] = \begin{cases} 1 \times \text{Pr\{even number of changes in} \\ \qquad\qquad\qquad\qquad\qquad (t, t + u)\} \\ -1 \times \text{Pr\{odd number of changes in} \\ \qquad\qquad\qquad\qquad\qquad (t, t + u)\} \end{cases}$$

$$= \sum_{k=0}^{\infty} (p_{2k} - p_{2k+1}),$$

where

$$p_k = \frac{e^{-\lambda|u|}(\lambda|u|)^k}{k!}.$$

On summing this series, it follows that

$$\gamma_{xx}(u) = e^{-\lambda|u|} \left[\frac{e^{\lambda|u|} + e^{-\lambda|u|}}{2} - \frac{e^{\lambda|u|} - e^{-\lambda|u|}}{2} \right]$$

$$= e^{-2\lambda|u|} = \rho_{xx}(u),$$

since $\gamma_{xx}(0) = 1$. If $\lambda = \frac{1}{2}T$, this agrees with the acf (5.2.25). Since the pdf of $X(t)$ is concentrated at two points ± 1, it follows that the behavior of this process will be markedly different from a Normal process with the same acf. In fact, such non-Normal processes have to be described by their higher moments $E[X(t)X(t + u_1) \cdots X(t + u_k)]$.

The importance of this section in the empirical analysis of time series is that a certain amount of care is required in the interpretation of an acf (and as will be seen later, of the corresponding spectrum), if the process is non-Normal. However, it may be possible to suggest a transformation, based on the empirical pdf, which results in a distribution which is more nearly Normal. For example, an essentially positive quantity, such as temperature or pressure, might be more nearly Normal if the logarithm were used. However, note that such a transformation, while it produces a univariate pdf which is more nearly Normal, need not necessarily have the same effect on all the multivariate distributions.

5.3 ESTIMATION OF AUTOCOVARIANCE FUNCTIONS

It was shown in Section 5.1.5 that the minimum mean square error estimator of the impulse response function of a system could be expressed in terms of the input–output covariance functions. In practice it is impossible to know these covariance functions exactly, and hence it is necessary to estimate them from finite lengths of records.

In Section 5.3.1 the least squares estimates of the impulse response function will be derived when finite-length records of the input and output are available. It will be shown that the results are analogous to those derived in Section

5.1.5, but with the theoretical covariance functions replaced by their sample estimates. In addition, it will be shown that the functions one is led to calculate from the data using this approach are natural estimates of the auto- and cross-covariance functions. In Section 5.3.2 other estimates of the autocovariance function are defined, and in Section 5.3.3 their sampling properties derived. Sections 5.3.4 and 5.3.5 consist of a discussion of some practical issues arising in the estimation of the autocovariance function.

5.3.1 Least squares system analysis

Suppose that, instead of the input and output stochastic processes $X(t)$ and $Y(t)$ to the system of Figure 5.7, only realizations $x(t)$ and $y(t)$ of finite length T are available. Then the model (5.1.10) may be rewritten

$$y(t) - \bar{y} = \int_0^\infty h(u)(x(t - u) - \bar{x})\, du + z(t), \qquad 0 \leqslant t \leqslant T, \quad (5.3.1)$$

where $\bar{x}$, $\bar{y}$ are the sample means, for example,

$$\bar{x} = \frac{1}{T} \int_0^T x(t)\, dt.$$

If the $Z(t)$ process is assumed to be white, then the continuous time least squares estimate of the function $h(u)$ is obtained by minimizing the integrated squared error

$$S = \int_0^T z^2(t)\, dt = \int_0^T \left\{ y(t) - \bar{y} - \int_0^\infty h(u)(x(t - u) - \bar{x})\, du \right\}^2 dt. \quad (5.3.2)$$

To be precise it would be necessary to estimate the parameter μ_Y occurring in (5.1.10). However, to a high degree of approximation this will be estimated by $\bar{y}$ and hence for ease of exposition, $\hat{\mu}_Y$ is replaced by $\bar{y}$ before considering the minimization with respect to the function $h(u)$.

Clearly $h(u)$ can only be estimated for $0 \leqslant u \leqslant T$, but in practice $h(u)$ will damp out fairly quickly relative to the length of the record. Thus one will usually be interested in estimating $h(u)$ in the range $0 \leqslant u \leqslant T_0$, where T_0 is considerably less than T. Note that despite the fact that $x(t)$ is a realization of a stochastic process $X(t)$, the least squares principle is still applied, treating $x(t)$ as fixed. As discussed in Section 4.4.4, knowledge of the joint distribution of the random variables $X(t)$ has no bearing on the estimation of $h(u)$.

Proceeding as in Section 5.1.5, S may be expanded in the form

$$S = \int_0^T (y(t) - \bar{y})^2\, dt - 2 \int_0^T \left\{ (y(t) - \bar{y}) \int_0^\infty (x(t - u) - \bar{x}) h(u)\, du \right\} dt$$

$$+ \int_0^T \left\{ \int_0^\infty \int_0^\infty (x(t - u) - \bar{x})(x(t - v) - \bar{x}) h(u) h(v)\, du\, dv \right\} dt.$$

Interchanging orders of integration gives

$$S = \int_0^T (y(t) - \bar{y})^2 \, dt - 2T \int_0^\infty h(u) \left\{ \frac{1}{T} \int_0^T (x(t - u) - \bar{x})(y(t) - \bar{y}) \, dt \right\} du$$
$$+ T \int_0^\infty \int_0^\infty h(u)h(v) \left\{ \frac{1}{T} \int_0^T (x(t - u) - \bar{x})(x(t - v) - \bar{x}) \, dt \right\} du \, dv.$$

$$(5.3.3)$$

Comparing (5.3.3) and (5.1.12), it is seen that the term

$$\frac{1}{T} \int_0^T (x(t - u) - \bar{x})(y(t) - \bar{y}) \, dt$$

in (5.3.3) is analagous to

$$E[(X(t - u) - \mu_X)(Y(t) - \mu_Y)] = \gamma_{XY}(u)$$

in (5.1.12). This suggests the following definition of the cross covariance function estimate

$$c_{xy}(u) = \frac{1}{T} \int_0^T (x(t - u) - \bar{x})(y(t) - \bar{y}) \, dt, \quad -T \leqslant u \leqslant T. \quad (5.3.4)$$

Similarly, the autocovariance function estimate is defined by

$$c_{xx}(u) = \frac{1}{T} \int_0^T (x(t) - \bar{x})(x(t + u) - \bar{x}) \, dt, \quad -T \leqslant u \leqslant T$$
$$= \frac{1}{T} \int_0^{T - |u|} (x(t) - \bar{x})(x(t + u) - \bar{x}) \, dt, \quad -T \leqslant u \leqslant T, \quad (5.3.5)$$

since $x(t) = 0$ for $t < 0$, $t > T$.

Equation (5.3.3) may then be rewritten

$$S = Tc_{yy}(0) - 2T \int_0^\infty h(u)c_{xy}(u) \, du + T \int_0^\infty \int_0^\infty c_{xx}(u - v)h(u)h(v) \, du \, dv,$$

$$(5.3.6)$$

which corresponds to (5.1.12). Thus, the integrated squared error is completely specified by the covariance function estimates and the impulse response $h(u)$, just as the mean square error was completely specified by the theoretical covariance functions and the impulse response. However, note that, whereas the mean square error approach required that the stochastic processes $X(t)$ and $Y(t)$ should be stationary, the least squares approach does not depend on this assumption. The $x(t)$ and $y(t)$ may be realizations of a non-stationary stochastic process.

Now that S has been expressed in terms of the covariance function estimates, or sample covariance functions, the least squares estimate $\hat{h}(u)$ is obtained using the calculus of variations as described in Appendix A5.1. It is shown that $\hat{h}(u)$ must satisfy the integral equation

$$c_{xy}(u) = \int_{-\infty}^\infty c_{xx}(u - v)\hat{h}(v) \, dv, \quad u \geqslant 0, \quad (5.3.7)$$

which is exactly the same as the Wiener–Hopf integral equation (5.1.13) with the γ's replaced by c's. As before, $\hat{h}(v) = 0$ for $v < 0$, in order that $h(v)$ be physically realizable.

5.3.2 Sample autocovariance functions

In the preceding section, the sample acvf $c_{xx}(u)$ was seen to arise quite naturally as an estimate of the theoretical autocovariance function $\gamma_{XX}(u)$. The estimator corresponding to (5.3.5) may be written

$$
c_{XX}(u) = \begin{cases} \dfrac{1}{T} \displaystyle\int_0^{T-|u|} (X(t) - \bar{X})(X(t + |u|) - \bar{X})\, dt, & 0 \leqslant |u| \leqslant T \\ 0, & |u| > T, \end{cases} \qquad (5.3.8)
$$

which makes explicit the fact that $x(t) = 0$ outside $(0, T)$. An alternative estimator which is also widely used is

$$
c'_{XX}(u) = \begin{cases} \dfrac{1}{T - |u|} \displaystyle\int_0^{T-|u|} (X(t) - \bar{X})(X(t + |u|) - \bar{X})\, dt, & 0 \leqslant |u| \leqslant T \\ 0, & |u| > T. \end{cases} \qquad (5.3.9)
$$

The estimators $c_{XX}(u)$ and $c'_{XX}(u)$ have been used in statistical work mainly because they have intuitive appeal, not because they are best in any known sense. Ideally, of course, what should be done in choosing an acvf estimator is to write down the likelihood function of the observed time series. Differentiation of this likelihood function would then give a set of equations for the maximum likelihood estimates of the autocorrelations. Assuming that the pdf is Normal, it is not difficult to write down the likelihood function, but unfortunately the equations obtained by differentiation are intractable. Thus one is restricted to choosing estimators such as $c_{XX}(u)$ and $c'_{XX}(u)$, which admittedly are based on intuitive appeal. However, these estimators may be compared according to some criterion, such as minimum mean square error, and the best of the available estimators then chosen. This is the approach adopted in the next section.

5.3.3 Properties of autocovariance function estimators

The first- and second-moment properties of the autocovariance function estimators $c_{XX}(u)$ and $c'_{XX}(u)$ are now derived, assuming that the signal $x(t)$,

$(0 \leqslant u \leqslant T)$, is a realization of a stationary stochastic process $X(t)$ which has the properties

$$E[X(t)] = 0 \qquad (5.3.10)$$

$$\text{Cov}\,[X(t), X(t + u)] = \gamma_{XX}(u) \qquad (5.3.11)$$

$$\begin{aligned}
\text{Cov}\,[X(t)X(t + u_1), X(v)X(v + u_2)] = {}& \gamma_{XX}(v - t)\gamma_{XX}(v - t + u_2 - u_1) \\
& + \gamma_{XX}(v - t + u_2)\gamma_{XX}(v - t - u_1) \\
& + K_4(v - t, u_1, u_2). \quad (5.3.12)
\end{aligned}$$

The function $K_4(v - t, u_1, u_2)$ in (5.3.12) is the fourth joint cumulant of the stochastic process $X(t)$, so that if $X(t)$ is Normal, $K_4 = 0$. For other processes it can be shown [8], when deriving properties of the autocovariance estimators, that the contributions due to this term may be neglected. Hence this term will be omitted from now on. Note also that $E[X(t)]$ is assumed to be zero for the present. The effect of allowing for a non-zero mean is discussed shortly.

Mean of autocovariance estimators. Using (5.3.11), the mean of the auto-covariance estimator (5.3.8) is

$$\begin{aligned}
E[c_{XX}(u)] &= E\left[\frac{1}{T} \int_0^{T-u} X(t)X(t + u)\, dt\right] \\
&= \frac{1}{T} \int_0^{T-u} \gamma_{XX}(u)\, dt = \begin{cases} \gamma_{XX}(u)\left(1 - \dfrac{|u|}{T}\right), & 0 \leqslant |u| \leqslant T \\ 0, & |u| > T. \end{cases}
\end{aligned}$$

Hence

$$E[c_{XX}(u)] = \begin{cases} \gamma_{XX}(u)\left(1 - \dfrac{|u|}{T}\right), & |u| \leqslant T \\ 0, & |u| > T. \end{cases} \qquad (5.3.13)$$

Similarly,

$$E[c'_{XX}(u)] = \begin{cases} \gamma_{XX}(u), & |u| \leqslant T \\ 0, & |u| > T. \end{cases} \qquad (5.3.14)$$

Thus, $c'_{XX}(u)$ is an unbiased estimator of $\gamma_{XX}(u)$, whereas $c_{XX}(u)$ is only asymptotically unbiased as the record length T tends to infinity. However, it is shown later that the biased estimator has a smaller mean square error.

Covariance of autocovariance estimators. The second-moment properties of the estimators $c_{XX}(u)$ and $c'_{XX}(u)$ may be derived using (5.3.12) with the K_4 term omitted. A detailed derivation of this result, explaining all the approximations, is given in Appendix A9.1. Here only a sketch of the derivation is given and the results illustrated by examples.

The covariance between two estimators* $c_{XX}(u_1)$ and $c_{XX}(u_2)$ at two lags u_1 and u_2, where $u_2 \geqslant u_1 \geqslant 0$, is

$$\text{Cov}\,[c_{XX}(u_1),\, c_{XX}(u_2)]$$

$$= \text{Cov}\left[\frac{1}{T}\int_0^{T-u_1} X(t)X(t+u_1)\,dt,\, \frac{1}{T}\int_0^{T-u_2} X(v)X(v+u_2)\,dv\right]$$

$$= \frac{1}{T^2}\int_0^{T-u_1}\int_0^{T-u_2} \text{Cov}\,[X(t)X(t+u_1),\, X(v)X(v+u_2)]\,dt\,dv. \quad (5.3.15)$$

(The conditions $u_2 \geqslant u_1 \geqslant 0$ are not restricting in any way, as is shown in Appendix A9.1.) Substituting (5.3.12) in the integral (5.3.15) gives

$$\text{Cov}\,[c_{XX}(u_1),\, c_{XX}(u_2)] = \frac{1}{T^2}\int_0^{T-u_1}\int_0^{T-u_2} \{\gamma_{XX}(v-t)\gamma_{XX}(v-t+u_2-u_1)$$

$$+ \gamma_{XX}(v-t+u_2)\gamma_{XX}(v-t-u_1)\}\,dt\,dv.$$

$$(5.3.16)$$

The transformation $v - t = r$, $t = s$ transforms the region of integration from a rectangle in the (t, v) plane to a parallelogram in the (r, s) plane as shown in Figure 5.11. Equation (5.3.16) then reduces to

$$\text{Cov}\,[c_{XX}(u_1),\, c_{XX}(u_2)]$$

$$= \frac{1}{T^2}\int_{-(T-u_1)}^{T-u_2} \{\gamma_{XX}(r)\gamma_{XX}(r+u_2-u_1) + \gamma_{XX}(r+u_2)\gamma_{XX}(r-u_1)\}\,dr\int ds,$$

$$(5.3.17)$$

where the limits of integration are determined from the parallelogram of Figure 5.11. Since the integrand is independent of s, integration with respect to s yields the length $\phi(r)$ of the segment at height r, namely,

$$\phi(r) = \begin{cases} T - u_2 - r, & r \geqslant 0 \\ T - u_2, & -(u_2 - u_1) \leqslant r \leqslant 0 \\ T - u_1 + r, & -(T - u_1) \leqslant r \leqslant -(u_2 - u_1). \end{cases} \quad (5.3.18)$$

Hence, from (5.3.17) and (5.3.18)

$$\text{Cov}\,[c_{XX}(u_1),\, c_{XX}(u_2)]$$

$$= \frac{1}{T^2}\int_{-(T-u_1)}^{T-u_2} \phi(r)\{\gamma_{XX}(r)\gamma_{XX}(r+u_2-u_1) + \gamma_{XX}(r+u_2)\gamma_{XX}(r-u_1)\}\,dr.$$

$$(5.3.19)$$

---

* The results for the estimators $c'_{XX}(u_1)$ and $c'_{XX}(u_2)$ are obtained from the results for $c_{XX}(u_1)$ and $c_{XX}(u_2)$ by replacing T by $T - |u_1|$ and $T - |u_2|$ in the denominator outside the integrals.

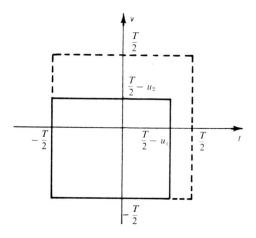

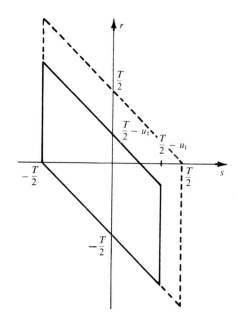

FIG. 5.11: Regions of integration for covariance calculation

The result (5.3.19) is exact and was first given in [8]. When $u_1 = u_2$, (5.3.19) reduces to the symmetrical form

$$\text{Var} [c_{XX}(u)] = \frac{1}{T^2} \int_{-(T-u)}^{T-u} (T - u - |r|)\{\gamma_{XX}^2(r) + \gamma_{XX}(r + u)\gamma_{XX}(r - u)\} \, dr.$$

$$(5.3.20)$$

For the unbiased estimator $c'_{XX}(u)$, the result corresponding to (5.3.20) is

$\text{Var}\left[c'_{XX}(u)\right]$

$$= \frac{1}{(T-|u|)^2} \int_{-(T-u)}^{(T-u)} (T - u - |r|)\{\gamma^2_{XX}(r) + \gamma_{XX}(r+u)\gamma_{XX}(r-u)\}\,dr.$$

$$(5.3.21)$$

Equation (5.3.19) shows, in general, that adjacent covariance function estimators will have strong correlations, and consequently that the sample autocovariance function may fail to damp out according to expectation. This effect is illustrated in Section 5.3.5.

A useful approximation. The computation of the covariance (5.3.19) is usually very difficult unless simple assumptions are made about the form of the auto-covariance functions. A useful approximation when T is large was suggested in [8]. This depends on the fact that

$$\lim_{T \to \infty} \{T \,\text{Cov}\,[c_{XX}(u_1), c_{XX}(u_2)]\}$$

$$= \int_{-\infty}^{\infty} \{\gamma_{XX}(r)\gamma_{XX}(r+u_2-u_1) + \gamma_{XX}(r+u_2)\gamma_{XX}(r-u_1)\}dr,$$

and hence for T large

$$\text{Cov}\,[c_{XX}(u_1), c_{XX}(u_2)]$$

$$\approx \frac{1}{T} \int_{-\infty}^{\infty} \{\gamma_{XX}(r)\gamma_{XX}(r+u_2-u_1) + \gamma_{XX}(r+u_2)\gamma_{XX}(r-u_1)\}\,dr. \quad (5.3.22)$$

An example. Consider the first-order continuous ar process with $\gamma_{XX}(u) = \sigma^2_X e^{-\lambda|u|}$ discussed in Section 5.2.4. Substituting $\gamma_{XX}(u)$ in (5.3.20) yields

$$\text{Var}\,[c_{XX}(u)] = \begin{cases} \dfrac{\sigma^4_X}{2\lambda^2 T^2}\{[e^{-\alpha(1-y)} + \alpha(1-y) - 1] + e^{-\alpha(1-y)} \\ \qquad + e^{-\alpha y}[\alpha(1-2y) - 1 + \alpha^2 y(1 - \tfrac{3}{2}y)]\}, \\ \qquad\qquad\qquad\qquad\qquad 0 \leqslant y \leqslant \tfrac{1}{2}, \\[2mm] \dfrac{\sigma^4_X}{2\lambda^2 T^2}\{[e^{-\alpha(1-y)} + \alpha(1-y) - 1] + e^{-\alpha y}(1-y^2)\}, \\ \qquad\qquad\qquad\qquad\qquad \tfrac{1}{2} \leqslant y \leqslant 1, \end{cases}$$

$$(5.3.23)$$

where $\alpha = 2\lambda T$, $y = u/T$, a result given in [9].

The exact result for the unbiased estimator $c'_{XX}(u)$ may be obtained by writing $(T - |u|)$ for T outside the brackets in (5.3.23). The approximation (5.3.22) for the estimator $c_{XX}(u)$ has the effect of removing the terms of order $1/T^2$, and yields

$$\text{Var}\,[c_{XX}(u)] \approx \frac{\sigma^4_X}{\lambda T}\{1 + e^{-\alpha y} + \alpha y\, e^{-\alpha y}\}. \qquad (5.3.24)$$

The variances of the two estimators $c_{XX}(u)$ and $c'_{XX}(u)$ are plotted against the lag u in Figure 5.12 for the case $\lambda T = 2.5$. It is seen that the two variances coincide when $u = 0$ but as u tends to T the variance of the biased estimator tends to zero, whereas the variance of the unbiased estimator tends to infinity. It is this behavior which makes the unbiased estimator $c'_{XX}(u)$ so unsatisfactory.

Mean square error of acv estimators. To make a valid comparison between the two estimators, it is necessary to compare their mean square errors. Using the result (4.2.12) for the mse, namely

$$E[\{c_{XX}(u) - \gamma_{XX}(u)\}^2] = \text{Var}\,[c_{XX}(u)] + B^2[c_{XX}(u)],$$

and the expression (5.3.13) to determine the bias $B[c_{XX}(u)]$, the mse's of the biased and unbiased estimators are

$$E[\{c_{XX}(u) - \gamma_{XX}(u)\}^2] = \text{Var}\,[c_{XX}(u)] + \sigma_X^4 \left(\frac{u}{T}\right)^2 e^{-2\lambda u}$$

and

$$E[\{c'_{XX}(u) - \gamma_{XX}(u)\}^2] = \text{Var}\,[c'_{XX}(u)].$$

These mean square errors are shown in Figure 5.12 together with the variances for the continuous first-order autoregressive process with $\lambda T = 2.5$. It is seen that the mean square error for $c'_{XX}(u)$ is consistently larger than that for $c_{XX}(u)$, a result mentioned in [10]. This fact has been demonstrated here only for the above acvf, but it is conjectured that it holds for most other acvf's [11].

Ergodicity. It follows from (5.3.13, 14) and (5.3.22) that for T large, the expected values of $c_{XX}(u)$ and $c'_{XX}(u)$ are $\gamma_{XX}(u)$ and that the variances are proportional to $1/T$. Hence the two covariance function estimators are asymptotically consistent. Thus the covariance function $E[X(t)X(t + u)]$ of the $X(t)$ process may be estimated with arbitrarily small error from a single sufficiently long record. For the covariance function, then, the *time average* over one record is equivalent to an *ensemble average*, and hence the covariance function is said to be *ergodic*. This property is given much prominence in many books, but is actually not of great practical interest since observed time series are of finite, not infinite, length.

Corrections for the mean. The bias of a covariance estimator of the form (5.3.8) may be obtained by writing (5.3.8) as

$$c_{XX}(u) = \frac{1}{T} \int_0^{T-|u|} (X(t) - \mu)(X(t + u) - \mu)\, dt - \left(1 - \frac{|u|}{T}\right)(\bar{X} - \mu)^2.$$

It follows that

$$E[c_{XX}(u)] = \left(1 - \frac{|u|}{T}\right)\gamma_{XX}(u) - \left(1 - \frac{|u|}{T}\right)\text{Var}\,[\bar{X}].$$

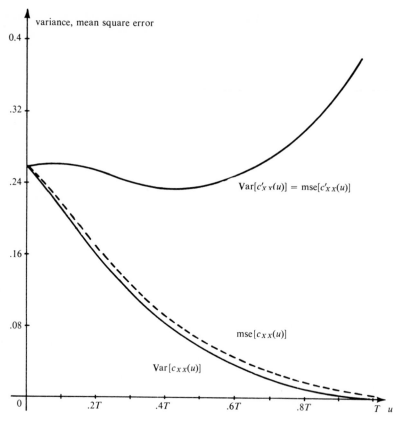

Fɪɢ. 5.12: Variances and mean square errors of autocovariance function estimators for a continuous first-order process

Now from (5.2.19),

$$\text{Var}\,[\bar{X}] = \frac{1}{T} \int_{-T}^{T} \left(1 - \frac{|y|}{T}\right) \gamma_{xx}(y)\,dy,$$

so the effect of correcting for the mean is to increase the bias still further by terms of order $(1/T)$ and higher.

5.3.4 Discrete time autocovariance estimates

If the observations $x_1, x_2, \ldots, x_N$ come from a discrete time series, the discrete estimate corresponding to the continuous estimate (5.3.5) is

$$c_{xx}(k) = \frac{1}{N} \sum_{t=1}^{N-k} (x_t - \bar{x})(x_{t+k} - \bar{x}), \qquad k = 0, 1, \ldots, N-1,$$

$$(5.3.25)$$

where

$$\bar{x} = \frac{1}{N} \sum_{t=1}^{N} x_t$$

is the sample mean of the whole series.

The approximate covariance between estimators corresponding to the estimates (5.3.25) may be obtained by replacing integrals by sums in (5.3.22), namely,

$$\text{Cov}\,[c_{xx}(k), c_{xx}(l)] \approx \frac{1}{N} \sum_{r=-\infty}^{\infty} \{\gamma_{xx}(r)\gamma_{xx}(r+l-k) + \gamma_{xx}(r+l)\gamma_{xx}(r-k)\}.$$

$$(5.3.26)$$

Covariance estimates for filtered data. It is sometimes necessary to calculate covariance estimates from *filtered* data. For example, it may be desired to remove trends in x_t by generating new data y_t according to the linear filtering operation

$$y_t = x_t - ax_{t-1}.$$ $$(5.3.27)$$

When $a = 1$, y_t is the differenced series, and when $a = -1$, y_t is the moving sum by twos of the original series. It is now shown that the covariance estimates $c_{yy}(k)$ for the filtered data may be expressed in terms of the covariance estimates $c_{xx}(k)$ of the original data. Hence, considerable savings in computer time are effected.

Using (5.3.25), the covariance estimate $c_{yy}(k)$ for the filtered estimate is

$$c_{yy}(k) = \frac{1}{N} \sum_{t=1}^{N-k} (y_t - \bar{y})(y_{t+k} - \bar{y}),$$ $$(5.3.28)$$

where

$$\bar{y} = \frac{1}{N} \sum_{t=1}^{N} (x_t - ax_{t-1}) \approx (1 - a)\bar{x}.$$

Substituting (5.3.27) in (5.3.28) gives

$$c_{yy}(k) \approx \frac{1}{N} \sum_{t=1}^{N-k} \{(x_t - ax_{t-1} - (1-a)\bar{x})(x_{t+k} - ax_{t+k-1} - (1-a)\bar{x})\}$$

$$= \frac{1}{N} \sum_{t=1}^{N-k} \{(x_t - \bar{x}) - a(x_{t-1} - \bar{x})\}\{(x_{t+k} - \bar{x}) - a(x_{t+k-1} - \bar{x})\}.$$

On expanding this expression,

$$c_{yy}(k) \approx c_{xx}(k) - ac_{xx}(k-1) - ac_{xx}(k+1) + a^2 c_{xx}(k)$$
$$= -ac_{xx}(k-1) + (1+a^2)c_{xx}(k) - ac_{xx}(k+1). \quad (5.3.29)$$

Thus, $c_{yy}(k)$ may be obtained by a simple linear filtering operation on the $c_{xx}(k)$. As an example, for filtering by differencing, $y_t = x_t - x_{t-1}$,

$$c_{yy}(k) \approx -c_{xx}(k-1) + 2c_{xx}(k) - c_{xx}(k+1), \qquad (5.3.30)$$

so that the covariances $c_{yy}(k)$ of the first differences of the data are the central *second* differences of the covariances $c_{xx}(k)$.

For the filtering operation

$$y_t = x_t - ax_{t-1} - bx_{t-2}, \qquad (5.3.31)$$

which may be used to remove oscillatory components in a time series, the covariances $c_{yy}(k)$ are

$$c_{yy}(k) \approx (1 + a^2 + b^2)c_{xx}(k) - a(1-b)\{c_{xx}(k-1) + c_{xx}(k+1)\}$$
$$- b\{c_{xx}(k-2) + c_{xx}(k+2)\}. \quad (5.3.32)$$

Estimating the acf. It is sometimes necessary to compare two time series with possibly different scales of measurement; thus estimates of the acf rather than the acvf are needed. Estimates of the acf may be obtained by dividing the above acvf estimates by the estimate of the variance. Thus

$$r_{xx}(k) = \frac{c_{xx}(k)}{c_{xx}(0)}, \qquad (5.3.33)$$

with $c_{xx}(k)$ defined as in (5.3.25).

An alternative correlation estimate. Another estimate of the acf which has been widely used by statisticians in the past is

$$r_{xx}(k) = \frac{\sum (x_t - \bar{x}_1)(x_{t+k} - \bar{x}_2)}{[\sum (x_t - \bar{x}_1)^2 (\sum (x_{t+k} - \bar{x}_2)^2)]^{1/2}}, \qquad (5.3.34)$$

where $\bar{x}_1$ and $\bar{x}_2$ are the means of the first $N - k$ and the last $N - k$ observations respectively, and the summations run from $t = 1$ to $t = N - k$. Equation (5.3.34) is based on the scatter diagram of x_{t+k} against x_t for $t = 1, 2, \ldots, N - k$. Figure 5.5, for example, corresponds to the case $k = 1$. If it is assumed that the joint pdf of the rv's X_t and X_{t+k} is bivariate Normal with correlation coefficient $\rho_{XX}(k)$, then (5.3.34) is the maximum likelihood estimate of $\rho_{XX}(k)$.

The use of the estimate (5.3.34) is not recommended on the grounds that, whereas it is a reasonable estimate of $\rho_{XX}(k)$ when considered in isolation from other values of the acf, it is not a satisfactory estimate when a *set of estimates* $r_{xx}(1), r_{xx}(2), \ldots, r_{xx}(m)$ is required for the first m autocorrelations $\rho_{XX}(1), \rho_{XX}(2), \ldots, \rho_{XX}(m)$.

The main disadvantage of (5.3.34) is that two means are used for the mean correction and that these change with lag; furthermore, the normalizing factor changes with lag k. The net result of these modifications is that the estimates are not positive definite in the sense of Property 4 of Section 5.2.1

and may lead to curious behavior of the estimates of the spectrum to be considered later.

5.3.5 Practical aspects of autocovariance function estimation

Two forms of motivation for the study of the acvf have been given in Section 5.1.5, namely that it enters into the design equations of a linear system and that it can be used for estimating impulse response functions. From a more general statistical point of view, an important reason for studying time series is to enable one to construct models for the underlying stochastic process. The model can then be used for prediction, systems design or for other purposes such as the simulation of a system. In such situations an empirical analysis of the acvf or the spectrum may provide a useful guide as to which models should be fitted to the time series.

An example. To illustrate how the acf can be used to summarize the information in the original series, consider the estimate of the acf for the batch data of Figure 5.2. Estimates for the first fifteen lags based on (5.3.33) and (5.3.25) are given in Table 5.2 and have been plotted in Figure 5.6. Examination of Table 5.2 reveals that the autocorrelations alternate in sign, reflecting the fact that a high yield from one batch tends to be followed by a low yield in the following batch and vice versa, and that the acf has almost completely damped out by lag 6, showing progressively weaker dependence between the observations as the lag between them increases.

TABLE 5.2: First 15 lags of the sample acf for the
data of Table 5.1

k	$r_{xx}(k)$	k	$r_{xx}(k)$	k	$r_{xx}(k)$
1	-0.39	6	-0.05	11	0.11
2	0.30	7	0.04	12	-0.07
3	-0.17	8	-0.04	13	0.15
4	0.07	9	-0.01	14	0.04
5	-0.10	10	0.01	15	-0.01

The basic mechanism generating this form of acf is well known for the above data. The industrial process from which the observations were obtained was a distillation column where the contents of the still were heated for some time and the distillate collected and run off. During distillation, tarry residues collect in the still and are run off at the end of each batch. However, the running off is not fully efficient, so a certain amount of tarry material is left behind. This has an adverse effect on the yield of the next batch, and so less distillate and hence less tarry material is generated. This explains the negative correlation between batches.

Computation of the autocorrelation function estimate. The computation of the acf estimate requires the use of an automatic computer, and a computer program for this purpose is described in Appendix A5.3. However, in order to appreciate the steps involved in the computations, it is advisable for the reader to work out one example on a desk calculator. To illustrate, consider the calculation of $r_{xx}(2)$ for the batch data of Table 5.1. Now the estimate (5.3.25) may be written

$$c_{xx}(k) = \frac{1}{N} \left\{ \sum_{t=1}^{N-k} x_t x_{t+k} - \bar{x} \left(\sum_{t=1}^{N-k} (x_t + x_{t+k}) \right) + (N - k)\bar{x}^2 \right\}, \quad (5.3.35)$$

and hence the bulk of the computation is concerned with the evaluation of the lagged sums of products $\sum_{t=1}^{N-k} x_t x_{t+k}$. For purposes of desk calculation, note that if an arbitrary constant is subtracted from each observation, the deviations $x_t - \bar{x}$ remain unaltered, and hence $c_{xx}(k)$ is unaffected. Therefore, to reduce the magnitude of the numbers which have to be multiplied, it is convenient to subtract from each value a constant, preferably one as close to the mean as possible. The data of Table 5.1 varies between 20 and 80, and hence 50 is a convenient constant to subtract from each number. Then

$$\sum_{t=1}^{68} (x_t - 50)(x_{t+2} - 50) = (-3)(-27) + (14)(21) + \cdots + (7)(-27)$$

$$= 3084.$$

Similarly,

$$\sum_{t=1}^{70} (x_t - 50) = 79, \qquad \sum_{t=1}^{68} (x_t - 50) = 102, \qquad \sum_{t=1}^{68} (x_{t+2} - 50) = 68.$$

Hence

$$c_{xx}(2) = \frac{1}{70} \left\{ 3084 - \frac{79}{70}(102 + 68) + 68 \left(\frac{79}{70}\right)^2 \right\}$$

$$= 42.55.$$

The variance $c_{xx}(0)$ of the series is 139.8 and hence

$$r_{xx}(2) = \frac{c_{xx}(2)}{c_{xx}(0)} = \frac{42.55}{139.8}$$

$$= 0.30,$$

which is the second value in Table 5.2.

Summary. The important points relating to the estimation of the autocorrelation function are now summarized:

(a) Estimators with divisors T usually have smaller mean square error than those based on $T - u$. In addition, the estimators based on a divisor T are positive definite, whereas those based on $T - u$ are not.

(b) Some form of correction for low frequency trends is required. In simple cases, as in (5.3.25), this can be achieved by removing a constant mean level. The mean correction preserves the positive definiteness of the estimate. In other cases, such as (5.3.27), the trends must be removed by a filtering operation and the autocovariances calculated from (5.3.29).

(c) Equation (5.3.19) shows that there will be strong correlation between the autocovariances if the correlation in the original series is moderately strong. The acvf plotted against lag may be regarded as a new time series derived from the original time series $x(t)$; thus (5.3.19) shows that, in general, this new time series will be more strongly correlated than the original time series.

(d) One of the consequences of the correlation between neighboring ordinates of the acvf is that the acvf may fail to damp out according to expectation. In order to illustrate this effect, Figure 5.13 shows the theoretical acf of the discrete second order autoregressive process

$$X_t = X_{t-1} - 0.5X_{t-2} + Z_t. \qquad (5.3.36)$$

The acf may be generated using the recurrence relation (5.2.43) when $m = 2$, namely,

$$\rho_{XX}(k) = \rho_{XX}(k-1) - 0.5\rho_{XX}(k-2).$$

The acf is a damped periodic function of the form (5.2.38) and has a period of 8 lags. Two sample acf's of an artificial series generated according to (5.3.36), with Z_t obtained from a table of random Normal deviates [7], are also plotted in Figure 5.13. The upper sample acf is based on 100 terms of the series while the lower sample acf is based on 400 terms. A feature of the acf based on 100 terms is the large periodicities which persist in the sample acf when the theoretical value should be close to zero. The explanation is that because of the large positive covariances between neighboring lags, a large positive autocorrelation tends to be followed by another large positive value, thus distorting the appearance of the acf. The acf based on 400 terms damps out more quickly but still differs considerably from the theoretical acf.

The main conclusion to be drawn from the above discussion is that it is sometimes dangerous to read too much into the visual appearance of an acf, especially from short series. In this book the main use of the acf is as an intermediate step in the estimation of the spectral density function, and also as a guide for designing a spectral analysis.

(e) Another consequence of (5.3.19) is that the variability of a single autocorrelation coefficient cannot be judged in isolation from the others. For example, suppose that a model is available for the time series, and that the acf of this model is known. One frequently finds in non-statistical texts that comparisons are made between the observed and theoretical acf under the assumption that neighboring points on the acf are independent. In view of the large covariances between neighboring lags, as shown by (5.3.19), this

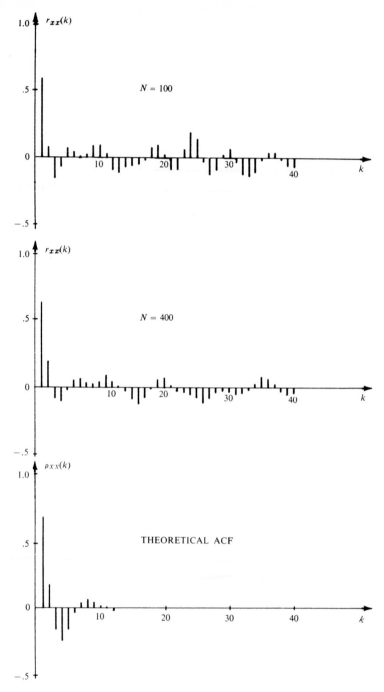

FIG. 5.13: Theoretical and sample autocorrelations for a second-order auto-regressive process

assumption can be quite misleading. A correct analysis would require that
the joint pdf of the autocorrelations be used in comparing the observed and
theoretical acf, but this comparison is then likely to be very complicated. In
a situation like this where a parametric model is specified, it is far better to
use a likelihood or least squares approach as described in Chapter 4.

A test for white noise. There is one situation where neighboring points of the
acf are virtually uncorrelated. This is when the time series is purely random or
white noise. In this case (5.3.19) shows that the covariance between the
autocorrelation estimators is zero if no mean correction is required. Correction for the mean introduces terms of order $1/T^2$ into the covariance and
hence may be neglected. It may be shown [12] that when the number of terms
in the series is sufficiently large, the distribution of $r_{xx}(k)$ can be taken to be
Normal with mean zero and variance $1/N$.

As an example, the data of Table 5.3 relate to the sample acf of sets of
random Normal deviates generated on a digital computer. The results of a

TABLE 5.3: Sample acf of samples of artificially generated white noise

Series 1:

k	$r_{xx}(k)$	k	$r_{xx}(k)$	k	$r_{xx}(k)$	k	$r_{xx}(k)$
1	0.041	9	-0.009	17	0.025	25	0.010
2	0.024	10	0.047	18	-0.020	26	0.029
3	0.045	11	0.061	19	0.032	27	0.011
4	0.330	12	0.083	20	0.075	28	0.068
5	0.007	13	0.026	21	-0.000	29	-0.004
6	0.012	14	-0.030	22	0.027	30	0.016
7	0.025	15	0.019	23	0.012	31	0.025
8	0.102	16	0.099	24	0.033	32	0.035

Series 2:

k	$r_{xx}(k)$	k	$r_{xx}(k)$	k	$r_{xx}(k)$	k	$r_{xx}(k)$
1	-0.014	9	0.020	17	-0.047	25	0.039
2	-0.008	10	0.013	18	-0.012	26	0.016
3	-0.038	11	0.007	19	0.025	27	0.025
4	0.011	12	-0.022	20	0.001	28	0.031
5	-0.047	13	0.017	21	0.009	29	-0.071
6	-0.051	14	-0.020	22	0.059	30	0.040
7	0.000	15	0.017	23	0.018	31	0.012
8	-0.041	16	-0.047	24	0.031	32	-0.025

simulation experiment suggested that the random deviates were far from
random and so blocks of approximately 1000 deviates were generated and
their sample acf's calculated. A typical acf based on 900 terms is partly

tabulated in Table 5.3 under the heading Series 1. Since the standard deviation
of a single acf estimate is $1/\sqrt{900} = 0.033$, the 95% confidence limits for a
single autocorrelation sample $\rho_{XX}(k)$ are approximately $r_{xx}(k) \pm 0.033(1.96)$
$= r_{xx}(k) \pm 0.065$. The 95% confidence intervals have been drawn on the
acf in Figure 5.14, where it is seen that 7 out of 32 confidence intervals

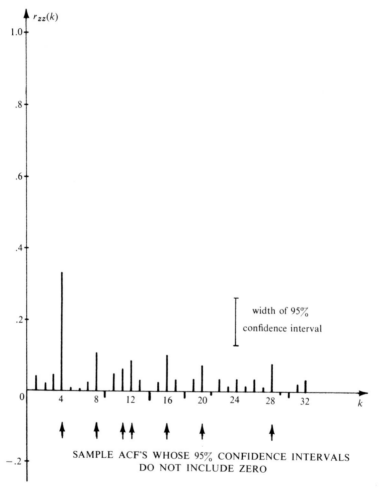

FIG. 5.14: Sample autocorrelation functions for two samples of random Normal
          deviates

do not include zero. On the basis of chance, one would expect approximately
5% or between 1 and 2 of the confidence intervals not to include zero. In fact,
the acf of Series 1 shows a periodicity of 4 due to a faulty method of generation of the random Normal deviates.

Under Series 2 of Table 5.3 is given a typical acf when the method of generation had been improved. Note now that only the confidence interval for $r_{xx}(22)$ does not include zero, a result which is not inconsistent with the hypothesis that the time series is purely random.

5.4 ESTIMATION OF THE PARAMETERS OF A LINEAR PROCESS

In this section the methods of Chapter 4 are applied to the estimation of the parameters of the ar and ma models introduced in Section 5.2. Suppose, for example, that it is required to fit the ar model

$$(X_t - \mu) = \alpha_1(X_{t-1} - \mu) + \cdots + \alpha_m(X_{t-m} - \mu) + Z_t \qquad (5.4.1)$$

to an observed time series $x_1, x_2, \ldots, x_N$. The fitting procedure involves two stages:

(1) Deciding the order m of the process.
(2) Given m, estimating the parameters $\mu, \alpha_1, \ldots, \alpha_m$.
Since it is only possible to decide on the order m by fitting processes of different orders, it is necessary to discuss *(2)* first.

5.4.1 *Maximum likelihood estimation of autoregressive parameters*

An approximate likelihood function. Assuming that the Z_t process is Normal, the log-likelihood function may be derived for fixed m as follows. First, it is noticed that the joint pdf of $Z_{m+1}, Z_{m+2}, \ldots, Z_N$ may be written

$$f_{m+1,\ldots,N}(z_{m+1}, z_{m+2}, \ldots, z_N) = \frac{1}{(\sqrt{2\pi}\,\sigma_Z)^{N-m}} \exp - \frac{1}{2\sigma_Z^2} \sum_{t=m+1}^{N} z_t^2,$$

where $E[Z_t] = 0$, $E[Z_t^2] = \sigma_Z^2$. If a transformation is made from the z's to the x's according to (5.4.1), then since the Jacobian is unity,

$$f_{m+1,\ldots,N}(x_{m+1}, x_{m+2}, \ldots, x_N \mid x_1, \ldots, x_m)$$

$$= \frac{1}{(\sqrt{2\pi}\,\sigma_Z)^{N-m}} \exp - \frac{1}{2\sigma_Z^2} \sum_{t=m+1}^{N} \{(x_t - \mu) - \alpha_1(x_{t-1} - \mu) - \cdots$$

$$- \alpha_m(x_{t-m} - \mu)\}^2 \qquad (5.4.2)$$

The notation on the left-hand side of (5.4.2) indicates that this represents the joint pdf of $x_{m+1}, \ldots, x_N$ conditional on the values $x_1, \ldots, x_m$ being fixed at their observed values. To obtain the overall pdf it would be necessary to multiply (5.4.2) by the joint pdf of $x_1, \ldots, x_m$. Since m will usually be small, the net effect of this end correction will be small and since it complicates the likelihood function considerably, it is omitted. When the x's are known, (5.4.2) is regarded as a function of $\mu, \alpha_1, \ldots, \alpha_m$, and represents the joint likelihood function of these parameters conditional on the values $x_1, \ldots, x_m$ being fixed. The log-likelihood function is thus

$$l(\mu, \alpha_1, \ldots, \alpha_m \,|\, x_1, \ldots, x_m)$$
$$= -(N - m) \ln \sqrt{2\pi} - (N - m) \ln \sigma_Z$$

$$-\frac{1}{2\sigma_Z^2} \sum_{t=m+1}^{N} \{(x_t - \mu) - \alpha_1(x_{t-1} - \mu) - \cdots - \alpha_m(x_{t-m} - \mu)\}^2. \quad (5.4.3)$$

For the estimation of $\mu, \alpha_1, \ldots, \alpha_m$, the important quantity is the sum-of-squares function

$$S(\mu, \alpha_1, \ldots, \alpha_m \,|\, x_1, \ldots, x_m)$$

$$= \sum_{t=m+1}^{N} \{(x_t - \mu) - \alpha_1(x_{t-1} - \mu) - \cdots - \alpha_m(x_{t-m} - \mu)\}^2. \quad (5.4.4)$$

The maximum likelihood or least squares estimates may then be obtained by differentiating (5.4.4). Some special cases are now considered.

First-order autoregressive process. Differentiation of the sum of squares

$$S(\mu, \alpha_1) = \sum_{t=2}^{N} \{(x_t - \mu) - \alpha_1(x_{t-1} - \mu)\}^2$$

gives rise to normal equations analogous to those obtained in Section 4.3.3. Thus

$$\bar{x}_2 - \hat{\mu} - \hat{\alpha}_1(\bar{x}_1 - \hat{\mu}) = 0,$$

$$\sum_{t=2}^{N} \{(x_{t-1} - \hat{\mu})[(x_t - \hat{\mu}) - \hat{\alpha}_1(x_{t-1} - \hat{\mu})]\} = 0,$$

where $\bar{x}_1, \bar{x}_2$ are the means of the first and last $N - 1$ observations. Hence

$$\hat{\mu} = \frac{\bar{x}_2 - \hat{\alpha}_1 \bar{x}_1}{1 - \hat{\alpha}_1}$$

$$\hat{\alpha}_1 = \frac{\sum_{t=2}^{N} (x_{t-1} - \hat{\mu})(x_t - \hat{\mu})}{\sum_{t=2}^{N} (x_{t-1} - \hat{\mu})^2}. \quad (5.4.5)$$

Since $\bar{x}_1$ and $\bar{x}_2$ will be very close to the overall mean $\bar{x}$, the estimate $\hat{\mu}$ may be approximated by $\bar{x}$ and hence $\hat{\alpha}_1$ by $r_{xx}(1)$.

The residual sum of squares

$$S(\hat{\mu}, \hat{\alpha}_1) = \sum_{t=2}^{N} \{(x_t - \hat{\mu}) - \hat{\alpha}_1(x_{t-1} - \hat{\mu})\}^2$$

may be simplified using (A4.1.11) to give

$$S(\hat{\mu}, \hat{\alpha}_1) = \sum_{t=2}^{N} (x_t - \hat{\mu})^2 - \hat{\alpha}_1 \sum_{t=2}^{N} (x_t - \hat{\mu})(x_{t-1} - \hat{\mu}). \quad (5.4.6)$$

Approximating (5.4.6), as was done for $\hat{\alpha}_1$ above, yields the simple expression

$$S(\hat{\mu}, \hat{\alpha}_1) \approx (N - 1)\{c_{xx}(0) - \hat{\alpha}_1 c_{xx}(1)\} = (N - 1)c_{xx}(0)\{1 - r_{xx}^2(1)\}. \quad (5.4.7)$$

Since there are effectively $N - 1$ observations in $S(\mu, \alpha_1)$ and two degrees of freedom are lost in fitting the constants μ, α_1, the variance of Z_t may be estimated by

$$s_z^2 = \frac{1}{N - 3} S(\hat{\mu}, \hat{\alpha}_1).$$

Using (A4.1.15) and the same method of approximation as above, the $100(1 - \alpha)\%$ confidence interval for α_1 is

$$(\alpha_1 - \hat{\alpha}_1)^2 \leqslant \frac{s_z^2 f_{1, N-3}(1 - \alpha)}{\sum_{t=1}^{N} (x_t - \bar{x})^2}. \quad (5.4.8)$$

Second-order autoregressive process. The mle's may be obtained by differentiating (5.4.3) with respect to μ, α_1 and α_2 and setting the derivatives equal to zero. This leads to the equations

$$(\bar{x}_3 - \hat{\mu}) = \hat{\alpha}_1(\bar{x}_2 - \hat{\mu}) + \hat{\alpha}_2(\bar{x}_1 - \hat{\mu}),$$

$$\sum (x_t - \hat{\mu})(x_{t-1} - \hat{\mu}) = \hat{\alpha}_1 \sum (x_{t-1} - \hat{\mu})^2 + \hat{\alpha}_2 \sum (x_{t-1} - \hat{\mu})(x_{t-2} - \hat{\mu}),$$

$$\sum (x_t - \hat{\mu})(x_{t-2} - \hat{\mu}) = \hat{\alpha}_1 \sum (x_{t-1} - \hat{\mu})(x_{t-2} - \hat{\mu}) + \hat{\alpha}_2 \sum (x_{t-2} - \hat{\mu})^2,$$

$$(5.4.9)$$

where

$$\bar{x}_j = \frac{1}{N - 3} \sum x_{t-3+j}$$

and all the summations extend from $t = 3$ to $t = N$. If the $\bar{x}_j$ are replaced by the overall mean $\bar{x}$, the six functions of the observations which appear in these equations may be linked in pairs and $\hat{\mu} = \bar{x}$. For example,

$$\sum (x_t - \hat{\mu})(x_{t-1} - \hat{\mu})$$

and

$$\sum (x_{t-1} - \hat{\mu})(x_{t-2} - \hat{\mu})$$

have $N - 3$ terms in common and differ only by one term at the beginning and end. To a good degree of approximation they may be replaced by $Nc_{xx}(1)$ where $c_{xx}(1)$ is the autocovariance estimate (5.3.25). The equations (5.4.9) may then be rewritten approximately as

$$c_{xx}(1) = \hat{\alpha}_1 c_{xx}(0) + \hat{\alpha}_2 c_{xx}(1),$$

$$c_{xx}(2) = \hat{\alpha}_1 c_{xx}(1) + \hat{\alpha}_2 c_{xx}(0).$$

Hence, converting to acf estimates $r_{xx}(k) = c_{xx}(k)/c_{xx}(0)$,

$$\hat{\alpha}_1 \approx \frac{r_{xx}(1)(1 - r_{xx}(2))}{1 - r_{xx}^2(1)},$$

$$\hat{\alpha}_2 \approx \frac{r_{xx}(2) - r_{xx}^2(1)}{1 - r_{xx}^2(1)}. \qquad (5.4.10)$$

Using the same approximation, the residual sum of squares $S(\hat{\mu}, \hat{\alpha}_1, \hat{\alpha}_2)$ reduces to

$$S(\hat{\mu}, \hat{\alpha}_1, \hat{\alpha}_2) = (N - 2)\{c_{xx}(0) - \hat{\alpha}_1 c_{xx}(1) - \hat{\alpha}_2 c_{xx}(2)\}. \qquad (5.4.11)$$

The residual variance is

$$s_z^2 = \frac{1}{N - 5} S(\hat{\mu}, \hat{\alpha}_1, \hat{\alpha}_2)$$

and has $N - 5$ degrees of freedom, since the original likelihood (5.4.13) involves $N - 2$ observations and a further 3 degrees of freedom are lost in fitting the three parameters μ, α_1 and α_2.

Again using the same approximation as in (A4.1.15), a $100(1 - \alpha)\%$ joint confidence region for the parameters (α_1, α_2) is

$$(\alpha_1 - \hat{\alpha}_1)^2 + 2r_{xx}(1)(\alpha_1 - \hat{\alpha}_1)(\alpha_2 - \hat{\alpha}_2) + (\alpha_2 - \hat{\alpha}_2)^2 \leqslant 2 \frac{s_z^2 f_{2,N-5}(1-\alpha)}{\sum_{t=1}^{N} (x_t - \bar{x})^2}.$$

As an example, consider the batch data of Figure 5.2. It will be shown in Section 5.4.3 that this can be adequately fitted by a second-order ar process. Using the values of $r_{xx}(1)$ and $r_{xx}(2)$ from Table 5.2 and (5.4.10), the estimates of the parameters are $\hat{\alpha}_1 = -0.32$ and $\hat{\alpha}_2 = +0.18$. The residual sum of squares $S(\hat{\alpha}_1, \hat{\alpha}_2)$ is 7768.5 so that $s_z^2 = 7768.5/65 = 119.6$. Hence the approximate 95% confidence interval is

$$(\alpha_1 + 0.32)^2 - 0.78(\alpha_1 + 0.32)(\alpha_2 - 0.18) + (\alpha_2 - 0.18)^2 \leqslant 0.077.$$

Figure 5.15 shows the exact sum-of-squares contours drawn in the stationarity region in the α_1, α_2 plane. The shaded region is the 95% confidence region and it is seen that this lies well within the stationarity region.

The general autoregressive process. Proceeding as before, the mle equations may be approximated by

$$c_{xx}(j) = \hat{\alpha}_1 c_{xx}(j - 1) + \hat{\alpha}_2 c_{xx}(j - 2) + \cdots + \hat{\alpha}_m c_{xx}(j - m), \qquad (5.4.12)$$

where $j = 1, 2, \ldots, m$. Similarly the residual sum of squares may be approximated by

$$S(\hat{\mu}, \hat{\alpha}_1, \ldots, \hat{\alpha}_m) = (N - m)\{c_{xx}(0) - \hat{\alpha}_1 c_{xx}(1) - \cdots - \hat{\alpha}_m c_{xx}(m)\}. \qquad (5.4.13)$$

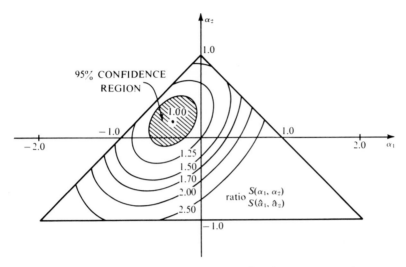

FIG. 5.15: Sum-of-squares contours for a second-order autoregressive process fitted to the batch data of Figure 5.2

From (5.4.13) an approximate estimate

$$s_z^2 = \frac{1}{N - 2m - 1} S(\hat{\mu}, \hat{\alpha}_1, \ldots, \hat{\alpha}_m)$$

of the residual variance may be obtained. Finally, using (A4.1.15) an approximate confidence region may be written in matrix notation

$$(\alpha - \hat{\alpha})'C(\alpha - \hat{\alpha}) \leqslant \frac{m}{N - 2m - 1} f_{m, N - 2m - 1}(1 - \alpha)s_z^2,$$

where $\alpha' = (\alpha_1, \alpha_2, \ldots, \alpha_m)$ and

$$C = \begin{pmatrix} c_{xx}(0) & c_{xx}(1) & \cdots & c_{xx}(m-1) \\ c_{xx}(1) & c_{xx}(0) & \cdots & c_{xx}(m-2) \\ \vdots & \vdots & & \vdots \\ c_{xx}(m-1) & c_{xx}(m-2) & \cdots & c_{xx}(0) \end{pmatrix}$$

5.4.2 Mean likelihood estimates for autoregressive parameters

Since the likelihood function (5.4.2) is a multivariate Normal distribution, apart from a multiplicative constant, it would appear at first sight that its description by means and covariances, as described in Section 4.4.1 would be adequate. However, when the mle's lie close to the boundaries of the stationarity region, the likelihood function is truncated and an alternative approach is required.

Mean likelihood estimates for a first-order autoregressive process. To illustrate, consider the first-order ar process with zero mean,

$$X_t = \alpha_1 X_{t-1} + Z_t.$$

The likelihood function (5.4.2) may then be rewritten

$$L(\alpha_1 | x_1) = K_1 \exp - \frac{\sum_{t=2}^{N} x_{t-1}^2 (\alpha_1 - \hat{\alpha}_1)^2}{2\sigma_Z^2}, \qquad (5.4.14)$$

where

$$\hat{\alpha}_1 = \frac{\sum_{t=2}^{N} x_{t-1} x_t}{\sum_{t=2}^{N} x_{t-1}^2} \qquad (5.4.15)$$

is the mle of α_1. Hence, provided σ_Z^2 is known, the likelihood function is a Normal distribution, apart from a multiplicative constant, with mean α_1 and variance

$$\frac{\sigma_Z^2}{\sum_{t=2}^{N} x_{t-1}^2}.$$

The description of the likelihood function (5.4.14) by its mean and variance would be adequate provided that the range of α_1 was infinite. However, since the model is stationary only if $|\alpha_1| < 1$, difficulties arise with the above description when the likelihood function has a maximum near $|\alpha_1| = 1$. In this case the likelihood function would be abruptly truncated at one of the points $\alpha_1 = 1$, $\alpha_1 = -1$, and so the Normal approximation is not valid.

The methods for transforming likelihoods discussed in Section 4.4.5 are also not applicable since no transformation which will provide a Normal approximation exists when the likelihood function terminates at a non-zero value. In this case, the best procedure is simply to evaluate the mean likelihood estimate (mele) for the range $(-1, 1)$ by

$$\bar{\alpha}_1 = \frac{\int_{-1}^{1} \alpha_1 L(\alpha_1) \, d\alpha_1}{\int_{-1}^{1} L(\alpha_1) \, d\alpha_1}.$$

Substituting for $L(\alpha_1)$ from (5.4.14), this becomes

$$\bar{\alpha}_1 = \hat{\alpha}_1 - \frac{\sigma_Z}{(\sum x_{t-1}^2)^{1/2}} \frac{f(L_2) - f(L_1)}{F(L_2) - F(L_1)}, \qquad (5.4.16)$$

where $f(x)$ and $F(x)$ are the pdf and cdf of the Normal distribution respectively, $\hat{\alpha}_1$ is the mle and

$$L_2 = \frac{\sum x_{t-1}^2}{\sigma_Z^2} (1 - \hat{\alpha}_1), \qquad L_1 = \frac{\sum x_{t-1}^2}{\sigma_Z^2} (-1 - \hat{\alpha}_1).$$

If σ_Z^2 is unknown, the marginal likelihood of α_1 may be obtained by integrating with respect to $d\sigma_Z^2/\sigma_Z^2$ as described in Section 4.4.6. It may be verified that, after performing this integration, the marginal likelihood for α_1 becomes

$$L_1(\alpha_1) = K[(N - 2)s_z^2 + \sum_{t=2}^{N} x_{t-1}^2 (\alpha_1 - \hat{\alpha}_1)^2]^{-(N-1)/2}. \qquad (5.4.17)$$

Apart from a constant multiplier, this is a t distribution with $(N - 2)$ degrees of freedom. The quantity s^2 in (5.4.17) is the usual estimate of σ_Z^2 obtained from the residual sum of squares, namely,

$$s_Z^2 = \frac{1}{N - 2} \left\{ \sum_{t=2}^{N} x_t^2 - \hat{\alpha}_1^2 \sum_{t=2}^{N} x_{t-1}^2 \right\}. \tag{5.4.18}$$

It may be verified that the mele of α_1 is now given by (5.4.16) but with σ_Z^2 replaced by s_Z^2 and $f(x)$, $F(x)$ referring to the pdf and cdf of the t distribution with $N - 2$ degrees of freedom.

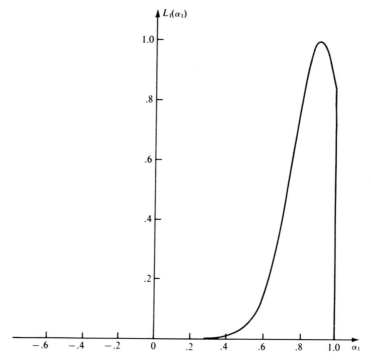

FIG. 5.16: Marginal likelihood function for a first-order autoregressive process

Suppose, for example, that a time series of length $N = 20$ gave rise to $s_Z^2 = 1.44$, $\sum x_{t-1}^2 = 64$, $\hat{\alpha}_1 = 0.9$. Then the marginal likelihood function for α_1 is a t distribution as shown in Figure 5.16. Using (5.4.16) with $f(x)$, $F(x)$ referring to a t distribution with 18 degrees of freedom, the mele is $\tilde{\alpha}_1 = 0.86$. Note that this has the effect of moving the mle $\hat{\alpha}_1 = 0.9$ inward from the stationarity boundary.

For simplicity the mean μ of the time series has been set equal to zero in the above discussion. A non-zero mean may be allowed for by replacing x_t by $x_t - \mu$. Integrating with respect to μ as well as σ_Z^2 gives a marginal likelihood for α which is the same as (5.4.17) except that x_t in (5.4.17) is replaced by the deviation from the mean $(x_t - \bar{x})$ and N is replaced by $N - 1$, that is,

$$L_1(\alpha_1) = K[(N - 3)s_z^2 + \sum_{t=2}^{N} (x_{t-1} - \bar{x})^2(\alpha_1 - \hat{\alpha}_1)^2]^{-(N-2)/2}.$$

Mean likelihood estimates for a second-order autoregressive process. Consider the second-order process

$$X_t - \mu = \alpha_1(X_{t-1} - \mu) + \alpha_2(X_{t-2} - \mu) + Z_t.$$

The likelihood function is

$$L(\alpha_1, \alpha_2, \mu, \sigma_Z^2 \mid x_1, x_2)$$

$$= \frac{1}{(\sqrt{2\pi}\,\sigma_Z)^{N-2}} \exp - \frac{1}{2\sigma_Z^2} \sum_{t=3}^{N} \{(x_t - \mu) - \alpha_1(x_{t-1} - \mu) - \alpha_2(x_{t-2} - \mu)\}^2.$$

On integrating with respect to $d\mu$ this becomes, apart from small end corrections,

$$L(\alpha_1, \alpha_2, \sigma_Z^2 \mid x_1, x_2)$$

$$= \frac{1}{(\sqrt{2\pi}\,\sigma_Z)^{N-3}} \exp - \frac{1}{2\sigma_Z^2} \sum_{t=3}^{N} \{(x_t - \bar{x}) - \alpha_1(x_{t-1} - \bar{x}) - \alpha_2(x_{t-2} - \bar{x})\}^2.$$

$$(5.4.19)$$

Integrating further with respect to $d\sigma_Z^2/\sigma_Z^2$ gives the joint likelihood of α_1, α_2

$$L(\alpha_1, \alpha_2 \mid x_1, x_2) = K\left[\sum_{t=3}^{N} \{(x_t - \bar{x}) - \alpha_1(x_{t-1} - \bar{x}) - \alpha_2(x_{t-2} - \bar{x})\}^2\right]^{-(N-3)/2}$$

$$(5.4.20)$$

When the 95% confidence region lies well within the stationarity region, as in Figure 5.15, the likelihood function is adequately described by its means and covariances. When the mle's lie near to the stationarity limits, the only safe procedure is to plot the likelihood contours. Instead of quoting the mle it is now more appropriate to evaluate the mele's. First, however, it is convenient to make the transformation

$$\phi_1 = \frac{\alpha_1}{1 - \alpha_2}, \qquad \phi_2 = \alpha_2. \qquad (5.4.21)$$

It may be verified using (5.4.20) that in the neighborhood of the mle's

$$\frac{\partial^2 l}{\partial \phi_1 \, \partial \phi_2} \approx 0,$$

and hence the parameters ϕ_1 and ϕ_2 are orthogonal.

The transformation (5.4.21) maps the triangular stability region into the square region $|\phi_1| < 1$, $|\phi_2| < 1$. The mean likelihood estimates of ϕ_1 and ϕ_2 may then be evaluated numerically, for example,

$$\bar{\phi}_1 = \frac{\int_{-1}^1 \int_{-1}^1 \phi_1 L(\phi_1, \phi_2)\, d\phi_1\, d\phi_2}{\int_{-1}^1 \int_{-1}^1 L(\phi_1, \phi_2)\, d\phi_1\, d\phi_2},$$

where

$$L(\phi_1, \phi_2) = K\left[\sum_{t=3}^N \{(x_t - \bar{x}) - \phi_1(1 - \phi_2)(x_{t-1} - \bar{x}) - \phi_2(x_{t-2} - \bar{x})\}^2\right]^{-(N-3)/2}$$

The mele's $\bar{\phi}_1$ and $\bar{\phi}_2$ may then be converted into mele's for α_1 and α_2 using the inverse transformation

$$\bar{\alpha}_1 = \bar{\phi}_1(1 - \bar{\phi}_2), \qquad \bar{\alpha}_2 = \bar{\phi}_2.$$

5.4.3 Determining the order of the autoregressive process

In this section the problem of determining the order m of the ar process is considered. A simple method is based on the fact that if an insufficient number of terms have been fitted in the model (5.4.1), the estimate of the residual variance σ_Z^2 will be inflated by those terms not yet included. Only when the correct number of terms has been included will a valid estimate of σ_Z^2 be obtained.

This suggests that if the estimate

$$s_z^2(m) = \frac{1}{N - 2m - 1}\, S(\hat{\mu}, \hat{\alpha}_1, \ldots, \hat{\alpha}_m)$$

of the residual variance is plotted versus m, the curve will flatten out or show a minimum at the point corresponding to the correct order of the process. Figure 5.17 shows a plot of $s_z^2(m)$ versus m for the batch data of Figure 5.2. It is seen that the curve flattens out around $m = 2$ and 3, indicating that a second- or third-order ar process would be adequate to fit this data.

The partial autocorrelation function. One criticism of the method based on $s_z^2(m)$ is that it may not always indicate strongly enough which value of m is required. For example, in Figure 5.17, is the decrease in $s_z^2(m)$ obtained by increasing m from 2 to 3 large enough to warrant using the third-order model? A more sensitive criterion is obtained by determining for each value of m the estimate $\hat{\pi}_m = \hat{\alpha}_m$ of the last coefficient α_m in the fitted model together with its confidence interval as described in Section 5.4.1. For reasons to be given in Chapter 11, the plot of $\hat{\pi}_m$ versus m is called the *partial autocorrelation function*. Using the results of Section 5.4.1, the first two values of $\hat{\pi}_m$ may be approximated by

$$\hat{\pi}_1 \approx r_{xx}(1), \qquad \hat{\pi}_2 \approx \frac{r_{xx}(2) - r_{xx}^2(1)}{1 - r_{xx}^2(1)}.$$

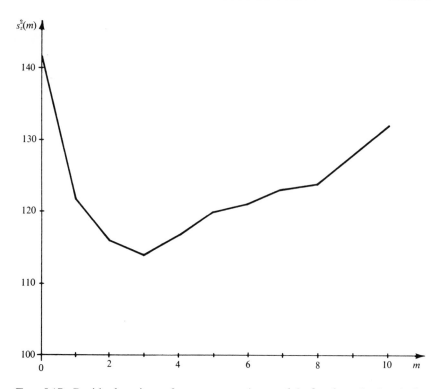

FIG. 5.17: Residual variance for autoregressive models fitted to the batch data of Figure 5.2

To interpret $\hat{\pi}_2$, it will be recalled that if the process is first order, the theoretical autocorrelations satisfy $\rho_{XX}(2) = \rho_{XX}^2(1)$ and hence the theoretical value of π_2 is zero. If the process is second order, π_2 measures the *excess* correlation in $\rho_{XX}(2)$ which would be expected over and above that if it were a first-order process.

An alternative interpretation for $\hat{\pi}_2$ is obtained by expressing the residual sums of squares in terms of the partial correlations. Thus, the residual sum of squares after fitting the first-order model is, from (5.4.7),

$$S(\hat{\alpha}_1) \approx (N - 1)c_{xx}(0)\{1 - \hat{\pi}_1^2\}.$$

Hence the factor $\{1 - \hat{\pi}_1^2\}$ gives the proportional reduction in the sum of squares as a result of fitting a first-order process. Similarly, the residual sum of squares (5.4.11) may be written

$$S(\hat{\alpha}_1, \hat{\alpha}_2) \approx (N - 2)c_{xx}(0)\{1 - \hat{\pi}_1^2\}\{1 - \hat{\pi}_2^2\}.$$

Hence the factor $\{1 - \hat{\pi}_2^2\}$ gives the *additional* reduction factor in the sum of squares, as a result of increasing the model to second order.

Figure 5.18 shows the partial autocorrelation function for the batch data of Figure 5.2. The confidence intervals in Figure 5.18 are 95% intervals and have been centred about zero in order to show up those coefficients which may be taken to be non-zero. It is seen that $\hat{\pi}_1$ lies outside the band, $\hat{\pi}_2$ lies very near the boundary, while the values beyond $m = 2$ lie well within. This indicates that a first-order process is adequate to describe this data and not a third-order

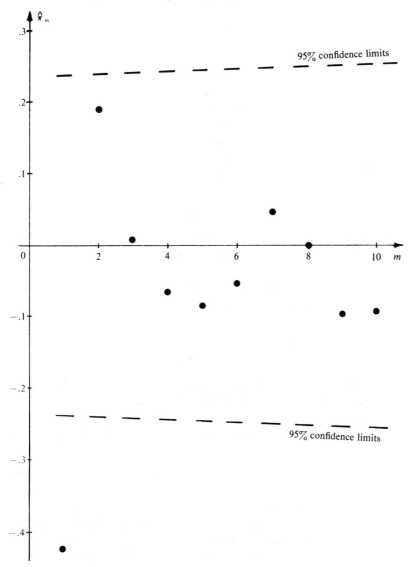

FIG. 5.18: Partial autocorrelations for autoregressive models fitted to the batch data of Figure 5.2

process as indicated by $s_z^2(m)$ in Figure 5.17. However, since $\hat{\pi}_2$ lies near one edge of the confidence interval, and since $s_z^2(2)$ is appreciably lower than $s_z^2(1)$, as shown in Figure 5.17, it is concluded that an adequate fit to this data requires a second-order model.

5.4.4 Estimation of the parameters of a moving average process

The first question which has to be decided when fitting an ma process

$$X_t = \mu + Z_t + \beta_1 Z_{t-1} + \cdots + \beta_l Z_{t-l} \qquad (5.4.22)$$

is the appropriate order l for the model. The method of analysis is more complicated than for the ar process and it is necessary, for simplicity, to determine the best value of l from the estimate of the residual variance $s_z^2(l)$. This is because it is difficult to write down an explicit form for the likelihood function of the process (5.4.22), although a special case has been given in [13]. However, a simple numerical technique given in [1] may be used to build up the log-likelihood function recursively.

To illustrate this approach, consider the first-order ma process

$$X_t = \mu + Z_1 + \beta_1 Z_{t-1}. \qquad (5.4.23)$$

For specified values of μ and β_1, (5.4.23) can be used to generate a set of z_t's from the observed x_t's. Since $E[Z_t] = 0$, a good starting value is $z_0 = 0$ and hence

$$z_1 = x_1 - \mu, \qquad z_2 = x_2 - \mu - \beta_1 z_1$$

and so on. Hence the sum of squares

$$S(\mu, \beta_1) = \sum_{t=1}^{N} z_t^2,$$

corresponding to a particular choice of (μ, β_1) may be readily obtained. The sum-of-squares surface can then be plotted for a grid of values of μ and β_1 and contours of constant sums of squares sketched in. If the minimum value of the sum of squares for a fixed value of l is denoted by $S(\hat{\mu}, \hat{\beta}_1, \ldots, \hat{\beta}_l)$, the criterion

$$s_z^2(l) = \frac{S(\hat{\mu}, \hat{\beta}_1, \ldots, \hat{\beta}_l)}{N - (l + 1)} \qquad (5.4.24)$$

may be used for deciding on the best value of l. The residual variance (5.4.24) is shown in Figure 5.19 for the batch data of Figure 5.2. It is seen that $s_z^2(l)$ levels out at $l = 2$ and then shows a pronounced decrease at $l = 8$. Hence an eighth-order ma process is required to give a fit to the data comparable to a second-order ar process. Clearly the simpler ar process is a much more realistic model.

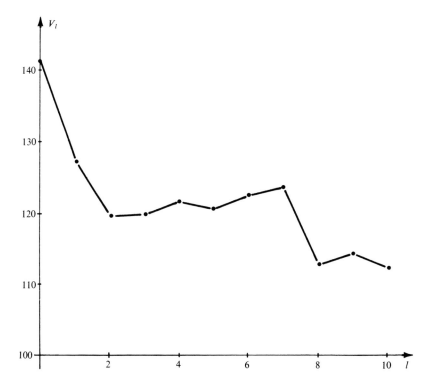

FIG. 5.19: Residual variances for moving average models fitted to the batch
data of Figure 5.2

Since it is difficult to write down an explicit form for the sum of squares, it
is necessary to consider an alternative method for deriving confidence
regions. If sum-of-squares contours have been plotted, the confidence region
may be obtained using (A4.1.17) by locating that contour for which

$$S(\mu, \beta_1, \ldots, \beta_l) = S(\hat{\mu}, \hat{\beta}_1, \ldots, \hat{\beta}_l)\left(1 + \frac{l+1}{N - (l+1)}f_{l+1, N-l-1}(1 - \alpha)\right).$$

$$(5.4.25)$$

To illustrate (5.4.25), a series of 50 terms of the process

$$X_t = 5 + Z_t + 0.5Z_{t-1}$$

was generated from random Normal deviates Z_t. Figure 5.20 shows the sum-
of-squares contours plotted with respect to μ and β_1 for this data. The lse's
of μ and β_1 are $\hat{\mu} = 4.90$, $\hat{\beta}_1 = 0.35$ and $S(\hat{\mu}, \hat{\beta}_1) = 38.91$. Hence using
(5.4.25), the 95% contour is

$$38.91\{1 + \tfrac{2}{48}(3.20)\} = 44.1.$$

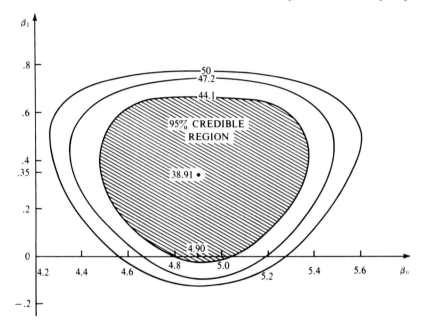

Fig. 5.20: Sum-of-squares contours for a first-order moving average process

Note that the starting values $z_{1-l}, \ldots, z_0$ could also be allowed to vary and the sum-of-squares surface plotted with respect to $z_{1-l}, \ldots, z_0$ regarded as parameters. However, the extra complication which occurs will usually not be justified by the results obtained.

5.4.5 Estimation of the parameters of a mixed autoregressive–moving average process

Because of the result (5.2.49) that when a continuous ar process of order m is sampled a discrete mixed ar–ma process is obtained, it would be expected that mixed models would be useful in fitting many time series. As an illustration of how the log-likelihood surface may be generated, consider the mixed process

$$X_t - \mu = \alpha_1(X_{t-1} - \mu) + \alpha_2(X_{t-2} - \mu) + Z_t + \beta_1 Z_{t-1}.$$

For fixed values of the parameters μ, α_1, α_2, and β_1, the z's may be generated according to

$$z_3 = (x_3 - \mu) - \alpha_1(x_2 - \mu) - \alpha_2(x_1 - \mu),$$
$$z_4 = (x_4 - \mu) - \alpha_1(x_3 - \mu) - \alpha_2(x_2 - \mu) - \beta_1 z_3$$

and so on. The sum-of-squares surface may then be calculated by plotting

$$S(\mu, \alpha_1, \alpha_2, \beta_1 \mid x_1, x_2, z_1 = 0, z_2 = 0) = \sum_{t=3}^{N} z_t^2$$

as a function of μ, α_1, α_2 and β_1. With the aid of a computer it is easy to scan these models by first fixing m, the order of the ar process, and then varying l, the order of the ma process. The residual variance

$$s_z^2(m, l) = \frac{1}{N - l - 2m - 1} S(\hat{\mu}, \ldots, \hat{\alpha}_m, \hat{\beta}_1, \ldots, \hat{\beta}_l)$$

may then be plotted as a function of l and m.

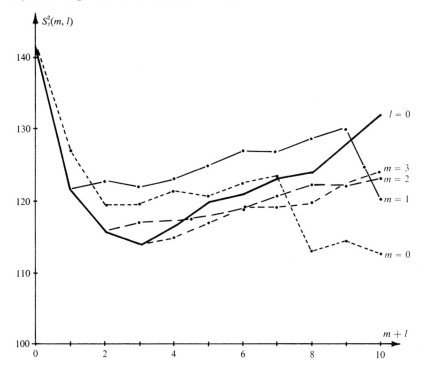

FIG. 5.21: Residual variances for mixed models fitted to the batch data of Figure 5.2

Figure 5.21 shows $s_z^2(m, l)$ versus $m + l$ for the batch data of Figure 5.2. It is seen that for $l + m$ less than 8 the best fit is obtained with a purely autoregressive model of order 3. It may be concluded on the basis of residual variances that the best fit to this data is achieved with an ar model of order three. However, as shown in Section 5.4.3, a second-order ar model is in fact adequate.

REFERENCES

[1] G. E. P. Box and G. M. Jenkins, "Some statistical aspects of adaptive optimization and control." *Jour. Royal Stat. Soc.* **B 24**, 297 (1962).

[2] G. E. P. Box and G. M. Jenkins, "Further contributions to adaptive quality control; simultaneous estimation of dynamics; non-zero costs." *Bulletin of I.S.I.*, 24th session, Ottawa, 943 (1963).

[3] G. E. P. Box and G. M. Jenkins, *Statistical Models for Forecasting and Control.* To be published, Holden-Day, San Francisco.

[4] N. Wiener, *The Extrapolation, Interpolation and Smoothing of Stationary Time Series with Engineering Applications.* John Wiley, New York, 1949.

[5] H. M. James, N. B. Nichols and R. S. Phillips, *Theory of Servomechanisms.* McGraw-Hill, New York, 1947.

[6] J. L. Doob, *Stochastic Processes.* John Wiley, New York, 1953.

[7] H. Wold, "Random Normal Deviates." *Tracts for Computers.* K. Pearson, Ed.

[8] M. S. Bartlett, "On the theoretical specification and sampling properties of autocorrelated time series." *Jour. Royal Stat. Soc.* **B 8**, 27 (1946).

[9] A. T. Fuller, "Sampling errors in the measurement of autocorrelation." *Jour. Electr. Contr.* **4**, 551 (1958).

[10] E. Parzen, "Mathematical considerations in the estimation of spectra." *Technometrics* **3**, 167 (1961).

[11] M. G. Schaerf, "Estimation of the covariance and autoregressive structure of a stationary time series." *Stanford U. Tech. Rep.*, 12 (1964).

[12] R. L. Anderson, "Distribution of the serial correlation coefficient." *Ann. Math. Stat.* **13**, 1 (1942).

[13] G. A. Barnard, G. M. Jenkins and C. B. Winsten, "Likelihood inference and time series." *Jour. Royal Stat. Soc.* **A 125**, 321 (1962).

APPENDIX A5.1   THE CALCULUS OF VARIATIONS

The linear system $\hat{h}(u)$, which produces the minimum mean square error (5.1.12), may be determined very simply by using the calculus of variations. It is assumed in what follows that the covariance functions $\gamma_{XX}(u)$ and $\gamma_{XY}(u)$ are known for all values of the lag u.

The first step is to note that (5.1.12) may be rewritten

$$\epsilon(h(u)) = \gamma_{YY}(0) - 2 \int_0^\infty h(u)\gamma_{XY}(u)\, du + \int_0^\infty \int_0^\infty h(u)h(v)\gamma_{XX}(u - v)\, du\, dv,$$

$$(A5.1.1)$$

since the function $h(u)$ is the only unknown. The general approach used in the calculus of variations is to assume that the answer is known and then find the conditions dictated by the fact that this answer is the correct one. Thus, in (A5.1.1), suppose that a particular function $\hat{h}(u)$ is *the* function which minimizes $\epsilon(h(u))$, that is,

$$\epsilon(\hat{h}(u)) < \epsilon(h(u)) \quad \text{for all} \quad h(u) \not\equiv \hat{h}(u). \qquad (A5.1.2)$$

Then, any function $h'(u) = \hat{h}(u) + g(u)$, where $g(u)$ is any function of u satisfying the boundary conditions on $h(u)$, will be such that $\epsilon(\hat{h}(u) + g(u)) > \epsilon(\hat{h}(u))$ for all $g(u)$ not identically zero.

More generally, if

$$h(u) = \hat{h}(u) + bg(u), \tag{A5.1.3}$$

$\epsilon(h(u))$ is a minimum when $h(u) = \hat{h}(u)$, that is, *when $b = 0$*. Expressing this condition for a minimum in terms of differentials gives the usual relations for a minimum, namely,

$$\frac{\partial\epsilon(h(u))}{\partial b} = 0, \quad (b = 0), \qquad \frac{\partial^2\epsilon(h(u))}{\partial b^2} > 0, \quad (b = 0). \tag{A5.1.4}$$

In particular, from (A5.1.1) and (A5.1.3)

$$\epsilon(h(u)) = \gamma_{YY}(0) - 2\int_0^\infty [\hat{h}(u) + bg(u)]\gamma_{XY}(u)\,du$$

$$+ \int_0^\infty\int_0^\infty [\hat{h}(u) + bg(u)][\hat{h}(v) + bg(v)]\gamma_{XX}(u - v)\,du\,dv \tag{A5.1.5}$$

and

$$\frac{\partial\epsilon(h(u))}{\partial b} = -2\int_0^\infty g(u)\gamma_{XY}(u)\,du$$

$$+ \int_0^\infty\int_0^\infty [\hat{h}(u)g(v) + g(u)\hat{h}(v) + 2bg(u)g(v)]\,\gamma_{XX}(u - v)\,du\,dv. \tag{A5.1.6}$$

On setting $b = 0$ in (A5.1.6) and using the first condition in (A5.1.4),

$$0 = -2\int_0^\infty g(u)[\gamma_{XY}(u) - \int_0^\infty \hat{h}(v)\gamma_{XX}(u - v)\,dv]\,du, \tag{A5.1.7}$$

since $\gamma_{XX}(u)$ is an even function, as shown in Section 5.2.1.

Since the equality (A5.1.7) must be true for *any* function $g(u)$, $\hat{h}(u)$ must satisfy the condition

$$\gamma_{XY}(u) = \int_0^\infty \hat{h}(v)\gamma_{XX}(u - v)\,dv, \quad u \geqslant 0. \tag{A5.1.8}$$

It may be verified that the second derivative with respect to b at $b = 0$ is positive, confirming that this solution corresponds to a minimum. Thus, $\hat{h}(u)$ must satisfy the integral equation (A5.1.8), which is called the Wiener–Hopf integral equation.

The qualification that the relation (A5.1.8) must be true for $u \geqslant 0$ occurs because of the physical realizability condition, namely, that $h(u) = 0$ for $u < 0$.

APPENDIX A5.2 MOMENTS OF LINEAR PROCESSES

Consider the general linear process (5.2.6), namely,

$$X(t) - \mu = \int_0^\infty h(v)Z(t - v)\,dv, \tag{A5.2.1}$$

where $Z(t)$ is white noise with the properties

$$E[Z(t)] = 0, \tag{A5.2.2}$$

$$\text{Cov}\,[Z(t), Z(t + u)] = \sigma_Z^2\, \delta(u), \tag{A5.2.3}$$

$$E[Z(t)Z(t + u_1)Z(t + u_2)] = \mu_3\, \delta(u_1)\, \delta(u_2), \tag{A5.2.4}$$

$$E[Z(t)Z(t + u_1)Z(v)Z(v + u_2)] = \sigma_Z^4[\delta(u_1)\, \delta(u_2) + \delta(v - t)\, \delta(v - t + u_2 - u_1)$$
$$+\, \delta(v - t + u_2)\, \delta(v - t - u_1)]$$
$$+\, K_4(Z)\, \delta(u_1)\, \delta(v - t)\, \delta(v - t + u_2). \tag{A5.2.5}$$

As before, $\delta(u)$ is the Dirac delta function. The lower-order moments of the stochastic process $X(t)$ will now be derived assuming that the process $Z(t)$ has the above properties.

From (A5.2.1) and (A5.2.2),

$$E[X(t) - \mu] = E\left[\int_0^\infty h(v)Z(t - v)\, dv\right]$$

$$= \int_0^\infty h(v)E[Z(t - v)]\, dv = 0. \tag{A5.2.6}$$

Similarly, from (A5.2.1) and (A5.2.3),

$$\text{Cov}\,[X(t), X(t + u)] = \text{Cov}\left[\int_0^\infty h(v)Z(t - v)\, dv, \int_0^\infty h(v')Z(t + u - v')\, dv'\right]$$

$$= \int_0^\infty \int_0^\infty h(v)h(v')\,\text{Cov}\,[Z(t - v), Z(t + u - v')]\, dv\, dv'$$

$$= \int_0^\infty \int_0^\infty h(v)h(v')\sigma_Z^2\, \delta(u - v' + v)\, dv\, dv'$$

$$= \sigma_Z^2 \int_0^\infty h(v)h(v + u)\, dv = \gamma_{XX}(u). \tag{A5.2.7}$$

When $u = 0$ this reduces to

$$\text{Var}\,[X(t)] = \sigma_Z^2 \int_0^\infty h^2(v)\, dv.$$

Hence, provided $\int_0^\infty h^2(v)\, dv$ is finite, $X(t)$ is a stationary process up to second order since the autocovariance function $\gamma_{XX}(u)$ is a function of the lag u only.

Similarly,

$$E[(X(t) - \mu)(X(t + u_1) - \mu)(X(t + u_2) - \mu)]$$
$$= \mu_3 \int_0^\infty h(v)h(v + u_1)h(v + u_2)\, dv \tag{A5.2.8}$$

and

$$\text{Cov}\,[(X(t) - \mu)(X(t + u_1) - \mu), (X(v) - \mu)(X(v + u_2) - \mu)]$$
$$= \gamma_{XX}(v - t)\gamma_{XX}(v - t + u_2 - u_1) + \gamma_{XX}(v - t + u_2)\gamma_{XX}(v - t - u_1)$$
$$+\, K_4(Z) \int_0^\infty h(v')h(v' + u_1)h(v' + v - t)h(v' + v - t + u_2)\, dv', \tag{A5.2.9}$$

where $\gamma_{XX}(u)$ is given by (A5.2.7). The result (A5.2.9) is used in Section 5.3.3 for the derivation of the expression for the covariances between covariance function estimators.

Note that (A5.2.9) implies that the fourth cumulant of the $X(t)$ process is given by the fourth cumulant of the $Z(t)$ process multiplied by the integral over the fourth product of the weighting functions, that is,

$$K_4(X) = K_4(Z) \int_0^\infty h(v)h(v + u_1)h(v + u_2)h(v + u_3) \, dv.$$

For Normal white noise $K_4(Z)$ is identically zero, and hence so is $K_4(X)$. For non-Normal white noise, the integral

$$\int_0^\infty h(v)h(v + u_1)h(v + u_2)h(v + u_3) \, dv$$

is generally small with respect to integrals of the form $\int_0^\infty h(v)h(v + u_1) \, dv$, and hence the cumulant term in (A5.2.9) may be neglected with respect to the terms in γ_{XX}. This approximation is used in the derivation of the moments of sample covariance function estimators in Section 5.3.3.

APPENDIX A5.3   FLOW CHART FOR COVARIANCE PROGRAM

The following is a flow chart for a computer program which accepts NS series, each of N data points, and calculates the NS autocovariances and NS(NS−1) cross covariances out to MAXM lags. The program also calculates the approximate auto- and cross covariances for the differenced data. The output consists of a printout of all covariances and differenced covariances, plots of all correlations with differenced correlations overlayed and tape or punched-card output of all covariances and differenced covariances for use in subsequent spectral programs. The print output is used mainly as an "echo check" when the covariances are input to the next program.

Program MULTICOR

1) *Read* NS, N, MAXM.

2) *Read* IDENT(J), X(I,J),   J = 1,N.

3) *Calculate* means $XM(J) = \dfrac{1}{N} \sum_{I=1}^{N} X(I,J)$,   J = 1,NS.

4) *Store* deviations $X(I,J) - XM(J) \rightarrow X(I,J)$.

5) *Calculate* covariances $COV(K,J,L) = \dfrac{1}{N} \sum_{I=1}^{N-K} X(I,J){*}X(I+K,L)$,

$$K = 0, \text{ MAXM} + 1; \ J = 1,NS; L = 1,NS.$$

6) *Calculate* differenced covariances
$$DCOV(K,J,L) = -COV(K-1,J,L) + 2{*}COV(K,J,L) - COV(K+1,J,L).$$
$$K = 0, \text{ MAXM}; \ J = 1,NS; \ L = 1,NS.$$

7) *Output* covariances and differenced covariances via printer and punched card or tape.

8) *Calculate* correlations

$$COR(K,J,L) = COV(K,J,L)/\sqrt{COV(0,J,J)*COV(0,L,L)}$$
$$DCOR(K,J,L) = DCOV(K,J,L)/\sqrt{DCOV(0,J,J)*DCOV(0,L,L)}$$
$$K = 0, \text{ MAXM}; \ J = 1,\text{NS}; \ L = 1,\text{NS}.$$

9) *Plot* correlations and overlay differenced correlations.

6

The Spectrum

In Chapter 5 it was shown that a stationary stochastic process is simply
described by its autocovariance function. In this chapter it is shown that an
equivalent description is provided by its power spectrum, which is the Fourier
transform of the autocovariance function. The power spectrum curve shows
how the variance of the stochastic process is distributed with frequency.

In Section 6.1 it is shown that classical Fourier methods fail when applied
to time series. Thus the estimator of the spectrum obtained from considerations of Fourier analysis, namely the sample spectrum, has the unfortunate
property that its variance does not decrease as the length of the time series
increases. Hence the methods of Chapter 2 must be modified for time
series analysis. These modifications lead to the definition of a spectrum appropriate to stochastic processes, which is given in Section 6.2. This section also
deals with the spectra of linear moving average and autoregressive processes.

In Section 6.3 it is shown that an improved estimator of the spectrum can
be obtained by smoothing the sample spectrum. The more one smooths
the smaller is the variance but the larger is the bias or distortion. Hence a
compromise has to be achieved between bias and variance.

Further properties of the smoothed estimators, including the notion of bandwidth, are derived in Section 6.4. It is also shown that confidence intervals
are easily obtained at each frequency by using the logarithm of the spectrum
estimate.

6.1 THE SAMPLE SPECTRUM

6.1.1 *Fourier methods applied to time series*

Fourier analysis. It was shown in Chapter 2 that the variance or average
power of a signal $x(t)$ in the range $-T/2 \leqslant t \leqslant T/2$ can be decomposed into
contributions at harmonics $f_m = m/T$ of the fundamental frequency $f_1 = 1/T$
according to

$$s_T^2 = \frac{1}{T} \int_{-T/2}^{T/2} x^2(t)\, dt = \sum_{m=-\infty}^{\infty} |X_m|^2. \qquad (6.1.1)$$

X_m is called the complex amplitude at the harmonic frequency $f_m = m/T$ and measures the amplitudes of the sine and cosine terms at frequency f_m in $x(t)$. The complex amplitude may be computed from

$$X_m = \frac{1}{T} \int_{-T/2}^{T/2} x(t)\, e^{-j2\pi mt/T}\, dt \qquad (6.1.2)$$

by writing

$$e^{-j2\pi mt/T} = \cos \frac{2\pi mt}{T} - j \sin \frac{2\pi mt}{T}.$$

Recall that the Fourier decomposition of $x(t)$ is

$$x(t) = \sum_{m=-\infty}^{\infty} X_m\, e^{+j2\pi mt/T}.$$

Similarly, for a discrete signal observed at times $t = -n\,\Delta,\ -(n-1)\,\Delta,$ $\ldots, (n-1)\,\Delta$, the average power is decomposed into contributions at a *finite* number of harmonics of the fundamental frequency $f_1 = 1/N\,\Delta$ ($N = 2n$), and the relations corresponding to (6.1.1) and (6.1.2) are

$$s_T^2 = \frac{1}{N} \sum_{t=-n}^{n-1} x_t^2 = \sum_{m=-n}^{n-1} |X_m|^2, \qquad (6.1.3)$$

$$X_m = \frac{1}{N} \sum_{t=-n}^{n-1} x_t\, e^{-j2\pi mt\, \Delta/N\, \Delta} = \frac{1}{N} \sum_{t=-n}^{n-1} x_t\, e^{-j2\pi mt/N}. \qquad (6.1.4)$$

The contribution $|X_m|^2$ to the average power at frequency f_m is called the *intensity* at this frequency, and the plot of $|X_m|^2$ versus m is called the *Fourier line spectrum*, an example of which is given in Figure 2.2.

The power spectrum of deterministic signals. It is when the record length tends to infinity that the main difference between the analysis of deterministic and stochastic signals arises. This distinction is not explained in many engineering texts, which use an argument similar to the following. From (6.1.1), the variance of the infinite record is

$$\sigma^2 = \lim_{T \to \infty} \frac{1}{T} \int_{-T/2}^{T/2} x^2(t)\, dt = \lim_{T \to \infty} \sum_{m=-\infty}^{\infty} (T|X_m|^2)\frac{1}{T} = \int_{-\infty}^{\infty} \Gamma(f)\, df,$$

where

$$\Gamma(f) = \lim_{T \to \infty} T|X_m|^2 \qquad (6.1.5)$$

is called a Fourier "*power spectrum.*" Using (6.1.2), the function $T|X_m|^2$ may be written

$$T|X_m|^2 = C_{xx}(f) = \frac{1}{T} \left| \int_{-T/2}^{T/2} x(t)\, e^{-j2\pi ft}\, dt \right|^2. \qquad (6.1.6)$$

Note that $C_{xx}(f)$ is defined for a continuous range of frequencies $-\infty \leqslant f \leqslant \infty$ and is called the *sample spectrum*. For the discrete case the sample spectrum is

$$C_{xx}(f) = \frac{\Delta}{N} \left| \sum_{t=-n}^{n-1} x_t e^{-j2\pi ft\Delta} \right|^2$$

$$= \frac{\Delta}{N} \left\{ \left(\sum_{t=-n}^{n-1} x_t \cos 2\pi ft\Delta \right)^2 + \left(\sum_{t=-n}^{n-1} x_t \sin 2\pi ft\Delta \right)^2 \right\},$$

$$\frac{1}{2\Delta} \leqslant f < \frac{1}{2\Delta}. \quad (6.1.7)$$

The frequency $1/2\Delta$ in (6.1.7) is the Nyquist frequency discussed in Chapter 2 and is the highest frequency which can be detected from data spaced at intervals Δ seconds apart.

Note that if $x(t)$ has a well-behaved Fourier transform, the limit (6.1.5) for $\Gamma(f)$ is zero. This is because $x(t)$ must tend to zero as f tends to $\pm\infty$ if its Fourier transform is to exist. However, provided $x(t)$ does not dissipate itself in this way, $C_{xx}(f)$ will usually tend to a well-defined limit $\Gamma(f)$. For deterministic signals, the convergence of $C_{xx}(f)$ to $\Gamma(f)$ is smooth in the sense that the function $C'_{xx}(f)$ obtained by increasing the record length from T to T' would be a smoother version of the function $C_{xx}(f)$ based on the record of length T.

It will be shown in the next section that the definition (6.1.5) is not a satisfactory one when $x(t)$ is a realization of a stochastic process. The basic difference between the Fourier analysis of a deterministic and stochastic signal is that the plot of $C'_{xx}(f)$ obtained from a record of length $T' > T$ of a stochastic signal is just as erratic as that obtained from a record of length T, that is, $C_{xx}(f)$ does not converge in any statistical sense to a limiting value as T tends to infinity.

6.1.2 *The sample spectrum of a white noise process*

To illustrate the effect of applying Fourier analysis to a stochastic process, a series of 400 random Normal deviates (Gaussian white noise) was generated. The sample spectrum $C_{zz}(f)$ was computed from the series consisting of the first 50 terms, the first 100, the first 200 and the entire series of 400 terms. Figure 6.1 shows the values of the sample spectrum $C_{zz}(f)$ computed according to (6.1.7) at the frequencies $f = 0.02, 0.04, \ldots, 0.50$ cps for the cases $N = 50$ and $N = 100$, with $\Delta = 1$ sec. Also indicated in the figure is the theoretical spectrum, which is shown in Section 6.2.3 to be a constant in the range $-\frac{1}{2} \leqslant f < \frac{1}{2}$.

Figure 6.1 shows that the fluctuations in $C_{zz}(f)$ are so erratic that it would be difficult to conclude on the basis of this diagram that the true spectrum

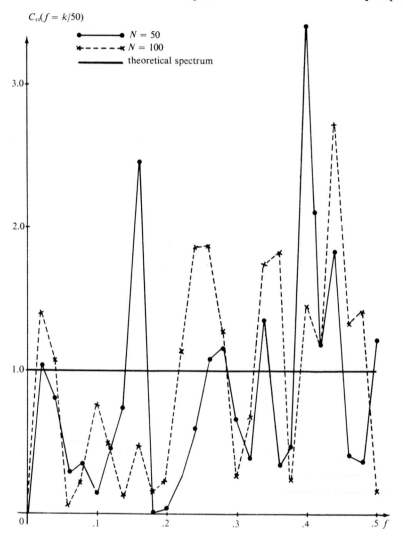

Fig. 6.1: Sample spectra for the first half ($N = 50$) and the whole ($N = 100$) of a realization of discrete Normal white noise

was a constant and hence that the time series was white noise. Note also that the fluctuations in $C_{zz}(f)$ for $N = 100$ are just as large as for $N = 50$, indicating lack of statistical convergence of any kind.

Table 6.1 summarizes the results obtained for the sample spectrum for series with $N = 50, 100, 200$ and 400 terms. Since the theoretical spectrum has the same value at all frequencies, the fluctuations in $C_{zz}(f)$ can be summarized by evaluating the mean, variance and mean square error over frequency. It is seen that the mean values for each series are close to unity, the value of the theoretical spectrum. Hence the $C_{zz}(f)$ seem to be clustering about some central value. However, Table 6.1 shows that the variances do not decrease as N increases, showing that the estimate of the spectrum obtained from a sample of $N = 100$, 200 or 400 is no better than that for $N = 50$.

TABLE 6.1: Behavior of sample spectra of white noise as the record length is increased

N	50	100	200	400
mean	0.85	1.07	1.00	0.95
variance	0.630	0.777	0.886	0.826
mean square error	0.652	0.782	0.886	0.828

It was seen in Chapter 4 that well-behaved estimators have the property that their variance decreases as N increases. Hence it can be concluded that $C_{zz}(f)$ is not a good estimate of the spectrum, at least not in its present form.

To show that the sample spectra for random processes other than white noise do not converge in any statistical sense, consider the auto-regressive process generated according to (5.3.36). The theoretical and sample acf's for a realization of 400 terms were shown in Figure 5.13. The theoretical spectrum and the sample spectrum for the same realization of 400 terms are shown in Figure 6.2. As for the white noise example, the sample spectrum is extremely erratic and bears little resemblance to the theoretical spectrum.

Summary. For deterministic signals, the spectrum is the limit, in the usual mathematical sense, of the sample spectrum $C_{xx}(f)$ as the record length tends to infinity. However, the white noise example above shows that when $C_{xx}(f)$ is used to analyze a time series its behavior is so erratic as to render it useless for estimation purposes. The basic reason why Fourier analysis breaks down when applied to time series is that it is based on the assumption of *fixed* amplitudes, frequencies and phases. Time series, on the other hand, are characterized by *random* changes of frequencies, amplitudes and phases. Therefore it is not surprising that Fourier methods need to be adapted to take account of the random nature of a time series.

6.1.3 The relation between the sample spectrum and the sample autocovariance function

Before giving a more precise definition of the spectrum of a stationary stochastic process, a fundamental relationship connecting the sample spectrum and the sample autocovariance function is proved.

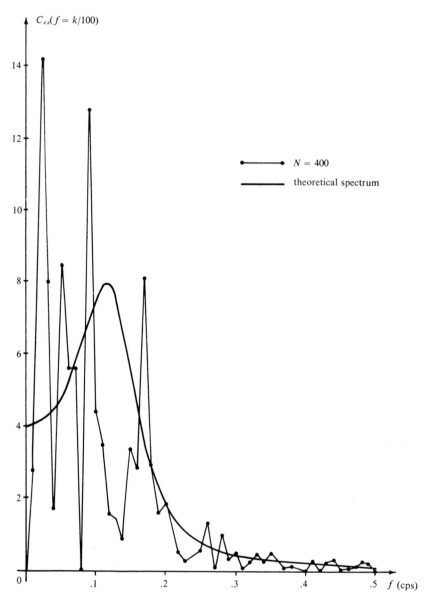

Fig. 6.2: Sample spectrum for a realization of a second-order autoregressive process

Using the definition (6.1.6) of the sample spectrum,

$$C_{xx}(f) = \frac{1}{T} \int_{-T/2}^{T/2} x(t)\, e^{-j2\pi ft}\, dt \int_{-T/2}^{T/2} x(t')\, e^{+j2\pi ft'}\, dt'. \qquad (6.1.8)$$

If the transformation

$$u = t - t', \qquad v = t'$$

is made in the double integral (6.1.8), the region of integration is transformed as shown in Figure 6.3. Then (6.1.8) becomes

$$C_{xx}(f) = \int_0^T \left[\frac{1}{T} \int_{-T/2}^{(T/2)-u} x(v)x(v+u)\, dv \right] e^{-j2\pi fu}\, du$$

$$+ \int_{-T}^0 \left[\frac{1}{T} \int_{-(T/2)-u}^{T/2} x(v)x(v+u)\, dv \right] e^{-j2\pi fu}\, du.$$

Using the definition (5.3.8) of $c_{xx}(u)$, this becomes

$$C_{xx}(f) = \int_{-T}^T c_{xx}(u)\, e^{-j2\pi fu}\, du, \qquad -\infty \leqslant f \leqslant \infty. \tag{6.1.9}$$

Hence *the sample spectrum is the Fourier transform of the sample acvf.* The inverse Fourier transform of (6.1.9) may be written

$$c_{xx}(u) = \int_{-\infty}^{\infty} C_{xx}(f)\, e^{j2\pi fu}\, df, \qquad -T \leqslant u \leqslant T, \tag{6.1.10}$$

which, for $u = 0$, becomes

$$c_{xx}(0) = s_T^2 = \int_{-\infty}^{\infty} C_{xx}(f)\, df. \tag{6.1.11}$$

Thus *the sample spectrum shows how the variance or average power of $x(t)$ is distributed over frequency.*

In discrete time, the sample spectrum is

$$C_{xx}(f) = \Delta \sum_{k=-(N-1)}^{(N-1)} c_{xx}(k)\, e^{-j2\pi fk\Delta}, \qquad -\frac{1}{2\Delta} \leqslant f < \frac{1}{2\Delta}, \tag{6.1.12}$$

which corresponds to (6.1.9). The inverse transform of (6.1.12) is

$$c_{xx}(u) = \int_{-1/2\Delta}^{1/2\Delta} C_{xx}(f)\, e^{j2\pi fu}\, df, \qquad -N\Delta \leqslant u \leqslant N\Delta, \tag{6.1.13}$$

which corresponds to (6.1.10).

The Fourier transform pairs (6.1.9, 10) and (6.1.12, 13) are mathematical identities which hold whether $x(t)$ is deterministic *or* a realization of a stochastic process. In the next section, an interpretation of the *limiting* value of $C_{xx}(f)$ is given when the function $x(t)$ is a realization of a stationary stochastic process.

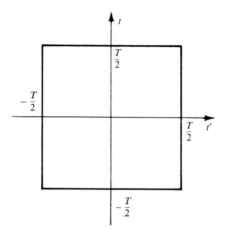

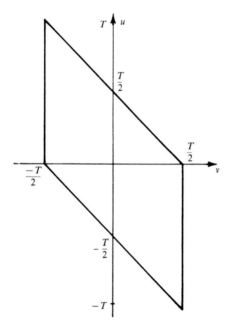

FIG. 6.3: Transformation of coordinates for the sample spectrum

6.2 THE SPECTRUM

6.2.1 *Definition of the spectrum of a stochastic process*

To describe the variability in $C_{xx}(f)$ demonstrated in Section 6.1.2, it is necessary to regard the record $x(t)$, $-T/2 \leqslant t \leqslant T/2$, as being one of many possible time series which might have been observed, that is, as a realization of a stochastic process. Thus, the variability in the record is characterized by rv's $X(t)$ for $-T/2 \leqslant t \leqslant T/2$, as indicated in Chapter 5. The sample spectrum $C_{XX}(f)$ is then regarded as a realization of the rv $C_{XX}(f)$, just as the sample covariance function $c_{XX}(u)$ was regarded as a realization of the rv $c_{XX}(u)$. By deriving the distribution of $C_{XX}(f)$, or its moments, the erratic behavior of $C_{XX}(f)$ demonstrated in Figures 6.1 and 6.2 can be explained.

Using (6.1.9), the first moment of the sample spectrum estimator $C_{XX}(f)$ is

$$E[C_{XX}(f)] = \int_{-T}^{T} E[c_{XX}(u)]\, e^{-j2\pi fu}\, du,$$

which becomes

$$E[C_{XX}(f)] = \int_{-T}^{T} \gamma_{XX}(u)\left(1 - \frac{|u|}{T}\right) e^{-j2\pi fu}\, du, \tag{6.2.1}$$

using (5.3.13). Thus (6.2.1) gives the average distribution (over all possible time series of length T) of power with frequency. As the record length T increases, $E[C_{XX}(f)]$ tends in the limit to

$$\Gamma_{XX}(f) = \lim_{T \to \infty} E[C_{XX}(f)] = \int_{-\infty}^{\infty} \gamma_{XX}(u)\, e^{-j2\pi fu}\, du. \tag{6.2.2}$$

The mathematics associated with this limiting operation is discussed more fully in [1].

The function $\Gamma_{XX}(f)$ is called the *power spectrum*, but from now on it will be referred to more concisely as the *spectrum*.

Equation (6.2.2) shows that the spectrum is the Fourier transform of the acvf of the $X(t)$ process. Using Table 2.3, there is an inverse transform

$$\gamma_{XX}(u) = \int_{-\infty}^{\infty} \Gamma_{XX}(f)\, e^{j2\pi fu}\, df. \tag{6.2.3}$$

Setting $u = 0$ in (6.2.3) gives

$$\gamma_{XX}(0) = \sigma_X^2 = \int_{-\infty}^{\infty} \Gamma_{XX}(f)\, df, \tag{6.2.4}$$

and hence $\Gamma_{XX}(f)$ *shows how the variance of the $X(t)$ process is distributed over frequency* in the same way that (6.1.9) shows how the variance of *one particular sample of length T* is distributed over frequency. Specifically, the variance of the $X(t)$ process which is due to frequencies in the range f to $f + df$ is approximately $\Gamma_{XX}(f)\, df$. Note from the definition (6.1.6) that $\Gamma_{XX}(f)$ is non-negative for all f.

For discrete time, the relations corresponding to (6.2.1) to (6.2.3) are

$$E[C_{XX}(f)] = \Delta \sum_{k=-(N-1)}^{N-1} \gamma_{XX}(k)\left(1 - \frac{|k|}{N}\right) e^{-j2\pi fk\Delta}, \quad -\frac{1}{2\Delta} \leqslant f < \frac{1}{2\Delta},$$

$$\tag{6.2.5}$$

$$\Gamma_{XX}(f) = \lim_{N \to \infty} E[C_{XX}(f)] = \Delta \sum_{k=-\infty}^{\infty} \gamma_{XX}(k)\, e^{-j2\pi k f\, \Delta}, \quad -\frac{1}{2\Delta} \leqslant f < \frac{1}{2\Delta},$$

$$(6.2.6)$$

and

$$\gamma_{XX}(k) = \int_{-1/(2\Delta)}^{1/(2\Delta)} \Gamma_{XX}(f)\, e^{j2\pi f k\, \Delta}\, df, \quad k = 0, \pm 1, \pm 2, \ldots . \quad (6.2.7)$$

Some examples. To provide some insight into the information contained in the spectrum, Figures 6.4 and 6.5 show the theoretical spectra of the first-order ar processes whose acfs were shown in Figures 5.7 and 5.8. Analytical expressions for the spectra of ar processes will be derived in Section 6.2.5.

Figure 6.4 shows that when the autoregressive parameter $\alpha_1 = 0.9$, the series is smooth, and this is reflected in an acf which damps out smoothly with lag. It is seen that the corresponding spectrum is large at low frequencies and small at high frequencies. Hence smooth series are characterized by spectra which have most of their power at low frequencies. Note that in Figures 6.4, 6.5 and 6.6, the spectrum is plotted on a *logarithmic scale*, which shows more detail in the spectrum over a wider amplitude range. Other reasons for plotting the logarithm of the spectrum will be given later on.

Figure 6.5 shows that when $\alpha_1 = -0.9$, the series oscillates very quickly, and this is reflected in an acf which changes sign. The corresponding spectrum has large power at high frequencies and small power at low frequencies. Hence quickly oscillating series are characterized by spectra which have most of their power at high frequencies.

Figure 6.6 illustrates a second-order autoregressive process. As discussed in Section 5.2.4, this is a quasi-periodic series with an "average" period of about 8 seconds. The acf reflects the periodic behavior and consists of a damped sine wave with a period of 8 seconds. The corresponding spectrum now has a peak at the frequency $f_0 = 0.125$ cps. Since the $X(t)$ process is not truly periodic, the spectrum is not concentrated at the single frequency $f = 0.125$ cps, but instead is spread over all frequencies in the range $-0.5 \leqslant f < +0.5$ cps. Most of the power, however, is near the frequency $f_0 = 0.125$ cps.

The spectral density function. It is sometimes necessary to compare time series which have different scales of measurement, and in these circumstances it is useful to normalize $\Gamma_{XX}(f)$ by dividing by the variance σ_X^2. The function

$$\frac{\Gamma_{XX}(f)}{\sigma_X^2}$$

is called the *spectral density function*. From (6.2.2) it follows that

$$\frac{\Gamma_{XX}(f)}{\sigma_X^2} = \int_{-\infty}^{\infty} \rho_{XX}(u)\, e^{-j2\pi f u}\, du, \quad (6.2.8)$$

so that the spectral density function is the Fourier transform of the acf.

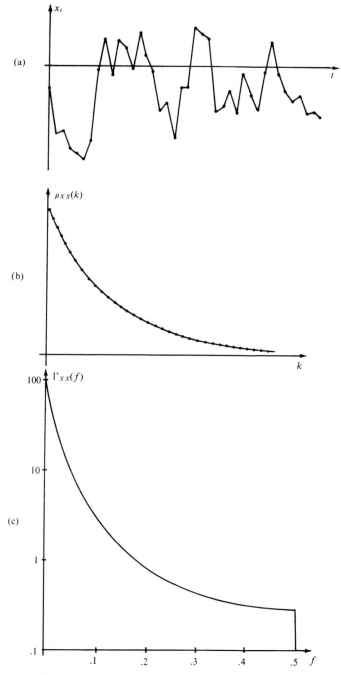

FIG. 6.4: A realization (a), the autocorrelation function (b) and spectrum (c) of a discrete first-order autoregressive process ($\alpha_1 = +0.9$)

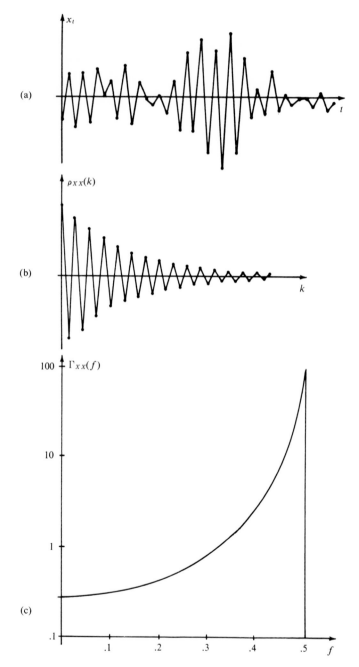

FIG. 6.5: A realization (a), the autocorrelation function (b) and spectrum (c) of a discrete first-order autoregressive process ($\alpha_1 = -0.9$)

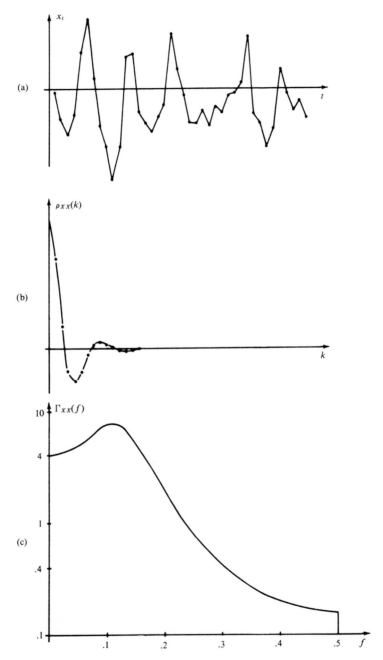

FIG. 6.6: A realization (a), the autocorrelation function (b) and spectrum (c) of a discrete second-order autoregressive process ($\alpha_1 = 1.0$, $\alpha_2 = -0.5$)

Now, the spectral density function, being the limit of a non-negative function, is also non-negative. Since it also integrates to unity, it follows that from a mathematical point of view it satisfies the same properties (3.1.8) as a pdf. It will be shown in Section 6.3 that the similarities between the spectral density function and the pdf also extend to the estimation of the two functions from finite lengths of records.

The method used to define the spectrum in this section is by no means unique. An alternative method based on the latent roots of the covariance matrix of the stochastic process is given in Section 11.1.2.

Comments on definitions of the spectrum used by engineers. Criticisms have already been given in Section 6.1.1 of the definition

$$\Gamma(f) = \lim_{T \to \infty} C_{xx}(f)$$

of the spectrum which is usually given in electrical engineering texts, for example [2] and [3]. The objection to this definition is that if $x(t)$ is a realization of a stationary stochastic process, then the corresponding random variable $C_{xx}(f)$ does not converge in any statistical sense to a limiting value.

A further source of confusion stems from the fundamental identity (6.1.9) proved above. It is falsely argued that since the sample autocovariance function $c_{xx}(u)$ tends in a well-behaved statistical sense to $\gamma_{xx}(u)$ as T tends to infinity, then it is permissible to state that

$$\lim_{T \to \infty} C_{xx}(f) = \int_{-T}^{T} \lim_{T \to \infty} c_{xx}(u)\, e^{-j2\pi f u}\, du$$

$$= \int_{-\infty}^{\infty} \gamma_{xx}(u)\, e^{-j2\pi f u}\, du$$

$$= \Gamma_{xx}(f).$$

As shown in Section 5.3.3, it is true that the mean squared error of the sample acvf estimator $c_{xx}(u)$ is of order $1/T$ and hence its distribution tends to be more clustered about $\gamma_{xx}(u)$ as T tends to infinity. Thus $c_{xx}(u)$ is a *consistent estimator* of $\gamma_{xx}(u)$. Another way of stating this fact is that the ensemble average $\gamma_{xx}(u)$ can be estimated by the *time average* $c_{xx}(u)$. This is usually referred to as the *ergodic property* and requires that $\gamma_{xx}(u)$ tend to zero at a sufficiently fast rate.

However, the fact that the ergodic property applies to $c_{xx}(u)$ *in no way implies that it holds for its Fourier transform* $C_{xx}(f)$. In fact, it is usually not true that, if there is a consistent estimator of a statistical parameter, its Fourier transform is a consistent estimator of the Fourier transform of that parameter. In other words $C_{xx}(f)$ is an example of a sample function for which the ergodic property does not hold.

An intuitive way of looking at this situation is to consider what happens to $c_{xx}(u)$ for fixed value of the lag u when the record length T increases. In this

case, more and more information in the form of products $x(t)x(t + u)$ are
included in $c_{xx}(u)$ and hence the information about $\gamma_{xx}(u)$ contained in $c_{xx}(u)$
increases indefinitely at T tends to infinity. It will be seen later that the information contained in $C_{xx}(f)$ concerning $\Gamma_{xx}(f)$ is spread over a band of
frequencies with effective width $\pm 1/T$ about f. As T increases, the total information contained in $C_{xx}(f)$ is distributed over an increasing number of
bands of decreasing width. The net result is that as T increases it is possible
to estimate the average power in narrower and narrower frequency bands;
however, the efficiency of the estimate of the power in the narrowing band
does not improve.

6.2.2 The integrated spectrum

Cases where no spectrum exists. In the previous section the power spectrum
was defined by

$$\lim_{T \to \infty} E[C_{xx}(f)] = \lim_{T \to \infty} \int_{-T}^{T} \gamma_{xx}(u) \left(1 - \frac{|u|}{T}\right) e^{-j2\pi fu} \, du,$$

provided this limit exists. Clearly, if $\Gamma_{xx}(f)$ is to be finite it is sufficient that

$$|\Gamma_{xx}(f)| = \left| \int_{-\infty}^{\infty} \gamma_{xx}(u) e^{-j2\pi fu} \, du \right|$$

$$\leqslant \int_{-\infty}^{\infty} |\gamma_{xx}(u)| \, du \leqslant M, \qquad (6.2.9)$$

where M is a finite constant. Hence if the spectrum is to be finite, it is sufficient
(but not necessary) for $\gamma_{xx}(u)$ to tend to zero as the lag u tends to infinity
at a sufficiently fast rate so that the integral (6.2.9) is finite.

As an example of a stochastic process for which this condition is not met,
consider the process

$$X(t) = A \cos 2\pi f_0 t + B \sin 2\pi f_0 t = R \cos (2\pi f_0 t + \phi), \qquad (6.2.10)$$

where A and B are independent rv's with mean zero and variance σ^2. For a
given realization, $x(t)$ is a cosine wave, $R \cos (2\pi f_0 t + \phi)$ having constant
amplitude, frequency and phase. Across the ensemble, the amplitude and
phase vary randomly, while the frequency remains fixed. From (6.2.10),

$$E[X(t)] = E[A] \cos 2\pi f_0 t + E[B] \sin 2\pi f_0 t = 0.$$

Hence

$$
\begin{aligned}
\gamma_{xx}(u) &= E[X(t)X(t + u)] \\
&= E[(A \cos 2\pi f_0 t + B \sin 2\pi f_0 t)(A \cos 2\pi f_0(t + u) + B \sin 2\pi f_0(t + u))] \\
&= \sigma^2[\cos 2\pi f_0 t \cos 2\pi f_0(t + u) + \sin 2\pi f_0 t \sin 2\pi f_0(t + u)] \\
&= \sigma^2 \cos 2\pi f_0 u.
\end{aligned}
$$

$\gamma_{XX}(u)$ does not tend to zero as u tends to infinity, and so the integral (6.2.9) diverges. However, a spectrum can be defined in terms of delta functions, using (2.2.12), so that

$$\Gamma_{XX}(f) = \frac{\sigma^2}{2} [\delta(f - f_0) + \delta(f + f_0)].$$

Hence the spectrum of the stochastic process (6.2.10) may be regarded as two delta functions of area $\sigma^2/2$ centered at the frequencies $f = \pm f_0$.

The integrated spectrum. Even when the spectrum contains delta functions, it is meaningful to talk about the variance of the series accounted for by frequencies less than or equal to some frequency f'. This may be obtained formally by integrating the expression for the spectrum. For example, integrating (6.2.2) from $f = -f'$ to $f = f'$ gives the *integrated spectrum*

$$I_{XX}(f') = \int_{-f'}^{f'} \Gamma_{XX}(f) \, df$$

$$= \int_{-\infty}^{\infty} \gamma_{XX}(u) \frac{\sin 2\pi f' u}{\pi u} \, du, \quad 0 \leqslant f' \leqslant \infty. \tag{6.2.11}$$

This function is analogous to the cumulative distribution function in the same way that the spectral density function is analogous to the probability density function. Thus

$$I(0) = 0,$$
$$I(\infty) = \sigma^2$$

and

$$I(f_1) \leqslant I(f_2)$$

when $f_1 \leqslant f_2$. If the spectral density has a delta function at $f = f_0$, that is, $\gamma_{XX}(u)$ contains a component $k \cos 2\pi f_0 u$, then the integrated power spectrum jumps by an amount k at the frequency f_0.

For the discrete case, the integrated spectrum is

$$I_{XX}(f') = \int_{-f'}^{f'} \Gamma_{XX}(f) \, df$$

$$= \Delta \sum_{k=-\infty}^{\infty} \gamma_{XX}(k) \frac{\sin \pi k f' \Delta}{\sin \pi f' \Delta}, \quad 0 \leqslant f' < \frac{1}{2\Delta}. \tag{6.2.12}$$

6.2.3 *The spectrum of white noise*

In Section 5.2.1, the completely random or white noise process $Z(t)$ was defined as one with an acvf $\gamma_{ZZ}(u) = \sigma_Z^2 \, \delta(u)$. This has infinite variance and as such cannot represent a valid stochastic process. However, it was shown that it could be regarded as the limit as τ tends to zero of the Bachelier–Wiener process $Y(t)$ which has the acvf

$$\gamma_{YY}(u) = \begin{cases} 0, & |u| > \tau \\ \dfrac{\sigma_Z^2}{\tau}\left(1 - \dfrac{|u|}{\tau}\right), & |u| \leqslant \tau. \end{cases}$$

Hence using the definition (6.2.2), the Bachelier–Wiener process has the spectrum

$$\Gamma_{YY}(f) = \int_{-\tau}^{\tau} \frac{\sigma_Z^2}{\tau}\left(1 - \frac{|u|}{\tau}\right) e^{-j2\pi fu}\, du$$

$$= \sigma_Z^2 \left(\frac{\sin \pi f\tau}{\pi f\tau}\right)^2, \quad -\infty < f < \infty.$$

In the limit as τ tends to zero, $\Gamma_{YY}(f)$ tends to

$$\lim_{\tau \to 0} \Gamma_{YY}(f) = \Gamma_{ZZ}(f) = \sigma_Z^2, \tag{6.2.13}$$

that is, a constant for all f.

The $Z(t)$ process is termed *white noise* by analogy with the optical spectrum of white light, which has all optical frequencies present with approximately the same intensity. True white noise is as physically impossible as an impulse function; indeed, it may be regarded as the statistician's analog of the engineer's impulse function.

Methods of generating white noise. There are no difficulties in defining white noise in discrete time since the acvf of discrete white noise Z_t is

$$\gamma_{ZZ}(u) = \begin{cases} \sigma_Z^2, & u = 0 \\ 0, & u = \pm \Delta, \pm 2\Delta, \pm 3\Delta, \ldots. \end{cases}$$

Using (6.2.6) it follows that

$$\Gamma_{ZZ}(f) = \sigma_Z^2 \Delta, \quad -\frac{1}{2\Delta} \leqslant f < \frac{1}{2\Delta}, \tag{6.2.14}$$

so that all frequencies in the range $-1/2\Delta \leqslant f < 1/2\Delta$ contribute the same amount of power or variance.

Discrete white noise may be generated from non-white continuous noise very simply. For example, suppose a source of continuous non-white noise is available which has an acvf which is zero when $u > u_0$. Clearly, sampling the $X(t)$ process at spacing $\Delta > u_0$ produces a Z_t process with the same acvf as (6.2.14).

The frequency-domain interpretation of this method of generating discrete white noise from continuous non-white noise is that the sampling frequency $1/\Delta$ is so low that many many aliasings of the spectrum $\Gamma_{XX}(f)$ occur (see Section 2.4.2). Hence, the spectrum of the discrete (sampled) signal which is the sum of the aliased segments tends to a flat-topped function, that is, $\Gamma_{zz}(f)$ tends to a constant in the range $-1/2\Delta \leqslant f < 1/2\Delta$. The flattening of the aliased spectrum is demonstrated in Figure 2.11 for one particular case. Note that in discussing white noise, nothing has been said about the pdf of $Z(t)$, that is, *white noise may have any amplitude pdf whatever.*

True white noise can never exist physically, but very good approximations to it can and do. For example, the fluctuating current in an electron tube provides a very good approximation, having an essentially flat power spectrum from 0 to 100 megacycles per second. This noise is usually referred to as *shot noise* and is due to the random emission of electrons from the cathode of the tube.

Another example of a physical source of noise which is approximately white over a wide frequency range is *thermal noise.* This is the voltage or current in a wire of resistance R due to the thermal motion of electrons. Its power spectrum is approximately constant over a wide range of frequencies and is equal to

$$\Gamma_{XX}(f) = 4RkT,$$

where T is the absolute temperature and k is Boltzmann's constant. A more detailed discussion of shot and thermal noise is given in [2].

6.2.4 The spectrum of a linear process

An expression is now derived for the spectrum of the output from a stable linear system when the input is a stationary process. When the input is white noise, the output spectrum is the spectrum of a stationary linear process.

Consider the output process $X(t)$ from a stable linear system with impulse response $h(u)$ and input process $Z(t)$. From (5.2.8), the acvf of the $X(t)$ process is

$$\gamma_{XX}(u) = \int_0^\infty \int_0^\infty h(v)h(v')\gamma_{ZZ}(u + v - v') \, dv \, dv',$$

and hence from (6.2.2) the spectrum of the output is

$$\Gamma_{XX}(f) = \int_{-\infty}^\infty \gamma_{XX}(u) \, e^{-j2\pi fu} \, du$$

$$= \int_{-\infty}^\infty e^{-j2\pi fu} \int_0^\infty \int_0^\infty h(v)h(v')\gamma_{ZZ}(u + v - v') \, dv \, dv' \, du$$

$$= \int_0^\infty h(v) \, e^{j2\pi fv} \, dv \int_0^\infty h(v') \, e^{-j2\pi fv'} \, dv' \int_{-\infty}^\infty \gamma_{ZZ}(y) \, e^{-j2\pi fy} \, dy,$$

where $y = u + v - v'$.
Hence

$$\Gamma_{XX}(f) = H(-f)H(f)\Gamma_{ZZ}(f)$$
$$= |H(f)|^2\Gamma_{ZZ}(f), \quad -\infty \leqslant f \leqslant \infty. \tag{6.2.15}$$

This fundamental property states that *the spectrum of the output from a linear system is obtained from the spectrum of the input by multiplying by the square of the modulus of the frequency response function.*

If $Z(t)$ is white noise with spectrum $\Gamma_{ZZ}(f) = \sigma_Z^2$, acvf $\gamma_{ZZ}(u) = \sigma_Z^2 \, \delta(u)$, then $X(t)$ is a linear process with spectrum

$$\Gamma_{XX}(f) = \sigma_Z^2 |H(f)|^2, \quad -\infty \leqslant f \leqslant \infty. \qquad (6.2.16)$$

In discrete time, the relation corresponding to (6.2.15) is

$$\Gamma_{XX}(f) = |H(f)|^2 \Gamma_{ZZ}(f), \quad -\frac{1}{2\Delta} \leqslant f < \frac{1}{2\Delta}, \qquad (6.2.17)$$

where $H(f) = \sum_{k=0}^{\infty} h_k \, e^{-j2\pi f k \, \Delta}$.

When the input is the completely random process with variance σ_Z^2, the output is a linear process with spectrum

$$\Gamma_{XX}(f) = \Delta\sigma_Z^2 |H(f)|^2, \quad -\frac{1}{2\Delta} \leqslant f < \frac{1}{2\Delta}. \qquad (6.2.18)$$

From (6.2.15) or (6.2.18) it is seen that, given a white noise source and a suitably versatile analog (or digital) filter it is possible to generate a stochastic process with any given spectrum. In the next section some examples are given of the wide variety of spectra which may be generated by linear filtering of white noise.

6.2.5 The spectra of autoregressive and moving average processes

Continuous first-order autoregressive processes. Consider the continuous first-order ar process

$$T\frac{dX(t)}{dt} + (X(t) - \mu) = Z(t),$$

where $Z(t)$ is white noise. This has the impulse response function

$$h(u) = \begin{cases} \dfrac{1}{T} \, e^{-u/T}, & 0 \leqslant u \leqslant \infty \\ 0, & u < 0 \end{cases}$$

and frequency response function

$$H(f) = \frac{1}{1 + j2\pi fT}.$$

Hence, using (6.2.16), the spectrum of $X(t)$ is

$$\Gamma_{XX}(f) = \frac{\sigma_Z^2}{1 + (2\pi fT)^2}, \quad -\infty \leqslant f \leqslant \infty. \qquad (6.2.19)$$

The function (6.2.19) has been plotted in Figure 2.3 (a), which shows that most of the power or variance is concentrated at low frequencies.

Discrete first-order autoregressive processes. In discrete time, the first-order ar process is

$$X_t - \mu = \alpha_1(X_{t-1} - \mu) + Z_t,$$

with

$$h_k = \alpha_1^k, \quad k = 0, 1, \ldots, \infty,$$

and

$$H(f) = \frac{1}{1 - \alpha_1 e^{-j2\pi f \Delta}}, \quad -\frac{1}{2\Delta} \leqslant f < \frac{1}{2\Delta}.$$

Hence, using (6.2.18), the spectrum of the X_t process is

$$\Gamma_{XX}(f) = \frac{\Delta \sigma_Z^2}{1 + \alpha_1^2 - 2\alpha_1 \cos 2\pi f \Delta}, \quad -\frac{1}{2\Delta} \leqslant f < \frac{1}{2\Delta}. \qquad (6.2.20)$$

The spectrum (6.2.20) has been plotted in Figures 6.4 and 6.5 for $\alpha_1 = +0.9$ and $\alpha_1 = -0.9$ respectively, $\Delta = 1$ and $\sigma_Z^2 = 1$. As discussed in Section 6.2.1, when α_1 is positive the spectrum has most power at low frequencies and when α_1 is negative the spectrum has most power at high frequencies. Note from (6.2.20) that $\Gamma_{XX}(f)$ for $\alpha_1 > 0$ equals $\Gamma_{XX}(1/2\Delta - f)$ for $\alpha_1 < 0$.

Continuous second-order autoregressive processes. Consider the continuous second-order ar process

$$a_2 \frac{d^2 X}{dt^2} + a_1 \frac{dX}{dt} + a_0(X(t) - \mu) = Z(t).$$

This has the frequency response function

$$H(f) = \frac{1}{a_2(j2\pi f)^2 + a_1(j2\pi f) + a_0},$$

and hence the spectrum

$$\Gamma_{XX}(f) = \frac{\sigma_Z^2}{(a_0 - a_2 4\pi^2 f^2)^2 + (2\pi f a_1)^2}. \qquad (6.2.21)$$

In addition to generating low-frequency spectra (a_1 or a_2 large), (6.2.21) can also generate a spectrum with a peak if the roots of the characteristic equation $a_2 p^2 + a_1 p + a_0 = 0$ are complex.

Discrete second-order autoregressive processes. The discrete second-order ar process (5.2.31), namely,

$$X_t - \mu = \alpha_1(X_{t-1} - \mu) + \alpha_2(X_{t-2} - \mu) + Z_t,$$

has the frequency response function

$$H(f) = \frac{1}{1 - \alpha_1 e^{-j2\pi f \Delta} - \alpha_2 e^{-j4\pi f \Delta}}, \quad -\frac{1}{2\Delta} \leqslant f < \frac{1}{2\Delta},$$

and hence the spectrum

$$\Gamma_{xx}(f) = \frac{\Delta\sigma_Z^2}{1 + \alpha_1^2 + \alpha_2^2 - 2\alpha_1(1 - \alpha_2)\cos 2\pi f\Delta - 2\alpha_2 \cos 4\pi f\Delta},$$

$$-\frac{1}{2\Delta} \leqslant f < \frac{1}{2\Delta}. \quad (6.2.22)$$

For certain values of the parameters α_1, α_2, (6.2.22) can give rise to a low-frequency or high-frequency spectrum like the first-order discrete process. In addition to these spectra, it is possible to obtain spectra with a peak or a trough at an intermediate frequency f_0. This occurs when $|\alpha_1(1 - \alpha_2)| < |4\alpha_2|$. The frequency f_0 at which the peak or trough occurs is given by

$$\cos 2\pi f_0\Delta = -\frac{\alpha_1(1 - \alpha_2)}{4\alpha_2}. \quad \leftarrow$$

For example, the time series shown in Figure 6.6 is based on a second-order process with parameters $\alpha_1 = 1$, $\alpha_2 = -0.5$ which produces a spectrum with a peak at $f_0 = 0.125/\Delta$ cps.

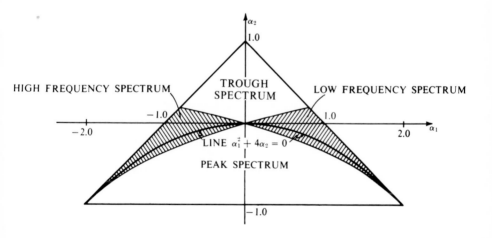

FIG. 6.7: Stability region and classification of spectra for discrete second-order autoregressive processes

The four types of spectra which can be generated with a second-order ar process are summarized in Figure 6.7. An interesting feature which is brought out by this diagram is that the region for which $\alpha_1^2 + 4\alpha_2 < 0$ (and hence for which the acf is a damped sine wave) lies partially in the region for which $|\alpha_1(1 - \alpha_2)| \geqslant |4\alpha_2|$ where the spectrum has no intermediate peak. For the high-frequency spectrum this is not surprising, since a first-order ar process with $\alpha_1 < 0$ has an oscillatory acf even though the spectrum does not have an intermediate peak. For the low-frequency spectrum, however, the acf can be oscillatory and yet no intermediate peak is evident. It is commonly assumed that a periodicity in the acf will appear as a peak in the spectrum, but this example shows that the amplitude of the damped sine wave must be large enough.

General autoregressive–moving average processes. The general continuous ar–ma process (5.2.51)

$$a_m \frac{d^m X}{dt^m} + \cdots + a_1 \frac{dX}{dt} + a_0(X(t) - \mu) = b_l \frac{d^l Z}{dt^l} + \cdots + b_1 \frac{dZ}{dt} + b_0 Z(t)$$

has the power spectrum

$$\Gamma_{XX}(f) = \sigma_Z^2 \left| \frac{b_0 + b_1 j2\pi f + \cdots + b_l(j2\pi f)^l}{a_0 + a_1 j2\pi f + \cdots + a_m(j2\pi f)^m} \right|^2, \quad -\infty \leqslant f \leqslant \infty. \quad (6.2.23)$$

Similarly, the discrete mixed process (5.2.50), namely

$$X_t - \mu = \alpha_1(X_{t-1} - \mu) + \cdots + \alpha_m(X_{t-m} - \mu) + Z_t + \beta_1 Z_{t-1} + \cdots + \beta_l Z_{t-l},$$

has the spectrum

$$\Gamma_{XX}(f) = \Delta\sigma_Z^2 \left| \frac{1 + \beta_1 e^{-j2\pi f \Delta} + \cdots + \beta_l e^{-j2\pi f \Delta l}}{1 - \alpha_1 e^{-j2\pi f \Delta} - \cdots - \alpha_m e^{-j2\pi f \Delta m}} \right|^2, \quad -\frac{1}{2\Delta} \leqslant f < \frac{1}{2\Delta}. \quad (6.2.24)$$

The expression (6.2.23) for the spectrum of the continuous process shows that if $\Gamma_{XX}(f)$ is to be a proper spectrum in the sense that it integrates out to a finite constant σ_X^2 corresponding to the variance of the $X(t)$ process, then l must satisfy $l \leqslant m - 1$. Note that there is no restriction on l for the discrete case.

The results (6.2.23) and (6.2.24) are obtained by substituting the frequency response functions (2.3.19) and (2.3.32) in (6.2.15) and (6.2.18) respectively. In general, these spectra may have multiple peaks or troughs if the roots of the corresponding characteristic equations are complex.

6.3 SPECTRAL ESTIMATORS

6.3.1 Distribution properties of sample spectral estimators for white noise

Introduction. Table 6.1 suggests that the sample spectrum estimator

$$C_{ZZ}(f) = \frac{\Delta}{N} \left[\left\{ \sum_{t=-n}^{n-1} Z_t \cos 2\pi f t \Delta \right\}^2 + \left\{ \sum_{t=-n}^{n-1} Z_t \sin 2\pi f t \Delta \right\}^2 \right],$$

$$-\frac{1}{2\Delta} \leqslant f < \frac{1}{2\Delta}, \quad (6.3.1)$$

for a purely random discrete process (discrete white noise) has a variance which is independent of the number of observations N. On the other hand, the average of the sample spectrum over frequency is close to the theoretical value of the spectrum. These results suggest that the sample spectrum is not a consistent estimator in the sense that its distribution does not tend to cluster more closely about the true spectrum as the sample size increases.

To see why this is so, consider the rv's associated with the real and imaginary Fourier components of a discrete process Z_t, $-n \leqslant t \leqslant n - 1$. These are

$$A(f) = \sum_{t=-n}^{n-1} Z_t \cos 2\pi ft\Delta,$$

$$B(f) = \sum_{t=-n}^{n-1} Z_t \sin 2\pi ft\Delta, \quad -\frac{1}{2\Delta} \leqslant f < \frac{1}{2\Delta}. \tag{6.3.2}$$

The sample spectrum estimator (6.3.1) is then

$$C_{ZZ}(f) = \frac{\Delta}{N} [A^2(f) + B^2(f)], \quad -\frac{1}{2\Delta} \leqslant f < \frac{1}{2\Delta}. \tag{6.3.3}$$

By investigating the properties of the rv's $A(f)$ and $B(f)$ it is possible to derive the sampling properties of the sample spectrum. In this section it is shown that if the Z_t process is a purely random Normal process with mean zero and variance σ_Z^2, then at the harmonic frequencies $f_k = k/N\Delta$:

(1) The random variables

$$Y(f_k) = \frac{2C_{ZZ}(f_k)}{\Delta\sigma_Z^2}, \quad k = \pm 1, \pm 2, \ldots, \pm(n - 1), \tag{6.3.4}$$

are distributed as χ_2^2 rv's.

(2) When $f_k = 0$ or $f_k = -1/2\Delta$, the rv's

$$Y(f_k) = \frac{C_{ZZ}(f_k)}{\Delta\sigma_Z^2} \tag{6.3.5}$$

are distributed as a χ_1^2.

(3) The rv's $Y(f_k)$ are mutually independent for $k = 0, \pm 1, \pm 2, \ldots,$ $\pm(n - 1)$, $-n$.

These results will be used to derive a test for white noise in Section 6.3.2. Section 6.3.3 contains a summary of more general results for the distribution properties of the sample spectrum estimators which apply for all frequencies f and for non-Normal and non-white processes. Proofs of these results are given in Appendix A9.1.

The chi-squared property of the sample spectrum estimator. Since $E[Z_t] = 0$, it follows from (6.3.2) that

$$E[A(f)] = 0 = E[B(f)].$$

Hence at the harmonic frequencies $f_k = k/N\Delta$,

$$\text{Var}\,[A(f_k)] = E[A^2(f_k)]$$

$$= \sigma_Z^2 \sum_{t=-n}^{n-1} \cos^2 2\pi f_k t\Delta = \begin{cases} \sigma_Z^2 \dfrac{N}{2}, & k = \pm 1, \pm 2, \ldots, \pm(n-1) \\ \sigma_Z^2 N, & k = 0, -n. \end{cases} \quad (6.3.6)$$

Similarly,

$$\text{Var}\,[B(f_k)] = \begin{cases} \sigma_Z^2 \dfrac{N}{2}, & k = \pm 1, \pm 2, \ldots, \pm(n-1) \\ 0, & k = 0, -n. \end{cases} \quad (6.3.7)$$

Furthermore, when $k \neq l$

$$\text{Cov}\,[A(f_k)A(f_l)] = \sigma_Z^2 \sum_{t=-n}^{n-1} \cos 2\pi f_k t\Delta \cos 2\pi f_l t\Delta$$

$$= 0, \quad (6.3.8)$$

$$\text{Cov}\,[B(f_k), B(f_l)] = 0.$$

In addition, for all k and l

$$\text{Cov}\,[A(f_k), B(f_l)] = 0. \quad (6.3.9)$$

Now since $A(f_k)$ and $B(f_k)$ are linear functions of Normal rv's, $A(f_k)$ and $B(f_k)$ are also distributed Normally. Hence the rv's

$$\frac{A^2(f_k)}{\text{Var}\,[A(f_k)]} = \frac{2A^2(f_k)}{N\sigma_Z^2}, \quad \frac{B^2(f_k)}{\text{Var}\,[B(f_k)]} = \frac{2B^2(f_k)}{N\sigma_Z^2}$$

are each distributed as χ_1^2. Moreover, (6.3.8) and (6.3.9) show that these rv's are uncorrelated and thus independent, since $A(f_k)$ and $B(f_k)$ are Normal rv's. Hence their sum

$$\frac{2}{N\sigma_Z^2}(A^2(f_k) + B^2(f_k)) = \frac{2C_{ZZ}(f_k)}{\Delta\sigma_Z^2} = Y(f_k)$$

is distributed as χ_2^2.

When $k = 0, -n$, $B(f_k)$ is identically zero. Hence

$$Y(f_k) = \frac{A^2(f_k)}{\text{Var}\,[A(f_k)]} = \frac{C_{ZZ}(f_k)}{\Delta\sigma_Z^2}, \quad k = 0, -n,$$

is distributed as χ_1^2. Equations (6.3.8) and (6.3.9) imply that the rv's $Y(f_k)$ at distinct frequencies are uncorrelated and hence independent because of the Normal assumption. Thus the results (1), (2) and (3) mentioned above have been established.

One immediate consequence of these results is that the erratic behavior of the sample spectrum in Figure 6.1 can be explained. Thus, for the purely random process, it was shown in Section 6.2.3 that the spectrum is

$$\Gamma_{ZZ}(f) = \sigma_Z^2 \Delta, \quad -\frac{1}{2\Delta} \leqslant f < \frac{1}{2\Delta}.$$

Using (3.3.6) and the results just derived,

$$E\left[\frac{2C_{zz}(f_k)}{\Delta\sigma_Z^2}\right] = 2,$$

that is,

$$E[C_{zz}(f_k)] = \sigma_Z^2\Delta = \Gamma_{zz}(f_k).$$

Hence, the sample spectrum at the harmonic frequencies provides an *unbiased estimator* of the spectrum for white noise. This explains why the mean values in Table 6.1 are close to the theoretical value.

Similarly, using (3.3.6),

$$\text{Var}\left[\frac{2C_{zz}(f_k)}{\Delta\sigma_Z^2}\right] = 4,$$

that is,

$$\text{Var}\,[C_{zz}(f_k)] = \sigma_Z^4\Delta^2 = \Gamma_{zz}^2(f_k). \tag{6.3.10}$$

Equation (6.3.10) shows that at the harmonic frequencies, at least, the variance of the estimator is a constant *independent of the sample size*. This explains the failure of the sample estimates of variance of $C_{zz}(f_k)$ to decrease with sample size as shown in Table 6.1. It is important to note that even if the Z_t process is not Normal, the rv's $A(f)$ and $B(f)$ will be very nearly Normal by the Central Limit Theorem. Hence the distribution of $C_{zz}(f)$ will be very nearly a χ_2^2 regardless of the distribution of the Z_t process.

Analysis of variance. The significance of the above results may be more readily appreciated by considering the decomposition of the total sum of squares of the rv's Z_t. Thus, using Parseval's theorem (6.1.3),

$$\sum_{t=-n}^{n-1} Z_t^2 = \sum_{t=-n}^{n-1} \frac{C_{zz}(f_k)}{\Delta}.$$

Making use of the fact that $C_{zz}(f_k) = C_{zz}(-f_k)$,

$$\frac{1}{\sigma_Z^2}\sum_{t=-n}^{n-1} Z_t^2 = \frac{1}{\Delta\sigma_Z^2}\left[C_{zz}(0) + 2\sum_{k=1}^{n-1} C_{zz}(f_k) + C_{zz}(f_n)\right]. \tag{6.3.11}$$

Since the Z_t/σ_Z are independent Normal rv's with zero means and unit standard deviations, the left-hand side of (6.3.11) will be distributed as χ_N^2. The above results then show that this χ_N^2 rv is decomposed into two χ_1^2 rv's and $(n-1)\chi_2^2$ rv's. Thus the total degrees of freedom is decomposed according to

$$N = 2n = 1 + 2(n-1) + 1.$$

When N is odd, the single degree of freedom component corresponding to $k = -n$ does not appear in (6.3.11). The decomposition is a special case of a technique called the *analysis of variance* by statisticians. When $E[Z_t] \neq 0$, the above analysis holds, but now the decomposition (6.3.11) is more conveniently written

$$\frac{1}{\sigma_Z^2} \sum_{t=-n}^{n-1} (Z_t - \bar{Z})^2 = \frac{1}{\Delta\sigma_Z^2} [2 \sum_{k=1}^{n-1} C_{ZZ}(f_k) + C_{ZZ}(f_n)], \qquad (6.3.12)$$

where $\bar{Z}$ is the sample mean of the rv's Z_t.

6.3.2 A test for white noise

Need for a test. Situations often occur in practice where it is necessary to test whether an observed time series could be regarded as a realization of a white noise process. One such example has been given in Section 5.3.5, where a test for white noise was applied to the Normal deviates generated by an automatic computer. Another example is to test the adequacy of a fitted model, for example, the ar process (5.2.39). The model can be regarded as being adequate if the residuals from the fitted model constitute a white noise process.

The test for white noise given in Section 5.3.5 is useful when one wants to detect "local correlation," that is, whether neighboring points of the time series are correlated. It is sometimes necessary to detect departures from whiteness caused by periodic effects. For example, after fitting a model to an economic time series containing seasonal variation, the inadequacy of the model might reflect itself in residuals which are periodic. In this situation a frequency domain test based on the sample spectrum is more appropriate. Such a test will now be described and should be regarded as complementary to the test based on the acf described in Section 5.3.5.

The test criterion. Equation (6.2.14) shows that the spectrum of a discrete white noise process is

$$\Gamma_{ZZ}(f) = \Delta\sigma_Z^2, \quad -\frac{1}{2\Delta} \leqslant f < \frac{1}{2\Delta}.$$

Hence the integrated spectrum

$$I_{ZZ}(f) = \int_{-f}^{f} \Gamma_{ZZ}(g)\, dg = 2\Delta\sigma_Z^2 f, \quad 0 \leqslant f \leqslant \frac{1}{2\Delta},$$

is a linear function of frequency.

Suppose that the sample spectrum estimate $C_{ZZ}(f)$ has been computed at the harmonic frequencies $f_k = k/N\Delta$, $k = 0, 1, \ldots, N/2$. Then $I(f_k)$ may be estimated from the sample integrated spectrum

$$I(f_k) = \frac{1}{N\Delta} \sum_{l=1}^{k} C_{ZZ}(f_l). \qquad (6.3.13)$$

Note that $C_{zz}(0)$ is zero if the mean is subtracted out. Since $E[C_{zz}(f_k)] = \Gamma_{zz}(f_k) = 2\,\Delta\sigma_Z^2$, it follows that

$$E[I(f_k)] = 2\,\Delta\sigma_Z^2 f_k = 2\,\Delta\sigma_Z^2 \frac{k}{N\Delta},$$

and hence $I(f_k)$ is an unbiased estimator of $I_{zz}(f_k)$. It is convenient in practice to normalize $I(f_k)$ by dividing by σ_Z^2; in this case, $I(1/2\Delta) = 1$. In practice σ_Z^2 is not known and has to be replaced by its estimator S_Z^2 so that the final form of the estimator is $I(f_k)/S_Z^2$. Thus if the estimate

$$\frac{I(f_k)}{s_z^2} = \frac{1}{N\Delta s_z^2} \sum_{l=1}^{k} C_{zz}(f_l)$$

obtained from an observed time series is plotted against $2\Delta f_k$, the points should be scattered about the straight line through the points $(0, 0)$, $(1, 1)$. Since $I(f_k)$ is the sum of rv's with the same distribution, the Kolmogoroff-Smirnov probability limits [4] applicable to cumulative distribution functions can be used to assess when a significant departure from linearity occurs.

Two examples. Table 6.2 gives the values of $C_{zz}(f_k)$ for one of the samples of random Normal deviates used for the calculations of Table 6.1. Here $N = 100$, $\Delta = 1$ and hence $f_k = 0.01, 0.02, \ldots, 0.50$. Figure 6.8 shows the plot of $I(f_k)/s^2$ versus k for this series, and from it can be seen that the deviations from the straight line are not large. To judge these deviations more precisely, a test of significance due to Kolmogoroff and Smirnov [4] may be used when N is large. This consists of constructing a band $\pm\lambda/((N/2) - 1)^{1/2}$ about the theoretical line. For significance levels of 0.95 and 0.75, λ is equal to 1.36 and 1.02 respectively. For the present example, $N/2 = 50$; hence the 95 percent

TABLE 6.2: Sample spectrum estimates at the harmonic frequencies for a sample of white noise

f_k	$C_{zz}(f_k)$	f_k	$C_{zz}(f_k)$	f_k	$C_{zz}(f_k)$
0.01	1.13	0.17	1.91	0.34	1.75
0.02	1.41	0.18	0.15	0.35	0.25
0.03	0.74	0.19	0.85	0.36	1.84
0.04	1.08	0.20	2.49	0.37	3.98
0.05	1.28	0.21	3.89	0.38	0.22
0.06	0.06	0.22	1.13	0.39	1.52
0.07	0.85	0.23	0.53	0.40	1.48
0.08	0.23	0.24	1.86	0.41	0.44
0.09	0.71	0.25	0.47	0.42	1.16
0.10	0.79	0.26	1.87	0.43	1.20
0.11	0.51	0.27	1.35	0.44	2.73
0.12	0.46	0.28	1.29	0.45	1.66
0.13	1.38	0.29	0.06	0.46	1.34
0.14	0.11	0.30	0.24	0.47	0.17
0.15	0.37	0.31	0.56	0.48	1.43
0.16	0.50	0.32	0.68	0.49	1.03
		0.33	0.44		

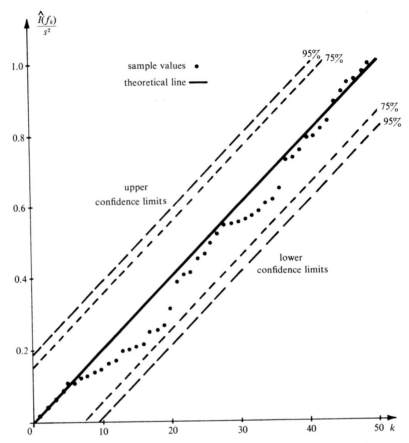

Fig. 6.8: A test for white noise using the sample integrated periodogram

limits are $\pm 1.36/\sqrt{49} = \pm 0.19$ and the 75 percent limits are ± 0.15. These limits are shown as broken lines in Figure 6.8, and it is seen that $I(f_k)/s^2$ falls well within them. Hence there is no evidence that the sample does not come from a white noise source. The interpretation of the 75 percent limits, for example, is that in one out of four plots, on average, the *maximum deviation* from the theoretical line will lie outside the limits if the process is in fact white noise.

Table 6.3 sets out the calculations for this test applied to the ionospheric data of Table 2.1, for which $s_z^2 = 196.4$. The values of $C_{zz}(f_k)$ in Table 6.3 may be obtained by multiplying the contributions to the mean square in Table 2.2 by $N = 12$.

Figure 6.9 shows that the sample integrated spectrum deviates widely from a straight line, since $I(f_1)/s^2$ is approximately twice the expected value for white noise and $I(f_2)/s^2$ is approximately three times the expected value.

The significance limits quoted above are not applicable here since N is so small. In fact, no test of significance is required in this case, since the values of $I(f_k)$ are so large when $f_k = 0.083$ and 0.166.

TABLE 6.3: White noise test applied
to ionospheric data

f_k	$C_{zz}(f_k)$	$\dfrac{1}{Ns^2} \displaystyle\sum_{l=1}^{k} C_{zz}(f_l)$
0.083	753.6	0.32
0.166	1322.4	0.88
0.250	38.4	0.90
0.333	18.0	0.91
0.417	78.0	0.94
0.500	146.0	1.00

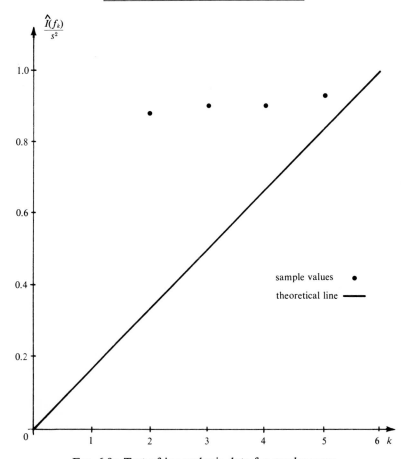

FIG. 6.9: Test of ionospheric data for randomness

6.3.3 General results for sample spectra for white noise

In Section 6.3.1 the mean and covariance of the sample spectrum estimator were derived for the harmonic frequencies $f_k = k/N\Delta$ under the assumption that the Z_t process is Normal. In Appendix A9.1 are derived more general results which apply for all frequencies and for non-Normal processes.

Moments of sample spectrum estimators for white noise. In discrete time these general results are

$$E[C_{ZZ}(f)] = \Gamma_{ZZ}(f) = \sigma_Z^2 \Delta, \quad -\frac{1}{2\Delta} \leqslant f < \frac{1}{2\Delta}, \tag{6.3.14}$$

and

$$
\begin{aligned}
&\text{Cov}\,[C_{ZZ}(f_1),\, C_{ZZ}(f_2)] \\
&= \frac{K_4 \Delta^2}{N} + \sigma_Z^4 \Delta^2 \left[\left(\frac{\sin \pi N \Delta (f_1 + f_2)}{N \sin \pi \Delta (f_1 + f_2)} \right)^2 + \left(\frac{\sin \pi N \Delta (f_1 - f_2)}{N \sin \pi \Delta (f_1 - f_2)} \right)^2 \right], \\
&\hspace{8cm} -\frac{1}{2\Delta} \leqslant f_1, f_2 < \frac{1}{2\Delta}, \quad (6.3.15)
\end{aligned}
$$

where K_4 is the fourth cumulant of the distribution of Z_t. It may be verified that (6.3.15) is zero when f_1 and f_2 are multiples of the fundamental frequency $1/N\Delta$ and the Z_t process is Normal, so that $K_4 = 0$. Hence, under these assumptions, the sample spectrum estimators at the harmonic frequencies are independent, as shown in Section 6.3.1.

For white noise in continuous time, the general results are

$$E[C_{ZZ}(f)] = \Gamma_{ZZ}(f) = \sigma_Z^2, \quad -\infty \leqslant f \leqslant \infty, \tag{6.3.16}$$

and

$$
\begin{aligned}
&\text{Cov}\,[C_{ZZ}(f_1),\, C_{ZZ}(f_2)] \\
&= \frac{K_4}{T} + \sigma_Z^4 \left[\left(\frac{\sin \pi T (f_1 + f_2)}{\pi T (f_1 + f_2)} \right)^2 + \left(\frac{\sin \pi T (f_1 - f_2)}{\pi T (f_1 - f_2)} \right)^2 \right], \\
&\hspace{8cm} -\infty \leqslant f_1, f_2 \leqslant \infty, \quad (6.3.17)
\end{aligned}
$$

where K_4 is the fourth cumulant of the $Z(t)$ process.

Note that the covariance between spectral estimators is of order $1/T$ for non-Normal processes, that is, when $K_4 \neq 0$. Observe also that for Normal processes $K_4 = 0$ and the covariance between spectral estimators is of order $1/T^2$. In the special case where f_1 and f_2 are multiples of $1/T$, the covariance is zero. Further, the variance of spectral estimators, neglecting terms of order $1/T$ and higher, is

$$\text{Var}\,[C_{ZZ}(f)] = \sigma_Z^4.$$

Hence, the variance is dominated by a constant term which remains finite as T tends to infinity. This shows in general that $C_{ZZ}(f)$ is not a consistent estimator of $\Gamma_{ZZ}(f)$.

Chi-squared properties of sample spectrum estimators for white noise. It was shown in Section 6.3.1 that for Z_t Normal white noise, $2C_{ZZ}(f)/\Delta\sigma_Z^2$ was distributed as a χ_2^2 at the harmonic frequencies $f_k = k/N\Delta$. In Appendix A9.1 this result is generalized to show that for Normal white noise processes, $2C_{ZZ}(f)/\Delta\sigma_Z^2$ is exactly distributed as a χ_2^2, while for non-Normal processes, $2C_{ZZ}(f)/\Delta\sigma_Z^2$ is approximately distributed as a χ_2^2 *for all f* when N is large. The results for continuous time are identical except that they refer to $C_{ZZ}(f)/\sigma_Z^2$.

6.3.4 Smoothing of spectral estimators

Bartlett's smoothing procedure. One device which can be used to produce spectrum estimators which have smaller variance than $C_{ZZ}(f)$ is due to Bartlett [5]. Suppose that instead of computing $C_{zz}(f)$ for a sample of white noise of length $N = 400$, as was done in Section 6.1.2, the series is split up into $k = 8$ series of length $N/k = 50$ and a sample spectrum $C_{zz}^{(i)}(f)$, $i = 1, 2, \ldots, 8$, evaluated for each sub-series. The mean of the eight sample spectra at the frequency f is

$$\bar{C}_{zz}(f) = \frac{1}{8} \sum_{i=1}^{8} C_{zz}^{(i)}(f), \quad -\frac{1}{2\Delta} \leqslant f < \frac{1}{2\Delta}, \qquad (6.3.18)$$

and is called a *smoothed spectral estimate* at the frequency f.

Figure 6.10 shows $\bar{C}_{zz}(f)$ and $C_{zz}(f)$ based on all 400 terms, plotted at the frequencies $f = 0, 0.02, \ldots, 0.5$ cps. Note that $\bar{C}_{zz}(f)$ is smoother than $C_{zz}(f)$ and much closer to $\Gamma_{ZZ}(f)$. Table 6.4 shows the mean, variance and

TABLE 6.4: Moments of unsmoothed and smoothed spectral estimates

	Mean	Variance	Mean square error
$C_{zz}(f)$	0.95	0.826	0.828
$\bar{C}_{zz}(f)$	0.94	0.139	0.143

mean square error of $\bar{C}_{zz}(f)$ and $C_{zz}(f)$ averaged over frequency. From (6.3.10), the variance of each $C_{zz}^{(i)}(f)$ is σ_Z^4. Because Z_t is white noise, it follows that the sub-series are independent and hence the variance of $\bar{C}_{ZZ}(f)$ is $\sigma_Z^4/8$. The observed ratio $(0.139/0.826 = 1/5.94)$ of the two variances from Table 6.4 is not inconsistent with the expected ratio $1/8$. Hence by averaging or smoothing over sub-series, the variance of the spectral estimator can be reduced to whatever size is required. As an extreme case, sub-series of size 2 could be used, in which case the variance would be reduced to $2\sigma_Z^4/N$. To see why this is not sensible, it is necessary to examine the above smoothing procedure more closely and to derive the moments of the smoothed estimator.

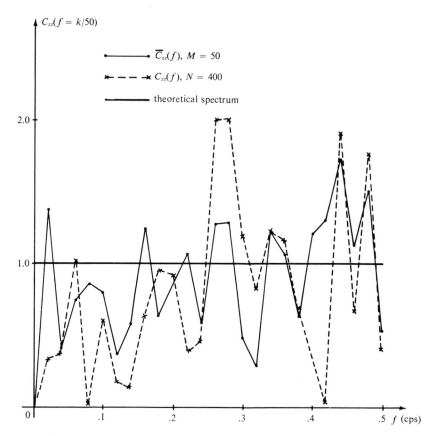

$C_{zz}(f = k/50)$

$\bullet\!\!-\!\!-\!\!-\!\!-\!\!\bullet$ $\overline{C}_{zz}(f)$, $M = 50$

$\times\!-\!-\!-\!\times$ $C_{zz}(f)$, $N = 400$

$\underline{\hspace{2cm}}$ theoretical spectrum

2.0

1.0

0   .1   .2   .3   .4   .5 f (cps)

FIG. 6.10: Sample spectrum and smoothed spectral estimates for Normal white noise

Lag and spectral windows. From (6.2.1), the mean of the sample spectrum estimator is

$$E[C_{XX}(f)] = \int_{-T}^{T} \left(1 - \frac{|u|}{T}\right) \gamma_{XX}(u)\, e^{-j2\pi f u}\, du. \qquad (6.3.19)$$

This is the Fourier transform of the product of $\gamma_{XX}(u)$ and the function

$$w(u) = \begin{cases} 1 - \dfrac{|u|}{T}, & |u| \leqslant T \\[2mm] 0, & |u| > T. \end{cases} \qquad (6.3.20)$$

Hence using the convolution theorem (2.4.3),

$$E[C_{XX}(f)] = \int_{-\infty}^{\infty} T\left\{\frac{\sin \pi T g}{\pi T g}\right\}^2 \Gamma_{XX}(f - g)\, dg, \qquad (6.3.21)$$

since the Fourier transform of $w(u)$ is

$$W(f) = T \left(\frac{\sin \pi Tf}{\pi Tf} \right)^2. \tag{6.3.22}$$

Equation (6.3.21) shows that the sample spectrum estimator has an expected value which corresponds to looking at the theoretical spectrum $\Gamma_{XX}(f)$ through the *spectral window* $W(f)$. In the terminology of Chapter 2, $E[C_{XX}(f)]$ corresponds to having passed the theoretical spectrum $\Gamma_{XX}(f)$ through a filter with an "impulse response" $W(f)$. The terms *spectral window* for $W(f)$ and *lag window* for $w(u)$ were introduced by Blackman and Tukey [6].

Since $W(f)$ in (6.3.22) behaves like a delta function for large T, it follows from (6.3.21) and (2.2.5) that

$$\lim_{T \to \infty} E[C_{XX}(f)] = \Gamma_{XX}(f),$$

that is, $C_{XX}(f)$ is an asymptotically unbiased estimator of $\Gamma_{XX}(f)$. For finite lengths of record, however, (6.3.21) shows that the sample spectrum is equivalent to looking at the true spectrum through the window (6.3.22). This means that $C_{XX}(f)$ is a biased estimator of $\Gamma_{XX}(f)$ with bias

$$B(f) = E[C_{XX}(f)] - \Gamma_{XX}(f).$$

For white noise, $\Gamma_{XX}(f) = \Delta \sigma_Z^2$, and (6.3.21) reduces to

$$E[C_{XX}(f)] = \Delta \sigma_Z^2$$

for all T. Hence for white noise, the sample spectrum estimator is an unbiased estimator of the spectrum for all T.

The spectral window $W(f)$ is a slit with width of order $1/T$, so that for large T it is reasonable to assume that $\Gamma_{XX}(f)$ is approximately constant over the slit. Hence (6.3.21) reduces to

$$E[C_{XX}(f)] \approx \Gamma_{XX}(f) \int_{-\infty}^{\infty} T \left(\frac{\sin \pi Tg}{\pi Tg} \right)^2 dg = \Gamma_{XX}(f).$$

Thus, the bias of the sample or unsmoothed spectrum estimate will always be small provided T is reasonably large.

The Bartlett spectral window. Now consider the expected value of the estimator $\bar{C}_{XX}(f)$ used in Bartlett's smoothing procedure. From (6.1.9) for the k sub-series, each of length M,

$$C_{XX}^{(i)}(f) = \int_{-M}^{M} c_{XX}^{(i)}(u) e^{-j2\pi fu} du.$$

Hence, the smoothed estimator is

$$\bar{C}_{XX}(f) = \frac{1}{k} \sum_{i=1}^{k} C_{XX}^{(i)}(f) = \int_{-M}^{M} \bar{c}_{XX}(u) e^{-j2\pi fu} du, \tag{6.3.23}$$

where

$$\bar{c}_{XX}(u) = \frac{1}{k} \sum_{i=1}^{k} \left\{ \frac{1}{M} \int_{(i-1)M}^{iM-u} X(t)X(t+u)\, dt \right\}, \quad u \geqslant 0, \qquad (6.3.24)$$

and it is defined in a similar way to (5.3.9) when $u < 0$. The expected value of $\bar{c}_{XX}(u)$ is then

$$E[\bar{c}_{XX}(u)] = \gamma_{XX}(u) \left(1 - \frac{|u|}{M} \right)$$

and

$$E[\bar{C}_{XX}(f)] = \int_{-M}^{M} \left(1 - \frac{|u|}{M} \right) \gamma_{XX}(u)\, e^{-j2\pi fu}\, du$$

$$= \int_{-\infty}^{\infty} \Gamma_{XX}(f-g)\, M \left(\frac{\sin \pi g M}{\pi g M} \right)^2 dg. \quad (6.3.25)$$

Hence, subdividing the record of length T into k section of length $M = T/k$ and forming the smoothed spectral estimator (6.3.23) is equivalent to smoothing the sample spectrum by the spectral window

$$W(f) = M \left(\frac{\sin \pi f M}{\pi f M} \right)^2. \qquad (6.3.26)$$

In the time domain, this is equivalent to multiplying the covariance function by the lag window

$$w(u) = \begin{cases} 1 - \dfrac{|u|}{M}, & |u| \leqslant M \\ 0, & |u| > M. \end{cases} \qquad (6.3.27)$$

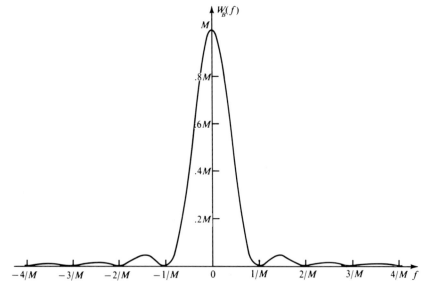

FIG. 6.11: The Bartlett spectral window $W_B(f) = M(\sin \pi f M/\pi f M)^2$

The windows (6.3.26) and (6.3.27) are called the Bartlett spectral window and Bartlett lag window. The Bartlett spectral window is plotted in Figure 6.11 and is seen to be symmetric about the origin and has zeros at $f = \pm 1/M$, $\pm 2/M, \ldots$. Thus the base width of the window, that is, the distance between the first zeros on either side, is $2/M$. Hence by controlling the length M of the sub-series it is possible to regulate the base width of the spectral window. It has already been shown that by making M small the variance can be made small. Since this corresponds to making the base width large, it follows that a small variance can be obtained by using a spectral window with a large base width. However, a large base width implies smoothing over a wide range of frequencies, that is, the "impulse response" $W(f)$ is very wide and so the bias $B(f) = E[\bar{C}_{xx}(f)] - \Gamma_{xx}(f)$ may be large. Thus, as with all statistical estimators, one is forced to compromise between variance and bias. In the next section this compromise is examined for a more general method of smoothing sample spectra.

6.3.5 Spectral windows and smoothed spectral estimators

A general class of smoothed spectral estimators. The Bartlett smoothing procedure described above shows that the large variance of the sample spectrum estimator can be reduced by introducing the lag window (6.3.27). More generally, this suggests that a smoothed spectral estimator of the form

$$\bar{C}_{xx}(f) = \int_{-\infty}^{\infty} w(u)c_{xx}(u)\, e^{-j2\pi fu}\, du = \int_{-\infty}^{\infty} \bar{c}_{xx}(u)\, e^{-j2\pi fu}\, du$$

(6.3.28)

will have a smaller variance than the sample spectrum estimator $C_{xx}(f)$. The lag window $w(u)$ in (6.3.28) is a function satisfying the conditions

$$
\begin{aligned}
&(1) \quad w(0) = 1,\\
&(2) \quad w(u) = w(-u),\\
&(3) \quad w(u) = 0, \quad |u| > T.
\end{aligned}
$$

(6.3.29)

In practice, condition *(3)* is replaced by

$$(4) \quad w(u) = 0, \quad |u| \geqslant M, \quad M < T,$$

since covariances need then be computed only up to lag M. Examples of lag windows which are widely used in spectral analysis are given in Table 6.5 and plotted in Figure 6.12. The Fourier transforms of these lag windows, that is, the spectral windows $W(f)$, are shown in Figure 6.13.

Using the convolution property (2.4.3), (6.3.28) may be written

$$\bar{C}_{xx}(f) = \int_{-\infty}^{\infty} W(g)C_{xx}(f - g)\, dg,$$

(6.3.30)

TABLE 6.5: Lag and spectral windows

Description	Lag window	Spectral window
rectangular	$w_R(u) = \begin{cases} 1, & |u| \leq M \\ 0, & |u| > M \end{cases}$	$W_R(f) = 2M\left(\dfrac{\sin 2\pi fM}{2\pi fM}\right)$, $\quad -\infty \leq f \leq \infty$
Bartlett	$w_B(u) = \begin{cases} 1 - \dfrac{|u|}{M}, & |u| \leq M \\ 0, & |u| > M \end{cases}$	$W_B(f) = M\left(\dfrac{\sin \pi fM}{\pi fM}\right)^2$, $\quad -\infty \leq f \leq \infty$
Tukey	$w_T(u) = \begin{cases} \dfrac{1}{2}\left(1 + \cos\dfrac{\pi u}{M}\right), & |u| \leq M \\ 0, & |u| > M \end{cases}$	$W_T(f) = M\left\{\dfrac{\sin 2\pi fM}{2\pi fM} + \dfrac{1}{2}\dfrac{\sin 2\pi M(f + \frac{1}{2}M)}{2\pi M(f + \frac{1}{2}M)} \right.$ $\left. + \dfrac{1}{2}\dfrac{\sin 2\pi M(f - \frac{1}{2}M)}{2\pi M(f - \frac{1}{2}M)}\right\}$ $= M\left(\dfrac{\sin 2\pi fM}{2\pi fM}\right)\left(\dfrac{1}{1 - (2fM)^2}\right)$, $\quad -\infty \leq f \leq \infty$
Parzen	$w_P(u) = \begin{cases} 1 - 6\left(\dfrac{u}{M}\right)^2 + 6\left(\dfrac{|u|}{M}\right)^3, & |u| \leq \dfrac{M}{2} \\ 2\left(1 - \dfrac{|u|}{M}\right)^3, & \dfrac{M}{2} < |u| \leq M \\ 0, & |u| > M \end{cases}$	$W_P(f) = \dfrac{3}{4}M\left(\dfrac{\sin \pi fM/2}{\pi fM/2}\right)^4$, $\quad -\infty \leq f \leq \infty$

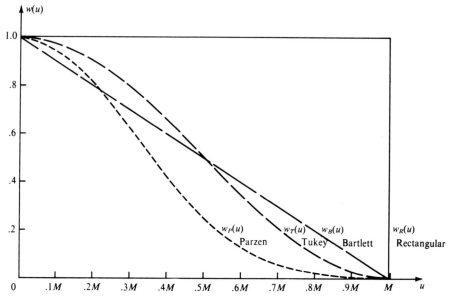

FIG. 6.12: Some common lag windows

where $C_{XX}(f)$ is the sample spectrum defined by (6.1.6) or (6.1.9) and

$$W(f) = \int_{-\infty}^{\infty} w(u) e^{-j2\pi f u} \, du. \tag{6.3.31}$$

The inverse transform

$$w(u) = \int_{-\infty}^{\infty} W(f) e^{j2\pi f u} \, df \tag{6.3.32}$$

enables the lag window $w(u)$ to be calculated from the spectral window $W(f)$. Analogous to the properties (6.3.29), the spectral window $W(f)$ satisfies the conditions

$(1) \quad \int_{-\infty}^{\infty} W(f) \, df = w(0) = 1,$

$(2) \quad W(f) = W(-f),$ (6.3.33)

$(3) \quad W(f)$ is a slit with base width of order $2/M$.

The expected value of a smoothed spectral estimator. Taking expectations in (6.3.30) gives

$$E[\bar{C}_{XX}(f)] = \int_{-\infty}^{\infty} W(g) E[C_{XX}(f - g)] \, dg. \tag{6.3.34}$$

However, for large T, (6.3.21) shows that

$$E[C_{XX}(g)] \approx \Gamma_{XX}(g),$$

and so

$$E[\bar{C}_{XX}(f)] \approx \int_{-\infty}^{\infty} W(g) \Gamma_{XX}(f - g) \, dg = \bar{\Gamma}_{XX}(f). \tag{6.3.35}$$

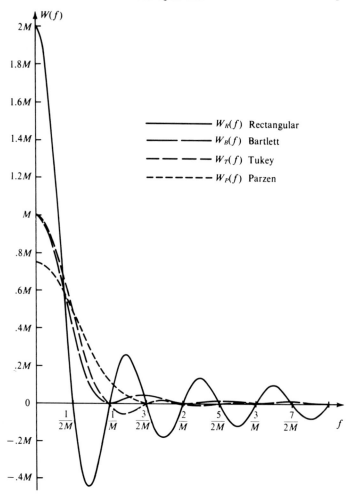

FIG. 6.13: Some common spectral windows

$\bar{\Gamma}_{XX}(f)$ will be called the *mean smoothed spectrum*.

The material of Section 2.4.1 is now relevant. Since the spectral window $W(f)$ satisfies condition *(3)* of (6.3.33), $\bar{\Gamma}_{XX}(f)$ will be a distorted version of $\Gamma_{XX}(f)$. This effect is demonstrated in Figure 2.10, where $\Gamma_{XX}(f)$ corresponds to $|S_i(f)|$, $\bar{\Gamma}_{XX}(f)$ corresponds to $|S_0(f)|$ and the lag windows $w(u)$ correspond to the data windows $w(t)$. From Figure 2.10 it is seen that the narrower the base width of the lag window, the more $\bar{\Gamma}_{XX}(f)$ differs from $\Gamma_{XX}(f)$. Hence, in order to keep the bias

$$B(f) = E[\bar{C}_{XX}] - \Gamma_{XX}(f) = \bar{\Gamma}_{XX}(f) - \Gamma_{XX}(f)$$

small, M must be large. This is contrary to the previous requirement that M

be small in order to keep Var $[\bar{C}_{XX}(f)]$ small. It has been shown in Section 4.2.3 that it is necessary to compromise between the variance and bias of an estimator. Similar considerations apply to estimators of the spectrum. The bias can only be made small by making $W(f)$ narrow or as close to a delta function as possible. On the other hand, a narrow spectral window $W(f)$ results in a large variance. Hence a sensible procedure is to compromise by making the mse

$$\text{Var } [\bar{C}_{XX}(f)] + B^2(f)$$

as small as possible [7].

The exact nature of the compromise which has to be made will depend on the degree of smoothness of the spectrum $\Gamma_{XX}(f)$. For example, if $\Gamma_{XX}(f)$ is very smooth, then the variance may be reduced by using a wide window without having serious effect on the bias. In particular, if $\Gamma_{XX}(f)$ is smooth over the range $-1/M \leqslant (f - g) \leqslant 1/M$, then (6.3.35) is approximately

$$E[\bar{C}_{XX}(f)] \approx \Gamma_{XX}(f) \int_{-\infty}^{\infty} W(g)\, dg$$
$$= \Gamma_{XX}(f), \tag{6.3.36}$$

by virtue of (6.3.33) and (6.3.34). Hence, if the spectrum is sufficiently smooth, a virtually unbiased estimator is obtained even though the spectral window has been made wide to reduce the variance.

Approximate expressions for bias. If the spectrum is not smooth relative to the spectral window, it is possible following Parzen [8] to compute approximations to the bias corresponding to a particular spectral window. Using (6.3.28) and (5.3.13), the bias may also be written

$$B(f) = E\left[\int_{-\infty}^{\infty} w(u)c_{XX}(u)\, e^{-j2\pi fu}\, du\right] - \int_{-\infty}^{\infty} \gamma_{XX}(u)\, e^{-j2\pi fu}\, du$$
$$\approx \int_{-\infty}^{\infty} (w(u) - 1)\gamma_{XX}(u)\, e^{-j2\pi fu}\, du, \tag{6.3.37}$$

for T large. Substituting for the lag windows $w(u)$ from Table 6.5, the following expressions are obtained for the bias associated with these windows:

$$B_B(f) \approx \frac{1}{M} \int_{-\infty}^{\infty} - |u|\gamma_{XX}(u)\, e^{-j2\pi fu}\, du,$$

$$B_T(f) \approx \frac{\pi^2}{4M^2} \int_{-\infty}^{\infty} - u^2\gamma_{XX}(u)\, e^{-j2\pi fu}\, du + 0\left(\frac{1}{M^4}\right)$$
$$= \frac{0.063}{M^2}\, \Gamma_{XX}^{(2)}(f) + 0\left(\frac{1}{M^4}\right), \tag{6.3.38}$$

$$B_P(f) \approx \frac{6}{M^2} \int_{-\infty}^{\infty} - u^2\gamma_{XX}(u)\, e^{-j2\pi fu}\, du + 0\left(\frac{1}{M^3}\right)$$
$$= \frac{0.152}{M^2}\, \Gamma_{XX}^{(2)}(f) + 0\left(\frac{1}{M^3}\right).$$

In the above expressions, $\Gamma_{XX}^{(2)}(f)$ is the second derivative of the spectrum at frequency f. These formulae show that:

(1) When $\Gamma_{XX}^{(2)}(f)$ is negative, as in the neighborhood of a peak, the bias is negative and hence peaks will tend to be underestimated. Conversely, when $\Gamma_{XX}^{(2)}(f)$ is positive, as in the neighborhood of a trough, the bias is positive, and hence troughs will be overestimated.

(2) The narrower the peak or trough, the larger $\Gamma_{XX}^{(2)}(f)$ and hence the greater the bias.

(3) The bias $B_B(f)$ for the Bartlett window is of order $1/M$ and hence will be larger in general than the bias of the Tukey and Parzen windows, which are of order $1/M^2$.

(4) The bias is reduced as M increases, that is, as the base width of the window is decreased.

(5) For the same truncation point M, the Parzen window has a larger bias than the Tukey window. This is because the Parzen spectral window is wider than the Tukey spectral window, as is seen from Figure 6.13. However, the Parzen estimator has a smaller variance than the Tukey estimator for the same values of M, as will be shown in Section 6.4.1.

The results (6.3.38) are useful in describing the qualitative features of bias but to obtain a quantitative picture it is necessary to plot the mean smoothed spectrum as a function of frequency, as will be shown in Section 7.1.

6.4 FURTHER PROPERTIES OF SMOOTHED SPECTRAL ESTIMATORS

One important property of a spectral estimator has already been derived, namely its bias. Another important property is its variance, for which an approximation was given in Section 6.3.4 for the special case of white noise using a Bartlett window. This result is now extended to any window and any stochastic process. Knowing the variance it is possible to construct a confidence interval for the true spectrum at any frequency. In this section it is shown that the covariance between two estimators at a sufficiently wide frequency spacing is approximately zero. Hence independent confidence intervals may be constructed at this frequency separation.

6.4.1 Covariance between smoothed spectral estimators

The precise derivation of the result for the covariance between smoothed spectral estimators at two frequencies is rather complicated. Hence the derivation given in this section is heuristic, but a more detailed analysis is given in Appendix A9.1.

The approach here will be to use the result (5.2.6), namely, that any stochastic process $X(t)$ with spectrum $\Gamma_{XX}(f)$ can be regarded as having been generated by passing white noise $Z(t)$ through a linear filter. Combining (5.2.6) with the results of Section 6.3.3 for the covariances between the sample spectrum estimators for white noise enables one to derive expressions for the covariances between sample spectrum estimators for any stochastic process. It is then a simple step to derive expressions for the covariances between smoothed spectral estimators.

Covariance of sample spectral estimators. Consider a stochastic process $X(t)$ with spectrum $\Gamma_{XX}(f)$, generated according to

$$X(t) = \int_0^\infty h(u)Z(t - u)\, du, \quad -\infty \leqslant t \leqslant \infty, \tag{6.4.1}$$

where $Z(t)$ is a white noise process. Hence, from (6.2.16), the spectrum can be written

$$\Gamma_{XX}(f) = \sigma_Z^2 |H(f)|^2, \quad -\infty \leqslant f \leqslant \infty. \tag{6.4.2}$$

For a finite segment of the $X(t)$ process, (6.4.1) may be written

$$X(t) = \int_0^\infty h(u)Z(t - u)\, du \approx X_T(t), \quad -T/2 \leqslant t \leqslant T/2, \tag{6.4.3}$$

where

$$X_T(t) = \int_0^\infty h(u)Z_T(t - u)\, du, \quad -T/2 \leqslant t \leqslant T/2. \tag{6.4.4}$$

In (6.4.4), $Z_T(t)$ is a finite segment of the $Z(t)$ process. Over the interval $-T/2 \leqslant t \leqslant T/2$, the two processes $X(t)$ and $X_T(t)$ will be identical except near the beginning of the interval, provided the impulse response $h(u)$ tends to zero in a short time compared with T. It will now be assumed that the "beginning effect" can be neglected.

The sample spectrum for the $X(t)$ process,

$$C_{XX}(f) = \frac{1}{T}\left| \int_{-T/2}^{T/2} X(t)\, e^{-j2\pi ft}\, dt \right|^2,$$

may then be written approximately

$$C_{XX}(f) \approx \frac{1}{T}\left| \int_{-T/2}^{T/2} X_T(t)\, e^{-j2\pi ft}\, dt \right|^2$$

$$= \frac{1}{T}\left| \int_{-T/2}^{T/2} \int_0^\infty h(u)Z_T(t - u)\, du\, e^{-j2\pi ft}\, dt \right|^2$$

$$= |H(f)|^2 C_{ZZ}(f). \tag{6.4.5}$$

Thus, the sample spectrum for the $X(t)$ process is approximately equal to the sample spectrum for the white noise process multiplied by the square of the modulus of the filter frequency response function. Since $2C_{ZZ}(f)/\sigma_Z^2$ is approximately distributed as a χ_2^2 for all f, (6.4.5) implies that

$$\frac{2C_{XX}(f)}{\sigma_Z^2|H(f)|^2} = \frac{2C_{XX}(f)}{\Gamma_{XX}(f)} \tag{6.4.6}$$

is approximately distributed as a χ_2^2. The results of Section 6.3.3 for the properties of spectral estimators of white noise may then be used to yield the following results. Since $E[C_{ZZ}(f)] = \sigma_Z^2$, from (6.3.16),

$$E[C_{XX}(f)] \approx |H(f)|^2\sigma_Z^2 = \Gamma_{XX}(f). \tag{6.4.7}$$

Similarly, since

$$\text{Cov} [C_{XX}(f_1), C_{XX}(f_2)] = \text{Cov} [|H(f_1)|^2C_{ZZ}(f_1), |H(f_2)|^2C_{ZZ}(f_2)]$$
$$= |H(f_1)|^2|H(f_2)|^2 \text{ Cov} [C_{ZZ}(f_1), C_{ZZ}(f_2)],$$

it follows from (6.3.17) that

$$\text{Cov} [C_{XX}(f_1), C_{XX}(f_2)]$$
$$\approx |H(f_1)|^2 |H(f_2)|^2 \sigma_Z^4 \left\{\left(\frac{\sin \pi T(f_1 + f_2)}{\pi T(f_1 + f_2)}\right)^2 + \left(\frac{\sin \pi T(f_1 - f_2)}{\pi T(f_1 - f_2)}\right)^2\right\},$$
$$\tag{6.4.8}$$

on neglecting the K_4 term. Since $\Gamma_{XX}(f) = \sigma_Z^2|H(f)|^2$, the covariance between the two sample spectrum estimators of the linear process at two distinct frequencies f_1 and f_2 is

$$\text{Cov} [C_{XX}(f_1), C_{XX}(f_2)]$$
$$\approx \Gamma_{XX}(f_1)\Gamma_{XX}(f_2) \left\{\left(\frac{\sin \pi T(f_1 + f_2)}{\pi T(f_1 + f_2)}\right)^2 + \left(\frac{\sin \pi T(f_1 - f_2)}{\pi T(f_1 - f_2)}\right)^2\right\}. \tag{6.4.9}$$

The result (6.4.9) shows that *for any Normal stochastic process* $X(t)$,

$$\text{Cov} [C_{XX}(f_1), C_{XX}(f_2)] \approx 0\left(\frac{1}{T^2}\right), \qquad f_1 \neq f_2,$$

$$\text{Var} [C_{XX}(f)] \approx \Gamma_{XX}^2(f),$$

and hence is an extension of the results of Section 6.3.3, which only applied to white noise processes. Note that for T large, the quantity in braces in (6.4.9) behaves like a delta function of area $1/T$. Furthermore, the covariance is identically zero when the frequencies $(f_1 \pm f_2)$ are multiples of $1/T$.

Covariance of smoothed spectral estimators. From (6.3.30), the smoothed spectral estimator $\bar{C}_{XX}(f)$ for the $X(t)$ process is

$$\bar{C}_{XX}(f) = \int_{-\infty}^{\infty} C_{XX}(g)W(f - g) \, dg,$$

and hence the covariance between $\bar{C}_{XX}(f_1)$ and $\bar{C}_{XX}(f_2)$ is

$$\text{Cov} [\bar{C}_{XX}(f_1), \bar{C}_{XX}(f_2)]$$
$$= \int_{-\infty}^{\infty} \int_{-\infty}^{\infty} W(f_1 - g)W(f_2 - h) \text{ Cov} [C_{XX}(g), C_{XX}(h)] \, dg \, dh.$$

Substituting for Cov $[C_{XX}(g), C_{XX}(h)]$ from (6.4.9) and integrating over h gives

Cov $[\bar{C}_{XX}(f_1), \bar{C}_{XX}(f_2)]$

$$\approx \frac{1}{T} \int_{-\infty}^{\infty} \Gamma_{XX}^2(g) W(f_1 - g)[W(f_2 + g) + W(f_2 - g)]\, dg, \quad (6.4.10)$$

provided T is large so that the $(\sin \pi f T/\pi f T)^2$ terms behave as delta functions. Equation (6.4.10) is the final result, but a useful approximation may be derived by making the assumption that $\Gamma_{XX}(f)$ is a smooth function over the width of the spectral window $W(f)$. Under this assumption, (6.4.10) becomes

Cov $[\bar{C}_{XX}(f_1), \bar{C}_{XX}(f_2)]$

$$\approx \frac{\Gamma_{XX}^2(f)}{T} \int_{-\infty}^{\infty} W(f_1 - g)[W(f_2 + g) + W(f_2 - g)]\, dg, \quad (6.4.11)$$

where $f_1 \leqslant f \leqslant f_2$.

Equation (6.4.11) shows that the covariance between smoothed spectral estimators is proportional to the amount of overlap of the spectral windows centered at f_1 and f_2. Hence, if the spectral windows overlap only slightly, the covariance will be very small. Some numerical values for the covariances of spectral windows will be given in Section 7.2.

Variance of smoothed spectral estimators. When $f_1 = f_2 = f$, (6.4.10) reduces to

$$\text{Var}\,[\bar{C}_{XX}(f)] \approx \frac{\Gamma_{XX}^2(f)}{T} \int_{-\infty}^{\infty} W^2(g)\, dg, \quad (6.4.12)$$

neglecting the term in $\int_{-\infty}^{\infty} W(g)W(g + 2f)\, dg$ which is small compared to $\int_{-\infty}^{\infty} W^2(g)\, dg$. Using Parseval's theorem, (6.4.12) may be written in the equivalent form

$$\text{Var}\,[\bar{C}_{XX}(f)] \approx \frac{\Gamma_{XX}^2(f)}{T} \int_{-\infty}^{\infty} w^2(u)\, du = \Gamma_{XX}^2(f)\frac{I}{T}. \quad (6.4.13)$$

For example, for the Bartlett window $w_B(u)$ of Table 6.5,

$$I = \int_{-M}^{M} \left(1 - \frac{|u|}{M}\right)^2 du = \tfrac{2}{3}M,$$

and hence

$$\text{Var}\,[\bar{C}_{XX}(f)] \approx \frac{\Gamma_{XX}^2(f)}{T}(\tfrac{2}{3}M).$$

This shows that the variance of the smoothed spectral estimator can be reduced by making the truncation point M of the lag window small. As discussed in Section 6.3.5, however, reducing M increases the bias and causes more distortion of the theoretical spectrum, since then the spectral window is wider. In this event, (6.4.10) shows that adjacent spectral estimators will be more highly correlated since the spectral windows will overlap more. Hence, the exact choice of M is a vital matter, and is discussed in Chapter 7.

Note that since $\text{Var}\,[C_{XX}(f)] \approx \Gamma_{XX}^2(f)$, the ratio

$$\frac{\text{Var}\,[\bar{C}_{XX}(f)]}{\Gamma_{XX}^2(f)} = \frac{1}{T}\int_{-\infty}^{\infty} w^2(u)\,du = I/T \qquad (6.4.14)$$

represents the proportional reduction in variance as a result of using a smoothed estimator as compared to the sample spectrum estimator. The values of the ratio (6.4.14) corresponding to the spectral windows of Table 6.5 are given in column 3 of Table 6.6. It is seen that they are all of the form $c(M/T)$, where c is a constant depending on the window.

TABLE 6.6: Properties of spectral windows

Description	Spectral window	Variance ratio I/T	Degrees of freedom	Standardized bandwidth b_1
rectangular	$2M\,\dfrac{\sin 2\pi fM}{2\pi fM}$	$2\,\dfrac{M}{T}$	$\dfrac{T}{M}$	0.5
Bartlett	$M\left(\dfrac{\sin \pi fM}{\pi fM}\right)^2$	$0.667\,\dfrac{M}{T}$	$3\,\dfrac{T}{M}$	1.5
Tukey	$M\left(\dfrac{\sin 2\pi fM}{2\pi fM} \times \dfrac{1}{1-(2fM)^2}\right)$	$0.75\,\dfrac{M}{T}$	$2.667\,\dfrac{T}{M}$	1.333
Parzen	$\tfrac{3}{4}M\left(\dfrac{\sin (\pi fM/2)}{\pi fM/2}\right)^4$	$0.539\,\dfrac{M}{T}$	$3.71\,\dfrac{T}{M}$	1.86

Suppose, for example, that the truncation point M is $0.1T$. Then I/T is $\tfrac{2}{3}(0.1) = 0.067$ for the Bartlett window. Hence by taking a truncation point which is 10% of the record length, the variance of the smoothed spectral estimator is reduced to 6.7% of the variance of the sample spectrum. The corresponding values for the Tukey and Parzen windows are 7.5% and 5.4% respectively. Hence for a given number of lags M, the Parzen window achieves the smallest variance among these three windows. Inspection of Figure 6.13 shows that this is due to the fact that the Parzen window is wider and flatter than the other two windows. As a result it tends to produce a larger bias and hence comparisons made on the basis of variance alone are misleading, as will be seen later.

6.4.2 *The chi-squared approximation to the distribution of smoothed spectral estimators*

In Section 6.3.5 it was shown that the sample spectrum estimator $C_{XX}(f)$ is such that $2C_{XX}(f)/\Gamma_{XX}(f)$ is approximately distributed as χ_2^2. In this section it is shown that the corresponding result for the smoothed spectral estimator is that $\nu \bar{C}_{XX}(f)/\Gamma_{XX}(f)$ is approximately distributed as χ_ν^2 where $\nu > 2$. This means that the smoothed spectral estimators will have many more degrees of freedom than the sample spectrum estimator, a consequence of their smaller variance.

The sample spectrum $C_{XX}(f)$ is the Fourier transform of the covariance function estimator $c_{XX}(u)$, where $c_{XX}(u)$ is zero outside the interval $-T \leqslant u \leqslant T$. If $c_{XX}(u)$ is represented over the interval $-T \leqslant u \leqslant T$ by a periodic function $c_{XX}^p(u)$, where $c_{XX}^p(u) = c_{XX}^p(u + 2T)$, then the function $c_{XX}^p(u)$ has a Fourier series representation

$$c_{XX}^p(u) = \sum_{l=-\infty}^{\infty} C_{XX}^p\left(\frac{l}{2T}\right) e^{j(2\pi l u/2T)}.$$

Since the lag window $w(u) = 0$ for $|u| \geqslant M$, the functions $\bar{c}_{XX}(u) = c_{XX}(u)w(u)$ and $\bar{c}_{XX}(u) = c_{XX}^p(u)w(u)$ are identical over all u, and so the smoothed spectrum $\bar{C}_{XX}(f)$ has the equivalent representations

$$\bar{C}_{XX}(f) = \int_{-\infty}^{\infty} W(f - g)C_{XX}(g)\, dg$$

and

$$\bar{C}_{XX}(f) = \sum_{l=-\infty}^{\infty} W\left(f - \frac{l}{2T}\right) C_{XX}^p\left(\frac{l}{2T}\right).$$

But

$$\frac{C_{XX}(l/2T)}{2T} = C_{XX}^p\left(\frac{l}{2T}\right),$$

and hence

$$\bar{C}_{XX}(f) = \frac{1}{2T} \sum_{l=-\infty}^{\infty} C_{XX}\left(\frac{l}{2T}\right) W\left(f - \frac{l}{2T}\right).$$

Thus the smoothed spectral estimator is a weighted sum of rv's $C_{XX}(l/2T)$ at the subharmonic frequencies $l/2T$. These rv's are distributed as a χ_2^2 and hence, using the results of Section 3.3.5, the distribution of $\bar{C}_{XX}(f)$ may be approximated by $a\chi_\nu^2$. Using (3.3.14, 15), the constants a and ν may be evaluated from

$$\nu \approx \frac{2\{E[\bar{C}_{XX}(f)]\}^2}{\text{Var}\,[\bar{C}_{XX}(f)]}, \tag{6.4.15}$$

$$a \approx \frac{E[\bar{C}_{XX}(f)]}{\nu}. \tag{6.4.16}$$

Under the assumption that the spectrum is smooth with respect to the spectral window,

$$E[\bar{C}_{XX}(f)] \approx \Gamma_{XX}(f),$$

from (6.3.36), and

$$\text{Var}\,[\bar{C}_{XX}(f)] \approx \frac{\Gamma_{XX}^2(f)}{T} \int_{-\infty}^{\infty} w^2(u)\, du,$$

from (6.4.13). Hence on substituting these results in (6.4.15) and (6.4.16),

$$v = \frac{2T}{\int_{-\infty}^{\infty} w^2(u)\, du} = \frac{2T}{I} \tag{6.4.17}$$

$$a = \frac{\Gamma_{XX}(f)}{v}. \tag{6.4.18}$$

Hence the rv $v\overline{C}_{XX}(f)/\Gamma_{XX}(f)$ is distributed as a χ_v^2 with degrees of freedom v given by (6.4.17). Thus the degrees of freedom of the smoothed spectral estimator depend on the window $w(u)$.

Column 4 of Table 6.6 shows the degrees of freedom associated with the spectral windows of column 2. For example, if the Bartlett window $w_B(u)$ is used with a truncation point M equal to one-tenth of the record length so that $M/T = 0.1$, the degrees of freedom of the estimator is $3/0.1 = 30$. The larger the number of degrees of freedom, the more reliable the estimator in the sense that its variance is smaller. However, there has to be a compromise between degrees of freedom and bias, as discussed above.

Referring to Table 6.6, it is seen that a wide window such as the Parzen window $W_P(f)$ provides a smaller variance and hence a larger number of degrees of freedom than a narrower window such as the Bartlett window $W_B(f)$. This is in accord with the previous remark that the wider the window, the smaller the variance.

6.4.3 Confidence limits for the spectrum

Since $v\overline{C}_{XX}(f)/\Gamma_{XX}(f)$ is distributed according to a χ_v^2 where v is given by (6.4.17), it follows that

$$\Pr\left\{ x_v\left(\frac{\alpha}{2}\right) < \frac{v\overline{C}_{XX}(f)}{\Gamma_{XX}(f)} \leqslant x_v\left(1 - \frac{\alpha}{2}\right) \right\} = 1 - \alpha, \tag{6.4.19}$$

where $\Pr\{\chi_v^2 \leqslant x_v(\alpha/2)\} = \alpha/2$. Hence by a similar argument to that used in Section 3.3.2, the interval between

$$\frac{v\overline{C}_{XX}(f)}{x_v(1 - (\alpha/2))}, \qquad \frac{v\overline{C}_{XX}(f)}{x_v(\alpha/2)} \tag{6.4.20}$$

is a $100(1 - \alpha)\%$ confidence interval for $\Gamma_{XX}(f)$. For a specified value of the ratio T/M the value of v corresponding to a given spectral window may be obtained from column 4 of Table 6.6, and then the confidence interval obtained from (6.4.20) and Figure 3.10, which gives the multiplying factors $v/x_v(\alpha/2)$ and $v/x_v(1 - (\alpha/2))$. For example, the smoothed spectral estimate shown in Figure 6.10 was based on the Bartlett window with $M/T = 0.125$. Hence from Table 6.5, $v = 3/0.125 = 24$. At the frequency $f = 0.1$ cps, $\overline{C}_{zz}(f) = 0.804$, and so the 95% confidence limits for $\Gamma_{zz}(f)$ are, from Figure 3.10,

$$(0.61)(0.804) = 0.49, \qquad (1.94)(0.804) = 1.56.$$

Similarly, the 95% confidence limits for $\Gamma_{zz}(f)$ based on the sample spectrum $C_{zz}(f)$ at $f = 0.1$ cps are

$$(0.27)(0.622) = 0.169, \qquad (39.5)(0.622) = 24.6.$$

These are considerably wider because of the smaller degrees of freedom associated with the estimate.

Note that (6.4.19) gives a confidence interval for $\Gamma_{xx}(f)$ at a *particular* frequency f only. If a confidence interval is given for q frequencies, at which the estimators are independent, the confidence coefficient will be $(1 - \alpha)^q$, which will usually be considerably less than $(1 - \alpha)$. Note also that the variance will only summarize the properties of the estimators if the bias is small, as discussed in Section 6.3.5. Hence the above confidence intervals will be of value only when the spectral window is sufficiently narrow so that no appreciable bias exists.

Confidence intervals on a logarithmic scale. It will be shown in Section 7.1.2 that spectral estimates should be plotted on a logarithmic scale so that the variation in the spectrum can be accommodated. The logarithmic scale is also a sensible choice from an engineering point of view, since it is usually *proportional* changes in power which are important. From a statistical point of view there is also a good reason to plot spectra on a logarithmic scale, since then the confidence interval for the spectrum is simply represented by a constant interval about the spectral estimate.

Thus using (6.4.20), the confidence interval for $\log \Gamma_{xx}(f)$ is

$$\log \bar{C}_{xx}(f) + \log \frac{\nu}{x_\nu(1 - (\alpha/2))}, \qquad \log \bar{C}_{xx}(f) + \log \frac{\nu}{x_\nu(\alpha/2)}. \qquad (6.4.21)$$

Therefore, when plotting the estimated spectrum, the confidence interval for all frequencies can be indicated by a single vertical line.

For example, consider the smoothed spectral estimate $\bar{C}_{xx}(f)$ of Figure 6.10 for which $\nu = 24$. From Figure 3.10 and (6.4.21) the 95% confidence intervals for $\log_{10} \Gamma_{xx}(f)$ are

$$\log_{10} \bar{C}_{xx}(f) + \log_{10} (0.61), \qquad \log_{10} \bar{C}_{xx}(f) + \log_{10} (1.94).$$

With $\bar{C}_{xx}(f)$ plotted on logarithmic paper, the 95% confidence interval would be obtained very simply by plotting the points (0.61, 1.0, 1.94) from Figure 3.10 in a vertical line on the log scale. This procedure will be illustrated in Section 7.2 and elsewhere throughout the book.

6.4.4 Bandwidth of a spectral window

It has been shown in Section 6.4.1 that one useful characteristic of a spectral window is $I = \int_{-\infty}^{\infty} w^2(u) \, du$, since I/T provides a measure of the reduction in variance of the estimator due to smoothing by the spectral window. Hence, to obtain a small variance it is necessary to choose $w(u)$ so that I is small. For a given window this can be achieved by making M small. A further useful characteristic of a window is its width. It will be shown in later sections that in order to obtain a good estimate of a peak in a spectrum, the "width" of a spectral window must be of the same order as the width of the peak. Since the spectral window is non-zero for most f in the range $-\infty \leqslant f \leqslant \infty$, it is necessary to define more precisely the notion of "width" of a spectral window.

One approach used by statisticians [9] to define the width, or *bandwidth*, of a spectral window is to consider a "bandpass" spectral window

$$W(f) = \frac{1}{h}, \quad -\frac{h}{2} \leqslant f \leqslant \frac{h}{2}.$$

This spectral window is rectangular in the frequency domain and has a unique width h, that is, its bandwidth $b = h$. Using (6.4.13), the variance of a smoothed spectral estimator based on this spectral window is

$$\mathrm{Var}\,[\bar{C}_{XX}(f)] \approx \frac{\Gamma^2_{XX}(f)}{T} \cdot \frac{1}{h} = \frac{\Gamma^2_{XX}(f)}{Tb}.$$

For an estimator based on a spectral window which is not rectangular, it is natural to define the bandwidth of the window as the width of a rectangular window which gives the same variance. That is,

$$\mathrm{Var}\,[\bar{C}_{XX}(f)] \approx \frac{\Gamma^2_{XX}(f)}{T} \cdot \frac{1}{b} = \frac{\Gamma^2_{XX}(f)}{T} \int_{-\infty}^{\infty} w^2(u)\,du. \qquad (6.4.22)$$

Hence the bandwidth is

$$b = \frac{1}{I} = \frac{1}{\int_{-\infty}^{\infty} w^2(u)\,du} = \frac{1}{\int_{-\infty}^{\infty} W^2(f)\,df}. \qquad (6.4.23)$$

For example, for the rectangular and Bartlett lag windows $w_R(u)$ and $w_B(u)$ of Table 6.5, the bandwidths are $1/2M$ and $3/2M$ respectively.

It is sometimes convenient to define the *standardized bandwidth* b_1 corresponding to $M = 1$, so that

$$b = \frac{b_1}{M} = \frac{1}{\int_{-\infty}^{\infty} w^2(u)\,du}. \qquad (6.4.24)$$

For example, the standarized bandwidths for the rectangular and Bartlett lag windows are $\frac{1}{2}$ and $\frac{3}{2}$ respectively. The standardized bandwidths for the windows of Table 6.5 are shown in column 5 of Table 6.6. It is seen that the Parzen window w_P has a standardized bandwidth which is approximately 1.4 times that of the Tukey window w_T.

Engineers will recognize (6.4.23) as being the inverse of the definition of the noise bandwidth of a filter. The precise definition of bandwidth is not very important, for example, some authors [10] use the distance between the half power points. Our preference for the definition (6.4.23) stems from the fact that it utilizes the full shape of the spectral window and is therefore more likely to distinguish between window shapes than the definition based on half power points. From (6.4.23) it is seen that the variance of the spectral estimator is inversely proportional to the bandwidth of the spectral window. In fact, from (6.4.22) and (6.4.23),

$$\text{Variance} \times \text{Bandwidth} = \text{Constant.} \qquad (6.4.25)$$

Hence small variance is associated with large bandwidths and large variance with small bandwidths. Furthermore, (6.4.17) shows that the number of degrees of freedom ν of the smoothed estimator is

$$\nu = \frac{2T}{I} = 2\left(\frac{T}{M}\right) b_1. \qquad (6.4.26)$$

Hence a large bandwidth implies that the number of degrees of freedom of the smoothed estimator is large and the variance small. Conversely a small bandwidth implies few degrees of freedom and hence large variance. Since it was shown in Section 6.3.5 that bias is reduced by making M large, it follows that small bias is associated with small bandwidth.

In the next chapter, the concepts introduced here are applied to the practical problem of estimating the spectrum of an observed time series.

REFERENCES

[1] J. L. Doob, *Stochastic Processes*. John Wiley, New York, 1953.

[2] J. H. Laning and R. H. Battin, *Random Processes in Automatic Control*. McGraw-Hill, New York, 1956.

[3] H. M. James, N. B. Nichols and R. S. Phillips, *Theory of Servomechanisms*. McGraw-Hill, New York, 1947.

[4] A. Hald, *Statistical Theory with Engineering Applications*. John Wiley, New York, 1952.

[5] M. S. Bartlett, *An Introduction to Stochastic Processes with Special Reference to Methods and Applications*. Cambridge University Press, Cambridge, 1953.

[6] R. B. Blackman and J. W. Tukey, *The Measurement of Power Spectra from the Point of View of Communications Engineering*. Dover, New York, 1958.

[7] U. Grenander and M. Rosenblatt, *Statistical Analysis of Stationary Time Series*. John Wiley, New York, 1957.

[8] E. Parzen, "Mathematical considerations in the estimation of spectra." *Technometrics* **3**, 167 (1961).

[9] G. M. Jenkins, "General considerations in the analysis of spectra." *Technometrics* **3**, 133 (1961).

[10] M. B. Priestley, "Basic considerations in the estimation of spectra." *Technometrics* **4**, 551 (1962).

7

Examples of Univariate
Spectral Analysis

In this chapter the theory of Chapter 6 is used to derive practical procedures for estimating spectra from observed time series. To provide the reader with experience in the numerical procedures involved, Section 7.1 illustrates the effect of varying bandwidth and window shape on the spectra of simulated time series. In Section 7.2 a practical method of estimating spectra, called *window closing*, is introduced. This requires the use of a wide bandwidth initially and then progressively smaller bandwidths until all the important detail in the spectrum has been brought out. This procedure can sometimes be badly affected by the instability of the estimate due to the shortness of the time series.

Section 7.3 discusses practical questions which arise in the estimation of spectra and gives a routine procedure which can be followed in practice. The importance of prefiltering the data to remove low frequency trends is emphasized. In Section 7.4 examples of spectral analysis are given in the three application areas of model building, design of experiments and frequency response studies.

7.1 SPECTRAL ANALYSIS USING SIMULATED TIME SERIES

In this section estimates of spectra are computed for simulated time series. This is intended to provide the reader with experience in interpreting spectral estimates. Section 7.1.1 presents the formulae for digital computation of smoothed spectral estimates, together with a sample calculation. Section 7.1.2 then illustrates the effect on spectra of changing the truncation point of the autocorrelation function. This is achieved by comparing $\bar{\Gamma}_{xx}(f)$ with $\Gamma_{xx}(f)$ and $\bar{C}_{xx}(f)$ with $\Gamma_{xx}(f)$ for first- and second-order autoregressive processes. To prepare for a discussion in Section 7.2 of practical methods of smoothing, an investigation is made of the effect of varying the truncation point (Section 7.1.2) and the shape (Section 7.1.3) of spectral windows.

7.1.1 Discrete estimation formulae

The statistical theory of spectral estimation has been derived in the previous sections assuming the data $x(t)$ are continuous. There are many situations in which the data is essentially discrete, for example, the batch data of Figure 5.2, and hence digital formulae are required. In addition, because of the accuracy, flexibility and relative availability of digital computers today, it may be assumed that most spectral analyses will be done using digital computers. This implies that the continuous or analog signal will have to be sampled in the manner of Chapter 2 and the sampled values converted to digital form. The process of converting from analog to digital form is termed *quantizing*, and a detailed analysis of its effects on correlation analysis has been given in [1]. It will be assumed that the quantizing is fine enough so that no errors are introduced in the conversion from analog to digital form. In practice this means that the data should be read to the nearest 1/10 to 1/100 of the full range of the signal.

Suppose that the digital data x_t, $t = 1, \ldots, N$, corresponds to values of the signal $x(t)$ at intervals Δ. In this case, the smoothed spectral estimate $\bar{C}_{xx}(f)$ is obtained by replacing the integral (6.3.28) by the corresponding sum

$$\bar{C}_{xx}(f) = \Delta \sum_{k=-(L-1)}^{L-1} w(k) c_{xx}(k) e^{-j2\pi f k \Delta}, \quad -\frac{1}{2\Delta} \leqslant f < \frac{1}{2\Delta}. \quad (7.1.1)$$

In (7.1.1) the acvf estimate $c_{xx}(k)$ is

$$c_{xx}(k) = \frac{1}{N} \sum_{t=1}^{N-k} (x_t - \bar{x})(x_{t+k} - \bar{x}), \quad -(N-1) \leqslant k \leqslant N - 1, \quad (7.1.2)$$

and $L = M/\Delta$. As before, $w(k)$ is the lag window with truncation point M, but it is now only defined at the discrete time points $u = k\Delta$. Note that it may be necessary to filter the data according to (5.3.27) or (5.3.31) before estimating the acvf.

Since $\bar{C}_{xx}(f)$ is an even function of frequency, it is only necessary to calculate it over the range $0 \leqslant f \leqslant 1/2\Delta$. However, to preserve the Fourier transform relationship between the sample spectrum and the sample acvf, it is necessary to double the power associated with each frequency in the range $0 \leqslant f \leqslant 1/2\Delta$. Hence, the formula generally used is

$$\bar{C}_{xx}(f) = 2\Delta \left\{ c_{xx}(0) + 2 \sum_{k=1}^{L-1} c_{xx}(k) w(k) \cos 2\pi f k \Delta \right\}, \quad 0 \leqslant f \leqslant \frac{1}{2\Delta}, \quad (7.1.3)$$

and the acvf (7.1.2) need only be computed for $k \geqslant 0$.

For purposes of computation it is more convenient to assume that $\Delta = 1$, in which case all sets of data may be processed alike. Thus the computing formula becomes

$$\bar{C}_{xx}(f) = 2\left\{c_{xx}(0) + 2\sum_{k=1}^{L-1} c_{xx}(k)w(k)\cos 2\pi fk\right\}, \quad 0 \leqslant f \leqslant \tfrac{1}{2}. \quad (7.1.4)$$

If $\Delta \neq 1$, then the estimate (7.1.1) can be recovered from (7.1.4) by multiplying by Δ and plotting the estimate against $f\Delta$ instead of f.

Finally, if autocorrelations are used instead of autocovariances, the smoothed spectral density estimate $\bar{R}_{xx}(f)$ is computed according to

$$\bar{R}_{xx}(f) = 2\left\{1 + 2\sum_{k=1}^{L-1} r_{xx}(k)w(k)\cos 2\pi fk\right\}, \quad 0 \leqslant f \leqslant \tfrac{1}{2},$$

where

$$r_{xx}(k) = \frac{c_{xx}(k)}{c_{xx}(0)}. \quad (7.1.5)$$

In practice it has been suggested [2] that $\bar{R}_{xx}(f)$ should only be computed at values of f corresponding to $f = 0, 1/L, 2/L, \ldots, \tfrac{1}{2}$. This frequency spacing is too wide, and it is recommended that $\bar{R}_{xx}(f)$ be evaluated at some fraction of this spacing so that a more detailed plot of $\bar{R}_{xx}(f)$ is obtained. In fact, it is not necessary that the frequency spacing for the values of $\bar{R}_{xx}(f)$ be at all related to the truncation point L. Thus, the f values may be computed at spacing $1/(2F)$, where F is 2 to 3 times L. Hence the final formula for digital computation of the smoothed spectral density function is

$$\bar{R}_{xx}(l) = 2\left\{1 + 2\sum_{k=1}^{L-1} r_{xx}(k)w(k)\cos\frac{\pi lk}{F}\right\}, \quad l = 0, 1, \ldots, F. \quad (7.1.6)$$

A flow chart for digital computer application is presented in Appendix A7.1.

A sample calculation. The sample autocorrelations for the discrete second-order ar process (5.3.36) are given in Table 5.2. These values may be used to derive an estimate of the spectral density function $2\Gamma_{xx}(f)/\sigma_X^2$ as follows. Using, for illustration, the Bartlett lag window

$$w(k) = \begin{cases} \left(1 - \dfrac{k}{L}\right), & 0 \leqslant k \leqslant L \\ 0, & k > L, \end{cases}$$

the smoothed spectral density function estimate is, from (7.1.6),

$$\bar{R}_{xx}(l) = 2\left\{1 + 2\sum_{k=1}^{L-1}\left(1 - \frac{k}{L}\right)r_{xx}(k)\cos\frac{\pi lk}{F}\right\}, \quad l = 0, 1, \ldots, F.$$

For example, if $L = 3$, the estimate is

$$\bar{R}_{xx}(l) = 2\left\{1 + 2\left(\frac{2}{3}\right) r_{xx}(1) \cos \frac{\pi l}{F} + 2\left(\frac{1}{3}\right) r_{xx}(2) \cos \frac{2\pi l}{F}\right\},$$

$$l = 0, 1, \ldots, F.$$

If the estimates are required at a frequency spacing of $1/16$ cps, so that $F = 8$, then using the values of the sample acf from Table 5.2, the calculation may be set out as shown in Table 7.1.

These spectral density estimates are shown in Figure 7.1. It is seen that a well-defined smooth curve can be drawn through the points. Also shown on the graph are the estimates plotted at spacing $\frac{1}{3}$ as suggested in [2]. It is seen that this spacing is too wide for plotting and interpolating purposes.

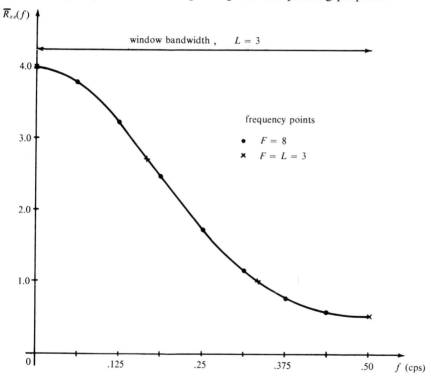

FIG. 7.1: A smoothed spectral density estimate for the second-order ar process ($\alpha_1 = 1.0$, $\alpha_2 = -0.5$) using the Bartlett window

Also shown on the graph is the bandwidth of the spectral window used. The bandwidth for the Bartlett window, with $L = 3$, is

$$b = b_1/L\Delta = 1.5/3(1) = 0.5 \text{ cps.}$$

This bandwidth is equal to the whole of the frequency range and hence the estimate has been smoothed considerably.

TABLE 7.1: An example of a spectral calculation

l/F	$f = \dfrac{l}{2F}$	$\cos \dfrac{\pi l}{F}$	① $2\left(\dfrac{2}{3}\right)(0.645)\cos \dfrac{\pi l}{F}$	$\cos \dfrac{2\pi l}{F}$	② $2\left(\dfrac{1}{3}\right)(0.195)\cos \dfrac{2\pi l}{F}$	$\bar{R}_{xx}(l) = 2(1 + ① + ②)$
0	0	1.0	0.860	1.0	0.130	3.980
$\frac{1}{8}$	$\frac{1}{16}$	0.924	0.794	0.707	0.092	3.773
$\frac{1}{4}$	$\frac{1}{8}$	0.707	0.608	0	0	3.216
$\frac{3}{8}$	$\frac{3}{16}$	0.383	0.329	-0.707	-0.092	2.474
$\frac{1}{2}$	$\frac{1}{4}$	0	0	-1.0	-0.130	1.740
$\frac{5}{8}$	$\frac{5}{16}$	-0.383	-0.329	-0.707	-0.092	1.158
$\frac{3}{4}$	$\frac{3}{8}$	-0.707	-0.608	0	0	0.784
$\frac{7}{8}$	$\frac{7}{16}$	-0.924	-0.794	0.707	0.092	0.596
1	$\frac{1}{2}$	-1.0	-0.860	1.0	0.130	0.540

7.1.2 Effect of bandwidth on smoothing

In this section an empirical investigation is made of the effect of varying the bandwidth of the window, or equivalently the truncation point L, on the smoothing of the spectral estimate. The time series used are realizations of first- and second-order ar processes with known spectra $\Gamma_{XX}(f)$. The quantities computed are the mean smoothed spectral density function

$$\frac{\bar{\Gamma}_{XX}(f)}{\sigma_X^2} = 2\left[1 + 2\sum_{k=1}^{L-1} \rho_{XX}(k)w(k)\cos 2\pi fk\right] \qquad (7.1.7)$$

and the smoothed spectral density estimate $\bar{R}_{XX}(f)$ (7.1.6). The mean smoothed spectral density $\bar{\Gamma}_{XX}(f)/\sigma_X^2$ is the expected value of the smoothed spectral density estimator, and hence when plotted alongside $\Gamma_{XX}(f)/\sigma_X^2$ shows how the bias varies with frequency. By plotting a series of curves for different values of L, the variation of bias with bandwidth is readily displayed. Similarly, by plotting the smoothed estimate $\bar{R}_{XX}(f)$ alongside $\Gamma_{XX}(f)/\sigma_X^2$ for various values of L, the effect of bandwidth on the variance of the estimator can be displayed visually.

A first-order ar process ($\alpha_1 = -0.4$). The stochastic process used for these computations is the first-order ar process (5.2.26), with $\alpha_1 = -0.4$, $\Delta = 1$, $\mu = 0$, that is,

$$X_t = -0.4X_{t-1} + Z_t.$$

Using (6.2.20), this process has the spectral density function

$$\frac{\Gamma_{XX}(f)}{\sigma_X^2} = \frac{2(0.84)}{1.16 + 0.8\cos 2\pi f}, \quad 0 \leqslant f \leqslant \tfrac{1}{2},$$

shown in Figure 7.2. It is seen that the spectral density function is very smooth with a wide peak at $f = 0.5$ cps, and that it varies only over a small vertical range. Also shown in the figure are the mean smoothed spectral density functions $\bar{\Gamma}_{XX}(f)/\sigma_X^2$ for values of $L = 4, 8$ and 16 based on the Tukey window. These curves show that for $L = 4$, the mean smoothed spectral density is quite biased, particularly near the peak, which is considerably underestimated. Doubling L to 8 improves the correspondence between $\bar{\Gamma}_{XX}(f)$ and $\Gamma_{XX}(f)$, particularly for frequencies less than 0.375 cps, in which cases $\bar{\Gamma}_{XX}(f)$ and $\Gamma_{XX}(f)$ are essentially indistinguishable. Therefore, $L = 8$ would be sufficient to give an estimate with an acceptably small bias over most of the frequency range. However, considerable bias persists near the peak, and hence a larger value of L is necessary to estimate the peak accurately. Doubling L again, to $L = 16$, shows that there is still a little bias near the peak. The reduction in bias achieved by doubling L to 16 is considerably less than that achieved by doubling L to 8. Hence a point of diminishing returns may have been reached.

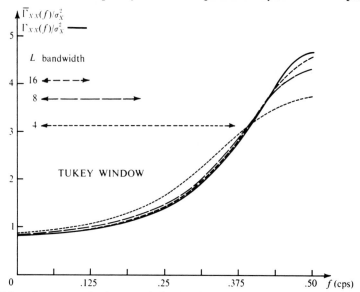

FIG. 7.2: Mean smoothed spectral density functions for a first-order ar process
($\alpha_1 = -0.4$)

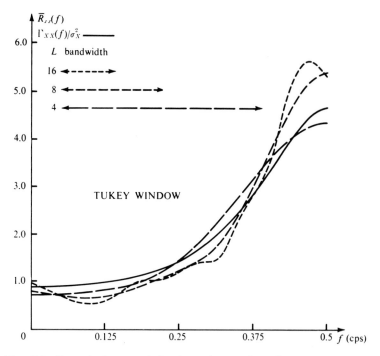

FIG. 7.3: Smoothed spectral density estimates for a first-order ar process
($\alpha_1 = -0.4$; $N = 400$)

This is simply explained by noting that for $k > 8$, $|\rho_{XX}(k)| < (0.4)^8 < 0.001$, and hence increasing L above 8 results in small changes in the sum of the series (7.1.7). Similar conclusions may be drawn from the mean smoothed spectra obtained using the Bartlett and Parzen windows. For the Bartlett window the number of lags which gives a good estimate is approximately $L = 12$ to 16 and for the Parzen window $L = 12$.

Smoothed spectral density estimates using the Tukey window for realizations of $N = 400$ and $N = 100$ terms of this process are shown in Figures 7.3 and 7.4. For $N = 400$, shown in Figure 7.3, changing L from 4 to 8 produces an appreciable change in the spectral estimate. A further increase from $L = 8$ to $L = 16$ produces only minor changes, and hence a reasonable estimate of the spectrum could be obtained with $L = 8$. The number of degrees of freedom per estimate in this case is 133 so that the confidence interval is very narrow.

The situation is different for the estimates, shown in Figure 7.4, obtained from the realization based on $N = 100$. Here, changing L from 4 to 8

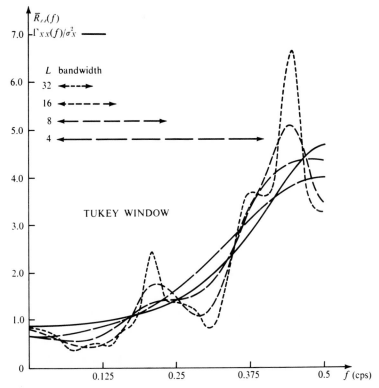

FIG. 7.4: Smoothed spectral density estimates for a first-order ar process ($\alpha_1 = -0.4$; $N = 100$)

produces significant changes in the spectrum, but even greater changes occur if L is increased to 16 or 32. Note that well-defined peaks occur at $f = 0.22$ cps and 0.44 cps which are spurious and are due to the increased variance of the estimator.

Note that the number of degrees of freedom per estimate is 33 for $L = 8$, 17 for $L = 16$ and 8 for $L = 32$. The estimate for $L = 8$ is reasonably close to the theoretical spectrum, but without knowing the correct answer one would be faced with a certain amount of ambiguity in interpreting these estimates. In particular, there would be doubt whether to accept the smooth estimate based on $L = 8$ or to decide for the apparent greater detail, but greater variance, of the estimate based on $L = 16$.

The bandwidths of the windows corresponding to various truncation points have been shown on Figures 7.3 and 7.4. This is a very useful feature since it enables the extent of the detail in the spectrum to be judged in relation to the bandwidth of the window.

A first-order ar process ($\alpha_1 = -0.9$). A similar investigation was conducted using the first-order ar process

$$X_t = -0.9X_{t-1} + Z_t. \tag{7.1.8}$$

This has the theoretical spectral density function

$$\frac{\Gamma_{XX}(f)}{\sigma_X^2} = \frac{2(0.19)}{1.81 + 1.8 \cos 2\pi f}, \quad 0 \leqslant f \leqslant \tfrac{1}{2},$$

and is shown in Figure 7.5. This spectrum has an extremely narrow peak near $f = 0.5$ cps. Note that for this process the spectrum ranges in value from 0.105 to 38.0 and so the spectral density has been plotted on a logarithmic scale. This has practical merit not only because it gives a better display of the detail in the spectrum but also because, as shown in Section 6.4.3, the confidence limits are the same for all frequencies and hence are easily displayed. Therefore, spectral density estimates should always be plotted on a logarithmic scale. Because the bandwidth is constant with frequency, the frequency scale should be linear.

The mean smoothed spectral densities $\bar{\Gamma}_{XX}(f)/\sigma_X^2$ for the process (7.1.8) are shown in Figure 7.5 for the Bartlett window using truncation points $L = 8$, 16 and 32. As before, considerable bias exists near the peak for all these values of L and the bias decreases with increasing L. No obviously good truncation point is apparent from these plots and hence it is concluded that a larger truncation point, perhaps $L = 48$, is necessary. This is also apparent from consideration of the acf $\rho_{XX}(k)$, since $|\rho_{XX}(k)|$ is 0.034 for $k = 32$ and 0.0012 for $k = 64$. Hence it may be concluded that for this process a very large L will be necessary to produce small bias. Therefore, in order to produce an estimate with small variance, it will be necessary to use a very large number

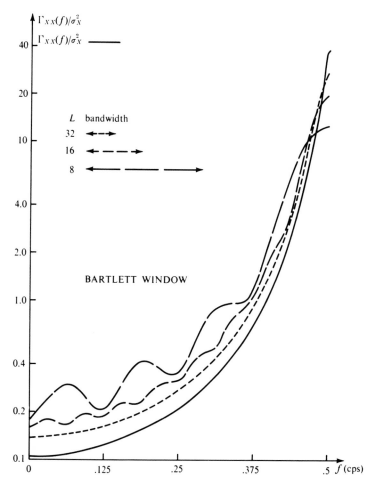

FIG. 7.5: Mean smoothed spectral density functions for a first-order ar process
$(\alpha_1 = -0.9)$

of data points. Figure 7.5 shows that for L small there are ripples in the
mean smoothed spectrum. These are due to the side lobes of the Bartlett
window which will be discussed in Section 7.2.5.

The difficulties of trying to estimate a narrow peak in the spectrum are
demonstrated in Figure 7.6. This shows $\bar{R}_{xx}(f)$ for the Bartlett window using
$L = 16$, 32 and 48 based on a realization of $N = 100$ terms of the process
(7.1.8). For $L = 16$ a reasonably smooth estimate is obtained, but the peak is
underestimated by a factor of three. Increasing L to 32 improves the estimate
near the peak slightly but more noticeably at lower frequencies. However,
oscillations now begin to appear due to the increased variance. For $L = 48$
the spectral estimate becomes very erratic, indicating that more data points

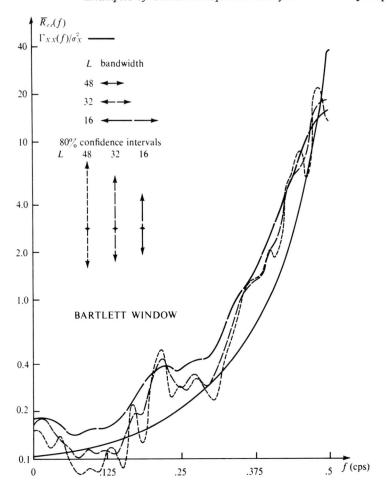

Fig. 7.6: Smoothed spectral density estimates for a first-order ar process
$(\alpha_1 = -0.9; N = 100)$

are needed in order to get a more reliable estimate in the neighborhood of the peak. Note, however, that it is possible to obtain a satisfactory estimate in the frequency range 0 to 0.45 cps with $L = 32$ or possibly a lower value, say $L = 24$.

Comparison of Figure 7.6 with Figure 7.4, which shows the spectral estimate for $\alpha_1 = -0.4$ and $N = 100$, brings out the important point that a series of length $N = 100$ may provide an acceptable estimate of a smooth spectrum but may be far too short to provide a good estimate of a spectrum which contains a narrow peak.

A second-order ar process. To illustrate the difficulties associated with estimating a spectrum which has a two-sided peak, as opposed to the one-sided peak in the previous example, consider the second-order ar process (5.3.36), that is,

$$X_t = X_{t-1} - 0.5X_{t-2} + Z_t. \qquad (7.1.9)$$

This has the spectral density function (6.2.22), namely

$$\frac{\Gamma_{XX}(f)}{\sigma_X^2} = \frac{2(0.417)}{2.25 - 3\cos 2\pi f + \cos 4\pi f}, \quad 0 \leqslant f \leqslant \tfrac{1}{2},$$

which is plotted in Figure 7.7. Also shown in the figure are the mean smoothed spectral densities $\overline{\Gamma}_{XX}(f)/\sigma_X^2$ based on the Parzen window with $L = 8$, 16 and 32. As before, these curves show that as L increases, $\overline{\Gamma}_{XX}(f)$ more closely resembles $\Gamma_{XX}(f)$. From Table 6.6 it is seen that the bandwidths of the spectral

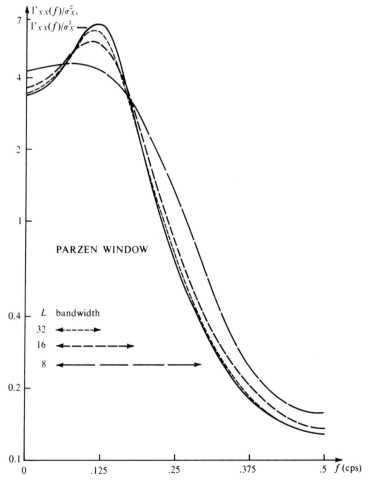

FIG. 7.7: Mean smoothed spectral density functions for a second-order ar process
$(\alpha_1 = 1.0, \alpha_2 = -0.5)$

windows corresponding to $L = 16$, $L = 32$ are 0.12 cps, 0.06 cps. The width of the peak, defined arbitrarily as the distance between the half power points, is about 0.08 cps. It is seen from Figure 7.7 that the peak is badly estimated when $L = 8$ or 16 but that the bias is acceptably low when $L = 32$. This is due to the fact that for $L = 32$ the bandwidth of the window equals 0.06 cps, which is less than the width 0.08 cps of the peak. This suggests that the number of lags of the acf necessary to give an estimate with acceptably low bias depends on the width of the peaks in the spectrum. This point will be returned to in Section 7.2.4.

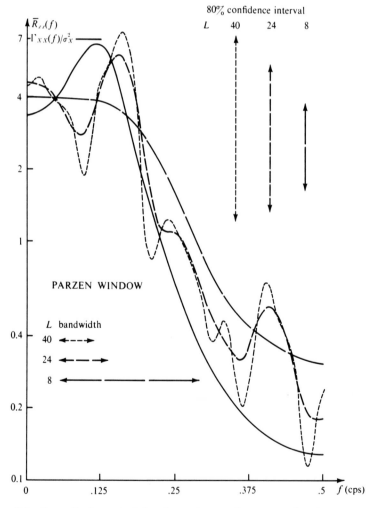

FIG. 7.8: Smoothed spectral density estimates for a second-order ar process ($\alpha_1 = 1.0$, $\alpha_2 = -0.5$; $N = 50$)

Smoothed spectral density estimates $\bar{R}_{xx}(f)$ based on a realization of $N = 50$ terms of the process (7.1.9) using the Parzen window are shown in Figure 7.8. The data used for this example were the first 50 values of the data listed in Appendix A7.4, Table A7.1. The acf for the first 50 values is given in Table A7.2. For $L = 8$ a smooth estimate is obtained but with no indication of a peak. Tripling L to 24 produces a flat peak near 0.125 cps, the position of the true peak.

As L is increased to 40, numerous other small peaks appear due to the increase in variance of the estimate, and hence doubts would remain about the true shape of the spectrum unless the theoretical spectrum were known.

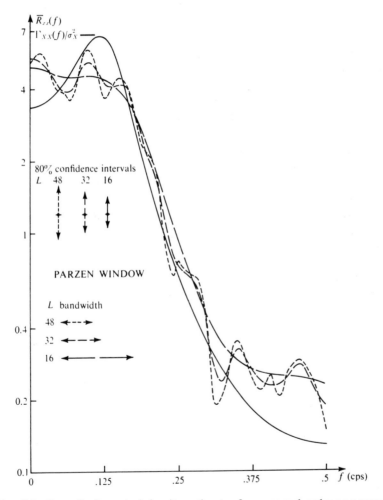

FIG. 7.9: Smoothed spectral density estimates for a second-order ar process $(\alpha_1 = 1.0, \alpha_2 = -0.5; N = 400)$

Figure 7.9 shows spectral estimates based on $N = 400$ for the same process. The data are given in Table A7.1, and the correlations based on 400 terms in Table A7.3. When $L = 48$ the estimate is closer to the true spectrum than any of the estimates based on $N = 50$, but the improvement is not as great as might be expected. Since the number of degrees of freedom per estimate is 31 when $L = 48$, it would probably be accepted that the peak is real. However, it is noticed that the peak is much narrower than the theoretical peak.

7.1.3 Effect of window shape on smoothing

The second aspect of smoothing investigated is the effect of using different spectral windows. Comparisons are made between the Bartlett, Tukey and Parzen windows.

The first-order process (7.1.8) has been used to calculate the mean smoothed spectral densities for the lag windows w_B, w_T and w_P for fixed values of the truncation point. These mean smoothed spectra, denoted by $\bar{\Gamma}_B/\sigma_X^2$, $\bar{\Gamma}_T/\sigma_X^2$ and $\bar{\Gamma}_P/\sigma_X^2$, are shown in Figure 7.10, together with the theoretical spectral density $\Gamma_{XX}(f)/\sigma_X^2$. All smoothed spectra are based on a truncation point $L = 12$.

The large bias and ripples in the estimate based on the Bartlett window for the lower frequencies are evident. However, near the peak the Bartlett window produces small bias. This is to be expected from (6.3.37), which gives the bias for the three windows. Thus the bias of the Bartlett window is related to the first derivative of the spectrum which is small in the neighborhood of a peak but large when the spectrum has large slope. Equation (6.3.37) shows that the important term in the bias of the Tukey and Parzen windows depends on the second derivative of the spectrum, and this is small in a region where the spectrum is linear and relatively large near a peak.

On the whole, the Tukey window has the smallest bias for a given number of lags. If the Parzen and Tukey windows are compared with equal bandwidths, however, the smoothed spectra are almost identical in shape.

The same conclusion can be drawn if comparisons are made between the variances of the estimators corresponding to two windows. From (6.4.25),

$$\text{Bandwidth} \times \text{Variance} = \text{Constant}.$$

Hence two estimators have the same variance if their bandwidths are equal. From Table 6.6 it is seen that the bandwidth of the Parzen window is 1.4 times that of the Tukey window. Hence a Tukey window with truncation point $L = 12$ has the same bandwidth and variance as a Parzen window with $L = 12 \times 1.4 = 16$.

Since both the variance and bias are approximately equal when the bandwidths are equal, it follows that, provided two spectral windows have reasonable shapes, the estimates of the spectrum obtained using equal bandwidths

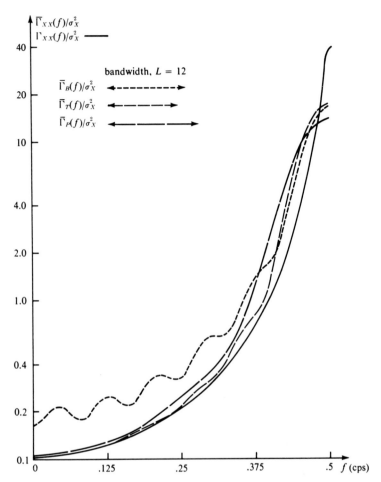

FIG. 7.10: Mean smoothed spectral density functions for a first-order ar process
($\alpha_1 = -0.9$)

should be very similar. Figure 7.11 shows equi-bandwidth comparisons for
the Tukey and Parzen windows for the first-order ar process with $\alpha_1 = -0.9$
and $N = 100$. The unbroken line shows the Tukey estimate based on $L = 32$
and the crosses are the Parzen estimate based on $L = 45$. Similarly, the broken
line shows the Tukey estimate based on $L = 8$ and the circles are the Parzen
estimate based on $L = 12$. The agreement is so close that it can be safely
concluded that no significant features in the spectrum would be missed as a
result of using one window rather than the other. *Hence the empirical results
of this section show that the important question in empirical spectral analysis is
the choice of bandwidth and not the choice of window.* These questions are
discussed more fully in Sections 7.2.4 and 7.2.5.

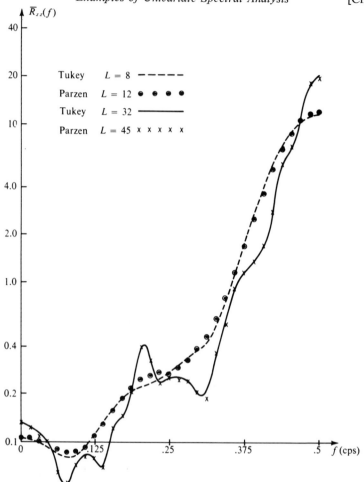

FIG. 7.11: Equi-bandwidth comparison of the Tukey and Parzen windows using a first-order ar process ($\alpha_1 = -0.9$, $N = 100$)

7.2 THE THEORY AND PRACTICE OF SMOOTHING

Section 7.2.1 contains a discussion of the various theoretical attempts to derive optimal methods of smoothing spectra. It is concluded that these theoretical solutions are not satisfactory and that a more empirical approach to spectral estimation is required. The main objectives in estimating spectra are *high stability* and *high fidelity*, and these are summarized in Section 7.2.2. In order to meet these objectives, an empirical approach to spectral estimation is introduced in Section 7.2.3. This process is termed *window closing* and is discussed in detail in Section 7.2.4. The final section deals with *window carpentry*, that is, the choice of spectral window shapes.

7.2.1 Optimal smoothing of spectral estimators

Several attempts have been made to determine smoothed spectral estimators which are optimal in some sense. Ideally, this involves choosing a lag window $w(u)$ in the range $0 \leqslant |u| \leqslant T$ so that some performance criterion is minimized. However, the practical constraint $w(u) = 0, |u| > M$, is usually imposed in order that the autocovariances need only be computed to lag M. Since the bulk of the computing time is spent on evaluating the autocovariances, there are good grounds for keeping M small relative to the record length T.

One criterion for determining an optimal lag window, mentioned in Section 6.3.5, is the mean square error

$$E[\{\overline{C}_{XX}(f) - \Gamma_{XX}(f)\}^2], \qquad (7.2.1)$$

suggested in [3]. One criticism which has been made of this approach is that a good estimator for one frequency may not be a good estimator for another frequency and hence a compromise is needed which will be best in some sense for all frequencies.

An overall criterion of optimality proposed in [4] is the integrated mean square error criterion

$$\int_{-\infty}^{\infty} E[\{\overline{C}_{XX}(f) - \Gamma_{XX}(f)\}^2] \, df. \qquad (7.2.2)$$

The lag window $w(u)$ which minimizes this criterion is

$$w(u) = \frac{\gamma_{XX}^2(u)}{\gamma_{XX}^2(u) + \text{Var}\,[c_{XX}(u)]}, \qquad 0 \leqslant |u| \leqslant T. \qquad (7.2.3)$$

Note that this estimator does not require truncation of the acvf. As mentioned above, the main function which truncation serves is to economize in the computation of the autocovariances.

The expression (7.2.3) for the optimum lag window will be recognized by communication and control engineers as being the exact analog of the expression for the frequency response for a minimum mean square error filter. Interpreting (7.2.2) in communication theory terminology, $\Gamma_{XX}(f)$ corresponds to the message and $\overline{C}_{XX}(f)$ corresponds to the message plus noise. Similarly in (7.2.3), $w(u)$ corresponds to the frequency response function of the optimum filter, $\gamma_{XX}^2(u)$ corresponds to the spectrum of the message and Var $[c_{XX}(u)]$ corresponds to the spectrum of the noise.

Another criterion suggested in [5], in an attempt to obtain a compromise estimator for all frequencies, is the expected maximum mean square error

$$E[\max_f |\overline{C}_{XX}(f) - \Gamma_{XX}(f)|^2]. \qquad (7.2.4)$$

A further criterion which could be proposed is to minimize the integral

$$\int_{-\infty}^{\infty} \left\{ \frac{E[\{\overline{C}_{XX}(f) - \Gamma_{XX}(f)\}^2]}{\Gamma_{XX}^2(f)} \right\} df. \qquad (7.2.5)$$

This differs from (7.2.2) in that the expected mean square error at a particular frequency is weighted in inverse proportion to the value of the theoretical spectrum at that frequency. Thus the integrated proportional mean square error is minimized, with the obvious advantage over (7.2.2) that the estimator is weighted inversely as its variance.

It is shown below that the value of the above criteria in spectral analysis is very limited. The only useful purpose which they serve is to enable spectral windows, such as those suggested by Bartlett, Tukey, Parzen and others, to be ranked according to the various criteria. For example, the rectangular window $w_R(u)$ of Table 6.5 performs badly according to all criteria and hence can be rejected. The other windows of Table 6.5 have similar performances according to these criteria, and hence it may be concluded that these window shapes are generally "good." However, other considerations, for example, the amount of leakage through side lobes, may be used to help to decide on good window shapes. Thus, as shown in Figure 7.10, the Bartlett window is inferior to the Tukey or Parzen windows since it produces large spurious ripples in the mean smoothed spectrum.

Criticisms of the optimality approach to smoothing. Several major criticisms can be made of the optimality approach to smoothing:

(1) The optimality. criteria are arbitrary. Therefore each criterion will produce a spectral window which is best is some arbitrary sense.

(2) The optimality criteria represent too rigid a mathematical formulation of the objectives of spectral analysis. For example, a physicist or an engineer may be interested in specific features of the spectrum, such as the width of a peak or the slope of the spectrum over a range of frequencies, and these criteria do not allow for this. Hence it will be shown in Section 7.2.2 that a more useful and flexible formulation of the objectives of spectral analysis is necessary and possible.

(3) Any optimum lag window, for example (7.2.3), will be a function of the unknown spectrum $\Gamma_{XX}(f)$. This criticism is not peculiar to spectral analysis since it is generally true that the best way to design anything must be based on guesses of the true picture. It is therefore of considerable importance to distinguish very clearly between *designing* a spectral analysis in advance of collecting the data and *analyzing* the data once they have been collected. We are therefore prepared to use mean square error or related criteria *in advance* of performing a spectral analysis to decide, for example, how long a record to take. After the data have been collected, it must be recognized that our guesses about $\Gamma_{XX}(f)$ may be wildly wrong. Hence any practical method of spectral analysis should be capable of standing on its own feet and should not depend critically on any major assumptions about $\Gamma_{XX}(f)$. In other words, the data must be allowed to speak for themselves.

(4) Even if there were situations where precise information about $\Gamma_{xx}(f)$ existed, the optimality approach only indicates what is best to do *on average*. Thus, the optimum lag window (7.2.3) is the best window *on average* when judged according to criterion (7.2.2). However, it might be very bad for a particular realization of a stochastic process. For example, it is possible to generate two realizations of equal length from a certain process, one of which requires a large bandwidth to give a good estimate of the spectrum, while the other requires a much narrower bandwidth.

These criticisms are major ones, and hence it must be concluded that a more robust and flexible approach to smoothing is required. In order to be able to suggest a suitable empirical procedure, it is necessary to review the general objectives of spectral analysis and to state them in useful precise terms. This is done in the next section, where the concepts of *fidelity* and *stability* are defined. An empirical procedure for smoothing of spectral estimates is then proposed in Section 7.2.3.

7.2.2 Fidelity and stability

The general objective in any spectral analysis is to estimate the function $\Gamma_{xx}(f)$ as accurately as possible. This involves two requirements:

(1) that the mean smoothed spectrum $\bar{\Gamma}_{xx}(f)$ be as close to $\Gamma_{xx}(f)$ as possible, that is, the bias

$$B(f) = \bar{\Gamma}_{xx}(f) - \Gamma_{xx}(f)$$

should be small. If this is true uniformly for all f, then $\bar{\Gamma}_{xx}(f)$ is said to reproduce $\Gamma_{xx}(f)$ with high *fidelity*.

(2) that the variance of the smoothed spectral estimator

$$\text{Var}\,[\bar{C}_{xx}(f)] \approx \frac{\Gamma_{xx}^2(f)}{T}\left(\frac{M}{b_1}\right)$$

be small. If this is the case, the estimator is said to have high *stability*.

To illustrate how the requirements of high fidelity and high stability conflict, some of the empirical findings of Section 7.1 are now reviewed.

High fidelity. First consider the plot of $\bar{\Gamma}_{xx}(f)$ for the first-order ar process with $\alpha_1 = -0.4$, shown in Figure 7.2. Using the Tukey window, high fidelity can be realized for frequencies less than 0.375 cps with a truncation point $L = 8$, and hence a bandwidth $b = 1.33/8 = 0.167$ cps. The true spectrum has a wide peak centered on $f = 0.5$ cps and in this neighborhood a truncation point of $L = 16$, or $b = 0.083$ cps, is necessary to give comparable fidelity.

The first-order ar process with $\alpha_1 = -0.9$ has a much narrower peak in the neighborhood of 0.5 cps. Figure 7.5 shows that for the Bartlett window, a truncation point of at least $L = 48$, or a bandwidth of 0.031 cps, is required to achieve reasonable fidelity. Note, however, that $\bar{\Gamma}_{xx}(f)$ is plotted on a logarithmic scale so that fidelity is measured by

$$\log \bar{\Gamma}_{xx}(f) - \log \Gamma_{xx}(f),$$

as opposed to

$$\bar{\Gamma}_{xx}(f) - \Gamma_{xx}(f)$$

as in the example above. In our opinion it is more logical to measure fidelity on a logarithmic scale than on a linear scale, since it is proportional changes in power that are relevant. Note that when $L = 32$, the fidelity near the peak is as high as it is in the range $0 - 0.375$ cps. Hence a constant bandwidth window is adequate to estimate this spectrum.

The second-order process shown in Figure 7.7 has a more complex spectrum in that the peak is now two-sided and not one-sided as in the previous examples. Figure 7.7 shows $\bar{\Gamma}_{xx}(f)$ for the Parzen window and it is seen that, whereas the plots for $L = 8$ and $L = 16$ tend to underestimate the peak badly, the plot for $L = 32$ reproduces the peak with high fidelity. If the width of the peak is defined by the distance between the half power points, it is seen from Figure 7.7 that this width is approximately 0.08 cps. The bandwidths of the Parzen window with $L = 16$ and 32 are 0.11 cps and 0.06 cps respectively. Hence for $L = 32$ the window bandwidth is less than the width of the peak and high fidelity is obtained.

Figure 7.12 shows an even more complex spectrum which corresponds to a stochastic process consisting of two narrow band white noise sources with

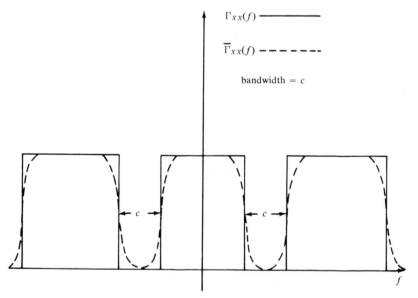

FIG. 7.12: Fidelity in the estimation of two narrow-band white noise sources

power in closely spaced bands. To achieve high fidelity for this spectrum it is necessary to use a spectral window whose bandwidth is of order c, the frequency width of the gap. Hence it can be concluded in general that to achieve high fidelity the *bandwidth of the window must be of the same order as the width of the narrowest important detail in the spectrum*. It follows that to design a spectral analysis in advance of collecting the data, it is useful to be able to guess at the width of the narrowest detail. This will be discussed in Section 7.3.1.

The word *resolution* has been used in [2] to describe a similar concept. This optical analogy presupposes that one is trying to resolve *lines* in the spectrum, that is, the spectrum is of the form

$$\Gamma_{xx}(f) = \frac{A_1}{2}\left[\delta(f-f_1) + \delta(f+f_1)\right] + \frac{A_2}{2}\left[\delta(f-f_2) + \delta(f+f_2)\right].$$

The delta functions or peaks in the spectrum are then said to be resolved if the bandwidth of the window is less than the frequency separation between the peaks. It is suggested that this is not a very useful concept in spectral analysis because real spectra can never be described in terms of delta functions, that is, the peaks are never of zero width. Further, as shown above, it is the width of the important *details* in the spectrum that are important and not merely the separation between the maxima of the peaks.

High stability. It was shown in Section 7.1 that high fidelity may be possible with a certain bandwidth but that bad estimates of the spectrum may still result if the record length is too small. For example, Figure 7.7 shows that the peak of the second-order process can be estimated with high fidelity when $L = 32$. However, Figure 7.8 shows that the estimate of the spectrum obtained with $N = 50$ gives a very bad picture of the peak. On the other hand, Figure 7.9, based on $N = 400$ terms, shows that a reasonable estimate of the spectrum is possible with $L = 32$. This is predicted by the theory of Section 6.3, since small variance, or high stability, is obtained with a large $T/M = N/L$ ratio. Hence an ideal spectral analysis is one for which M is sufficiently large for high fidelity and T/M is sufficiently large for high stability. This ideal situation is approached in the estimate of the first-order ar spectrum shown in Figure 7.3. However, in many practical problems some form of compromise is necessary between high fidelity and high stability. The practical realization of this compromise is discussed in the next section.

7.2.3 Empirical smoothing of spectral estimates

The discussion of the optimal approach to smoothing in Section 7.2.1, and specifically the criticisms of that approach, indicate the need for an empirical approach to smoothing. In particular, criticisms *(2)*, *(3)* and *(4)* call for an approach which is deliberately left *flexible*, so that many courses of action suggested by analysis of the data are possible, and a method which allows for the possibility of *learning* from the data enough about the spectrum $\Gamma_{xx}(f)$ to choose adequate smoothing for any frequency ranges of interest.

In the terminology of the preceding section, it must be possible to infer from the data when a reasonable compromise has been achieved between high fidelity and high stability. If it is accepted that economy in the computation of the autocovariances is desirable and that smoothed spectral estimators of the form (6.3.28) are suitable, then the smoothing of a spectral estimator is completely determined by the *shape* or *mathematical form* of the window and the *bandwidth* or, equivalently, the *truncation point* of the window.

Since the effect of window shape on spectral estimates is of secondary importance, as demonstrated in Figure 7.11, an empirical approach must be based on varying the bandwidth. The following is an empirical approach to smoothing which meets the requirements and falls within the framework set out above. First, use a spectral window with an acceptable shape. Then compute smoothed spectral estimates using a wide bandwidth initially and then progressively smaller bandwidths. This empirical approach to spectral analysis was suggested in [6] and illustrated in practice in [7] and [8]. From now on this procedure of using a progressively smaller bandwidth will be referred to as *window closing*. It is discussed more fully in Section 7.2.4. The less important problem of designing spectral windows with acceptable shapes, termed *window carpentry* by J. W. Tukey, is discussed in Section 7.2.5.

7.2.4 Window closing

The technique of window closing involves computing smoothed spectral estimates with a wide bandwidth and then using progressively smaller bandwidths. The first objective of this approach is flexibility, so that any significant features of the spectrum which are of practical interest, or which suggest themselves during the process of analysis, can be explored further.

The method allows one to *learn* about the shape of the spectrum, and thus the initial choice of a wide bandwidth will usually mask a certain amount of detail in the spectrum. By allowing the bandwidth to become smaller, more significant detail can be explored. Finally, as discussed in Section 7.2.2, when the bandwidth of the window is less than the smallest significant detail in the spectrum, there is no point in making the bandwidth smaller. However, practical problems of interpretation arise due to the instability of the estimates and these will be discussed below.

Since certain records yield uninformative spectra in the same way that some uninformative likelihood functions are flat, the method enables the best bandwidth to be chosen to suit the record available.

The important practical question is when to stop the process of narrowing the bandwidth, that is, when should one stop looking for more detail in the interest of maintaining stability. No rigid rules can be given to answer this question, since the best time to stop will depend on factors such as the degree of detail in the spectrum, the amount of prior knowledge of $\Gamma(f)$ available and the extent to which it is possible to discriminate between real detail and sampling fluctuations due to instability. Nevertheless, it is possible to distinguish between three types of situation which can occur in practice.

(1) It is sometimes possible to narrow the bandwidth sufficiently to reveal most of the significant detail without running into instability. In this case no major changes in the spectrum occur after quite large changes in bandwidth. Such a happy state of affairs is illustrated in Figure 7.3 by the spectral estimates of the first-order ar process. It is seen that only minor changes occur in the shape of the spectrum as a result of a fourfold decrease in bandwidth from $L = 4$ to $L = 16$. It can be concluded that a satisfactory estimate of the spectrum is obtained in the range 0 to 0.375 cps with a truncation point of $L = 8$, but that a higher truncation point, say $L = 12$, is required in the neighborhood of the peak.

(2) Sometimes it is clear that in no sense is the spectrum converging to a stable value. An example of this is given in Figure 7.8, which shows estimates of the second-order ar spectrum based on $N = 50$. The estimate for $L = 8$ is relatively smooth but it is impossible to conclude whether the large change from $L = 8$ to $L = 24$ is due to instability or to the appearance of more detail in the spectrum. Hence it would probably be concluded that the estimate based on $L = 8$ shows the broad features in the spectrum but that a longer series would be required to reveal more detail. Notice, however, that the spectrum based on $L = 8$ contains a great deal of useful information and hence the analysis is by no means worthless.

(3) Usually the situation falls somewhere between *(1)* and *(2)*. For example, consider the spectral estimates of the first-order ar process with $\alpha_1 = -0.4$, $N = 100$, shown in Figure 7.4. Note that well-defined peaks appear at $f = 0.22$ cps and $f = 0.44$ cps when $L = 16$. Without knowledge of the structure of this process it might be tempting to conclude that these peaks were real, since the estimate has approximately 17 degrees of freedom. The peaks become still more well-defined for $L = 32$, so there is doubt as to when to stop the window closing process. Similar comments apply to the estimates shown in Figure 7.6.

These situations are all characterized by a tendency for the estimates to converge initially, but then to diverge due to instability before definite conclusions can be drawn. Since it is not possible to say which of these spectra is closest to the truth, it is suggested that three spectra should be presented in the region where convergence is followed by divergence. However, it is important to remember that as the bandwidth is narrowed, the spectral estimate is a polynomial of high degree in $\cos 2\pi f$ and hence it is easy to produce spurious peaks. In the limit as the estimate tends to that of the unsmoothed spectrum, it is possible to produce peaks almost anywhere. Hence a certain amount of caution is required in interpreting spectral estimates. Finally, *the spectrum has to make sense physically*, or else the analysis is of little value. In summary, the main objective of window closing is to aid physical insight in the process of estimating and interpreting spectra.

7.2.5 Window carpentry

It was shown empirically in Section 7.1 that window closing is much more important than window carpentry. Nevertheless, it is of some importance to pay attention to the design of the window which is to be used. As stated previously, one approach to the design problem is the optimal smoothing approach of Section 7.2.1. However, windows which perform badly on mean square error and related criteria can be shown to have bad shapes on other grounds. In this section a list is given of some of the important properties which spectral windows should possess. An analytic approach to this problem has been given elsewhere [9]; a more descriptive account is given here.

(1) For a given truncation point M, the bias due to the spectral window $W(f)$ will be small if it is concentrated about zero. From Figures 6.12 and 6.13, it is seen that $W_R(f)$ corresponding to the rectangular lag window $w_R(u)$ is more concentrated about the center frequency than any of the other windows. As shown in Table 6.6, the spectral window $W_R(f)$ has the smallest bandwidth. Hence bandwidth gives a *measure of the concentration of the spectral window*.

(2) The spectral window $W_R(f)$ has the smallest bandwidth, but the price which has to be paid is that it also has the largest side lobes, as is seen from Figure 6.13. The effect of side lobes is to permit values of $\Gamma_{XX}(g)$ at frequencies distant from f to make large contributions to the bias at the frequency f. This effect is known as *leakage*. Figure 6.13 shows that windows W_B, W_T and W_P have much smaller side lobes than W_R. However, the Bartlett window W_B has larger side lobes than windows W_T and W_P, and Figure 7.5 shows that these can be troublesome if the spectrum has a narrow peak. If side lobes are to be minimized, then window W_P is preferable to the other windows.

(3) The spectral windows $W_R(f)$, $W_B(f)$ and $W_P(f)$ are of the form

$$W(f) \propto \left\{ \frac{\sin{(2\pi f M/n)}}{2\pi f M/n} \right\}^n, \quad n = 1, 2, 4, \qquad (7.2.6)$$

and hence the lag windows $w_R(u)$, $w_B(u)$ and $w_P(u)$ are related by convolution. That is, the lag window $w_B(u) = (1 - |u|/M)$, $0 \leqslant |u| \leqslant M$, may be obtained by convolving the lag window $w_R(u) = 1$, $0 \leqslant |u| \leqslant M/2$, with itself. Similarly, the lag window $w_P(u)$ is obtained by convolving the lag window $w_R(u) = 1$, $0 \leqslant |u| \leqslant M/4$, with itself four times

An equivalent way of saying this is that window w_R is proportional to the pdf of a uniform rv, window w_B is proportional to the pdf of the mean of two uniformly distributed rv's and window w_P is proportional to the pdf of the mean of four uniformly distributed rv's. Clearly, the mean of n uniformly distributed rv's will tend to a Normal or Gaussian distribution as n tends to infinity. Thus the lag window tends to a Normal curve, and hence so does the spectral window (7.2.6), as shown in Chapter 2. In fact, Daniels [10] recommends the use of a Normal window for spectral analysis.

One effect of increasing n is to decrease the height of the side lobes, as is evident from (7.2.6). However, the spectral window also becomes flatter and wider, since the first zero occurs at $f = 2^{n-1}/2M$ and hence requires a large M in order to achieve a specified bandwidth. For example, the Parzen window w_P requires approximately 40% more lags than the Tukey window w_T to achieve a given bandwidth.

(4) The effect of altering the window shape for a given truncation point may be shown by plotting the correlation between smoothed spectral estimators separated in frequency by $f_1 - f_2$. From (6.4.11) this correlation is

$$\rho_{\bar{c}\bar{c}}(f_1, f_2) \approx \frac{\int_{-\infty}^{\infty} W(f_1 - g)[W(f_2 + g) + W(f_2 - g)]\, dg}{I}. \quad (7.2.7)$$

Figure 7.13 shows the correlation function (7.2.7) plotted as a function of $f_1 - f_2$ for the windows W_B, W_T and W_P of Table 6.5. It is seen that for a wide window like W_P, the correlation between neighboring estimators is large, whereas the correlation between distant estimators is small. Conversely, for a narrow window like W_B, the correlation between neighboring estimators is relatively small and between distant estimators is relatively large.

Blackman and Tukey [2] have suggested that because of the correlation between neighboring estimators, only the uncorrelated estimates should be plotted. This is a dangerous rule to apply since it is possible, for example, to miss a peak whose frequency lies halfway between the uncorrelated estimates. In our experience it is advisable to plot the estimate at a frequency spacing of at least one-half the frequency spacing between uncorrelated estimators, that is, $F \geqslant 2L$.

The above considerations suggest that windows W_B, W_T and W_P have reasonable shapes but that one should probably reject W_B because of its bad side lobe properties. Windows W_B and W_P always give positive estimates of the spectrum, whereas W_T can sometimes give negative estimates, which is undesirable. Although W_P has smaller side lobes than W_B and W_T, it is a wider window and hence requires more autocovariances to achieve a given bandwidth. This means that if the window closing procedure is applied to W_P, the spectral estimate will take a longer time to settle down to a steady value than if W_T were used.

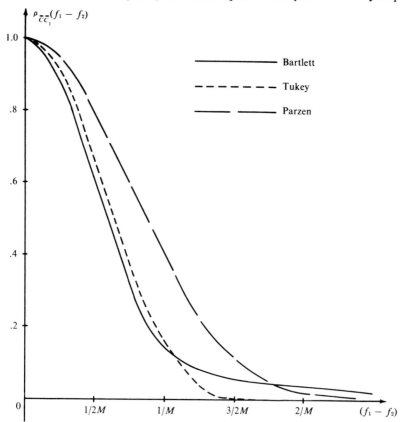

FIG. 7.13: Correlation between smoothed spectral estimators for different windows with the same truncation point

7.3 PRACTICAL ASPECTS OF SPECTRAL ESTIMATION

In this section some of the more practical aspects of spectral estimation are discussed. The first of these, discussed in Section 7.3.1, deals with the planning of a spectral analysis. The next section describes the pilot estimation of a spectrum, and this is illustrated using the batch data of Figure 5.2. Then Section 7.3.3 presents a useful practical procedure to follow in performing a spectral analysis. This procedure is illustrated in Section 7.3.4 by two practical examples which show the usefulness of the window closing technique. In Section 7.3.5 it is shown how digital filtering can be used to improve spectral estimates.

7.3.1 The design of a spectral analysis

It is now shown how a spectral analysis calculation can be designed in advance of collecting the data, and in particular, how the record length can be chosen to meet certain specifications. There are four basic requirements which have to be met:

(1) The sampling interval Δ must be small enough so that the spectrum can be estimated in the range of interest $0 \leqslant f \leqslant f_0$. Hence Δ must be, at the most, $1/2f_0$.

(2) Care must be taken to avoid *aliasing*. This may be done in one of two ways. The first involves choosing Δ so that $\Gamma_{XX}(f)$ is effectively zero for $f > 1/2\Delta$. This requires initial knowledge of the spectrum which may not be available. Furthermore, $\Gamma_{XX}(f)$ may only be required for frequencies less than some value f_0. If f_0 is much less than the frequency beyond which $\Gamma_{XX}(f)$ is effectively zero, then it may be necessary to read the data at a much finer sampling interval than is really necessary if information is only required for frequencies $f \leqslant f_0$. The second method is to filter the signal *before sampling* so that the power above f_0 is effectively removed. This is most easily done electronically. It should be noted that a certain amount of care at this stage of the data processing may save considerable trouble and expense later on.

(3) Suppose that a guess can be made of the width a of the narrowest important peak in the spectrum, or alternatively that it is required to "detect" detail of width a or more in the spectrum. Then the truncation point M should be chosen so that the bandwidth b is less than a. For example, for the Tukey window this means that $b = 1.33/M \leqslant a$, or $M = L\Delta \geqslant 1.33/a$. The number of lags of the discrete acvf which must be computed is then $L \geqslant 1.33/a\Delta$. In general the truncation point should be chosen according to

$$M = \frac{b_1}{a},\qquad (7.3.1)$$

where b_1 is the standardized bandwidth. Hence the number of lags required is

$$L = M/\Delta = b_1/a\Delta. \qquad (7.3.2)$$

(4) For finite records, the extent to which the width of peaks can be estimated or fine detail detected is also influenced by the variance of the estimator. Hence, to be able to trust the fine structure in the spectrum, it must be possible to tie down the estimate to a given stability. This may be accomplished by specifying the number of degrees of freedom ν desired with each estimate, say 15 to 30, and then determining the length of record T from (6.4.26) and (7.3.1). This gives

$$T = \frac{\nu}{2}\frac{M}{b_1} = \frac{\nu}{2a}, \qquad (7.3.3)$$

and hence

$$N = \frac{\nu}{2a\Delta} = \frac{\nu L}{2b_1}, \qquad (7.3.4)$$

using (7.3.2). From Figure 3.10 it is then possible to read off the width of the 80% or 95% confidence interval for the given number of degrees of freedom. If the confidence interval so obtained is too large, increasing v and hence N will reduce it, but at the expense of computing and data-gathering time.

A simple interpretation of (7.3.4) is obtained by considering smoothed spectral estimators separated in frequency by an amount equal to the band-width b of the spectral window. The covariance between these estimators will be approximately zero since there is negligible overlap of the spectral window at this spacing. The number of independent smoothed spectral estimators in the frequency band 0 to $1/2\Delta$ is therefore $(1/2\Delta)b = L/2b_1$ since $b = b_1/L\Delta$. However, unsmoothed spectral estimators separated by a frequency spacing $1/T = 1/N\Delta$ are distributed as independent χ^2 with 2 degrees of freedom. Since there are $T/2\Delta$ of these in the interval 0 to $1/2\Delta$, the total number of degrees of freedom associated with each smoothed estimator is $v = 2(T/2\Delta)/(L/2b_1) = 2b_1 N/L$. Hence $N = vL/2b_1$.

The important feature of (7.3.3) is that the record length can be specified independently of the spectral window and that it depends only on v and a.

An example. Suppose that it is required to estimate the power up to $f_0 = 2$ cps in the spectrum and that it can be safely assumed there is no appreciable power beyond this point. Thus there will be no trouble arising from aliasing. Then according to requirement *(1)*

$$\Delta = \frac{1}{2f_0} = \frac{1}{4} = 0.25 \text{ seconds.}$$

If it can be assumed that the width of the narrowest peak in the spectrum is at least 0.20 cps, and 30 degrees of freedom are deemed adequate, then (7.3.3) shows that the record duration must be at least

$$T = 30/2(0.2) = 75 \text{ seconds.}$$

Hence $N = 300$ data points are required. From Figure 3.10 it is found that 30 degrees of freedom give an 80% confidence interval for $\Gamma_{XX}(f)$ of approximately $(0.7\bar{C}_{xx}(f), 1.3\bar{C}_{xx}(f))$, that is, a 30% proportional error. To decrease this confidence interval to, say, $(0.8\bar{C}_{xx}(f), 1.2\bar{C}_{xx}(f))$ would require $v = 80$ and hence $T = 200$ seconds and $N = 800$.

The above calculations are of some value in deciding in advance how long a record to take but it should be emphasized that once the data have been collected, a different approach is required. Thus, if the analysis has been designed to separate peaks of width a, it may be found when the data comes to be analyzed that our guesses about a were wrong. Hence, as described in Section 7.2, it is necessary to tailor the actual analysis of the spectrum to the data available, that is, an attempt must be made to learn about the structure of the spectrum from the data. This forms the basis of the window closing procedure described in Section 7.2.4.

7.3.2 Pilot analysis

It is occasionally useful to obtain a rough estimate of the shape of a spectrum without having to compute first the acvf and then a smoothed estimate of the form (7.1.6). In particular, if it is required to prefilter the data, as will be necessary in certain problems in Chapters 9, 10 and 11, then a rough pilot analysis may be sufficient to make a guess of a good frequency response function for the filter. Since these pilot analyses are easily carried out without using an automatic computer, they also serve as useful exercises to illustrate the information contained in a spectrum.

The form of pilot analysis described below is useful when the number of observations N is 2^p, for some integer p. As will be shown in Section 7.3.5, it is capable of modification for use with any value of N. To explain the procedure, imagine that the first 64 observations of the batch data of Table 5.1 had been obtained from an experiment in which certain process variables had been deliberately varied according to the scheme in Table 7.2. In the experimental

TABLE 7.2: A fictitious experimental design for the batch data

Modification	1								2							
Week	1				2				3				4			
Day	1		2		3		4		5		6		7		8	
Shift	1	2	1	2	1	2	1	2	1	2	1	2	1	2	1	2
Batch 1	47	38	59	56	80	51	44	25	56	45	48	50	43	55	34	68
	64	65	48	40	55	58	57	59	74	54	55	62	52	41	35	38
Batch 2	23	55	71	58	37	50	50	50	50	36	45	44	38	53	54	50
	71	41	35	44	74	60	45	71	58	54	57	64	60	49	45	60

arrangement it is assumed that the yields were influenced by the batch of raw material used, shifts, days, weekly cleaning of the distillation column and two major process modifications. Note that it is only meaningful to make comparisons of the type "between batches within shifts, within days, within weeks, within modifications" since the batches being used are different each time. Hence it is natural to analyze these data by a technique called the nested analysis of variance. Thus the total variance may be decomposed as

$$\frac{1}{N} \sum_{t=1}^{N} (x_t - \bar{x})^2 = \frac{S_R}{N} + \frac{S_B}{N} + \frac{S_S}{N} + \frac{S_D}{N} + \frac{S_W}{N} + \frac{S_M}{N}, \qquad (7.3.5)$$

where the right-hand side of (7.3.5) denotes the contribution to the total variance from differences between replicates, batches, shifts, days, weeks and modifications. Thus

$$S_R = \frac{(x_2 - x_1)^2}{2} + \frac{(x_4 - x_3)^2}{2} + \cdots,$$

$$S_B = \frac{(x_4 + x_3 - x_2 - x_1)^2}{4} + \frac{(x_8 + x_7 - x_6 - x_5)^2}{4} + \cdots,$$

$$S_S = \frac{(x_8 + x_7 + x_6 + x_5 - x_4 - x_3 - x_2 - x_1)^2}{8} + \cdots,$$

$$S_D = \frac{(x_{16} + x_{15} + \cdots + x_9 - x_8 - x_7 - \cdots - x_1)^2}{16} + \cdots,$$

$$S_W = \frac{(x_{32} + x_{31} + \cdots + x_{17} - x_{16} - x_{15} - \cdots - x_1)^2}{32} + \cdots,$$

$$S_M = \frac{(x_{64} + x_{63} + \cdots + x_{33} - x_{32} - x_{31} - \cdots - x_1)^2}{64}.$$

It is seen that S_R is obtained by correlating the data with a square wave of period 2 and then squaring. Hence S_R will tend to be large if the data contains strong periodic components with period 2. Similarly, S_B will be reinforced by components of period 4, and so on. Table 7.3 shows the contributions to the mean square from each of these sources.

TABLE 7.3: Pilot spectral estimate for batch data

Source	Contribution to mean square	Estimate of spectrum	Frequency range
between replications	99.30	397.20	0.25 –0.50 cycles
between batches	15.24	121.92	0.125 –0.25 cycles
between shifts	11.77	188.32	0.0625–0.125 cycles
between days	4.10	131.20	0.0313–0.0625 cycles
between weeks	4.16	266.24	0.0156–0.0313 cycles
between modifications	0.71	90.88	0.0078–0.0156 cycles

The sum of squares S_R contains contributions not only from components with period 2 units but, as will be shown in Section 7.3.5, S_R represents contributions from components with periods between 2 and 4, that is, in the frequency range 0.25 to 0.5 cycles. Hence the average power over the frequency range 0.25 to 0.5 cycles is $99.30/0.25 = 397.2$ (yield units)^2 per cycle. Similarly, S_M represents the total power from frequencies in the range 0.125 to 0.25 cycles, and hence the average power over this band is $15.24/0.125 = 121.92$ (yield units)^2 per cycle.

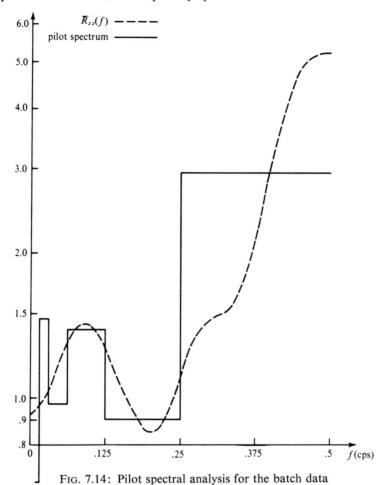

Fig. 7.14: Pilot spectral analysis for the batch data

The estimate of the spectrum obtained from the pilot analysis is plotted in Figure 7.14, together with the spectral estimate obtained from the more refined analysis of Section 7.1.1 using a Tukey window with $M = 12$. It is seen that the pilot spectral estimate agrees quite well with the refined estimate.

7.3.3 A practical procedure for spectral estimation

In this section a useful practical procedure to follow in estimating spectra is described. This consists of the following four stages:

(1) Preliminary stage. The series is examined to see if any obvious trends or periodicities are present. This is helpful in deciding whether to use the original or filtered data as will be described in Section 7.3.5. A particularly useful and

simple form of filter, which will be used extensively from now on, is the first difference filter

$$y_t = x_t - x_{t-1}.$$

A pilot analysis might also be made at this stage. The number of lags L_{max} for which the autocorrelations or autocovariances are to be computed is decided. Initially L_{max} should be chosen to be approximately $N/4$ unless this requires too much computing time. In rare cases where it is found that $N/4$ lags are not sufficient, further autocorrelations can be computed.

(2) First computation stage. The sample acf for the original and differenced data are then computed for $k = 0, 1, \ldots, L_{max}$. Plots of these functions are made to assist in deciding whether to use the original or differenced data, and what range of truncation values to use. The truncation points may be decided by scanning the chosen correlation function to see where it becomes negligible. A set of truncation values L_1, L_2, L_3 to be used in the window closing procedure is chosen to cover a fairly wide range, for example, $L_3/L_1 = 4$.

(3) Second computation stage. The spectral estimates corresponding to these truncation values are computed and plotted on a logarithmic scale, all on the same graph. The frequency spacing $1/2F$ should be chosen so that $F \approx 2L$ or $3L$. Horizontal lines corresponding to the window bandwidths (6.4.24) should be drawn on the graph to indicate the detail in the estimated spectrum relative to these bandwidths. Vertical lines corresponding to the confidence interval (6.4.21) should also be drawn for each bandwidth.

(4) Interpretation of spectral estimates. In general, the composite spectral plot obtained at stage *(3)* will fall into one of three categories, which are described below as ideal, intermediate and poor.

(a) *Ideal spectral analysis.* The variation in the spectral estimates is examined as the truncation point is increased, that is, as the bandwidth is decreased. If only minor changes occur in the estimates when L is changed beyond a certain value L^*, then it can be concluded that the window-closing procedure has revealed most of the detail in the spectrum. If the confidence interval for the spectrum at a single frequency is considered to be small enough, then the estimate based on L^* can be accepted. It is then concluded that the estimate has high fidelity and high stability. Occasionally the largest value of the truncation point L_M will be too small. In this case the spectral estimate may show a tendency to converge to some limiting form, but further estimates based on higher values of $L > L_M$ may have to be computed to confirm this behavior.

(b) *Intermediate spectral analysis.* In practice, situations where high fidelity and high stability can be attained simultaneously are rare. Usually the estimate tends to converge for small values of L but then diverges with larger values of L. This usually implies that the estimate has become unstable before the fine detail in the spectrum has been revealed. In such situations it is suggested that a series of spectra should be presented covering the intermediate cases where convergence of the spectral estimates gives way to divergence, so that these effects are evident when the spectra are interpreted. As shown in Section 7.1, it is very easy to generate spurious peaks in the spectra by narrowing the bandwidth and hence it is better to be cautious on the side of using small rather than large truncation points.

It sometimes happens that the spectrum converges very quickly in certain frequency ranges where the spectrum is smooth and slowly in other ranges where the spectrum changes quickly. Hence different values of L may be required in different parts of the frequency range.

(c) *Poor spectral analysis.* In some cases the spectral estimates change so markedly as the bandwidth is changed that it is impossible to recommend even a range of spectra. In this badly-behaved situation, the spectral estimate corresponding to a small truncation value may have to be accepted even though it is realized that there may be considerable fine detail masked by the wide spectral window. However, the basic trouble is that N is too small and so the final conclusion should be to collect more data.

It is to be emphasized that the above rules are not rigid and should be regarded only as rough guides. Special problems may dictate other courses of action. For example, one may only be interested in a peak whose frequency is *known* but whose width is only approximately known. Hence the bandwidth could be narrowed at this frequency in order to investigate this particular peak without much concern for problems of stability at other frequencies. The above procedure is now illustrated using two practical examples.

7.3.4 Two practical examples of spectral estimation

Spectral analysis of the batch data

(1) Preliminary analysis. Inspection of the batch data of Figure 5.2 did not reveal any obvious trend in the data. Hence the acvf estimate (7.1.2) was used and computed up to $I_{\text{-max}} = 18$ lags. Inspection of the pilot spectrum, Figure 7.14, revealed that the spectrum was quite smooth since the range of variation was only about four. Hence differencing was not considered necessary.

(2) First computation stage. The sample acf $r_{xx}(k)$ for these data was plotted in Figure 5.6. From this plot it is seen that the acf is essentially zero for $k > 10$, and hence it was decided to use truncation values of $L = 4$, 8, and 16.

(3) Second computation stage. The spectral estimates for these values of L using the Tukey window were computed and plotted together in Figure 7.15.

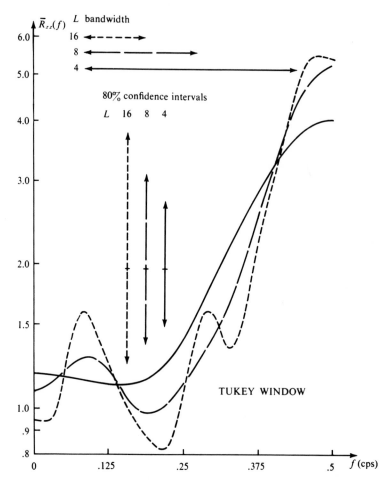

FIG. 7.15: Smoothed spectral density estimates for the batch data

Also shown are the window bandwidths and confidence interval for each value of L.

The similarity in the behavior of this spectrum and the spectrum of the simulated first-order ar process with $\alpha_1 = -0.4$, $N = 100$, shown in Figure 7.4, should be noted. It is clear that the bandwidth corresponding to $L = 4$ is too wide to reveal all the detail in the spectrum, but the changes from $L = 8$ to $L = 16$ indicate that the spectrum is very smooth and that there is no point in closing the window any further. Despite the fact that N is small, it may be concluded that this is a satisfactory spectral analysis and that little would be lost in accepting the value based on $L = 8$. The number of degrees of freedom corresponding to $L = 8$ using the Tukey window is 23, which is acceptable.

Spectral analysis of the radar data. As another example of the approach of
Section 7.3.3, Figure 7.16 shows the sample acf of the radar return signal of
Figure 5.1. Figure 7.17 shows estimates of the spectral density function using
the Bartlett window with $L = 16$, 48 and 60 for a series consisting of $N = 448$
terms. The frequency range is shown as 0 to 0.5 cps, since the actual frequency
range is not of great importance. It is seen that the estimate based on $L = 16$
is smooth and does not reveal the peak which might be expected because of the
oscillatory acf. For $L = 32$, not shown in the diagram, well-defined peaks
appear at approximately $f = 0.07$ cps and $f = 0.25$ cps. Increasing L to 48
reveals these peaks nicely, and it is seen that little change in the spectrum
occurs by increasing L to 60. Hence the final spectral window used has an
equivalent bandwidth of $1.5/60 = 0.025$ cps, and the estimate at any frequency has $3(448)/60 \approx 22$ degrees of freedom, which is adequate. The confidence interval and bandwidth corresponding to $L = 60$ are shown in the
figure as vertical and horizontal lines.

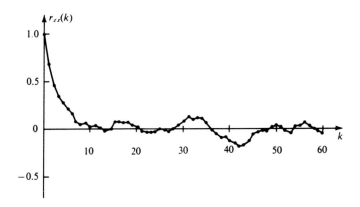

FIG. 7.16: Autocorrelation function estimate for the radar return signal of Figure
5.1

    In this particular experiment it was necessary to use 60 lags in order to
describe adequately the narrow peak at 0.07 cps. The spectrum for frequencies
greater than 0.1 cps, however, is quite adequately defined with only 32 lags.
This again illustrates the important practical point that whereas very large
values of L may be needed to show up a very narrow peak in a certain part of
the spectrum, the remainder of the spectrum may be very successfully
analyzed using much smaller values. In this radar example, the peak at $f =
0.07$ cps was of little interest since it was related to the scanning frequency of
the radar. In fact, the region of greatest practical interest is that beyond about
0.1 cps, and this could be successfully analyzed with relatively small values of
L, such as 32 or 40.

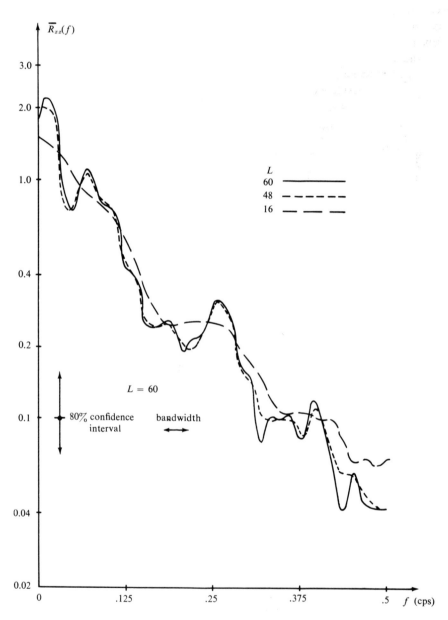

Fɪɢ. 7.17: Smoothed spectral density estimates for the radar return signal of
    Figure 5.1

7.3.5 *Digital filtering*

It is sometimes apparent from preliminary investigation of data, such as pilot analyses or visual inspection, that the spectrum is badly behaved. By this is meant that most of the power is contained in one or a few very narrow bands. Because of leakage from spectral windows, such peaks can cause errors in the spectral estimates where there is less power. Hence it may be advantageous to filter the data digitally in order to improve the spectral estimates at these frequencies.

Digital filtering is simply the process by which a set of input data x_t is transformed into a set of output data y_t by means of a linear relationship such as

$$y_t = \sum_{l=-\infty}^{\infty} h_l x_{t-l}, \tag{7.3.5}$$

where the h_l are suitably chosen weights. Note that it is not necessary to invoke the condition of "physical realizability" which implies $h_l = 0, l < 0$. Hence the filter (7.3.5) can operate on values of x to the left of y_t ("past" values of x) and on values of x to the right of y_t ("future" values of x). As shown in Chapter 2, the transfer function of the digital filter (7.3.5) is

$$H(\mathcal{Z}) = \sum_{l=-\infty}^{+\infty} h_l \mathcal{Z}^{-l}, \tag{7.3.6}$$

using $\mathcal{Z}$ transform notation.

Substituting $\mathcal{Z} = e^{+j2\pi f \Delta}$ in (7.3.6) gives the frequency response function of the filter. A special case of some importance in what follows occurs when $h_l = h_{-l}$. For these *symmetric filters*, the frequency response function is

$$H(f) = h_0 + 2 \sum_{l=1}^{\infty} h_l \cos 2\pi f l \, \Delta, \quad -\frac{1}{2\Delta} \leqslant f < \frac{1}{2\Delta}. \tag{7.3.7}$$

Hence the phase shift between input and output will either be zero or π since (7.3.7) contains no imaginary part. The gain $G(f)$ is obtained by taking the modulus of $H(f)$ in (7.3.6).

It has been noted in Section 7.3.2 that pilot estimation of a power spectrum consists of applying suitable digital filters to the time series and then squaring the output from these filters. An older application of digital filters is the smoothing of time series. For example, economic time series are sometimes smoothed to reduce the effect of short term (high-frequency) fluctuations and hence to enable a study of trends in economic variables to be made.

Examples of digital filters. Some simple digital filters are now defined and their properties discussed. For simplicity, it is assumed in these examples that the sampling interval Δ equals unity.

(1) Smoothing by threes. A time series may be "smoothed by threes" by combining the observations according to

$$y_t = h_{-1}x_{t+1} + h_0 x_t + h_1 x_{t-1}.$$

If the weights are equal, this reduces to the symmetric form

$$y_t = \tfrac{1}{3}(x_{t+1} + x_t + x_{t-1}),$$

which has the transfer function

$$H(\mathcal{Z}) = \tfrac{1}{3}(\mathcal{Z} + 1 + \mathcal{Z}^{-1}).$$

The frequency response function is

$$H(f) = \tfrac{1}{3}(1 + 2\cos 2\pi f) = \frac{\sin 3\pi f}{3 \sin \pi f}, \quad -\tfrac{1}{2} \leqslant f < \tfrac{1}{2}.$$

Hence the gain and phase functions are

$$G(f) = \left| \frac{\sin 3\pi f}{3 \sin \pi f} \right|, \quad -\tfrac{1}{2} \leqslant f < \tfrac{1}{2}$$

$$\phi(f) = \begin{cases} 0, & |f| \leqslant \tfrac{1}{3} \\ \pi, & \tfrac{1}{3} < |f| < \tfrac{1}{2}. \end{cases}$$

(2) Summing. Consider the sum filter

$$y_t = (x_t + x_{t-1}).$$

This filter has the transfer function

$$H(\mathcal{Z}) = (1 + \mathcal{Z}^{-1}),$$

and hence the frequency response function

$$H(f) = (1 + e^{-j2\pi f}) = 2e^{-j\pi f} \cos \pi f, \quad -\tfrac{1}{2} \leqslant f < \tfrac{1}{2}.$$

The gain and phase functions are

$$G(f) = 2\cos \pi f, \quad -\tfrac{1}{2} \leqslant f < \tfrac{1}{2}$$
$$\phi(f) = \pi f,$$

and hence it acts as a low-pass filter.

(3) Differencing. A difference filter is defined by

$$y_t = (x_t - x_{t-1}) \tag{7.3.8}$$

and has the frequency response function

$$H(f) = 2je^{-j\pi f} \sin \pi f = 2e^{-j\pi(f-1/2)} \sin \pi f, \quad -\tfrac{1}{2} \leqslant f < \tfrac{1}{2}.$$

The gain and phase functions are

$$G(f) = 2|\sin \pi f|, \quad -\tfrac{1}{2} \leqslant f < \tfrac{1}{2}$$
$$\phi(f) = \begin{cases} \pi(f + \tfrac{1}{2}), & -\tfrac{1}{2} \leqslant f < 0 \\ \pi(f - \tfrac{1}{2}), & 0 \leqslant f < \tfrac{1}{2}. \end{cases}$$

Hence the difference filter acts as a high-pass filter. The gain function for the difference filter is shown in Figure 1.4.

(4) Sum and difference filters. Consider now a filter corresponding to m summings and n differencings. From (2.3.26) and (2.3.27), the overall gain and phase functions are

$$G_{m,n}(f) = 2^{m+n} (\cos \pi f)^m |\sin \pi f|^n, \quad -\tfrac{1}{2} \leqslant f < \tfrac{1}{2}, \qquad (7.3.9)$$

and

$$\phi(f) = \begin{cases} \pi f(m+n) + n\pi/2, & -\tfrac{1}{2} \leqslant f < 0, \\ \pi f(m+n) - n\pi/2, & 0 \leqslant f < \tfrac{1}{2}. \end{cases}$$

Note that the gain is a maximum at the frequency

$$f_0 = \frac{1}{2\pi} \arccos\left(\frac{m-n}{m+n}\right). \qquad (7.3.10)$$

Slutsky's Theorem. Using (7.3.9), if a time series with spectrum $\Gamma_{ZZ}(f)$ is the input to the above sum and difference filter, the output spectrum is

$$\Gamma_{XX}(f) = 2^{m+n+1}(\cos \pi f)^{2m}(\sin \pi f)^{2n}\Gamma_{ZZ}(f), \quad 0 \leqslant f \leqslant \tfrac{1}{2}.$$

For white noise, that is, $\Gamma_{ZZ}(f) = 2, 0 \leqslant f \leqslant \tfrac{1}{2}$, it may be verified that as m and n tend to infinity, such that the ratio n/m tends to a constant θ, $\Gamma_{XX}(f)$ tends to a delta function $\delta(f - f_0)$, where

$$\cos 2\pi f_0 = \frac{1-\theta}{1+\theta},$$

using (7.3.10). It was shown in Section 6.2.2 that a stochastic process whose spectrum is a delta function is a sine or cosine wave. Hence this result shows that if white noise is summed and differenced sufficiently, the output becomes a sine wave. This result is due to Slutsky [11], who suggested that some apparently periodic or pseudo-periodic behavior in economic time series could be accounted for by the smoothing procedures used on the data.

(5) Pilot analysis filters. The filters used for the pilot analysis in Section 7.3.2 are made up of summing and differencing operations with suitable delays. For example, the Z-transform of the filter associated with the sum of squares S_M in Section 7.3.2 is

$$H(Z) = \frac{(Z^{32} - 1)^2}{8(Z - 1)},$$

and hence the gain function is

$$G(f) = \frac{2(\sin 32 \pi f)^2}{|\sin \pi f|}, \quad -\tfrac{1}{2} \leqslant f < \tfrac{1}{2}.$$

Similar expressions may be obtained for the other filters. As noted in Section 7.3.2, the filter corresponding to S_R has a maximum at $f = 0.5$ cps and its first

zero at $f = 0.25$ cps. Hence the output from this filter needs to be averaged roughly over the range 0.25 cps to 0.5 cps if an estimate of the average
power in this frequency band is required.

(6) *Autoregressive–moving average filters.* Autoregressive–moving average
filters are generalizations of the above filters and are defined by

$$\sum_{i=-m}^{m} \alpha_i y_{t+i} = \sum_{i=-l}^{l} \beta_i x_{t+i}. \qquad (7.3.11)$$

The main difference between the filter (7.3.11) and those previously considered
is that the output y_t depends on other values of the output as well as on
values of the input, that is, these filters use *feedback.* The transfer function
for the filter (7.3.11) is

$$H(\mathcal{Z}) = \frac{\beta_{-l}\mathcal{Z}^l + \cdots + \beta_0 + \beta_1 \mathcal{Z}^{-1} + \cdots + \beta_l \mathcal{Z}^{-l}}{\alpha_{-m}\mathcal{Z}^m + \cdots + \alpha_0 + \alpha_1 \mathcal{Z}^{-1} + \cdots + \alpha_m \mathcal{Z}^{-m}}.$$

Filters of this form have greater flexibility than those described previously and
are also more economical, in the sense that a good approximation to a given
filter shape can be achieved with a small number of terms using parameters on
both sides of (7.3.11). This fact was illustrated in Figure 5.20, where it was
shown that an ar process of two terms gave a better fit to the data than did
an ma process of order ten.

For most applications of digital filtering, it is possible to use the sum and
difference filters or generalizations of them. However, if special care is required in the design of the filter, then the parameters α_i, β_i in (7.3.11) can be
chosen empirically as described in [12]. First the ideal filter shape is specified
and then the parameters chosen so as to minimize some performance criterion
at a fixed number of frequency points. For example, one could choose the
parameters to minimize the mean square error of deviations between the
actual and ideal filter shapes at selected frequency points. Alternatively one
could use a Tschebysheff criterion, that is, minimize the maximum distance
between the actual and ideal filter shape. With the aid of a digital computer,
such calculations are easily performed.

Uses of digital filters. Some of the most important uses of digital filters are as
follows:

(a) *For pilot estimation of spectra.* This requires a bank of band-pass filters,
for example, those given in [13].

(b) *For smoothing data.* This removes high frequency oscillations and
requires a low-pass filter.

(c) *For removing trends from data.* This requires a high-pass filter, which
may be obtained by using a low-pass filter and subtracting the output of the
low-pass filter from the original data. Removal of low-frequency trend is

often a necessary preliminary to estimating a spectrum. An example is given below where failure to remove trends produced a serious bias in the spectral estimate.

(d) *For partitioning time series.* In studying relations between time series it is often better to split up the original time series x_t according to

$$x_t = x_t^{(1)} + x_t^{(2)} + \cdots + x_t^{(k)} \tag{7.3.12}$$

by using a bank of band-pass filters. For example, prior information may suggest that the low-frequency components in x_t can be predicted more accurately from a knowledge of the low-frequency components in some other series y_t than from either x_t or y_t directly. Hence each series $x_t^{(i)}$ in (7.3.12) can be used as a separate time series for further analysis. Applications of this approach to the analysis of meteorological time series have been given in [14] and to economic time series in [13].

Binomial filters. A particularly simple set of filters which could be used for this purpose has been given in [15]. These make use of the sum and difference filters introduced earlier. Thus, using $\mathcal{Z}$ transforms,

$$\begin{aligned} x_t &= [\tfrac{1}{2}(1 + \mathcal{Z}^{-1}) + \tfrac{1}{2}(1 - \mathcal{Z}^{-1})]^k x_t \\ &= (\tfrac{1}{2})^k[(1 + \mathcal{Z}^{-1})^k + k(1 + \mathcal{Z}^{-1})^{k-1}(1 - \mathcal{Z}^{-1}) + \cdots \\ &\quad + \binom{k}{i}(1 + \mathcal{Z}^{-1})^{k-i}(1 - \mathcal{Z}^{-1})^i + \cdots + (1 - \mathcal{Z}^{-1})^k]x_t. \end{aligned}$$

Hence the time series x_t can be filtered into $k + 1$ time series using $(k + 1)$ filters, the ith filter having $\mathcal{Z}$ transform

$$H_i(\mathcal{Z}) = \left(\frac{1}{2}\right)^k \binom{k}{i}(1 + \mathcal{Z}^{-1})^{k-i}(1 - \mathcal{Z}^{-1})^i.$$

Hence the output $x_t^{(i)}$ from this filter is obtained by passing the original series through $k - i$ summation filters and i difference filters and then multiplying by the coefficient $(\tfrac{1}{2})^k\binom{k}{i}$.

Using (7.3.10) it is seen that the ith filter has a peak frequency at

$$\cos 2\pi f_0 = \frac{k - 2i}{k}, \quad i = 0, 1, 2, \ldots, k.$$

For example, with $k = 4$, the peak frequencies are at 0, 0.167, 0.25, 0.417 and 0.5 cps.

An example of digital filtering. This example relates to the estimation of the spectrum of a radar return signal and is described in greater detail in [16]. For technical reasons the return signal cannot be measured independently of the yawing motion of the aircraft which is being tracked by the radar. Figure 7.18 shows a section of record where the yaw motion is extreme and dominates the high-frequency noise whose spectrum was required.

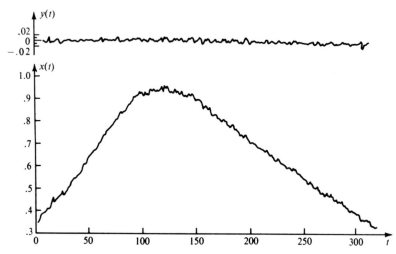

FIG. 7.18: Original and filtered radar return signals

The record was read at 320 points and then filtered using the symmetric filter (7.3.5) with

$$h_0 = 1 - \frac{1}{m+1},$$

$$h_i = h_{-i} = -\frac{1}{m+1}\left(\frac{1}{2} + \frac{1}{2}\cos\frac{i\pi}{m+1}\right), \quad i = 1, 2, \ldots, m,$$

and $m = 9$. These weights are the same as the Tukey window w_T of Table 6.5 but they have been modified to make the filter a high-pass filter and normalized to make the sum of the weights equal to one.

The filtered series y_t is shown above the original series x_t in Figure 7.18 and the effectiveness of the filter in removing the low frequencies can be seen.

The acvf's of the original and filtered series were calculated and spectral estimates obtained for different values of the truncation point L using the Bartlett window. The estimate of the spectrum of the filtered series did not change for values of L greater than 30, but a much higher value of L was required for the original series. To compare the high frequency ends of the two spectra, Figure 7.19 shows the spectra for the same value of L for both series. It is seen that at higher frequencies the original series has a spectrum which is approximately 10 times higher than that of the filtered series. This is because the low-frequency power is so great in the original series that it leaks into the estimates at high frequencies, producing large biases.

Several records of this type exhibiting various degrees of yaw were available, and some contained no yaw motion at all. When the records containing yaw were filtered before estimating the spectrum, excellent agreement was obtained with the spectra estimated when yaw was absent.

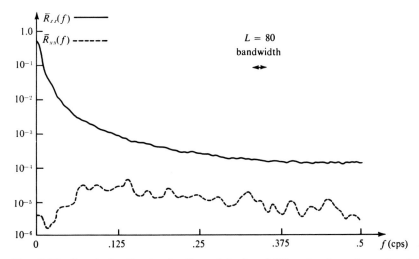

Fig. 7.19: Spectral estimates for the original and filtered radar return signals

7.4 USES AND EXAMPLES OF SPECTRAL ANALYSIS

Since spectral methods were introduced by M. S. Bartlett and J. W. Tukey about fifteen years ago, a wide variety of applications of the technique have been reported in the literature. Most of these applications can be classified according to the following three broad areas: model building, the design of experiments and frequency response studies.

Further applications of spectral analysis will be given later on in the book, but for the present it is convenient to show how knowledge of the spectrum of a single time series is useful in these three areas.

7.4.1 Model building

The shape of a spectrum will sometimes suggest features which need to be explained in any model which may be proposed for the time series. For example, the presence and magnitudes of peaks in the spectrum may throw light on some basic periodicities which require physical interpretation.

In situations where spectra are being studied to obtain a better understanding of the physical mechanism generating the time series, a single spectrum will rarely be very useful. The most important clues concerning the model may be obtained when external conditions change and hence several spectra need to be studied. These external conditions may be beyond one's control as in the first example below, or may be deliberately varied in the form of a planned experiment as in the second example.

Example 1. Figure 7.20 shows the spectrum of the horizontal velocity component of atmospheric turbulence, given in [17]. The upper spectrum was

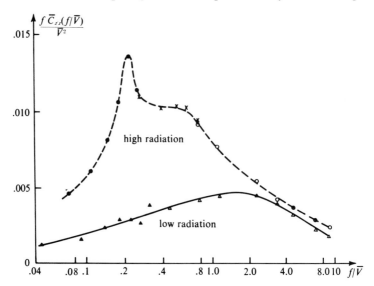

FIG. 7.20: Velocity spectra for horizontal wind components

obtained from measurements made under clear skies (high solar radiation) and the lower spectrum from measurements made under cloudy skies (low solar radiation). Note that the spectrum contains much more power during periods of high radiation and that most of this power appears at low frequencies. In particular, the peak in the spectrum moves toward lower frequencies with increasing radiation and the power at higher frequencies seems to be independent of radiation. These conclusions are borne out in more detailed studies given in [18], where the following physical explanation for this behavior is suggested: at high frequencies the main causes of atmospheric turbulence are *mechanical* or frictional forces, and at low frequencies the main causes are heat *convection* due to solar radiation.

In Figure 7.20 the ordinate plotted is proportional to $f\overline{C}_{xx}(f)$, since the abscissa is $\log f$. As a result, the area under the curve is still the total variance or power. Since the mean wind speed $\overline{V}$ changes the intensity of turbulence, and also its distribution with frequency, in a known manner, the quantities actually plotted in Figure 7.20 are non-dimensional quantities $f\overline{C}_{xx}(f)/\overline{V}^2$ and $f/\overline{V}$.

Example 2. Figure 7.21 shows three spectra relating to measurements of the vertical velocity component of atmospheric turbulence made at three different heights and described in [18]. The variables actually plotted in Figure 7.21 are the non-dimensional quantities $f\overline{C}_{xx}(f)/\overline{V}^2$ and $fZ/\overline{V}$ where Z is the height from the ground. The figures show that the upper two spectra are very similar in shape and also have maxima at the same frequency. The lower spectrum is not directly comparable to the others. On the basis of these and

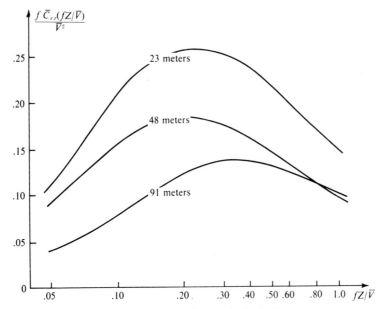

FIG. 7.21: Velocity spectra for vertical wind components

other spectra reported in [18], good agreement was found over the important regions of the spectrum, between the empirical spectra and two suggested theoretical expressions,

$$\Gamma_{XX}(h) = 2h(1 + h)^{-3}$$
$$\Gamma_{XX}(h) = \tfrac{10}{9}h(1 + h)^{-8/3},$$

where $h = \gamma Zf/\bar{V}$ and γ is a constant. Further examples may be found in the literature of explanations for complex physical phenomena which have been suggested or partially verified by means of spectral analysis.

7.4.2 The design of experiments

As a simple example of this type of application, suppose that it is required to design an experiment to estimate the slope of a response surface $\eta(v_1, \ldots, v_n)$ with a view to maximizing or minimizing η. For example, when $n = 1$, $\eta(v)$ might be the yield or cost per ton of a chemical product and v the flow rate of feedstock into the reactor. Two situations can be distinguished in practice. In the first, the process is a batch process and the variables v_i are set at the beginning of a run. Alternatively, the process is a continuous process but adjustments are made so infrequently that the dynamics of the process can be neglected. In the second, the process is continuous and the slope is measured on a continuous basis as in a maximum-seeking or hill-climbing

control system [19]. On the basis of the estimated slope the control system
can adjust the operating conditions in order to maximize yield or minimize
cost.

Suppose in the first situation that adjustments are made to v at unit time
intervals according to

$$v_t = a \cos \frac{\pi t}{b}, \quad t = 1, 2, \ldots, N. \tag{7.4.1}$$

Suppose that the amplitude a of the cosine wave is fixed and that it is required
to choose its period $2b$ so as to minimize the variance of the estimated slope.
Assuming a linear model

$$Y_t = \eta(v_t) + Z_t = \theta_1 v_t + Z_t,$$

where Z_t is a noise or error term, the usual least squares estimate of θ_1 is

$$\hat{\theta}_1 = \frac{\sum_{t=1}^N y_t v_t}{\sum_{t=1}^N v_t^2} = \frac{2}{Na^2} \sum_{t=1}^N y_t v_t.$$

It is shown in appendix A7.2 that the variance of the corresponding estimator
$\hat{\Theta}_1$ is approximately

$$\text{Var}\,[\hat{\Theta}_1] \approx \frac{4}{Na^2}\, \Gamma_{zz}\!\left(\frac{1}{2b}\right). \tag{7.4.2}$$

Hence, for fixed a, the variance is a minimum when the frequency $1/2b$ of
the perturbation signal corresponds to the minimum in the spectrum
of the noise. In other words, the signal-to-noise ratio $a^2/2\Gamma_{zz}(1/2b)$ is
maximized.

For the second situation the perturbation signal is a continuous cosine wave

$$v(t) = a \cos 2\pi f_0 t.$$

It is shown in Appendix A7.2 that the variance of the slope is then minimized when the signal-to-noise ratio

$$\frac{a^2 G^2(f_0)}{2\Gamma_{zz}(f_0)} \tag{7.4.3}$$

is a maximum. In (7.4.3), $G(f_0)$ is the gain of the system at frequency f_0.

Example 3. The batch data of Figure 5.2 was obtained from a process when
no deliberate changes were made in the process variables. Thus the smoothed
spectrum $\bar{C}_{xx}(f)$ shown in Figure 7.15 gives an estimate of the spectrum
$\Gamma_{zz}(f)$ of the noise in the process. This information can be used to design an
experiment in which some process variable is deliberately varied according
to the cosine wave (7.4.1) or some other periodic signal, say a square wave of
period $2b$.

Figure 7.15 shows that the spectrum is approximately flat between $f = 0$ and $f = 0.25$ cps but rises sharply when $f > 0.25$ cps. Since $b = 1$ corresponds to $f = 0.5$ cps and $b \geqslant 2$ corresponds to the frequency range 0 to 0.25 cps, it is seen that any value of $b \geqslant 2$ would be acceptable. However, there are strong practical grounds for using as high a frequency as possible, since low frequency drifts or trends are likely to occur and increase the variance at low frequencies. Hence $b = 2$ would be a reasonable choice on the basis of the estimated spectrum.

7.4.3 Frequency response studies

These applications of spectral analysis are centered on the relation (6.2.15) connecting the spectra of the input $Z(t)$ and the output $X(t)$ to a linear system, that is,

$$\Gamma_{xx}(f) = \Gamma_{zz}(f)G^2(f). \tag{7.4.4}$$

It is possible to distinguish between two types of situations which occur in practice. Either the gain function $G(f)$ of the system is fixed and the only quantity which can be altered in (7.4.4) is the input spectrum $\Gamma_{zz}(f)$, or the input spectrum $\Gamma_{zz}(f)$ is fixed but the gain function can be changed.

Example 4. As an example of a system with fixed gain function consider the problem of runway roughness [20]. This presents a problem to aircraft designers which has increased in severity over the last few years since it is responsible for structural failure, reduction of fatigue life of an aircraft, difficulties in reading instruments and passenger discomfort.

The way in which runway roughness affects an aircraft is governed by the frequency response characteristic of the landing gear. For example, the landing gear of a typical commercial aircraft has a gain plot which has a predominant response in the frequency range between 1.5 and 2 cycles per second.

One way of measuring the roughness of a runway is to take readings of the runway elevation at intervals of the order of a foot along the runway. These readings may be used to characterize the runway roughness by computing an estimate of the spectrum of the runway. The spectrum $\Gamma_{zz}(f)$ would then be measured in terms of (elevation units)^2 per cycle per foot, that is, ft^2/cpf. From a knowledge of the gain function of the landing gear and the runway roughness spectrum, it is then possible to investigate how much stress the wings of the aircraft will be subjected to, and so on.

Suppose, for example, that the roughness spectrum is as shown in Figure 7.22(a) and has a definite peak due to a large concentration of roughness at a particular wave length. The squared gain of the landing gear response is shown in Figure 7.22(b) for two different speeds $V = 40$ mph, curve 3, and $V = 20$ mph, curve 2, at constant damping and at two different dampings at the same speed $V = 20$ mph, curve 1 referring to light damping and 2 to

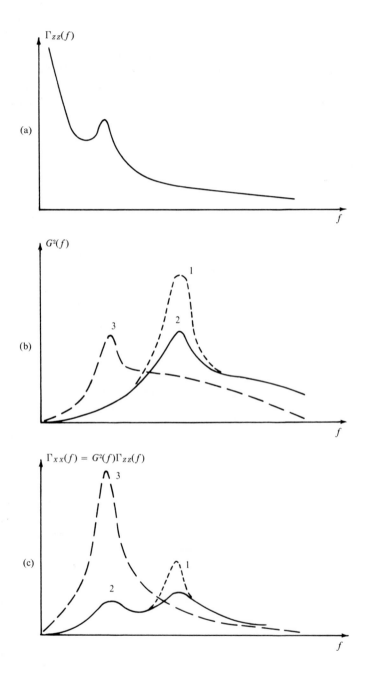

Fɪɢ. 7.22: Effects of input peaks, damping and velocity on aircraft response

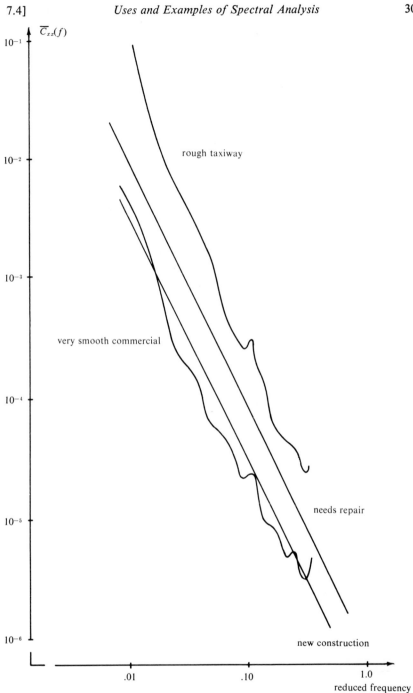

FIG. 7.23: Typical spectra of runway elevation

heavy damping. The predicted response obtained from (7.4.4) is shown in Figure 7.22(c) for these three cases.

Notice that at a given speed the effect of low damping is to increase the power under the spectral curve and hence to produce more damaging effects. Moreover, increasing the speed shifts the maximum in the gain to lower frequencies where the roughness spectrum increases and again the output power is increased. Finally, a shift in the gain plot as a result of an increased speed may interact with the roughness spectrum to produce a very sharp reinforcement in the output spectrum, as in curve 3 of Figure 7.22(c). (An example of this occurs when a car is driven over a washboard road at a speed which produces vehicle resonance.)

Some typical runway elevation spectra are shown in Figure 7.23. On the basis of the above calculations it is possible to lay down norms for the spectra of new runway constructions and for runways needing repair. These norms are indicated by the straight lines in Figure 7.23.

An example of a system with fixed input spectrum is the problem of designing the suspension of motorcycles and cars. Since road surfaces tend to differ widely in different countries, measurements of road surface spectra are beginning to have a considerable influence on the design of frequency response characteristics of cars and motorcycles, especially those designed for export. Another example of this type arises in the design of aircraft to minimize fatigue due to atmospheric turbulence. This is discussed below.

Example 5. Figure 7.24 shows the spectral estimate of the tail shear on an aircraft flown at low altitude in gusty conditions. The spectrum is characterized by a narrow peak at $f = 4.85$ cps, corresponding roughly to the natural

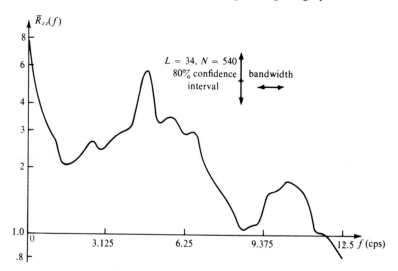

FIG. 7.24: Spectrum of tail shear

frequency of oscillation of the aircraft. There is also a wider peak at $f = 10.3$ cps corresponding to the natural frequency of oscillation of the tail, as would be expected since the measurements were made on the tail. These spectra are useful to design engineers in suggesting how various parts of the aircraft structure need to be modified to minimize the risk of structural damage due to the buffeting of turbulent air.

REFERENCES

[1] D. G. Watts, "A general theory of amplitude quantization with application to correlation determination." *Proc. Inst. Electr. Engrs.*, Part C **109**, 209 (May, 1962).

[2] R. B. Blackman and J. W. Tukey, *The Measurement of Power Spectra from the Point of View of Communications Engineering*. Dover, New York, 1958.

[3] U. Grenander and M. Rosenblatt, *Statistical Analysis of Stationary Time Series*. John Wiley, New York, 1957.

[4] A. A. Lomnicki and S. K. Zaremba, "On estimating the spectral density function of a stochastic process." *Jour. Royal Stat. Soc.* **B 19**, 13 (1957).

[5] E. Parzen, "Mathematical considerations in the estimation of spectra." *Technometrics* **3**, 167 (1961).

[6] G. M. Jenkins, "General considerations in the analysis of spectra." *Technometrics* **3**, 133 (1961).

[7] G. M. Jenkins, "An example of the estimation of a linear open loop transfer function." *Technometrics* **5**, 227 (1963).

[8] G. M. Jenkins, "A survey of spectral analysis." *Applied Statistics* **14**, 2 (1965).

[9] D. G. Watts, "Optimal windows for power spectra estimation." Mathematics Research Center Technical Summary Report 506 (Sept., 1964).

[10] H. E. Daniels, "The estimation of spectral densities." *Jour. Royal Stat. Soc.* **B 24**, 185 (1962).

[11] E. Slutsky, "The summation of random causes as the source of cyclic processes." *Econometria* **5**, 105 (1937).

[12] H. Robertson, "Approximate design of digital filters." *Technometrics* **7**, 387 (1965).

[13] J. M. Craddock, "An analysis of the slower temperature variations at Kew Observatory by means of mutually exclusive band-pass filters." *Jour. Royal Stat. Soc.* **A 120**, 387 (1957).

[14] M. D. Godfrey, "Frequency methods in economic analysis." Ph.D. Thesis. London University (1962).

[15] L. J. Tick, "Some time series techniques useful in life sciences." Proc. I.B.M. Scientific Computing Symposium. *Statistics*, 265 (1963).

[16] A. S. Alavi and G. M. Jenkins, "An example of digital filtering." *Applied Statistics* **14**, 70 (1965).

[17] H. A. Panofsky and I. Van der Hoven, "Spectra and cross-spectra of velocity components in the mesometeorological range." *Quart J. Roy. Meteorol. Soc.* **81**, 603 (1955).

[18] H. A. Panofsky and R. A. McCormick, "Properties of spectra of atmospheric turbulence at 100 meters." *Quart. J. Roy. Meteorol. Soc.* **80**, 546 (1954).

[19] G. E. P. Box and J. R. Chanmugam, "Adaptive optimization of continuous processes." *Industrial and Engineering Chemistry (Fundamentals)* **1**, 2 (1962).

[20] J. C. Houbolt, "Runway roughness studies in the aeronautical field." *Jour. Air Transport Div., Amer. Soc. Civ. Engr.* **87**, 11 (1961).

APPENDIX A7.1   FLOW CHART FOR AUTOSPECTRUM SUBROUTINE

The following is a flow chart for a computer subroutine which accepts autocovariance estimates COV(K,J,J) or DCOV(K,J,J), K = 0, MAXM, from program MULTICOR described in Appendix A5.3. Additional inputs are the sampling interval DELTA, the number of frequency points NF at which the smoothed autospectrum estimate is to be computed, and values of lag M ≤ MAXM for which smoothed autospectra are to be computed. In general NF = 2 or 3 times the largest M used. The spectral window used is the Tukey window (Table 6.5). Output consists of printout of the autocovariances (echo check), the smoothed spectra values for each truncation point M and a plot of the logarithm of the smoothed spectrum versus frequency for each truncation point M, overlayed on one graph.

Subroutine AUTOSPEC

1) *Input* parameters N, MAXM, DELTA, NF.

2) *Read* IDENT, COV(K); K = 0, MAXM.

3) *Read* M, *calculate* weights

$$W(K) = 0.5*(1. + COS(\pi K/M)), \ K = 1, \ M - 1.$$

4) *Calculate* smoothed autospectral estimate

$$SPEC(I) = 2*DELTA*\left\{ COV(0) + 2 \sum_{K=1}^{M-1} COV(K)*W(K)*COS\frac{\pi KI}{NF} \right\}; \quad I = 0, \ NF.$$

This transform can be performed very rapidly using either the fast Fourier transform [1], or the algorithm listed below in which the transform is obtained as the solution of a difference equation.

5) *Calculate* the logarithm of the spectrum LOGSPEC(I) = LOG10(SPEC(I)); I = 0, NF.

Care must be taken here to ensure that SPEC(I) is positive. If SPEC(I) is negative or zero, set LOGSPEC(I) = −100. for plotting purposes.

6) *Print* the smoothed spectral estimates SPEC(I) I = 0, NF, the bandwidth B = 4/(3M*DELTA) and the degrees of freedom D = (8*N)/(3*M) for the Tukey window and the appropriate values of N, M and DELTA.

7) *Plot* and *overlay* the logarithm of the smoothed spectrum versus frequency for all values of M used.

A search procedure is used to find the maximum value MLOG of LOGSPEC(I), which can then be used in plotting the graph. The procedure used by the authors is to choose the nearest decade value D above MLOG and plot the logspectrum over four decades. For example, suppose that the maximum spectral value was 2, so that MLOG $= 0.303$ and hence D $= 1$. Then the logspectrum values would be plotted over the range -3 to 1 corresponding to spectral values from 0.001 to 10. A range of four decades was considered adequate for most purposes, since if more than four decades are required it is probably better to filter the data in order to get a better spectral estimate at lower power levels. A value of LOGSPEC(I) $= -100$ will automatically be plotted along the lowest decade line.

Algorithm

To find SPEC(I),

Set $C = COS \dfrac{\pi I}{NF}$, V0 $= 0.$, V1 $= 0.$

Do 1, K $= M-1$, 1

    V2 $= 2.*C*V1 - V0 + W(K)*COV(K)$

    V0 $= V1$

1   V1 $= V2.$

    SPEC(I) $= 2.*DELTA*(COV(0) + 2.*(V1*C - V0)).$

Example: Consider the example given in Section 7.1.1 for which M $= 3$, DELTA $= 1.0$, NF $= 8$ and COV(0) $= 1$, W(1)*COV(1) $= 0.430$, W(2)*COV(2) $= 0.065$. Then for I $= 0$, $C = COS\frac{\pi}{8}(0) = 1$, V0 $= 0.$, V1 $= 0.$, and going through the do-loop,

    K $= 2$, V2 $= 2(1)(0) - 0 + 0.065 = 0.065$

        V0 $= 0$

        V1 $= 0.065$;

    K $= 1$, V2 $= 2(1)(0.065) - 0 + 0.430 = 0.560$

        V0 $= 0.065$

        V1 $= 0.560.$

Then SPEC(0) $= 2(1)\{1 + 2((0.560)(1) - 0.065)\} = 3.980$, which agrees with the value obtained in Table 7.1.

For I $= 1$,

$C = COS(\pi/8) = 0.924$, V0 $= 0$, V1 $= 0$. Going through the do-loop,

K $= 2$, V2 $= 2(0.924)(0) - 0 + 0.065 = 0.065$

    V0 $= 0$

    V1 $= 0.065$;

$K = 1,\ V2 = 2(0.924)(0.065) - 0 + 0.430 = 0.550$

$\qquad V0 = 0.065$

$\qquad V1 = 0.550.$

Then $\text{SPEC}(1) = 2(1)(1 + 2((0.550)(0.924) - 0.065)) = 3.772.$

This algorithm, while not as fast as the fast Fourier transform, nevertheless enjoys the advantages of relatively high speed, high accuracy and the need to compute only one cosine function for each frequency point.

APPENDIX REFERENCE

[1] J. W. Cooley and J. W. Tukey, "An algorithm for the machine calculation of complex Fourier series." *Mathematics of Computation,* **19**, 90, 297 (1965).

APPENDIX A7.2   VARIANCE OF SLOPE ESTIMATORS

Discrete Time. The estimate of the slope θ_1 in the model

$$Y_t = \theta_1 x_t + Z_t, \qquad (A7.2.1)$$

introduced in Section 7.4.2, is of the form

$$\hat{\theta}_1 = \sum_{t=1}^{N} w_t y_t, \qquad (A7.2.2)$$

with $w_t = (2/Na) \cos(\pi t/b)$. Proceeding as in the derivation of (5.2.9), the variance of the corresponding estimator is

$$\text{Var}[\hat{\theta}_1] = \sum_{t=1}^{N} \sum_{r=1}^{N} w_t w_r \gamma_{YY}(t - r). \qquad (A7.2.3)$$

Now if the observations are made at unit time intervals,

$$\gamma_{YY}(k) = \int_{-1/2}^{1/2} \Gamma_{YY}(f)\, e^{j2\pi fk}\, df. \qquad (A7.2.4)$$

Substituting (A7.2.4) in (A7.2.3),

$$\text{Var}[\hat{\theta}_1] = \int_{-1/2}^{1/2} |W(f)|^2 \Gamma_{YY}(f)\, df, \qquad (A7.2.5)$$

where

$$W(f) = \sum_{t=1}^{N} w_t\, e^{j2\pi ft}. \qquad (A7.2.6)$$

Now, suppose that $w_t = (2/Na) \cos(\pi t/b)$ as in (7.4.1). Then

$$W(f) = \frac{1}{Na} \left\{ \frac{1 - \exp[j(N + 1)2\pi(f - 1/2b)]}{1 - \exp[j2\pi(f - 1/2b)]} \right.$$
$$\left. + \frac{1 - \exp[j(N + 1)2\pi(f + 1/2b)]}{1 - \exp[j2\pi(f + 1/2b)]} \right\}.$$

Substituting the modulus squared in (A7.2.5) gives

$$\text{Var}\,[\hat{\Theta}_1] = \frac{1}{Na^2} \int_{-1/2}^{1/2} \left\{ \frac{\sin^2 (N+1)\pi(f - 1/2b)}{N \sin^2 \pi(f - 1/2b)} \right.$$
$$\left. + \frac{\sin^2 (N+1)\pi(f + 1/2b)}{N \sin^2 \pi(f + 1/2b)} \right\} \Gamma_{YY}(f)\,df,$$

plus cross-product terms.

Making use of the fact that the quantity in braces tends to

$$\delta(f - 1/2b) + \delta(f + 1/2b)$$

as N tends to infinity, while the cross-product terms are of order $1/N^2$, gives

$$\lim_{N \to \infty} N \,\text{Var}\,[\hat{\Theta}_1] = \frac{4}{a^2}\,\Gamma_{YY}\left(\frac{1}{2b}\right). \tag{A7.2.7}$$

For finite N, it follows that

$$\text{Var}\,[\hat{\Theta}_1] \approx \frac{4}{Na^2}\,\Gamma_{YY}\left(\frac{1}{2b}\right). \tag{A7.2.8}$$

Since the model (A7.2.1) implies that $\Gamma_{YY}(1/2b) = \Gamma_{ZZ}(1/2b)$, (A7.2.8) is equivalent to (7.4.2). Thus the variance is a minimum if the perturbation frequency $1/2b$ is equal to the frequency for which the spectrum of the noise is a minimum.

Continuous Time. In discrete time, the dynamics of the process were ignored. If a continuous sinusoidal perturbation $x(t) = a \cos 2\pi f_0 t$ is applied to an input variable, the model (A7.2.1) needs to be modified to

$$Y(t) = \theta_1 a G(f_0) \cos 2\pi f_0 t + Z(t),$$

where $G(f_0)$ is the gain at frequency f_0. The analysis is then similar to that for the discrete case. The final result is

$$\text{Var}\,[\hat{\Theta}_1] \approx \frac{4}{Ta^2}\,\frac{\Gamma_{YY}(f_0)}{G^2(f_0)}.$$

Hence the variance is a minimum if the perturbation frequency f_0 corresponds to the maximum of the signal to noise ratio $G^2(f_0)/\Gamma_{YY}(f_0)$.

APPENDIX A7.3   THE FAST FOURIER TRANSFORM

A recent innovation in spectral analysis is the fast Fourier transform (FFT). This is an algorithm for computing discrete Fourier transforms much more quickly than the direct method given in Section 2.1.2, but at the same time retaining accuracy. Thus, using the direct approach, the discrete Fourier transform of a series of N terms would require approximately N^2 operations, whereas the FFT requires only $2N \log_2 N$ operations. Savings in computer time can be very large if one is interested in the Fourier analysis of long series. For example, computation of the Fourier coefficients for a series of $N = 8192$ terms [1] required about 5 seconds on an IBM 8094 computer, as compared with almost 30 minutes using the direct approach.

The relevance of the FFT to spectral analysis is that it is now faster to compute the sample spectrum directly using a FFT, then smooth the sample spectrum rather than compute the autocorrelation function, smooth with a lag window and finally transform. Despite this computing advantage we do not believe that the case for using the FFT in spectral analysis is as strong as in Fourier analysis for the following reasons:

(1) In the authors' experience, the fast computers which are now available are more than adequate for purposes of spectral analysis. Our present computing facilities are greatly in excess of our ability to make sense of practical data.

(2) We regard the autocorrelation function as an invaluable intermediate stage in spectral analysis. Thus the autocorrelation function of the original and an appropriately differenced series should be plotted to decide

(a) whether differencing is necessary or not
(b) the choice of a suitable range of truncation points
(c) the degree of alignment necessary when cross correlating series.

Description of the Fast Fourier Transform. A complete description of the FFT is given in [1] and its history of discovery and repeated discovery in [2]. These papers are part of a special journal issue [3], which also includes a paper on some additional uses of the FFT [4, 5]. The treatment here follows [1].

Suppose it is required to find the Fourier transform X_m, $m = 0, 1, \ldots, N - 1$, of the series x_t, $t = 1, 2, \ldots, N$, where N is even. One approach [5] is to partition the series x_t into two half-series y_t and z_t, where

$$y_t = x_{2t-1};$$

$$z_t = x_{2t}, \qquad t = 1, 2, \ldots, \frac{N}{2}. \tag{A7.3.1}$$

The series y_t, z_t each consist of $N/2$ values and hence have Fourier transforms

$$Y_m^{(N/2)} = \frac{2}{N} \sum_{t=1}^{N/2} y_t \, e^{-j(4\pi tm/N)},$$

$$Z_m^{(N/2)} = \frac{2}{N} \sum_{t=1}^{N/2} z_t \, e^{-j(4\pi tm/N)}, \tag{A7.3.2}$$

where the superscript on the transform denotes the number of terms in the series and the transform. But $X_m^{(N)}$ and $Y_m^{(N/2)}$, $Z_m^{(N/2)}$ are related, since

$$X_m^{(N)} = \frac{1}{N} \sum_{t=1}^{N} x_t \, e^{-j(2\pi tm/N)}$$

$$= \frac{1}{N} \sum_{t=1}^{N/2} \left\{ y_t \, e^{-j(2\pi m/N)(2t-1)} + z_t \, e^{-j(2\pi m/N)(2t)} \right\}$$

$$= e^{j(2\pi m/N)} \frac{1}{N} \sum_{t=1}^{N/2} y_t \, e^{-j(4\pi mt/N)} + \frac{1}{N} \sum_{t=1}^{N/2} z_t \, e^{-j(4\pi mt/N)}$$

$$= \frac{e^{j(2\pi m/N)}}{2} Y_m^{(N/2)} + \frac{1}{2} Z_m^{(N/2)}, \qquad 0 \le m \le \frac{N}{2} - 1. \tag{A7.3.3}$$

Also,

$$Y_{m+(N/2)}^{(N/2)} = Y_m^{(N/2)},$$

$$Z_{m+(N/2)}^{(N/2)} = Z_m^{(N/2)}, \qquad 0 \le m \le \frac{N}{2} - 1,$$

so that

$$X_{m+(N/2)}^{(N)} = \frac{e^{j(2\pi/N)(m+N/2)}}{2} Y_m^{(N/2)} + \frac{1}{2} Z_m^{(N/2)}$$

$$= -\frac{e^{j(2\pi m/N)}}{2} Y_m^{(N/2)} + \frac{1}{2} Z_m^{(N/2)}, \qquad 0 \le m \le \frac{N}{2} - 1. \quad (A7.3.4)$$

Hence, summarizing (A7.3.3) and (A7.3.4),

$$X_m^{(N)} = \frac{e^{j(2\pi m/N)}}{2} Y_m^{(N/2)} + \frac{1}{2} Z_m^{(N/2)}$$

$$X_{m+(N/2)}^{(N)} = -\frac{e^{j(2\pi m/N)}}{2} Y_m^{(N/2)} + \frac{1}{2} Z_m^{(N/2)}, \qquad 0 \le m \le \frac{N}{2} - 1, \quad (A7.3.5)$$

and it is seen that the Fourier transform for the series x_t is easily obtained from the Fourier series of the half-series y_t and z_t. Likewise, if $N/2$ is even, the series y_t and z_t may be partitioned into two series, y_t', z_t' and y_t'', z_t'' respectively, and an appropriate version of (A7.3.5) may be used to construct the transforms $Y_m^{(N/2)}$ and $Z_m^{(N/2)}$ from the transforms of the series of length $N/4$.

For series of length $N = 2^k$, the procedure is followed until partitions of only one term are obtained, for which the Fourier transform equals the term itself. Otherwise the procedure is followed until the reduced series can be simply transformed or until a new factor of N, say $n = 3$, is encountered. The procedure is the same as above then, except that the remaining partitions are partitioned by threes. Details are given in [1]. An example follows.

An example. Consider the ionosphere data of Chapter 2, with $n = 12 = 2^2 3$. The data are as follows:

t	1	2	3	4	5	6	7	8	9	10	11	12
x_t	-6	-20	-28	-8	-1	7	-20	-6	-7	14	19	12

Partitioning into two gives

t	1	2	3	4	5	6
y_t	-6	-28	-1	-20	-7	19
z_t	-20	-8	7	-6	14	12

Partitioning y_t and z_t into two gives

t	1	2	3
y_t'	-6	-1	-7
z_t'	-28	-20	19
y_t''	-20	7	14
z_t''	-8	-6	12

The Fourier transforms of y'_t, z'_t, y''_t and z''_t are easily calculated and each consists of three terms, as shown below.

Harmonic Transform	m		
	0	1	2
$Y_m'^{(3)}$	-4.6667	$-1.1667 + j1.4433$	$-1.1667 - j1.4433$
$Z_m'^{(3)}$	-9.6667	$14.3333 + j2.3093$	$14.3333 - j2.3093$
$Y_m''^{(3)}$	0.3333	$6.8333 + j7.7940$	$6.8333 - j7.7940$
$Z_m''^{(3)}$	-0.6667	$6.3333 + j0.5773$	$6.3333 - j0.5773$

The Fourier transforms $Y_m^{(6)}$, $Z_m^{(6)}$, $(0 \le m \le 5)$, are then calculated using (A7.3.5). For example,

$$Y_0^{(6)} = \frac{1}{2} Y_0'^{(3)} + \frac{1}{2} Z_0'^{(3)} \qquad\qquad = -7.1666$$

$$Y_1^{(6)} = \frac{1}{2}\left(\frac{1}{2} + j\frac{\sqrt{3}}{2}\right) Y_1'^{(3)} + \frac{1}{2} Z_1'^{(3)} \quad = 6.2500 + j1.0103$$

$$Y_2^{(6)} = \frac{1}{2}\left(\frac{1}{2} + j\frac{\sqrt{3}}{2}\right)^2 Y_2'^{(3)} + \frac{1}{2} Z_2'^{(3)} \quad = 8.0833 - j1.2990$$

$$Y_3^{(6)} = -\frac{1}{2} Y_0'^{(3)} + \frac{1}{2} Z_0'^{(3)} \qquad\qquad = -2.5000$$

$$Y_4^{(6)} = -\frac{1}{2}\left(\frac{1}{2} + j\frac{\sqrt{3}}{2}\right) Y_1'^{(3)} + \frac{1}{2} Z_1'^{(3)} = 8.0833 + j1.2990$$

$$Y_5^{(6)} = -\frac{1}{2}\left(\frac{1}{2} + j\frac{\sqrt{3}}{2}\right)^2 Y_2'^{(3)} + \frac{1}{2} Z_2'^{(3)} = 6.2500 - j1.0103.$$

The transform $Z_m^{(6)}$ is obtained similarly, to give the following:

Harmonic Transform	m					
	0	1	2	3	4	5
$Y_m^{(6)}$	-7.1667	6.2500 $+j1.0103$	8.0833 $-j1.2990$	-2.5000	8.0883 $+j1.2990$	6.2500 $-j1.0103$
$Z_m^{(6)}$	-0.1666	1.5000 $+j5.1960$	4.8333 $+j4.6187$	-0.5000	4.8333 $-j4.6187$	1.5000 $-j5.1960$

These values are combined, using (A7.3.5), to give the final transform $X_m^{(12)}$. For example,

$$X_0^{(12)} = \frac{1}{2} Y_0^{(6)} + \frac{1}{2} Z_0^{(6)} \qquad\qquad = -3.667$$

$$X_1^{(12)} = \frac{1}{2}\left(\frac{\sqrt{3}}{2} + j\frac{1}{2}\right) Y_1^{(6)} + \frac{1}{2} Z_1^{(6)} = 3.204 + j4.598.$$

The complete transform is as follows:

m	0	1	2	3	4	5
$X_m^{(12)}$	-3.667	3.204 $+j4.598$	5.000 $+j5.485$	-0.250 $-j1.250$	-0.167 $+j0.866$	-1.704 $-j0.598$

m	6	7	8	9	10	11
$X_m^{(12)}$	-3.500	-1.704 $+j0.598$	-0.167 $-j0.866$	-0.250 $+j1.250$	5.000 $-j5.485$	3.204 $-j4.598$

Except for the phase shift due to the shift in origin, these are the same as the results in Table 2.2, obtained using the difference equation method of Appendix A7.1 or the straightforward method of Chapter 2.

REFERENCES

[1] Cochran, W. T. et al., "What is the Fast Fourier Transform?" IEEE *Transactions on Audio and Electroacoustics*, Vol. AU-15, No. 2, p. 45, June 1967.

[2] Cooley, J. W., P. A. W. Lewis and P. D. Welch, "Historical Notes on the Fast Fourier Transform," IEEE *Transactions on Audio and Electroacoustics*, Vol. AU-15, No. 2, p. 76, June 1967.

[3] IEEE *Transactions on Audio and Electroacoustics*, Vol. AU-15, No. 2, June 1967.

[4] Cooley, J. W., P. A. W. Lewis and P. D. Welch, "Application of the Fast Fourier Transform to Computation of Fourier Integrals, Fourier Series, and Convolution Integrals," IEEE *Transactions on Audio and Electroacoustics*, Vol. AU-15, No. 2, p. 79, June 1967.

[5] Helms, H. D., "Fast Fourier Transform Method of Computing Difference Equations and Simulating Filters," IEEE *Transactions on Audio and Electroacoustics*, Vol. AU-15, No. 2, p. 85, June 1967.

APPENDIX A7.4: DATA AND AUTOCORRELATIONS FOR A SIMULATED SECOND-ORDER AR PROCESS

TABLE A7.1: 400 values of the second-order ar process $X_t = X_{t-1} - 0.5X_{t-2} + Z_t$

t					x_t					
1– 10	−0.88	−0.12	−0.89	−1.38	−0.07	1.03	2.14	0.35	−1.10	−1.78
11– 20	−2.76	−1.77	0.98	1.00	−0.70	−1.01	−1.30	−0.85	−0.46	1.63
21– 30	0.06	−0.17	−1.01	−1.04	−0.66	−1.12	−0.51	−0.71	−0.20	−0.13
31– 40	0.14	1.59	−0.76	−1.08	−1.77	−1.20	0.45	−0.07	−0.63	−0.35
41– 50	−0.87	−0.62	0.28	1.90	2.14	1.05	0.31	1.07	2.67	2.44
51– 60	1.31	1.10	1.94	0.33	1.82	1.15	0.61	−1.08	−1.62	−0.39
61– 70	0.19	−1.59	−2.25	0.29	1.73	2.30	0.80	−0.40	0.30	−0.50
71– 80	−2.11	−2.43	0.72	3.09	4.96	1.81	−0.46	−0.33	0.04	0.82
81– 90	−1.63	−2.29	−0.77	1.91	1.92	0.85	−0.65	0.35	0.78	1.62
91–100	3.24	1.86	0.76	2.24	0.76	−0.15	0.18	0.60	0.92	−0.70
101–110	−0.03	1.07	0.28	−1.38	−0.63	−1.48	0.19	−1.14	0.31	0.39
111–120	−0.17	0.70	2.14	1.24	0.42	0.61	−0.76	−1.75	−0.37	1.21
121–130	1.40	2.46	1.74	0.78	0.90	1.11	2.20	0.52	−0.22	1.12
131–140	1.02	1.10	1.72	1.80	−0.46	−1.27	0.39	0.93	0.55	−0.45
141–150	−0.87	−0.90	0.64	2.29	2.75	1.43	0.47	1.80	0.46	0.32
151–160	−0.81	−1.81	−2.07	0.96	1.20	0.77	−0.98	−1.46	−1.30	−2.29
161–170	−1.81	−1.61	−1.01	−1.36	−1.78	0.04	1.44	2.58	0.54	0.27
171–180	−0.75	−0.70	0.45	−0.13	−1.03	−1.19	−0.31	1.77	1.89	0.88
181–190	0.58	0.70	−0.32	−1.62	1.08	1.25	0.19	−0.93	−0.61	0.83
191–200	0.46	1.12	0.11	−1.11	−0.85	−1.86	−0.74	−1.04	−0.42	0.16

201–210	0.55	−0.37	−0.62	−1.23	−0.76	−0.79	−1.99	−1.56	−0.36	1.00
211–220	0.02	−0.30	−0.23	−0.63	−1.61	−1.66	−0.80	−1.71	−0.87	−0.74
221–230	1.55	1.39	1.51	2.39	1.68	−0.04	−1.24	−2.24	−1.31	−0.10
231–240	0.46	1.06	1.37	1.67	0.29	−0.31	−2.08	−2.67	−1.50	−1.71
241–250	−0.70	−1.25	−0.25	0.14	1.43	0.47	−1.16	−3.68	−3.41	−1.43
251–260	1.06	2.86	0.72	−1.79	−2.26	−1.87	−1.53	−0.25	1.40	3.37
261–270	0.85	−0.36	0.25	1.57	−0.08	0.78	−0.56	−1.22	0.07	−0.33
271–280	−0.15	1.56	2.23	2.01	0.42	−0.75	−0.47	1.55	3.60	2.07
281–290	1.32	0.06	0.87	0.51	−0.25	0.12	1.54	1.37	1.97	0.81
291–300	−0.67	−2.41	−1.82	−0.45	0.31	0.12	−1.01	−1.12	−1.69	−1.52
301–310	−0.82	−0.81	−0.33	−0.65	1.86	−0.94	0.50	1.05	1.40	1.52
311–320	0.20	0.64	1.95	1.55	1.74	−0.22	−2.14	−2.33	−1.01	0.42
321–330	2.54	0.86	0.10	−0.04	−1.18	−0.40	−0.53	0.70	−0.14	−0.20
331–340	0.47	1.07	0.85	−0.35	−0.69	−0.63	−2.08	−1.56	−1.00	0.55
341–350	2.08	1.74	−0.34	−1.85	−1.29	1.74	2.58	1.64	1.85	−0.01
351–360	−0.16	−0.29	−0.66	−3.41	−2.33	−2.57	−1.78	−1.31	−2.69	−1.77
361–370	−0.57	1.58	1.78	1.09	−0.54	0.29	−0.26	0.01	1.05	0.94
371–380	−0.91	−2.09	−2.01	−1.12	−0.02	0.98	0.50	2.12	1.68	2.28
381–390	2.59	3.04	1.16	0.50	0.56	0.45	0.35	0.10	2.16	2.60
391–400	1.40	0.62	0.36	−0.09	1.93	1.80	1.13	−1.34	−1.94	−0.89

TABLE A7.2: Autocorrelation estimates for a second-order ar process,
$$X_t = X_{t-1} - 0.5X_{t-2} + Z_t, \quad N = 50$$

k	$r_{xx}(k)$	k	$r_{xx}(k)$	k	$r_{xx}(k)$	k	$r_{xx}(k)$
1	0.574	11	-0.068	21	-0.217	31	0.049
2	0.086	12	0.124	22	-0.124	32	-0.051
3	-0.166	13	0.109	23	0.035	33	-0.200
4	-0.130	14	0.000	24	0.165	34	-0.213
5	0.096	15	-0.063	25	0.137	35	-0.097
6	0.225	16	-0.043	26	-0.045	36	0.004
7	0.244	17	0.062	27	-0.136	37	0.007
8	0.032	18	0.103	28	-0.156	38	-0.060
9	-0.180	19	-0.047	29	-0.027	39	-0.096
10	-0.199	20	-0.152	30	0.109	40	-0.086

TABLE A7.3: Autocorrelation estimates for a second-order ar process,
$$X_t = X_{t-1} - 0.5X_{t-2} + Z_t, \quad N = 400$$

k	$r_{xx}(k)$	k	$r_{xx}(k)$	k	$r_{xx}(k)$	k	$r_{xx}(k)$
1	0.645	13	0.012	25	-0.075	37	0.019
2	0.196	14	-0.021	26	-0.116	38	-0.020
3	-0.080	15	-0.074	27	-0.078	39	-0.045
4	-0.099	16	-0.119	28	-0.038	40	-0.035
5	-0.009	17	-0.070	29	-0.013	41	0.021
6	0.057	18	0.008	30	-0.036	42	0.083
7	0.066	19	0.064	31	-0.044	43	0.081
8	0.040	20	0.069	32	-0.037	44	0.017
9	0.030	21	0.017	33	-0.015	45	-0.004
10	0.052	22	-0.026	34	0.047	46	0.042
11	0.088	23	-0.032	35	0.080	47	0.081
12	0.051	24	-0.044	36	0.066	48	0.069

8

The Cross Correlation
Function and Cross Spectrum

In this chapter the concepts introduced in Chapters 5 and 6 are extended to deal with pairs of time series and stochastic processes. The first generalization, given in Section 8.1, is the cross correlation function of a stationary bivariate stochastic process, which measures the correlation between the two processes at different lags. The second generalization is the bivariate linear process which can be generated by linear operations on two white noise sources. Important special cases of the bivariate linear process are the bivariate autoregressive and moving average processes.

The estimation of the cross correlation function is discussed in Section 8.2, where it is shown that unless a filtering operation is applied to both series to convert them to white noise, spurious cross correlations may arise. The third generalization, the cross spectrum of a stationary bivariate process, is given in Section 8.3. The cross spectrum contains two different types of information about the dependence between the two processes. The first is the coherency spectrum, which effectively measures the correlation between the two processes at each frequency, and the second is the phase spectrum, which measures the phase difference between the two processes at each frequency. In Section 8.4 the information contained in the coherency and phase spectrum is illustrated by simple examples.

8.1 THE CROSS CORRELATION FUNCTION

8.1.1 Introduction

This chapter is concerned with describing *pairs* of time series or *bivariate* time series. The methods used are extensions of those developed in Chapters 5 and 6, and hence all the general considerations relating to time series discussed in Section 5.1 apply. It was briefly mentioned in Section 5.1 under the heading of multivariate time series that the individual series in a multivariate time series may not arise on equal footing. For example, consider the system shown in Figure 8.1, which has two *inputs* $x_1(t)$, $x_2(t)$, and two *outputs* $x_3(t)$, $x_4(t)$.

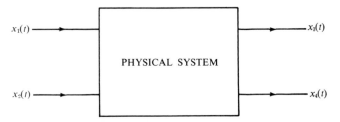

FIG. 8.1: A physical system with two inputs and two outputs

Two situations may be distinguished. The first occurs when the two series arise on a *similar footing*, for example, the two inputs in Figure 8.1. Thus $x_1(t)$, $x_2(t)$ may be two correlated control variables whose interactions are to be studied. An example of a pair of time series which falls into this category is given in Figure 8.2, which shows records of the in-phase and out-of-phase current inputs to a turbo-alternator.

The second situation arises when a pair of series are *causally related*, for example, the output $x_3(t)$ of Figure 8.1 depends on the input $x_1(t)$. In this situation it is usually required to estimate the properties of the system so that the output can be predicted from the input. An example of a pair of time series of this type is given in Figure 8.3, which shows the input gas rate $x_1(t)$ and the concentration $x_2(t)$ of carbon dioxide in the output from a gas furnace. It is seen that the input $x_1(t)$ lags behind the output $x_2(t)$ due to the delay in the transfer of the gases through the reactor.

In the first situation one is interested in describing the interaction or correlation between the two time series so that this interaction can be allowed for in any further studies. For example, if an output $x_3(t)$ is to be controlled by means of two control variables which are cross correlated, then allowance must be made for the cross correlation if the desired effect is to be produced at the output. On the other hand, in the second situation one is interested in relating $x_2(t)$ to $x_1(t)$, for example, by means of a relationship such as

$$x_2(t) = \int_0^\infty h(u)x_1(t - u)\, du,$$

so that $x_2(t)$ can be predicted from $x_1(t)$, as discussed briefly in Section 5.1.5. This chapter and the next will be devoted to series which arise on a similar footing, while series which are causally related will be discussed in Chapter 10.

8.1.2 Cross covariance and cross correlation functions

As in the univariate case discussed in Chapter 5, a useful way of describing pairs of stochastic processes is by their lower-order moments. Thus the

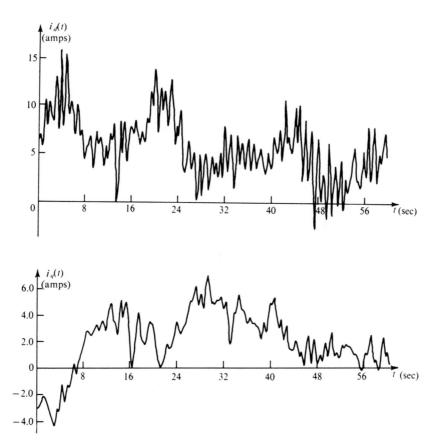

FIG. 8.2: In-phase and out-of-phase current inputs to a turbo-alternator

observed bivariate time series $\{x_1(t), x_2(t)\}$ is regarded as a realization of the bivariate stochastic process $\{X_1(t), X_2(t)\}$. The four rv's $X_1(t)$, $X_2(t)$, $X_1(t+u)$ and $X_2(t+u)$ at times t and $t+u$ will have a joint pdf which can be partially described by its first- and second-order moments. If it is assumed that the processes are *stationary*, then these moments will be functions of time differences u and not of the absolute time t. Thus the first moments are

$$E[X_i(t)] = \mu_i, \quad i = 1, 2,$$

and are independent of time t. The second moments of the joint pdf are the *autocovariance functions*

$$\gamma_{X_1 X_1}(u) = E[(X_1(t) - \mu_1)(X_1(t + u) - \mu_1)],$$
$$\gamma_{X_2 X_2}(u) = E[(X_2(t) - \mu_2)(X_2(t + u) - \mu_2)]$$

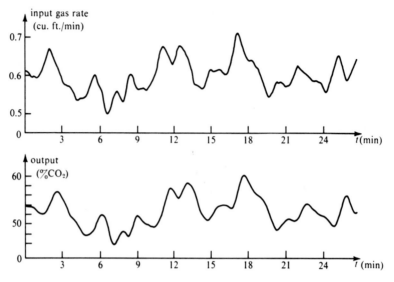

FIG. 8.3: Input and output signals to a chemical reactor

and the *cross covariance functions*

$$\begin{aligned}
\gamma_{X_1X_2}(u) &= E[(X_1(t) - \mu_1)(X_2(t + u) - \mu_2)], \\
\gamma_{X_2X_1}(u) &= E[(X_2(t) - \mu_2)(X_1(t + u) - \mu_1)].
\end{aligned} \qquad (8.1.1)$$

The function $\gamma_{X_1X_2}(u)$ is called the *cross covariance function* (ccvf) of lag u with $X_2(t)$ leading $X_1(t)$ and $\gamma_{X_2X_1}(u)$ the ccvf of lag u with $X_1(t)$ leading $X_2(t)$. For conciseness when no confusion is likely, the notation $\gamma_{11}(u)$, $\gamma_{22}(u)$, $\gamma_{12}(u)$ and $\gamma_{21}(u)$ will be used to denote the acvf's and ccvf's $\gamma_{X_1X_1}(u)$, $\gamma_{X_2X_2}(u)$, $\gamma_{X_1X_2}(u)$ and $\gamma_{X_2X_1}(u)$ respectively.

Properties of covariance functions. The properties of the acvf's of a real bivariate process are the same as those for the acvf of a univariate process, that is,

$$\left.\begin{aligned}
\gamma_{ii}(0) &= \text{Var}\,[X_i(t)] = \sigma_{X_i}^2 \\
\gamma_{ii}(u) &= \gamma_{ii}(-u)
\end{aligned}\right\} \quad i = 1, 2. \qquad (8.1.2)$$

Hence the acvf's are *even* functions of the lag u.

The ccvf $\gamma_{12}(u)$ of two real processes has the property

$$\gamma_{12}(u) = \gamma_{21}(-u), \qquad (8.1.3)$$

since

$$\begin{aligned}
\gamma_{12}(u) &= E[(X_1(t) - \mu_1)(X_2(t + u) - \mu_2)] \\
&= E[(X_1(t - u) - \mu_1)(X_2(t) - \mu_2)] \\
&= E[(X_2(t) - \mu_2)(X_1(t - u) - \mu_1)] \\
&= \gamma_{21}(-u).
\end{aligned}$$

Similarly, $\gamma_{21}(u) = \gamma_{12}(-u)$. Hence the covariance between the two stochastic processes can be described by means of the single ccvf $\gamma_{12}(u)$ where
$-\infty \leqslant u \leqslant \infty$. Note that although the acvf is an even function of lag, the
ccvf will *not* be an even function in general.

The cross correlation function. In general it may be necessary to study the
interactions between two processes with possibly different scales of measurement or different variances. In this situation it is necessary to define the
cross correlation function (ccf)

$$\rho_{12}(u) = \frac{\gamma_{12}(u)}{\sqrt{\gamma_{11}(0)\gamma_{22}(0)}} = \frac{\gamma_{12}(u)}{\sigma_1\sigma_2}. \tag{8.1.4}$$

The first property of the ccf is that

$$|\rho_{12}(u)| \leqslant 1,$$

which follows from the fact that the rv

$$Y(t) = \lambda_1 X_1(t) + \lambda_2 X_2(t + u)$$

has positive variance. The second property is that

$$\rho_{12}(u) = \rho_{21}(-u),$$

which follows from (8.1.3).

Like the ccvf, the ccf is in general *not* an even function of lag. For example,
Figure 8.4 shows the sample ccf of the gas furnace data of Figure 8.3. This
ccf has a large peak at $u = 5$ and is clearly not symmetrical about $u = 0$.

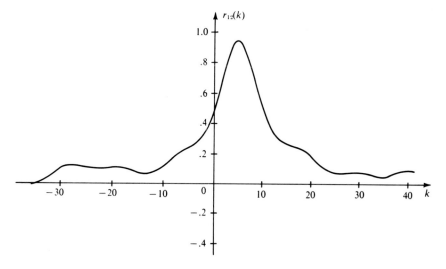

FIG. 8.4: Sample cross correlation function for gas furnace data

Note also that most of the cross correlations are positive. This is due to the fact that a positive change in the input gas rate results in a positive change in the output concentration.

The most trivial case of cross correlation between two stochastic processes occurs when the cross correlation function is identically zero for all lags. This implies that the two processes are completely uncorrelated. If, in addition, the processes $\{X_1(t), X_2(t)\}$ are Normal, then they will also be *independent*, as shown in Chapter 3.

Another simple case of cross correlation is when $\rho_{12}(u)$ is non-zero for $u = 0$, and zero for all other lags. This implies that the stochastic processes are correlated at simultaneous times but otherwise are uncorrelated. More general models for describing cross correlation between two stochastic processes will be given in Sections 8.1.3 and 8.1.4.

8.1.3 The cross correlation function of a linear process

One of the simplest ways in which two correlated stochastic processes $\{X_1(t), X_2(t)\}$ can occur is when $X_1(t)$ is the input to a linear system and $X_2(t)$ is the corresponding output plus noise, that is,

$$X_2(t) = \int_0^\infty h(u)X_1(t - u)\, du + Z(t). \tag{8.1.5}$$

In discrete time, the corresponding model is

$$X_{2t} = \sum_{r=0}^\infty h_r X_{1t-r} + Z_t. \tag{8.1.6}$$

Example 1. As a special case of (8.1.6), consider the simple regression model (4.3.5) which in this notation is written

$$X_{2t} = h_0 X_{1t} + Z_t.$$

If X_{1t} and Z_t have zero means, the ccvf between the input X_{1t} and output X_{2t} is, from (8.1.1),

$$\gamma_{12}(k) = E[X_{1t}(h_0 X_{1t+k} + Z_{t+k})]$$
$$= h_0 E[X_{1t}X_{1t+k}] + E[X_{1t}Z_{t+k}].$$

If it is further assumed that the noise Z_t is uncorrelated with the input X_{1t}, then

$$\gamma_{12}(k) = h_0\gamma_{11}(k),$$

that is, the ccvf is a constant times the acvf of the input. In the special case where $X_1(t)$ is white noise, the only non-zero cross covariance occurs when $k = 0$, that is,

$$\gamma_{12}(0) = h_0\gamma_{11}(0).$$

Note that while the noise Z_t does not seem to enter into these calculations, its effect is to increase the variance of X_{2t}. Thus

$$
\begin{aligned}
\text{Var } [X_{2t}] &= E[X_{2t}^2] \\
&= E[(h_0 X_{1t} + Z_t)^2] \\
&= h_0^2 \gamma_{11}(0) + \gamma_{zz}(0).
\end{aligned}
$$

Hence the cross correlation function for the above example is

$$
\begin{aligned}
\rho_{12}(0) &= \frac{h_0 \gamma_{11}(0)}{\sqrt{\gamma_{11}(0)\{h_0^2 \gamma_{11}(0) + \gamma_{zz}(0)\}}} \\
&= \frac{h_0}{\sqrt{h_0^2 + (\gamma_{zz}(0)/\gamma_{11}(0))}}, \qquad (8.1.7)
\end{aligned}
$$

$$
\rho_{12}(k) = 0, \quad k \neq 0.
$$

Thus the correlation between the input and output depends on the *signal-to-noise ratio* $\gamma_{11}(0)/\gamma_{zz}(0)$, that is, the ratio of the input and noise variances. If this ratio is large, then $\rho_{12}(0)$ is close to one, but if it is small, the noise dominates and $\rho_{12}(0)$ is correspondingly small.

Example 2. To consider a less trivial example, suppose that

$$
X_{2t} = h_0 X_{1t} + h_1 X_{1t-1} + Z_t,
$$

where X_{1t} and Z_t are uncorrelated white noise processes with the same variance σ^2.

Then

$$
\begin{aligned}
\gamma_{12}(0) &= E[X_{1t}\{h_0 X_{1t} + h_1 X_{1t-1} + Z_t\}] \\
&= h_0 \sigma^2, \\
\gamma_{12}(1) &= E[X_{1t}\{h_0 X_{1t+1} + h_1 X_{1t} + Z_{t+1}\}] \\
&= h_1 \sigma^2, \\
\gamma_{12}(k) &= 0, \quad k \neq 0, 1.
\end{aligned}
$$

The variances of the two processes are

$$
\begin{aligned}
\gamma_{22}(0) &= E[(h_0 X_{1t} + h_1 X_{1t-1} + Z_t)(h_0 X_{1t} + h_1 X_{1t-1} + Z_t)] \\
&= (h_0^2 + h_1^2 + 1)\sigma^2, \\
\gamma_{11}(0) &= \sigma^2.
\end{aligned}
$$

Hence the ccf's are

$$
\rho_{12}(0) = \frac{h_0}{\sqrt{1 + h_0^2 + h_1^2}},
$$

$$
\rho_{12}(1) = \frac{h_1}{\sqrt{1 + h_0^2 + h_1^2}},
$$

$$
\rho_{12}(k) = 0, \quad k \neq 0, 1.
$$

If the weights h_k in (8.1.6) are positive, the two processes $X_1(t)$, $X_2(t)$ will tend to "look alike" and the cross correlation function will be positive. Conversely if the weights are negative, the two processes will tend to be mirror images of each other, that is, positive changes in one process are associated with negative changes in the other.

The cross correlation function of a general linear process. The general expression for the ccvf of the model (8.1.5) may be obtained by multiplying (8.1.5) by $X_1(t - u)$ and taking expectations. If the $X_1(t)$ and $Z(t)$ processes have zero means, the ccvf is

$$\gamma_{12}(u) = E\left[X_1(t - u)\int_0^\infty h(v)X_1(t - v)\,dv + X_1(t - u)Z(t)\right]$$

$$= \int_0^\infty h(v)\gamma_{11}(u - v)\,dv, \quad -\infty \leqslant u \leqslant \infty, \tag{8.1.8}$$

provided $\gamma_{X_1 Z}(u) = 0$ for all u.

Another result required later is the expression for the autocovariance function of the output. This may be obtained from (8.1.5) by squaring and taking expectations. The final result, assuming $E[X_1(t)] = E[Z(t)] = 0$ and $\gamma_{X_1 Z}(u) = 0$, is

$$\gamma_{22}(u) = \int_0^\infty \int_0^\infty h(v)h(v')\gamma_{11}(u + v - v')\,dv\,dv' + \gamma_{ZZ}(u), \quad -\infty \leqslant u \leqslant \infty, \tag{8.1.9}$$

which is a simple extension of (5.2.9).

The cross correlation function is then obtained from

$$\rho_{12}(u) = \frac{\gamma_{12}(u)}{\sqrt{\gamma_{11}(0)\gamma_{22}(0)}}, \tag{8.1.10}$$

with $\gamma_{22}(0)$ obtained from (8.1.9) by setting $u = 0$.

For discrete processes, the results corresponding to (8.1.8), (8.1.9) and (8.1.10) are readily obtained from (8.1.6). Thus

$$\gamma_{12}(k) = \sum_{r=0}^\infty h_r\gamma_{11}(k - r), \quad k = 0, \pm 1, \pm 2, \ldots, \tag{8.1.11}$$

$$\gamma_{22}(k) = \sum_{r=0}^\infty \sum_{s=0}^\infty h_r h_s\gamma_{11}(k + r - s) + \gamma_{ZZ}(k), \quad k = 0, \pm 1, \pm 2, \ldots, \tag{8.1.12}$$

$$\rho_{12}(k) = \frac{\gamma_{12}(k)}{\sqrt{\gamma_{11}(0)\gamma_{22}(0)}}. \tag{8.1.13}$$

8.1.4 Bivariate linear processes

The model (8.1.5) assumed that the fluctuations in $X_1(t)$ *caused* the fluctuations in $X_2(t)$. A more general model for cross correlation between two stochastic processes occurs when it is assumed that the fluctuations in $X_1(t)$ and $X_2(t)$ are caused by two other sources $Z_1(t)$ and $Z_2(t)$ which affect them in different ways. For example, in the simplest possible situation,

$$X_1(t) = h_{11}Z_1(t) + h_{12}Z_2(t),$$
$$X_2(t) = h_{21}Z_1(t) + h_{22}Z_2(t),$$

where $Z_1(t)$, $Z_2(t)$ are uncorrelated white noise processes with variances σ_1^2, σ_2^2. Hence

$$\gamma_{12}(0) = E[\{h_{11}Z_1(t) + h_{12}Z_2(t)\}\{h_{21}Z_1(t) + h_{22}Z_2(t)\}]$$
$$= h_{11}h_{21}\sigma_1^2 + h_{12}h_{22}\sigma_2^2,$$
$$\gamma_{12}(k) = 0, \quad k \neq 0.$$

More generally, suppose that the bivariate stochastic process $\{X_1(t), X_2(t)\}$ is generated according to the lattice diagram of Figure 8.5. Two white noise sources $Z_i(t)$, $i = 1, 2$, are fed into four linear systems with impulse response functions $h_{11}(u)$, $h_{12}(u)$, $h_{21}(u)$ and $h_{22}(u)$ respectively. The outputs from the

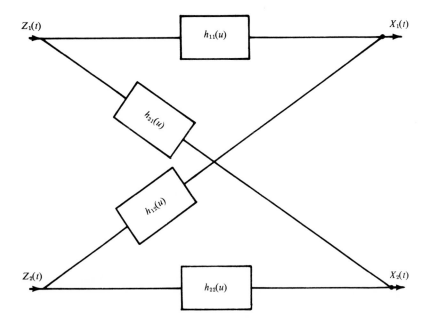

FIG. 8.5: Lattice representation of a bivariate linear process

first and third systems are summed to give $X_1(t)$, and the outputs from the second and fourth systems are summed to give $X_2(t)$. Thus

$$X_1(t) = \int_0^\infty h_{11}(v)Z_1(t-v)\,dv + \int_0^\infty h_{12}(v)Z_2(t-v)\,dv,$$

$$(8.1.14)$$

$$X_2(t) = \int_0^\infty h_{21}(v)Z_1(t-v)\,dv + \int_0^\infty h_{22}(v)Z_2(t-v)\,dv.$$

The stochastic process (8.1.14) is called a *bivariate linear process*.

Covariance functions of a bivariate linear process. If the white noise sources are mutually uncorrelated, that is,

$$E[Z_i(t)Z_j(t')] = 0, \quad \text{all } t, t', \quad i = 1, 2, \quad j = 1, 2,$$

then using (5.2.10),

$$\gamma_{11}(u) = \sigma_1^2 \int_0^\infty h_{11}(v)h_{11}(v+u)\,dv + \sigma_2^2 \int_0^\infty h_{12}(v)h_{12}(v+u)\,dv,$$

$$\gamma_{22}(u) = \sigma_1^2 \int_0^\infty h_{21}(v)h_{21}(v+u)\,dv + \sigma_2^2 \int_0^\infty h_{22}(v)h_{22}(v+u)\,dv,$$

$$(8.1.15)$$

$$\gamma_{21}(u) = \sigma_1^2 \int_0^\infty h_{21}(v)h_{11}(v+u)\,dv + \sigma_2^2 \int_0^\infty h_{22}(v)h_{12}(v+u)\,dv,$$

$$\gamma_{12}(u) = \sigma_1^2 \int_0^\infty h_{11}(v)h_{21}(v+u)\,dv + \sigma_2^2 \int_0^\infty h_{12}(v)h_{22}(v+u)\,dv.$$

In the discrete case the formulae are similar except that integrals are replaced by the corresponding sums. The formulae (8.1.15) show that by adjusting the impulse response functions $h_{ij}(u)$, it is possible to generate a bivariate stochastic process $\{X_1(t), X_2(t)\}$ with any specified cross covariance function and autocovariance functions.

A more general model still is possible by allowing the white noise processes in (8.1.14) to be correlated at simultaneous times, that is,

$$E[Z_1(t), Z_2(t')] = \sigma_{12}\,\delta(t-t').$$

8.1.5 Bivariate autoregressive and moving average processes

The simplest type of bivariate linear process occurs when the impulse response functions $h_{ij}(u)$ are zero beyond a certain point. For example, consider the discrete process

$$X_{1t} = Z_{1t} + \beta_{11}Z_{1t-1} + \beta_{12}Z_{2t-1},$$

$$X_{2t} = Z_{2t} + \beta_{21}Z_{1t-1} + \beta_{22}Z_{2t-1}.$$

$$(8.1.16)$$

Then if the Z_{1t}, Z_{2t} are uncorrelated white noise processes with variances σ_1^2 and σ_2^2, the ccvf of the bivariate process $\{X_{1t}, X_{2t}\}$ is

$$\gamma_{12}(-1) = \beta_{12}\sigma_2^2,$$
$$\gamma_{12}(0) = \beta_{11}\beta_{21}\sigma_1^2 + \beta_{12}\beta_{22}\sigma_2^2,$$
$$\gamma_{12}(1) = \beta_{21}\sigma_1^2,$$
$$\gamma_{12}(k) = 0, \quad k \neq 0, \pm 1.$$

Note that the above ccvf is not one-sided like the one given in example 2 of Section 8.1.3.

Bivariate autoregressive processes. These processes have the property that the impulse response functions $h_{ij}(u)$ in (8.1.14) do not vanish after a finite lag. For example, it is possible to define a continuous first-order process which is a generalization of (5.2.24). Thus, if $Z_1(t)$ and $Z_2(t)$ are white noise processes, correlated at simultaneous times only, a bivariate ar process is defined in continuous time by

$$\frac{dX_1(t)}{dt} + a_{11}X_1(t) + a_{12}X_2(t) = Z_1(t),$$
$$\frac{dX_2(t)}{dt} + a_{21}X_1(t) + a_{22}X_2(t) = Z_2(t),$$
(8.1.17)

and in discrete time by

$$X_{1t} = \alpha_{11}X_{1t-1} + \alpha_{12}X_{2t-1} + Z_{1t},$$
$$X_{2t} = \alpha_{21}X_{1t-1} + \alpha_{22}X_{2t-1} + Z_{2t},$$
(8.1.18)

where without loss of generality we assume the processes have zero means.

The computation of the auto- and cross covariances of the continuous process (8.1.17) using (8.1.15) is laborious and is achieved more elegantly using matrix methods to be developed in Chapter 11. For the present it is noted that the auto- and cross covariances of the process (8.1.17) may be written

$$\gamma_{11}(u) = b_{11}\,e^{-a_{11}u} + b_{21}\,e^{-a_{12}u},$$
$$\gamma_{22}(u) = b_{12}\,e^{-a_{21}u} + b_{22}\,e^{-a_{22}u},$$
$$\gamma_{12}(u) = b_{12}\,e^{-a_{11}u} + b_{22}\,e^{-a_{12}u},$$
$$\gamma_{21}(u) = b_{11}\,e^{-a_{21}u} + b_{21}\,e^{-a_{22}u},$$

where the b_{ij} are functions of the a_{ij}. It is interesting to note that the acf of the bivariate first-order process has the same form as the acf (5.2.35) of a univariate *second-order* ar process.

Explicit expressions for the auto- and cross covariances of the discrete process (8.1.18) are derived very simply in Chapter 11 using matrix theory. However, they may also be generated recursively using a scalar recurrence relation for the covariances, analogous to (5.2.43). Thus, multiplying the first equation in (8.1.18) by X_{2t-k} and taking expectations gives

$$E[X_{2t-k}X_{1t}] = \alpha_{11}E[X_{2t-k}X_{1t-1}] + \alpha_{12}E[X_{2t-k}X_{2t-1}] + E[X_{2t-k}Z_{1t}],$$

or

$$\gamma_{21}(k) = \alpha_{11}\gamma_{21}(k-1) + \alpha_{12}\gamma_{22}(k-1), \quad k \geq 1.$$

Similarly,

$$\gamma_{12}(k) = \alpha_{21}\gamma_{11}(k-1) + \alpha_{22}\gamma_{12}(k-1), \quad k \geq 1,$$
$$\gamma_{11}(k) = \alpha_{11}\gamma_{11}(k-1) + \alpha_{12}\gamma_{12}(k-1), \quad k \geq 1, \qquad (8.1.19)$$
$$\gamma_{22}(k) = \alpha_{21}\gamma_{21}(k-1) + \alpha_{22}\gamma_{22}(k-1), \quad k \geq 1.$$

Hence the values of the covariances at lag k are easily generated from the values at lag $k - 1$. To start the process it is necessary to know the values for $k = 0$. These may be obtained by squaring and multiplying the equations (8.1.18) and then taking expectations.

Thus

$$\gamma_{11}(0) = \alpha_{11}^2\gamma_{11}(0) + \alpha_{12}^2\gamma_{22}(0) + 2\alpha_{11}\alpha_{12}\gamma_{12}(0) + \sigma_1^2,$$
$$\gamma_{22}(0) = \alpha_{21}^2\gamma_{11}(0) + \alpha_{22}^2\gamma_{22}(0) + 2\alpha_{21}\alpha_{22}\gamma_{12}(0) + \sigma_2^2,$$
$$\gamma_{12}(0) = \alpha_{11}\alpha_{21}\gamma_{11}(0) + \alpha_{12}\alpha_{22}\gamma_{22}(0) + (\alpha_{11}\alpha_{22} + \alpha_{12}\alpha_{21})\gamma_{12}(0) + \sigma_{12}^2,$$

where $\sigma_1^2 = E[Z_{1t}^2]$, $\sigma_2^2 = E[Z_{2t}^2]$ and $\sigma_{12}^2 = E[Z_{1t}Z_{2t}]$. The values of $\gamma_{11}(0)$, $\gamma_{12}(0)$ and $\gamma_{22}(0)$ may then be obtained by solving the above equations in terms of the known parameters α_{ij}, σ_1^2, σ_2^2 and σ_{12}^2.

Example 1. A realization of $N = 100$ terms of the process

$$X_{1t} = 0.6X_{1t-1} - 0.5X_{2t-1} + Z_{1t},$$
$$X_{2t} = 0.4X_{1t-1} + 0.5X_{2t-1} + Z_{2t} \qquad (8.1.20)$$

was generated using two independent sets of random Normal deviates with $E[Z_{it}] = 0$, $E[Z_{1t}Z_{2t}] = 0$, Var $[Z_{it}] = 1$. The values of the two series are given in Appendix A8.1 and plotted in Figure 8.6, where it is seen that the pattern in both series is similar. Thus both series tend to have the same sign, and there is also a tendency for a peak or trough in X_{1t} to be followed after one or two observations by a peak or trough in X_{2t}. To explain this behavior it is necessary to calculate the auto- and cross correlation functions of the bivariate process. Using the above procedure, the recurrence relations for the *covariances* are

$$\left.\begin{array}{l}\gamma_{11}(k) = 0.6\gamma_{11}(k-1) - 0.5\gamma_{12}(k-1) \\ \gamma_{12}(k) = 0.4\gamma_{11}(k-1) + 0.5\gamma_{12}(k-1) \\ \gamma_{21}(k) = 0.6\gamma_{21}(k-1) - 0.5\gamma_{22}(k-1) \\ \gamma_{22}(k) = 0.4\gamma_{21}(k-1) + 0.5\gamma_{22}(k-1)\end{array}\right\} \quad k \geq 1,$$

with

$$0.64\gamma_{11}(0) - 0.25\gamma_{22}(0) + 0.6\gamma_{12}(0) = 1,$$
$$-0.16\gamma_{11}(0) + 0.75\gamma_{22}(0) - 0.4\gamma_{12}(0) = 1,$$
$$0.24\gamma_{11}(0) - 0.25\gamma_{22}(0) - 0.9\gamma_{12}(0) = 0.$$

Hence

$$\gamma_{11}(0) = 1.15/0.52 = 2.21,$$
$$\gamma_{12}(0) = 0.04/0.52 = 0.08,$$
$$\gamma_{22}(0) = 0.96/0.52 = 1.85.$$

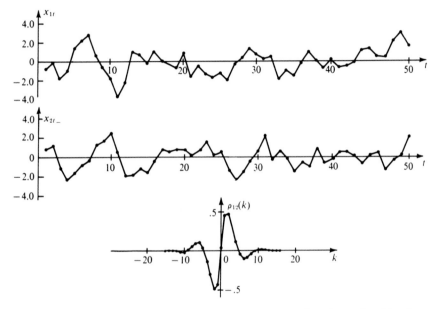

FIG. 8.6: Realization and theoretical cross correlation function of a bivariate autoregressive process

The recurrence relations for the *correlations* are

$$\rho_{11}(k) = 0.6\rho_{11}(k - 1) - 0.5\sqrt{(0.96/1.15)}\rho_{12}(k - 1),$$
$$\rho_{12}(k) = 0.4\sqrt{(1.15/0.96)}\rho_{11}(k - 1) + 0.5\rho_{12}(k - 1),$$
$$\rho_{21}(k) = 0.6\rho_{21}(k) - 0.5\sqrt{(0.96/1.15)}\rho_{22}(k), \qquad (8.1.21)$$
$$\rho_{22}(k) = 0.4\sqrt{(1.15/0.96)}\rho_{21}(k) + 0.5\rho_{22}(k),$$

with $\rho_{11}(0) = \rho_{22}(0) = 1$ and $\rho_{12}(0) = 0.04/\sqrt{(1.15)(0.96)} = 0.038$.

The correlation function values are shown in Table 8.1 and the ccf is plotted in Figure 8.6. It is seen that whereas $\rho_{12}(0)$ is very small, $\rho_{12}(1)$ and

TABLE 8.1: Theoretical correlations for the bivariate
autoregressive process (8.1.20)

k	$\rho_{11}(k)$	$\rho_{22}(k)$	$\rho_{12}(k)$	$\rho_{21}(k)$
0	1.00	1.00	0.04	0.04
1	0.52	0.58	0.46	−0.43
2	0.07	0.14	0.48	−0.50
3	−0.18	−0.14	0.30	−0.33
4	−0.24	−0.22	0.09	−0.11
5	−0.17	−0.17	−0.05	0.04
6	−0.07	−0.08	−0.10	0.10
7	0.01	0.00	−0.09	0.09
8	0.04	0.04	−0.04	0.05
9	0.04	0.04	−0.01	0.01
10	0.03	0.03	0.02	−0.01
11	0.01	0.01	0.02	−0.02
12	0.01	0.00	0.01	−0.02
13	−0.01	−0.01	0.01	−0.01
14	−0.01	−0.01	0.00	0.00
15	−0.01	0.00	—	—
16	0.00	—	—	—
17	—	—	—	—

$\rho_{12}(2)$ are large and positive. This explains the tendency, mentioned earlier, for X_{2t} to lead X_{1t} by one observation. Examination of Figure 8.6 also shows that there is a definite periodicity in the ccf with a period of roughly 10 or a frequency of 0.1 cps. This implies that any pattern in one series will tend to recur or resonate in the other series. The realizations of the two processes shown in Figure 8.6 indicate that there is a tendency for peaks and troughs in X_{1t} to be followed by peaks and troughs at intervals of about 10 in X_{2t}.

Example 2. As a second example of a bivariate linear process consider the process

$$X_{1t} = 0.6X_{1t-1} + Z_{1t},$$
$$X_{2t} = 0.5X_{2t-1} + 2X_{1t-10} + Y_{2t}, \qquad (8.1.22)$$

where

$$Y_{2t} = 0.5Y_{2t-1} + Z_{2t},$$

and Z_{1t} and Z_{2t} are uncorrelated white noise processes with unit variance.

This is an example of the model (8.1.6) given in Section 8.1.3. Thus the process X_{2t} is generated by passing X_{1t} through a linear filter and adding non-white noise. Note that there is an initial delay period of 10 units before X_{1t} begins to affect X_{2t}.

Proceeding as above, the following recurrence relations may be derived for the covariances:

$$\left.\begin{aligned}
\gamma_{11}(k) &= 0.6\gamma_{11}(k-1)\\
\gamma_{12}(k) &= 2\gamma_{11}(k-10) + 0.5\gamma_{12}(k-1)\\
\gamma_{21}(k) &= 0.6\gamma_{21}(k-1)\\
\gamma_{22}(k) &= 2\gamma_{21}(k-10) + 0.5\gamma_{22}(k-1) + \gamma_{X_2Y}(k-1)
\end{aligned}\right\} \quad k \geqslant 1, \quad (8.1.23)$$

with

$$\gamma_{X_1Y}(k) = 0, \qquad\qquad\qquad\qquad\qquad \text{all } k$$

$$\left.\begin{aligned}
\gamma_{X_2Y}(k) &= 0.5\gamma_{X_2Y}(k-1)\\
\gamma_{YX_2}(k) &= 0.5\gamma_{YX_2}(k-1) + \gamma_{YY}(k)\\
\gamma_{YY}(k) &= 0.5\gamma_{YY}(k-1)
\end{aligned}\right\} \quad k \geqslant 1,$$

and

$$\gamma_{11}(0) = 1/0.64 = 1.56,$$
$$\gamma_{YY}(0) = 1/0.75 = 1.33,$$
$$-4\gamma_{11}(0) + 0.75\gamma_{22}(0) - 2\gamma_{12}(9) = \gamma_{YY}(0) + \gamma_{X_2Y}(1), \quad (8.1.24)$$
$$1.2\gamma_{11}(9) - 0.7\gamma_{12}(0) = 0,$$
$$0.75\gamma_{X_2Y}(0) - 0.5\gamma_{YY}(1) = 1.$$

Solving the equations (8.1.24) for $k = 0$ and substituting the solutions in the recurrence relations (8.1.23) enables the covariances to be calculated. Normalizing these gives the correlations for the process, and these are tabulated in Table 8.2. The ccf has a fairly wide peak centered at lag 10, as would be expected because of the delay of 10 units between the two processes.

Bivariate autoregressive–moving average processes. A more general bivariate process can be obtained by including both ar and ma terms. For example, the discrete process

$$X_{1t} = \alpha_{11}X_{1t-1} + \alpha_{12}X_{2t-1} + Z_{1t} + \beta_{11}Z_{1t-1} + \beta_{12}Z_{2t-1},$$

$$(8.1.25)$$

$$X_{2t} = \alpha_{21}X_{1t-1} + \alpha_{22}X_{2t-1} + Z_{2t} + \beta_{21}Z_{1t-1} + \beta_{22}Z_{2t-1}$$

is obtained by combining the models (8.1.16) and (8.1.18).

As stated above, these processes are most easily expressed in matrix form for mathematical conciseness, and a more general treatment of their properties is postponed until Chapter 11.

TABLE 8.2: Theoretical correlations for the bivariate
linear process with delay (8.1.22)

k	$\rho_{11}(k)$	$\rho_{22}(k)$	$\rho_{12}(k)$	$\rho_{21}(k)$
0	1.00	1.00	0.00	0.00
1	0.60	0.84	0.01	—
2	0.36	0.62	0.01	—
3	0.22	0.43	0.02	—
4	0.13	0.28	0.04	—
5	0.08	0.18	0.06	—
6	0.05	0.12	0.11	—
7	0.03	0.07	0.18	—
8	0.02	0.04	0.30	—
9	0.01	0.03	0.50	—
10	0.01	0.02	0.83	—
11	0.00	0.01	0.77	—
12	—	0.01	0.59	—
13	—	0.00	0.42	—
14	—	—	0.29	—
15	—	—	0.19	—
16	—	—	0.12	—
17	—	—	0.08	—
18	—	—	0.05	—
19	—	—	0.03	—
20	—	—	0.02	—

8.2 ESTIMATION OF THE CROSS COVARIANCE FUNCTION

8.2.1 The sample cross covariance function

It was shown in Section 5.3.1 that a reasonable estimator of the ccvf at lag u, if the means of the two processes are zero, is

$$
c_{X_1X_2}(u) = \begin{cases} \dfrac{1}{T} \displaystyle\int_{-T/2}^{T/2-u} X_1(t)X_2(t+u)\,du, & 0 \leqslant u \leqslant T, \\[3mm] \dfrac{1}{T} \displaystyle\int_{-T/2+u}^{T/2} X_1(t)X_2(t+u)\,du, & -T \leqslant u \leqslant 0. \end{cases} \tag{8.2.1}
$$

As with the estimation of autocovariances, the divisor T is preferable to $T - u$ since the estimator has smaller mean square error.

Taking expectations in (8.2.1),

$$
E[c_{X_1X_2}(u)] = \left(1 - \frac{|u|}{T}\right)\gamma_{X_1X_2}(u),
$$

which shows that $c_{X_1X_2}(u)$ is a biased estimator of $\gamma_{12}(u)$ and only becomes unbiased as T tends to infinity.

If allowance is made for a non-zero mean by using the estimator

$$c_{X_1 X_2}(u) = \begin{cases} \dfrac{1}{T} \displaystyle\int_{-T/2}^{T/2-u} (X_1(t) - \bar{X}_1)(X_2(t+u) - \bar{X}_2)\, du, & 0 \leqslant u \leqslant T, \\[4mm] \dfrac{1}{T} \displaystyle\int_{-T/2+u}^{T/2} (X_1(t) - \bar{X}_1)(X_2(t+u) - \bar{X}_2)\, du, & -T \leqslant u \leqslant 0, \end{cases}$$

(8.2.2)

where

$$\bar{X}_i = \frac{1}{T} \int_{-T/2}^{T/2} X_i(t)\, dt, \quad i = 1, 2,$$

then a similar calculation to that made in Section 5.3.3 shows that

$$E[c_{X_1 X_2}(u)] = \left(1 - \frac{|u|}{T}\right) \gamma_{X_1 X_2}(u) + \frac{1}{T} \int_{-T}^{T} \left(1 - \frac{|u|}{T}\right) \gamma_{X_1 X_2}(u)\, du.$$

Hence the bias is increased by a term of order $1/T$ by introducing a correction for the mean.

The sample ccvf suffers from the same disadvantages as the sample acvf, namely that neighboring values tend to be highly correlated. It is shown in Appendix A9.1 that the covariance between the estimators $c_{X_1 X_2}(u_1)$, $c_{X_1 X_2}(u_2)$ at two different lags u_1 and u_2 is given by Bartlett's formula

$$\text{Cov}\,[c_{X_1 X_2}(u_1), c_{X_1 X_2}(u_2)]$$

$$= \frac{1}{T^2} \left\{ T' \int_{-T'}^{T'} \gamma(r) \left(1 - \frac{|r|}{T'}\right) dr - T'' \int_{-T''}^{T''} \gamma(r) \left(1 - \frac{|r|}{T''}\right) dr \right\}, \quad (8.2.3)$$

where

$$T' = T - \frac{|u_1| + |u_2|}{2}, \qquad T'' = \frac{|u_2| - |u_1|}{2},$$

$$\gamma(r) = \gamma_{X_1 X_1}\left(r - \frac{u_2 - u_1}{2}\right) \gamma_{X_2 X_2}\left(r + \frac{u_2 - u_1}{2}\right)$$

$$+ \gamma_{X_1 X_2}\left(r + \frac{u_2 + u_1}{2}\right) \gamma_{X_2 X_1}\left(r + \frac{u_2 + u_1}{2}\right) + K(r, u_1, u_2),$$

and $K(r, u_1, u_2)$ is the joint cumulant of the rv's $X_1(t)$, $X_1(t + u_1)$, $X_2(t + r)$ and $X_2(t + r + u_2)$.

For large T, (8.2.3) may be approximated by the following expression, which is analogous to (5.3.22):

$$\text{Cov}\,[c_{X_1 X_2}(u_1), c_{X_1 X_2}(u_2)] \approx \frac{1}{T} \int_{-\infty}^{\infty} \gamma(r)\, dr. \qquad (8.2.4)$$

In the discrete case, the approximation is

$$\text{Cov}\,[c_{X_1 X_2}(k), c_{X_1 X_2}(l)] \approx$$

$$\frac{1}{N} \sum_{r=-\infty}^{\infty} \{\gamma_{X_1 X_1}(r)\gamma_{X_2 X_2}(r+l-k) + \gamma_{X_1 X_2}(r+l)\gamma_{X_2 X_1}(r-k)\}. \quad (8.2.5)$$

Effect of autocorrelation on the cross correlation between two time series. An interesting case of (8.2.4) occurs when $\gamma_{X_1X_2}(u) = 0$ for all u, that is, the two processes are uncorrelated. Then (8.2.4) becomes

$$\text{Cov}\,[c_{X_1X_2}(u_1),\, c_{X_1X_2}(u_2)]$$

$$\approx \frac{1}{T} \int_{-\infty}^{\infty} \gamma_{X_1X_1}\left(r - \frac{u_2 - u_1}{2}\right) \gamma_{X_2X_2}\left(r + \frac{u_2 - u_1}{2}\right) dr, \quad (8.2.6)$$

on neglecting the non-Normality term.

Similarly for two uncorrelated discrete processes, (8.2.5) becomes

$$\text{Cov}\,[c_{X_1X_2}(k),\, c_{X_1X_2}(l)] \approx \frac{1}{N} \sum_{r=-\infty}^{\infty} \gamma_{X_1X_1}(r)\gamma_{X_2X_2}(r + l - k). \quad (8.2.7)$$

For $X_1(t)$, $X_2(t)$ first-order ar processes with parameters α_1 and β_1 respectively,

$$\gamma_{X_1X_1}(k) = \sigma_1^2\alpha_1^{|k|}, \quad \gamma_{X_2X_2}(k) = \sigma_2^2\beta_1^{|k|},$$

and substitution in (8.2.7) with $l = k$ yields

$$\text{Var}\,[c_{X_1X_2}(k)] \approx \frac{\sigma_1^2\sigma_2^2}{N}\left(\frac{1 + \alpha_1\beta_1}{1 - \alpha_1\beta_1}\right). \quad (8.2.8)$$

For white noise the corresponding result is

$$\text{Var}\,[c_{X_1X_2}(k)] \approx \frac{\sigma_1^2\sigma_2^2}{N}. \quad (8.2.9)$$

Hence if $\alpha_1\beta_1$ is positive, the variance (8.2.8) of the cross covariance estimator is inflated relative to (8.2.9) for two white noise sources, whereas if $\alpha_1\beta_1$ is negative, (8.2.8) is deflated. It is usually the case that $\alpha_1\beta_1$ is positive, that is, the two processes are either both positively correlated or both negatively correlated. Equation (8.2.8) then shows that very large cross covariances, all of them spurious, can be generated *between* two uncorrelated processes as a result of the large autocovariances *within* the two processes.

An example. To illustrate this effect, the sample ccf $r_{x_1x_2}(k)$ is computed for realizations of two independent first-order ar processes with parameters $\alpha_1 = \beta_1 = -0.9$ and $N = 100$. The estimate used is based on the discrete analog of (8.2.2), namely

$$r_{x_1x_2}(k) = \frac{c_{x_1x_2}(k)}{\sqrt{c_{x_1x_1}(0)c_{x_2x_2}(0)}},$$

where

$$c_{x_ix_j}(k) = \frac{1}{N} \sum_{t=1}^{N-k} (x_{it} - \bar{x}_i)(x_{jt+k} - \bar{x}_j), \quad k \geqslant 0. \quad (8.2.10)$$

and

$$\bar{x}_i = \frac{1}{N} \sum_{t=1}^{N} x_{it} \quad i,j = 1, 2.$$

The cross correlation estimate is shown in Figure 8.7 as a broken line. It is seen that values of $r_{x_1 x_2}(k)$ as large as ± 0.3 can occur, whereas the theoretical ccf is, of course, zero.

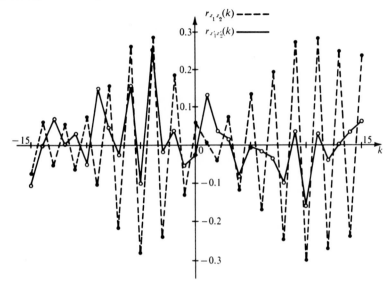

FIG. 8.7: Sample cross correlations of two first-order ar processes before and after filtering

8.2.2 Improvement of the sample cross correlation function estimator

To see how the estimation properties of the ccvf estimator can be improved, consider the following model for two cross correlated first-order ar processes:

$$\begin{aligned} X_{1t} &= \alpha_1 X_{1t-1} + Z_{1t}, \\ X_{2t} &= \beta_1 X_{2t-1} + Z_{2t}. \end{aligned} \qquad (8.2.11)$$

Suppose that the covariance between Z_{1t} and Z_{2t-k} is zero for k not equal to zero. Then assuming that Z_{1t}, Z_{2t} are bivariate Normal, using (3.1.17), the log likelihood function of the parameters $\alpha_1, \beta_1, \gamma_{12}$ is

$$l(\alpha_1, \beta_1, \gamma_{12}(k)) = -(N-k)\log 2\pi - (N-k)\log \sigma_1 - (N-k)\log \sigma_2$$

$$-\frac{\sigma_1^2 \sigma_2^2}{2(\sigma_1^2 \sigma_2^2 - \gamma_{12}^2(k))^2} \left[\sum_{t=1}^{N-k} \left\{ \frac{z_{1t}^2}{\sigma_1^2} + \frac{z_{2t-k}^2}{\sigma_2^2} - \frac{2\gamma_{12}(k)}{\sigma_1^2 \sigma_2^2} z_{1t} z_{2t-k} \right\} \right],$$

where

$$z_{1t} = x_{1t} - \alpha_1 x_{1t-1},$$
$$z_{2t-k} = x_{2t-k} - \beta_1 x_{2t-k-1}.$$

On differentiating $l(\alpha_1, \beta_1, \gamma_{12}(k))$ with respect to all three parameters, and setting the derivatives equal to zero, the mle of $\gamma_{12}(k)$ is

$$\hat{\gamma}_{12}(k) = \frac{1}{N-k} \sum_{t=1}^{N-k} (x_{1t} - \hat{\alpha}_1 x_{1t-1})(x_{2t-k} - \hat{\beta}_1 x_{2t-k-1}), \quad (8.2.12)$$

where $\hat{\alpha}_1$, $\hat{\beta}_1$ are the mle's of α_1, β_1. The logic behind this estimate is clear:

If a test is required for non-zero correlation between two time series, a filtering operation should be carried out on the two series x_{1t} and x_{2t} to convert them to white noise before computing the cross covariance function.

For the two independent processes in the example of section 8.2.1, the parameters were estimated using the mle (5.4.5). For example,

$$\hat{\alpha}_1 = \frac{\sum_{t=2}^{N} (x_{1t} - \bar{x}_1)(x_{1t-1} - \bar{x}_1)}{\sum_{t=2}^{N} (x_{1t-1} - \bar{x}_1)^2}.$$

Then the two series were filtered according to

$$x'_{1t} = x_{1t} - \hat{\alpha}_1 x_{1t-1},$$
$$x'_{2t} = x_{2t} - \hat{\beta}_1 x_{2t-1},$$

and the ccf of the filtered series (x'_{1t}, x'_{2t}) calculated using (8.2.12). This ccf is plotted as the solid line in Figure 8.7, and it is seen that the values are much smaller than those before filtering. Since the filtered series are random, the standard error of the cross correlation estimate is $\sqrt{1/N} = 0.1$, using (8.2.9). Hence the 95% confidence limits are ± 0.2 about their actual values. It is seen that only one interval fails to enclose zero. Since two intervals would be expected not to enclose zero on average if the two processes were uncorrelated, the observed ccf is not inconsistent with the hypothesis that the two processes are uncorrelated.

8.3 THE CROSS SPECTRUM

This section deals with the frequency-domain description of bivariate time series. It is shown that the sample ccvf discussed in the preceding section has a Fourier transform called the *sample cross spectrum*. This sample cross spectrum is a complex quantity and may be written as the product of a real function called the sample cross *amplitude spectrum* and a complex function called the sample *phase spectrum*. Similarly, the theoretical cross covariance function has a Fourier transform called the cross spectrum, which can be represented as the product of the cross amplitude spectrum and the phase spectrum. The cross amplitude spectrum shows whether frequency components in one series are associated with large or small amplitudes at the same frequency in the other series. Similarly, the phase spectrum shows whether frequency components in one series lag or lead the components at the same frequency in the other series. The following section contains examples of cross amplitude and phase spectra, based on the cross spectrum of the bivariate linear process (8.1.14). A more useful quantity than the cross amplitude spectrum, namely the coherency spectrum, is then introduced. The coherency spectrum and the phase spectrum are shown to provide a complete description of a bivariate Normal stochastic process.

8.3.1 Fourier analysis applied to bivariate time series

Fourier analysis may be applied to bivariate time series as well as univariate time series. For example, suppose $x_1(t)$, $x_2(t)$ are two cosine waves with the same frequency f_0, different amplitudes A_1 and A_2, and different phases ϕ_1 and ϕ_2 respectively. That is,

$$x_i(t) = A_i \cos (2\pi f_0 t + \phi_i), \quad i = 1, 2. \tag{8.3.1}$$

If records of length T are available, then using (2.2.11) the Fourier transforms of $x_i(t)$, $-T/2 \leqslant t \leqslant T/2$, are

$$X_i(f) = \frac{A_i}{2} \left[e^{j\phi_i} \left\{ \frac{\sin \pi(f - f_0)T}{\pi(f - f_0)} \right\} + e^{-j\phi_i} \left\{ \frac{\sin \pi(f + f_0)T}{\pi(f + f_0)} \right\} \right], \quad i = 1, 2. \tag{8.3.2}$$

Hence the sample spectra (6.1.6) of the two signals are

$$C_{x_i x_i}(f) = \frac{|X_i(f)|^2}{T}, \quad i = 1, 2,$$

which tend to

$$\tfrac{1}{4} A_i^2 [\delta(f - f_0) + \delta(f + f_0)]$$

as T tends to infinity. Thus the variance or average power of a cosine wave is equal to $(1/2)A_i^2$ distributed as delta functions at the frequencies $f = \pm f_0$.

Suppose now that it is required to describe the *covariance* between the two cosine waves. Then a natural function to use is the sample cross power spectrum or, more concisely, the *sample cross spectrum*

$$C_{x_1 x_2}(f) = \frac{X_1^*(f) X_2(f)}{T}, \tag{8.3.3}$$

where the asterisk denotes a complex conjugate. Substituting (8.3.2) in (8.3.3) shows that the sample cross spectrum of two cosine waves is

$$C_{x_1x_2}(f) = \frac{A_1A_2}{4T}\left\{e^{-j\phi_1}\left[\frac{\sin \pi(f - f_0)T}{\pi(f - f_0)}\right] + e^{j\phi_1}\left[\frac{\sin \pi(f + f_0)T}{\pi(f + f_0)}\right]\right\}$$

$$\times \left\{e^{j\phi_2}\left[\frac{\sin \pi(f - f_0)T}{\pi(f - f_0)}\right] + e^{-j\phi_2}\left[\frac{\sin \pi(f + f_0)T}{\pi(f + f_0)}\right]\right\}, \quad (8.3.4)$$

which tends to

$$\tfrac{1}{4}A_1A_2[e^{-j(\phi_2 - \phi_1)}\,\delta(f + f_0) + e^{j(\phi_2 - \phi_1)}\,\delta(f - f_0)] \qquad (8.3.5)$$

as T tends to infinity.

The definition (8.3.3) is a natural one to adopt since it summarizes all the information about the dependence between the two signals. For the special case of two cosine waves, (8.3.5) shows that this information is summarized by the *phase difference* $\phi_2 - \phi_1$, which shows how one cosine wave leads or lags the other, and the *cross amplitude* A_1A_2, which shows whether a large amplitude at a particular frequency in one wave is associated with a large amplitude at the same frequency in the other.

Sample phase and cross amplitude spectra. More generally, suppose that $x_1(t)$ and $x_2(t)$ are arbitrary real signals with Fourier transforms $X_1(f)$ and $X_2(f)$ respectively. These Fourier transforms give the amplitude and phase distribution of the signals, that is,

$$X_i(f) = A_i(f)\,e^{jF_i(f)}, \quad i = 1, 2, \qquad (8.3.6)$$

where $A_i(f)$ is a *positive even function* and $F_i(f)$ is an *odd function*. From (8.3.3), the sample cross spectrum is then

$$C_{x_1x_2}(f) = A_1(f)A_2(f)\,e^{j(F_2(f) - F_1(f))}/T, \qquad (8.3.7)$$

which may be written

$$C_{12}(f) = A_{12}(f)\,e^{jF_{12}(f)}. \qquad (8.3.8)$$

Hence the covariance between the two series $x_1(t)$ and $x_2(t)$ may be described by the *sample phase spectrum*

$$F_{12}(f) = F_2(f) - F_1(f) \qquad (8.3.9)$$

and the *sample cross amplitude spectrum*

$$A_{12}(f) = A_1(f)A_2(f)/T. \qquad (8.3.10)$$

The sample phase spectrum $F_{12}(f)$ shows whether the frequency components in one series lead or lag the components at the same frequency in the other series. Similarly, the sample cross amplitude spectrum $A_{12}(f)$ shows whether the amplitude of the component at a particular frequency in one series is associated with a large or small amplitude at the same frequency in the other series. Note that $A_{12}(f)$ is a positive even function of frequency and that $F_{12}(f)$ is an odd function of frequency.

Sample co- and quadrature spectra. Since (8.3.8) is a complex quantity, it may be written as the product of an amplitude function times a phase function as in (8.3.7). An alternative expression for (8.3.8) is as a sum of a real and imaginary part, that is,

$$C_{12}(f) = L_{12}(f) - jQ_{12}(f),$$

where

$$L_{12}(f) = A_{12}(f) \cos F_{12}(f), \qquad Q_{12}(f) = -A_{12}(f) \sin F_{12}(f),$$

and

$$A_{12}^2(f) = L_{12}^2(f) + Q_{12}^2(f), \qquad F_{12}(f) = \arctan\left(\frac{Q_{12}(f)}{L_{12}(f)}\right)$$

$$(8.3.11)$$

Note that $L_{12}(f)$ is an *even* function of frequency and $Q_{12}(f)$ is an *odd* function of frequency because $A_{12}(f)$ is an even and $F_{12}(f)$ an odd function of frequency. To illustrate, consider the bivariate cosine wave example used above.

In the limiting case as T tends to infinity, it may be shown that

$$L_{12}(f) = \frac{A_1 A_2}{4} \cos(\phi_2 - \phi_1)[\delta(f + f_0) + \delta(f - f_0)]$$

$$= \left\{\frac{A_1 \cos\phi_1 A_2 \cos\phi_2}{4} + \frac{A_1 \sin\phi_1 A_2 \sin\phi_2}{4}\right\} [\delta(f + f_0) + \delta(f - f_0)].$$

Since the signals $x_i(t)$ may be written

$$x_1(t) = A_1 \cos(2\pi f_0 t + \phi_1)$$
$$= (A_1 \cos\phi_1) \cos 2\pi f_0 t - (A_1 \sin\phi_1) \sin 2\pi f_0 t,$$
$$x_2(t) = A_2 \cos(2\pi f_0 t + \phi_2)$$
$$= (A_2 \cos\phi_2) \cos 2\pi f_0 t - (A_2 \sin\phi_2) \sin 2\pi f_0 t,$$

it follows that $L_{12}(f)$ measures the covariance between the two cosine components and the covariance between the two sine terms, that is, the covariance between the *in-phase* components. Hence $L_{12}(f)$ is called the sample in-phase or *sample co-spectrum*. Similarly,

$$Q_{12}(f) = \frac{A_1 A_2}{4} \sin(\phi_2 - \phi_1)[\delta(f + f_0) + \delta(f - f_0)]$$

$$= \left\{\frac{A_1 \cos\phi_1 A_2 \sin\phi_2}{4} - \frac{A_1 \sin\phi_1 A_2 \cos\phi_2}{4}\right\} [\delta(f + f_0) + \delta(f - f_0)]$$

measures the covariance between the sine and cosine components, that is, the *out-of-phase* or *quadrature* components. Hence $Q_{12}(f)$ is called the *sample quadrature spectrum*.

Similarly for general signals $x_1(t)$, $x_2(t)$, the Fourier representations

$$L_{12}(f) = A_{12}(f) \cos F_{12}(f)$$

and

$$Q_{12}(f) = A_{12}(f) \sin F_{12}(f)$$

measure the covariance between the in-phase and quadrature components at frequency f.

8.3.2 *The relation between the sample cross spectrum and the sample cross covariance function*

It was shown in Chapter 6 that the sample acvf and the sample spectrum are related by the Fourier transform (6.1.9). In this section, (6.1.9) is generalized to show that the sample ccvf and the sample cross spectrum likewise form a Fourier transform pair.

From the definition (8.3.3) of the sample cross spectrum,

$$C_{12}(f) = \frac{1}{T} X_1^*(f) X_2(f)$$

$$= \frac{1}{T} \int_{-T/2}^{T/2} \int_{-T/2}^{T/2} x_1(t) x_2(t') \, e^{-j2\pi f(t' - t)} \, dt \, dt'.$$

Making the transformation $t' - t = u$, $t = v$ and proceeding as in Section 6.1.3,

$$C_{12}(f) = \int_{-T}^{T} c_{12}(u) \, e^{-j2\pi fu} \, du. \tag{8.3.12}$$

Thus the sample cross spectrum is the Fourier transform of the sample ccvf defined by

$$c_{12}(u) = \frac{1}{T} \int_{-T/2}^{T/2 - u} x_1(t) x_2(t + u) \, dt, \qquad 0 \leqslant u \leqslant T,$$

$$= \frac{1}{T} \int_{-T/2 + u}^{T/2} x_1(t) x_2(t + u) \, dt, \qquad -T \leqslant u \leqslant 0, \tag{8.3.13}$$

$$= 0, \qquad\qquad |u| > T.$$

The transform (8.3.12) has the inverse

$$c_{12}(u) = \int_{-\infty}^{\infty} C_{12}(f) \, e^{j2\pi fu} \, df. \tag{8.3.14}$$

Substituting (8.3.11) in (8.3.14) yields the important identity

$$c_{12}(u) = \int_{-\infty}^{\infty} (L_{12}(f) - jQ_{12}(f)) \, e^{j2\pi fu} \, df$$

$$= \int_{-\infty}^{\infty} L_{12}(f) \cos 2\pi fu \, df + \int_{-\infty}^{\infty} Q_{12}(f) \sin 2\pi fu \, df, \tag{8.3.15}$$

since $L_{12}(f)$ is an even function of f and $Q_{12}(f)$ is an odd function of f. Finally, substituting $u = 0$ in (8.3.15) gives

$$c_{12}(0) = \int_{-\infty}^{\infty} L_{12}(f) \, df, \qquad (8.3.16)$$

and hence the sample co-spectrum gives the decomposition of the zero lag cross covariance with frequency in the same way that the sample spectrum (6.1.11) gives the decomposition of the sample variance with frequency.

Now suppose that (8.3.15) is written

$$c_{12}(u) = l_{12}(u) + q_{12}(u), \qquad (8.3.17)$$

where

$$L_{12}(f) = \int_{-T}^{T} l_{12}(u) \cos 2\pi f u \, du,$$

$$Q_{12}(f) = \int_{-T}^{T} q_{12}(u) \sin 2\pi f u \, du. \qquad (8.3.18)$$

It may be verified that $l_{12}(u)$ is the even part of $c_{12}(u)$, that is,

$$l_{12}(u) = \tfrac{1}{2}(c_{12}(u) + c_{12}(-u)). \qquad (8.3.19)$$

Similarly, $q_{12}(u)$ is the odd part of $c_{12}(u)$, namely,

$$q_{12}(u) = \tfrac{1}{2}(c_{12}(u) - c_{12}(-u)). \qquad (8.3.20)$$

8.3.3 The cross spectrum

The analysis of the previous section assumed that $x_1(t)$ and $x_2(t)$ were mathematical functions of time t. If $\{x_1(t), x_2(t)\}$ are realizations of a stationary bivariate stochastic process $\{X_1(t), X_2(t)\}$, the same problems arise as for univariate spectra. Thus if the sample co- and quadrature spectra are computed for a realization of a bivariate stochastic process, they do not tend to a limiting value, in any statistical sense, as the record length T tends to infinity. In fact, their behavior is identical to that of the sample spectrum as shown in Figure 6.1. To see why this is so it is necessary to examine the properties of the rv $C_{X_1 X_2}(f)$ associated with the sample cross spectrum.

From (8.3.12) the sample cross spectrum estimator is

$$C_{X_1 X_2}(f) = \int_{-T}^{T} c_{X_1 X_2}(u) \, e^{-j 2\pi f u} \, du, \qquad -\infty \leqslant f \leqslant \infty.$$

Using (8.2.2), this has mean value

$$E[C_{X_1 X_2}(f)] = \int_{-T}^{T} \left(1 - \frac{|u|}{T}\right) \gamma_{X_1 X_2}(u) \, e^{-j 2\pi f u} \, du, \qquad (8.3.21)$$

and as T tends to infinity, this mean value tends to the cross power spectrum or, more concisely, the *cross spectrum*. Thus

$$\lim_{T \to \infty} E[C_{X_1 X_2}(f)] = \Gamma_{X_1 X_2}(f) = \int_{-\infty}^{\infty} \gamma_{X_1 X_2}(u) \, e^{-j2\pi f u} \, du, \quad -\infty \leqslant f \leqslant \infty.$$
(8.3.22)

Equation (8.3.22) shows that the cross spectrum is the Fourier transform of the ccvf. Note that in the stochastic definition (8.3.22), the cross spectrum is a continuous function of frequency in the range $-\infty \leqslant f \leqslant \infty$.

It is emphasized once again that the definition

$$\Gamma_{X_1 X_2}(f) = \lim_{T \to \infty} C_{X_1 X_2}(f)$$

usually given in engineering texts has no meaning for stochastic processes since the variances of the real and imaginary parts of the rv $C_{X_1 X_2}(f)$ do not tend to zero as T tends to infinity, as will be shown in Section 9.1.

Co- and quadrature spectra. Writing $\gamma_{X_1 X_2}(u)$ as the sum of an even part $\lambda_{12}(u)$ and an odd part $\psi_{12}(u)$ gives

$$\begin{aligned}
\lambda_{12}(u) &= \tfrac{1}{2}(\gamma_{12}(u) + \gamma_{12}(-u)), \\
\psi_{12}(u) &= \tfrac{1}{2}(\gamma_{12}(u) - \gamma_{12}(-u)),
\end{aligned}$$
(8.3.23)

and substitution in (8.3.22) yields

$$\Gamma_{12}(f) = \Lambda_{12}(f) - j\Psi_{12}(f),$$
(8.3.24)

where

$$\Lambda_{12}(f) = \int_{-\infty}^{\infty} \lambda_{12}(u) \cos 2\pi f u \, du$$
(8.3.25)

and

$$\Psi_{12}(f) = \int_{-\infty}^{\infty} \psi_{12}(u) \sin 2\pi f u \, du.$$
(8.3.26)

$\Lambda_{12}(f)$ is called the *co-spectrum* and $\Psi_{12}(f)$ the *quadrature spectrum* of the $\{X_1(t), X_2(t)\}$ process. Equivalent definitions for these quantities may be obtained from (8.3.21) and (8.3.22). Thus

$$\Lambda_{12}(f) = \lim_{T \to \infty} E[L_{12}(f)], \quad \Psi_{12}(f) = \lim_{T \to \infty} E[Q_{12}(f)].$$

Cross amplitude and phase spectra. The cross spectrum may also be written

$$\Gamma_{12}(f) = \alpha_{12}(f) \, e^{j\phi_{12}(f)},$$
(8.3.27)

where $\alpha_{12}(f)$, $\phi_{12}(f)$ are called the *cross amplitude spectrum* and the *phase spectrum* respectively. From (8.3.11), it is seen that

$$\alpha_{12}(f) = \sqrt{\Lambda_{12}^2(f) + \Psi_{12}^2(f)},$$
(8.3.28)

$$\phi_{12}(f) = \arctan -\frac{\Psi_{12}(f)}{\Lambda_{12}(f)}.$$
(8.3.29)

TABLE 8.3: **Summary of cross spectral formulae**

Function		Theoretical values			Sample values
	Symbol	Definition	Symbol		Definition
auto-spectrum	$\Gamma_{11}(f)$	$\Gamma_{11}(f) = \int_{-\infty}^{\infty} \gamma_{11}(u)\, e^{-j2\pi fu}\, du$	$C_{11}(f)$		$C_{11}(f) = \int_{-T}^{T} c_{11}(u)\, e^{-j2\pi fu}\, du$
cross spectrum	$\Gamma_{12}(f)$	$\Gamma_{12}(f) = \int_{-\infty}^{\infty} \gamma_{12}(u)\, e^{-j2\pi fu}\, du$ $= \alpha_{12}(f)\, e^{+j\phi_{12}(f)}$ $= \Lambda_{12}(f) - j\Psi_{12}(f)$	$C_{12}(f)$		$C_{12}(f) = \int_{-T}^{T} c_{12}(u)\, e^{-j2\pi fu}\, du$ $= A_{12}(f)\, e^{+jF_{12}(f)}$ $= L_{12}(f) - jQ_{12}(f)$
cross amplitude spectrum	$\alpha_{12}(f)$	$\alpha_{12}(f) = \lvert\Gamma_{12}(f)\rvert$ $= \sqrt{\Lambda_{12}^2(f) + \Psi_{12}^2(f)}$	$A_{12}(f)$		$A_{12}(f) = \lvert C_{12}(f)\rvert$ $= \sqrt{L_{12}^2(f) + Q_{12}^2(f)}$
phase spectrum	$\phi_{12}(f)$	$\phi_{12}(f) = \arctan\left\{-\dfrac{\Psi_{12}(f)}{\Lambda_{12}(f)}\right\}$	$F_{12}(f)$		$F_{12}(f) = \arctan\left\{-\dfrac{Q_{12}(f)}{L_{12}(f)}\right\}$
co-spectrum	$\Lambda_{12}(f)$	$\Lambda_{12}(f) = \int_{-\infty}^{\infty} \lambda_{12}(u)\, e^{-j2\pi fu}\, du$ $= \tfrac{1}{2}\int_{-\infty}^{\infty} \{\gamma_{12}(u) + \gamma_{12}(-u)\}\cos 2\pi fu\, du$	$L_{12}(f)$		$L_{12}(f) = \int_{-T}^{T} l_{12}(u)\, e^{-j2\pi fu}\, du$ $= \tfrac{1}{2}\int_{-T}^{T} \{c_{12}(u) + c_{12}(-u)\}\cos 2\pi fu\, du$
quadrature spectrum	$\Psi_{12}(f)$	$\Psi_{12}(f) = \int_{-\infty}^{\infty} \psi_{12}(u)\, e^{-j2\pi fu}\, du$ $= \tfrac{1}{2}\int_{-\infty}^{\infty} \{\gamma_{12}(u) - \gamma_{12}(-u)\}\sin 2\pi fu\, du$	$Q_{12}(f)$		$Q_{12}(f) = \int_{-T}^{T} q_{12}(u)\, e^{-j2\pi fu}\, du$ $= \tfrac{1}{2}\int_{-T}^{T} \{c_{12}(u) - c_{12}(-u)\}\sin 2\pi fu\, du$

Hence the cross amplitude and phase spectra may be calculated by computing $\lambda_{12}(u)$ and $\psi_{12}(u)$ from the cross covariance function according to (8.3.23), by computing the co- and quadrature spectra using (8.3.25) and (8.3.26), and by substituting in (8.3.28) and (8.3.29).

Summary. Table 8.3 summarizes the spectra which have been defined in this chapter.

8.4 CROSS SPECTRA OF LINEAR PROCESSES

8.4.1 Simple examples of cross spectra

Before deriving the cross spectrum of the general bivariate process (8.1.14) it is instructive to consider some simple examples of cross spectra. These examples will be used to demonstrate what information is contained in the cross spectrum. For this purpose the cross spectra of some simple discrete processes are derived. For discrete processes, the cross spectrum is

$$\Gamma_{12}(f) = \Delta \sum_{k=-\infty}^{\infty} \gamma_{12}(k)\, e^{-j2\pi fk}, \quad -\frac{1}{2\Delta} \leqslant f < \frac{1}{2\Delta}. \tag{8.4.1}$$

In the following examples it is assumed that $E[Z_{1t}] = 0$, $E[Z_{2t}] = 0$, $E[Z_{1t}^2] = \sigma_1^2$, $E[Z_{2t}^2] = \sigma_2^2$ and $\Delta = 1$ so that $-\frac{1}{2} \leqslant f < \frac{1}{2}$.

Example 1. Suppose

$$X_{2t} = Z_{2t}, \qquad X_{1t} = Z_{1t},$$

where Z_{1t} and Z_{2t} are mutually uncorrelated white noise sources. Hence

$$\gamma_{12}(k) = E[Z_{1t}Z_{2t+k}] = 0, \quad \text{all } k,$$

and using (8.3.22),

$$\Gamma_{12}(f) = \alpha_{12}(f)\, e^{j\phi} e^{j\phi_{12}(f)} = \sqrt{\Lambda_{12}^2(f) + \Psi_{12}^2(f)} = 0.$$

This implies that the cross amplitude spectrum is zero everywhere and hence the co- and quadrature spectra are identically zero. This would seem to imply that the phase spectrum is indeterminate. It may be shown, however, that the phase spectrum is uniformly distributed in the range $(-\pi/2, \pi/2)$ so that the average phase difference between the two processes is zero but the phase difference at any frequency is equally likely to lie anywhere in the range $(-\pi/2, \pi/2)$.

Example 2 (the bivariate equivalent of white noise). Suppose

$$X_{2t} = Z_{2t} + \beta_1 Z_{1t}, \qquad X_{1t} = Z_{1t},$$

so that

$$X_{2t} = \beta_1 X_{1t} + Z_{2t}. \tag{8.4.2}$$

Hence

$$\gamma_{12}(0) = E[Z_{1t}(Z_{2t} + \beta_1 Z_{1t})]$$
$$= \beta_1 \sigma_1^2,$$
$$\gamma_{12}(k) = 0, \quad k \neq 0.$$

From (8.4.1)

$$\Gamma_{12}(f) = \beta_1 \sigma_1^2,$$

which implies that

$$\alpha_{12}(f) = \beta_1 \sigma_1^2, \qquad \phi_{12}(f) = 0,$$
$$\Lambda_{12}(f) = \beta_1 \sigma_1^2, \qquad \Psi_{12}(f) = 0.$$

Hence if the two processes are cross correlated only at simultaneous times, the cross amplitude spectrum is a constant, like the spectrum of white noise. Further, the two processes are in phase, since $\phi_{12}(f) = 0$. The cross amplitude and phase spectra for this example are shown in Figure 8.8(a). *Thus (8.4.2) may be regarded as a fundamental model for cross spectra in the same way that white noise is fundamental for univariate spectra.*

Example 3 (*the effect of delay*). Suppose

$$X_{2t} = Z_{2t} + \beta_1 Z_{1t-d}, \qquad X_{1t} = Z_{1t},$$

so that

$$X_{2t} = \beta_1 X_{1t-d} + Z_{2t},$$

that is, the two series are shifted by a time interval d relative to each other. Hence

$$\gamma_{12}(k) = \begin{cases} \beta_1 \sigma_1^2, & k = d \\ 0, & \text{otherwise.} \end{cases}$$

Therefore, from (8.4.1),

$$\Gamma_{12}(f) = \beta_1 \sigma_1^2 e^{-j2\pi f d},$$

$$\alpha_{12}(f) = \beta_1 \sigma_1^2, \qquad\qquad \phi_{12}(f) = -2\pi f d,$$
$$\Lambda_{12}(f) = \beta_1 \sigma_1^2 \cos 2\pi f d, \qquad \psi_{12}(f) = \beta_1 \sigma_1^2 \sin 2\pi f d.$$

Again the cross amplitude spectrum is a constant, but the phase spectrum is now a linear function of frequency as shown in Figure 8.8(b). This means that a cosinusoidal wave of frequency f cycles per second takes fd cycles to cover the delay time d seconds and hence the phase lag is $2\pi f d$ radians.

Example 4. A more interesting case occurs with the model

$$X_{2t} = \beta_1 Z_{1t} + \beta_2 Z_{1t-1} + Z_{2t}, \qquad X_{1t} = Z_{1t},$$

which may be rewritten

$$X_{2t} = \beta_1 X_{1t} + \beta_2 X_{1t-1} + Z_{2t}.$$

Hence, as shown in the second example of Section 8.1.3,

$$\gamma_{12}(k) = \begin{cases} \beta_1 \sigma_1^2, & k = 0, \\ \beta_2 \sigma_1^2, & k = 1, \\ 0, & \text{otherwise.} \end{cases}$$

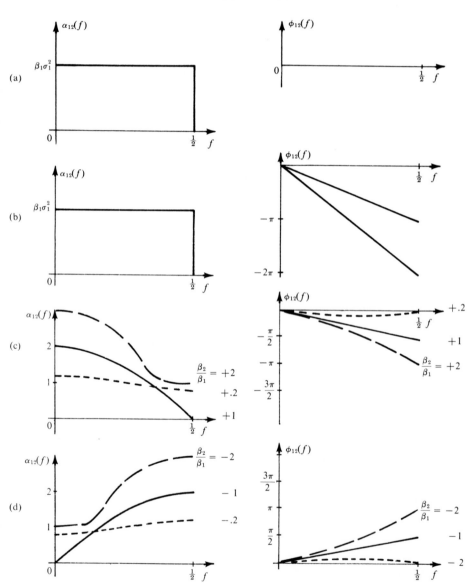

Fig. 8.8: Cross amplitude and phase spectra for some simple bivariate processes

Therefore

$$\Gamma_{12}(f) = \sigma_1^2[\beta_1 + \beta_2 e^{-j2\pi f}],$$

$$\alpha_{12}(f) = \sigma_1^2 \sqrt{\beta_1^2 + \beta_2^2 + 2\beta_1\beta_2 \cos 2\pi f},$$

$$\phi_{12}(f) = \arctan\left(\frac{-\beta_2 \sin 2\pi f}{\beta_1 + \beta_2 \cos 2\pi f}\right),$$

$$\Lambda_{12}(f) = \sigma_1^2(\beta_1 + \beta_2 \cos 2\pi f),$$

$$\Psi_{12}(f) = \sigma_1^2\beta_2 \sin 2\pi f.$$

The cross amplitude spectrum shows that the covariance between the two processes is dominated by low frequencies if $\beta_2/\beta_1 > 0$ and by high frequencies if $\beta_2/\beta_1 < 0$. Hence cross correlations all of one sign produce low-frequency cross amplitude spectra and oscillatory cross correlations produce high-frequency cross amplitude spectra. The corresponding phase diagrams are shown in Figure 8.8(c) and (d), and it is seen that when $\beta_2/\beta_1 > 0$, X_{1t} leads X_{2t} and when $\beta_2/\beta_1 < 0$, X_{1t} lags behind X_{2t}.

By using more sophisticated models it is possible to generate a wide variety of cross amplitude and phase spectra. An important point which needs emphasizing at this stage is that examination of the cross amplitude spectra of two empirical time series may indicate that *a different model may be required in different frequency ranges*. For example, a phase diagram made up of straight lines with different slopes would indicate that one series was delayed relative to the other but that the time domain delay between the two series changes from one frequency band to the next.

Hence it is seen that a study of the cross spectra of empirical time series can provide a very flexible tool for suggesting models to describe their behavior. If it is suspected that different models may be operating in different frequency bands, a more efficient analysis results if, as discussed in Section 7.3.5, the two series are filtered into component series using a bank of band-pass filters. Then the cross spectra are calculated using the component series.

8.4.2 The cross spectrum of a linear system

It was shown in Section 8.1.3 that two stochastic processes $X_1(t)$, $X_2(t)$ are sometimes related linearly as

$$X_2(t) = \int_0^\infty h(u)X_1(t - u)\,du + Z(t).$$

Thus $X_1(t)$ is the input process to a linear system and $X_2(t)$ is the corresponding output plus an independent noise $Z(t)$. From (8.1.8) the ccvf of the output is

$$\gamma_{12}(u) = \int_0^\infty \gamma_{11}(u - v)h(v)\,dv, \quad -\infty \leqslant u \leqslant \infty. \tag{8.4.3}$$

Transforming (8.4.3) gives

$$\Gamma_{12}(f) = H(f)\Gamma_{11}(f).\tag{8.4.4}$$

Hence the frequency response function may be determined from

$$H(f) = \frac{\Gamma_{12}(f)}{\Gamma_{11}(f)}.\tag{8.4.5}$$

Comparison of equations (8.4.3) and (8.4.4) shows how the analysis of linear systems is simplified by using Fourier techniques. Thus the convolution in (8.4.3) is converted into a multiplication in (8.4.4). Rewriting (8.4.5) in the form

$$H(f) = G(f)\,e^{+j\phi(f)} = \frac{\Lambda_{12}(f) - j\,\Psi_{12}(f)}{\Gamma_{11}(f)}$$

yields expressions for the gain $G(f)$ and phase $\phi(f)$ of the linear system. Thus

$$G(f) = \frac{\sqrt{\Lambda_{12}^2(f) + \Psi_{12}^2(f)}}{\Gamma_{11}(f)} = \frac{\alpha_{12}(f)}{\Gamma_{11}(f)},\tag{8.4.6}$$

$$\phi(f) = \arctan -\frac{\Psi_{12}(f)}{\Lambda_{12}(f)}.\tag{8.4.7}$$

Remembering that the cross amplitude $\alpha_{12}(f)$ is a measure of the "covariance" between $X_1(t)$ and $X_2(t)$ at frequency f and $\Gamma_{11}(f)$ the "variance" in the input at frequency f, it is seen that the gain $G(f)$ behaves like the regression coefficient (4.3.7) but is now evaluated at each frequency f.

Squared coherency spectrum. This analogy may be pursued further using the relation (8.1.9) for the autocovariance of the output, namely,

$$\gamma_{22}(u) = \int_{-\infty}^{\infty} \int_{-\infty}^{\infty} h(v)h(v')\gamma_{11}(u + v - v')\,dv\,dv' + \gamma_{zz}(u).$$

On transforming this equation,

$$\Gamma_{22}(f) = G^2(f)\Gamma_{11}(f) + \Gamma_{zz}(f),\tag{8.4.8}$$

which differs from (6.2.15) only in that the spectrum of the noise $Z(t)$ is added to the contribution from the input. Substituting for (8.4.6) in (8.4.8),

$$\Gamma_{22}(f) - \frac{\alpha_{12}^2(f)}{\Gamma_{11}(f)} = \Gamma_{zz}(f)$$

or

$$\Gamma_{zz}(f) = \Gamma_{22}(f)[1 - \kappa_{12}^2(f)],\tag{8.4.9}$$

where

$$\kappa_{12}^2(f) = \frac{\alpha_{12}^2(f)}{\Gamma_{11}(f)\Gamma_{22}(f)}\tag{8.4.10}$$

is called the *squared coherency* between the input and output at frequency f. The plot of $\kappa_{12}^2(f)$ versus f is called the *squared coherency spectrum*.

The resemblance between (8.4.9) and the ordinary correlation coefficient (3.2.19) should be noted. In fact, the coherency plays the role of a correlation coefficient defined at each frequency f. Thus (8.4.9) shows that when the noise spectrum is identical to the output spectrum, the squared coherency is zero. In other words, the squared coherency is zero when the output consists entirely of noise. When $\Gamma_{ZZ}(f) = 0$, the squared coherency is unity and the output spectrum is simply the input spectrum multiplied by the square of the gain of the system. Eliminating $\Gamma_{22}(f)$ between (8.4.8) and (8.4.10),

$$\kappa_{12}^2(f) = \frac{1}{1 + (\Gamma_{ZZ}(f)/G^2(f)\Gamma_{11}(f))}. \tag{8.4.11}$$

Equation (8.4.11) shows that the squared coherency is small when the output-signal to noise ratio $G^2(f)\Gamma_{11}(f)/\Gamma_{ZZ}(f)$ is small and large when the ratio is large.

8.4.3 Cross spectra of bivariate linear processes

It was shown in Section 8.1.4 that a very general model for generating bivariate stochastic processes is obtained by passing two white noise sources $Z_1(t)$ and $Z_2(t)$ through the system shown in Figure 8.5. The auto- and cross covariances of this process are given by (8.1.15). These results will now be used to derive the corresponding auto- and cross spectra. Denote by

$$H_{ij}(f) = \int_{-\infty}^{\infty} h_{ij}(u)\, e^{-j2\pi fu}\, du, \quad i,j = 1, 2,$$

the frequency response functions of the four systems in the lattice diagram of Figure 8.5. The results for the auto- and cross spectra may now be obtained by transforming the equations (8.1.15). Transforming the first two equations and using (6.2.16), the autospectra are

$$\begin{aligned}
\Gamma_{11}(f) &= \sigma_1^2 |H_{11}(f)|^2 + \sigma_2^2 |H_{12}(f)|^2, \\
\Gamma_{22}(f) &= \sigma_1^2 |H_{21}(f)|^2 + \sigma_2^2 |H_{22}(f)|^2.
\end{aligned} \tag{8.4.12}$$

To derive the cross spectrum, note that the last two of the equations (8.1.15) can be combined to give

$$\gamma_{12}(u) = \sigma_1^2 \int_{-\infty}^{\infty} h_{11}(v)h_{21}(v + u)\, dv + \sigma_2^2 \int_{-\infty}^{\infty} h_{12}(v)h_{22}(v + u)\, dv, \tag{8.4.13}$$

which now holds for $-\infty \leqslant u \leqslant \infty$. On taking Fourier transforms of both sides of (8.4.13), the cross spectrum is

$$\Gamma_{12}(f) = \sigma_1^2 H_{11}^*(f)H_{21}(f) + \sigma_2^2 H_{12}^*(f)H_{22}(f). \tag{8.4.14}$$

Thus the computation of the cross spectrum reduces to computation of the frequency response functions of the associated bivariate linear process (8.1.14).

The frequency response functions $H_{ij}(f)$ may be obtained very simply by transforming equations (8.1.14). On substituting the $H_{ij}(f)$ in (8.4.12) and (8.4.14), explicit expressions for the auto- and cross spectra may be obtained. This procedure is best illustrated by an example.

An example. Consider the continuous bivariate ar process

$$\frac{dX_1(t)}{dt} + a_{11}X_1(t) + a_{12}X_2(t) = Z_1(t),$$

$$\frac{dX_2(t)}{dt} + a_{21}X_1(t) + a_{22}X_2(t) = Z_2(t).$$

Transforming these equations and using the differentiation property (A2.1.2) gives

$$[a_{11} + j2\pi f]X_1(f) + a_{12}X_2(f) = Z_1(f),$$
$$a_{21}X_1(f) + [a_{22} + j2\pi f]X_2(f) = Z_2(f),$$

which may be solved to give

$$X_1(f) = \frac{(a_{22} + j2\pi f)Z_1(f) - a_{12}Z_2(f)}{(a_{11} + j2\pi f)(a_{22} + j2\pi f) - a_{12}a_{21}},$$

$$X_2(f) = \frac{-a_{21}Z_1(f) + (a_{11} + j2\pi f)Z_2(f)}{(a_{11} + j2\pi f)(a_{22} + j2\pi f) - a_{12}a_{21}}.$$

Likewise, transforming (8.1.14) gives

$$X_1(f) = H_{11}(f)Z_1(f) + H_{12}(f)Z_2(f),$$
$$X_2(f) = H_{21}(f)Z_1(f) + H_{22}(f)Z_{22}(f).$$

Hence,

$$H_{11}(f) = \frac{a_{22} + j2\pi f}{D}, \qquad H_{12}(f) = -\frac{a_{12}}{D},$$

$$H_{21}(f) = \frac{-a_{21}}{D}, \qquad H_{22}(f) = \frac{a_{11} + j2\pi f}{D},$$

where $D = a_{11}a_{22} - a_{12}a_{21} - (2\pi f)^2 + j2\pi f(a_{11} + a_{22})$. Finally, using (8.4.12) and (8.4.14), the auto- and cross spectra for the bivariate process are

$$\Gamma_{11}(f) = \frac{[a_{22}^2 + (2\pi f)^2]\sigma_1^2 + a_{12}^2\sigma_2^2}{|D|^2},$$

$$\Gamma_{22}(f) = \frac{a_{21}^2\sigma_1^2 + [a_{11}^2 + (2\pi f)^2]\sigma_2^2}{|D|^2},$$

$$\Gamma_{12}(f) = \frac{-a_{22}a_{21}\sigma_1^2 - a_{11}a_{12}\sigma_2^2 - j2\pi f(a_{12}\sigma_2^2 - a_{21}\sigma_1^2)}{|D|^2}.$$

Cross spectra of discrete bivariate linear processes. Expressions for the auto- and cross spectra of discrete bivariate linear processes may be obtained in a similar way. To illustrate, consider the discrete bivariate process (8.1.20)

$$X_{1t} = 0.6X_{1t-1} - 0.5X_{2t-1} + Z_{1t},$$
$$X_{2t} = 0.4X_{1t-1} + 0.5X_{2t-1} + Z_{2t},$$

where Z_{1t}, Z_{2t} are uncorrelated white noise processes. Taking Z transforms,

$$X_1(Z) = 0.6Z^{-1}X_1(Z) - 0.5Z^{-1}X_2(Z) + Z_1(Z),$$
$$X_2(Z) = 0.4Z^{-1}X_1(Z) + 0.5Z^{-1}X_2(Z) + Z_2(Z).$$

These equations may be solved to give

$$X_1(Z) = \frac{(1 - 0.5Z^{-1})Z_1(Z) - 0.5Z^{-1}Z_2(Z)}{1 - 1.1Z^{-1} + 0.5Z^{-2}},$$

$$X_2(Z) = \frac{0.4Z^{-1}Z_1(Z) + (1 - 0.6Z^{-1})Z_2(Z)}{1 - 1.1Z^{-1} + 0.5Z^{-2}}.$$

Substituting $Z = e^{j2\pi f}$ gives the frequency response functions

$$H_{11}(f) = \frac{(1 - 0.5e^{-j2\pi f})}{D}, \qquad H_{12}(f) = \frac{-0.5e^{-j2\pi f}}{D},$$

$$H_{21}(f) = \frac{0.4e^{-j2\pi f}}{D}, \qquad H_{22}(f) = \frac{1 - 0.6e^{-j2\pi f}}{D},$$

where

$$D = 1 - 1.1e^{-j2\pi f} + 0.5e^{-j4\pi f}$$
$$= 1 - 1.1\cos 2\pi f + 0.5\cos 4\pi f + j(1.1\sin 2\pi f - 0.5\sin 4\pi f).$$

Finally, using (8.4.12) and (8.4.14), the auto- and cross spectra for the bivariate process are

$$\Gamma_{11}(f) = \frac{\sigma_1^2(1.25 - \cos 2\pi f) + \sigma_2^2(0.25)}{|D|^2},$$

$$\Gamma_{22}(f) = \frac{\sigma_1^2(0.16) + \sigma_2^2(1.36 - 1.2\cos 2\pi f)}{|D|^2}, \qquad (8.4.15)$$

$$\Gamma_{12}(f)$$
$$= \frac{\sigma_1^2(-0.2 + 0.4\cos 2\pi f) + \sigma_2^2(0.3 - 0.5\cos 2\pi f) - j\sin 2\pi f\,(0.4\sigma_1^2 + 0.5\sigma_2^2)}{|D|^2},$$

where $|D|^2 = 2.46 - 3.3\cos 2\pi f + \cos 4\pi f$.

In the particular case where $\sigma_1^2 = \sigma_2^2 = 1$, (8.4.15) reduces to

$$\Gamma_{11}(f) = \frac{1.5 - \cos 2\pi f}{|D|^2},$$

$$\Gamma_{22}(f) = \frac{1.52 - 1.2\cos 2\pi f}{|D|^2}, \qquad (8.4.16)$$

$$\Gamma_{12}(f) = \frac{0.1(1 - \cos 2\pi f) - j(0.9)\sin 2\pi f}{|D|^2}.$$

8.4.4 The squared coherency spectrum

It was shown in Section 8.4.2 that the correlation at frequency f between the input and output of a linear system could be described by the squared coherency $\kappa_{12}^2(f)$. This resembles a correlation coefficient at each frequency and measures the influence of the noise in the system, a large noise spectrum resulting in a low squared coherency and vice versa. It will be shown in Chapter 11 that any bivariate stochastic process has a coherency spectrum. In this section, the basic idea is illustrated by calculating the coherency spectrum of a bivariate linear process.

Consider the bivariate linear process of Figure 8.5, which has auto- and cross spectra

$$\Gamma_{11}(f) = \sigma_1^2|H_{11}(f)|^2 + \sigma_2^2|H_{12}(f)|^2,$$
$$\Gamma_{22}(f) = \sigma_1^2|H_{21}(f)|^2 + \sigma_2^2|H_{22}(f)|^2, \qquad (8.4.17)$$
$$\Gamma_{12}(f) = \sigma_1^2 H_{11}^*(f)H_{21}(f) + \sigma_2^2 H_{12}^*(f)H_{22}(f).$$

The squared coherency spectrum of the bivariate linear process can then be obtained by substituting (8.4.17) in the definition (8.4.10). That is,

$$\kappa_{12}^2(f) = \frac{\alpha_{12}^2(f)}{\Gamma_{11}(f)\Gamma_{22}(f)} = \frac{|\Gamma_{12}(f)|^2}{\Gamma_{11}(f)\Gamma_{22}(f)}. \qquad (8.4.18)$$

Some special cases of (8.4.17) and (8.4.18) are now considered.

Case 1. Suppose that $h_{12}(u) = 0$, $h_{22}(u) = 0$, so that $H_{12}(f) = 0$, $H_{22}(f) = 0$. Then

$$\kappa_{12}^2(f) = \frac{\sigma_1^4|H_{11}^*(f)H_{21}(f)|^2}{\sigma_1^4|H_{11}(f)|^2|H_{21}(f)|^2} = 1.$$

Referring to (8.1.14), if $h_{12}(u) = 0$, $h_{22}(u) = 0$,

$$X_1(t) = \int_0^\infty h_{11}(u)Z_1(t-u)\,du,$$

$$X_2(t) = \int_0^\infty h_{21}(u)Z_1(t-u)\,du.$$

Hence a squared coherency which is everywhere unity means that $X_2(t)$ could be completely recovered from $X_1(t)$. To do this, it would be necessary to convert $X_1(t)$ to white noise $Z_1(t)$ using a filter with frequency response function $1/H_{11}(f)$ and then generate $X_2(t)$ from $Z_1(t)$.

Case 2. Suppose that $h_{21}(u) = 0$, $h_{12}(u) = 0$ in (8.1.14) so that

$$X_1(t) = \int_0^\infty h_{11}(u)Z_1(t-u)\,du,$$

$$X_2(t) = \int_0^\infty h_{22}(u)Z_2(t-u)\,du.$$

From (8.4.17) it is seen that $\Gamma_{12}(f) = 0$ and hence $\kappa_{12}^2(f) = 0$. Since $Z_1(t)$ and $Z_2(t)$ are two different white noise sources, a squared coherency of zero implies that it is impossible to recover or predict $X_2(t)$ from $X_1(t)$.

Case 3 (example 2 of Section 8.4.1). Values of the squared coherency between 0 and 1 correspond to situations where $X_2(t)$ can be partially recovered or predicted from $X_1(t)$. For example, consider the bivariate process (8.4.2) for which

$$X_{1t} = Z_{1t},$$
$$X_{2t} = Z_{2t} + \beta_1 Z_{1t}.$$

Hence $H_{11}(f) = 1$, $H_{22}(f) = 1$, $H_{12}(f) = 0$, $H_{21}(f) = \beta_1$ and

$$\kappa_{12}^2(f) = \frac{\beta_1^2}{1 + \beta_1^2},$$

if $\sigma_1^2 = \sigma_2^2$. Thus the squared coherency spectrum is zero if $\beta_1 = 0$ and tends to unity if β_1 tends to infinity. This is to be expected, since when β_1 tends to zero, the noise Z_{2t} dominates, and when β_1 tends to infinity, the signal $\beta_1 Z_{1t}$ dominates.

Case 4 (effect of delay). Consider the bivariate process discussed in the third example of Section 8.4.1, namely,

$$X_{2t} = Z_{2t} + \beta_1 Z_{1t-d},$$
$$X_{1t} = Z_{1t}.$$

When $\sigma_1^2 = \sigma_2^2$, the squared coherency spectrum is

$$\kappa_{12}^2(f) = \frac{\beta_1^2}{1 + \beta_1^2},$$

which is identical to that of the preceding case.

However, it was shown in Section 8.4.1 and Figures 8.8(a) and (b) that these two processes have markedly different phase functions. Thus the squared coherency spectrum gives no indication of any phase differences between the two processes, and hence a complete frequency domain description of a bivariate process requires a phase spectrum as well as a coherency spectrum.

Case 5. Consider the discrete bivariate process (8.1.20), which has the auto- and cross spectra (8.4.16) when $\sigma_1^2 = \sigma_2^2$. The corresponding coherency spectrum is

$$\kappa_{12}^2(f) = \frac{0.42 - 0.02 \cos 2\pi f - 0.4 \cos 4\pi f}{2.88 - 3.32 \cos 2\pi f + 0.6 \cos 4\pi f}, \quad -\tfrac{1}{2} \leqslant f < \tfrac{1}{2}, \quad (8.4.19)$$

which is shown in Figure 8.9.

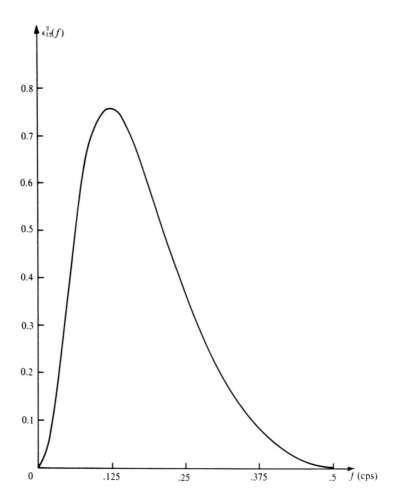

FIG. 8.9: Theoretical coherency spectrum for the bivariate autoregressive process
(8.1.20)

The most important features of this coherency spectrum are the large peak at
approximately 0.125 cps and the fact that the coherency tends to zero at both
low and high frequencies. The peak is to be expected because of the periodicity
in the ccf and shows that the bulk of the correlation between the two processes is confined to a band of frequencies in the neighborhood of 0.125 cps.
Using (8.4.16), the phase spectrum for this process is

$$\phi_{12}(f) = \arctan \frac{-0.9 \sin 2\pi f}{0.1(1 - \cos 2\pi f)}$$

$$= \arctan \left(-9 \cot \pi f\right), \tag{8.4.20}$$

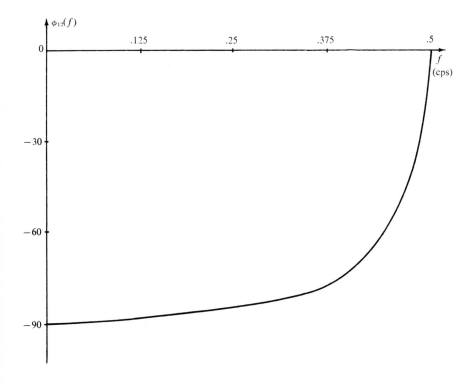

Fig. 8.10: Theoretical phase spectrum for the bivariate autoregressive process (8.1.20)

which is shown in Figure 8.10. This figure shows that the low-frequency components of series 1 lag those of series 2 by essentially 90°, but the phase difference tends to zero at higher frequencies.

Practical use of squared coherency. The coherency spectrum is useful in practice because it provides a non-dimensional measure of the correlation between two time series as a function of frequency. Thus it is to be preferred to the cross amplitude spectrum, which depends on the scale of measurement of $X_1(t)$ and $X_2(t)$. Hence the cross correlation properties of two time series can be described by the squared coherency spectrum $\kappa_{12}^2(f)$ and the phase spectrum $\phi_{12}(f)$. In Section 9.2 it is shown how to estimate these spectra from finite lengths of record.

8.4.5 *Linear operations on bivariate time series*

In Section 9.4.2 it will be necessary to prefilter the time series before conducting a cross spectral analysis. In this section an investigation is made of the effect of this prefiltering operation on coherency and phase spectra.

It is assumed that different filtering operations are performed on the $X_1(t)$, $X_2(t)$ processes leading to new processes $Y_1(t)$, $Y_2(t)$ according to

$$Y_1(t) = \int_0^\infty h_1(v)X_1(t - v) \, dv,$$
$$Y_2(t) = \int_0^\infty h_2(v)X_2(t - v) \, dv. \tag{8.4.21}$$

Proceeding as in Section 5.2.2, the cross covariance function of the filtered process is

$$\gamma_{Y_1Y_2}(u) = \int_0^\infty \int_0^\infty h_1(v)h_2(v')\gamma_{X_1X_2}(u + v - v') \, dv \, dv'. \tag{8.4.22}$$

On transforming (8.4.22), the cross spectrum is

$$\Gamma_{Y_1Y_2}(f) = H_1^*(f)H_2(f)\Gamma_{X_1X_2}(f). \tag{8.4.23}$$

Since

$$\Gamma_{Y_iY_i}(f) = |H_i(f)|^2\Gamma_{X_iX_i}(f), \quad i = 1, 2,$$

the coherency spectrum of the filtered bivariate series is

$$\kappa_{Y_1Y_2}^2(f) = \frac{|H_1^*(f)|^2|H_2(f)|^2\Gamma_{X_1X_2}(f)}{|H_1^*(f)|^2|H_2(f)|^2\Gamma_{X_1X_1}(f)\Gamma_{X_2X_2}(f)}$$
$$= \kappa_{X_1X_2}^2(f).$$

Hence the coherency spectrum is unaltered by the filtering.
    From (8.3.27) and (2.3.17),

$$\Gamma_{X_1X_2}(f) = \alpha_{X_1X_2}(f) \, e^{j\phi_{X_1X_2}(f)},$$
$$H_i(f) = G_i(f) \, e^{j\phi_i(f)},$$

and

$$\Gamma_{Y_1Y_2}(f) = G_1(f)G_2(f)\alpha_{X_1X_2}(f) \, e^{j\{\phi_2(f) - \phi_1(f) + \phi_{12}(f)\}}$$
$$= G_1(f)G_2(f) \, e^{j\{\phi_2(f) - \phi_1(f)\}}\Gamma_{X_1X_2}(f).$$

Thus the phase spectrum is changed by $\phi_2(f) - \phi_1(f)$. However, note that if $h_1(u) = h_2(u)$, $\phi_1(f) = \phi_2(f)$ and the phase is unaltered. Hence, if the same filtering operation is applied to both processes, the cross amplitude spectrum is altered by $G^2(f)$ but the coherency and phase spectra are unaltered. The residual spectrum (see Chapter 10) for the filtered data will be affected in the same way as the autospectrum $\Gamma_{Y_2Y_2}(f)$, that is, the residual spectrum for the filtered data equals $G_2^2(f)$ times the residual spectrum for the original data.

APPENDIX A8.1 REALIZATIONS OF TWO BIVARIATE LINEAR PROCESSES

TABLE A8.1: A realization of a bivariate linear process

$$x_{1t} = 0.6x_{1t-1} - 0.5x_{2t-1} + z_{1t} \qquad x_{2t} = 0.4x_{1t-1} + 0.5x_{2t-1} + z_{2t}$$

$t = 1\text{-}25$	$t = 26\text{-}50$	$t = 51\text{-}75$	$t = 76\text{-}100$	$t = 1\text{-}25$	$t = 26\text{-}50$	$t = 51\text{-}75$	$t = 76\text{-}100$
−0.88	−2.00	0.37	0.15	0.79	−1.40	2.96	2.69
−0.16	−0.22	−0.24	−1.04	1.12	−2.55	1.56	0.57
−1.87	0.38	0.57	0.12	−1.10	−1.66	−0.36	0.29
−1.12	1.31	−0.53	0.08	−2.39	−0.43	−0.59	1.10
1.38	0.71	2.44	0.11	−1.75	0.58	−0.12	0.48
2.13	0.32	1.02	−2.62	−0.82	2.18	3.03	−1.06
2.76	0.48	−0.53	−1.28	−0.36	−0.24	2.11	−2.28
0.56	−1.88	−2.49	1.07	1.27	0.58	0.78	−2.03
−0.69	−0.94	−2.12	3.20	1.75	−0.18	0.89	−0.75
−1.79	−1.54	−1.04	1.92	2.44	−1.55	−1.45	1.00
−3.82	−0.13	−0.12	0.53	0.36	−0.64	−0.36	1.71
−2.38	1.02	−1.88	−1.08	−2.10	−1.09	−0.37	0.58
1.00	0.02	−1.50	0.49	−1.93	0.90	−1.39	1.97
0.70	−0.77	1.54	−0.58	−1.30	−0.66	−4.19	0.99
−0.15	0.11	3.33	0.17	−1.75	−0.35	−0.73	1.94
0.98	−0.60	3.08	1.15	−0.34	0.48	−0.98	2.18
0.11	−0.52	1.71	−0.97	0.74	0.50	0.36	3.14
−0.35	−0.09	0.79	−1.63	0.49	0.05	0.06	0.60
−0.73	1.23	1.55	1.14	0.70	−0.68	−1.94	0.51
0.89	1.46	0.89	−0.67	0.71	0.24	−0.08	1.35
−1.63	0.61	−0.89	−0.88	0.09	0.58	0.17	0.56
−0.44	0.42	−1.18	−0.07	0.59	−1.26	1.00	0.11
−1.37	2.16	0.89	0.24	1.54	−0.25	−0.05	0.00
−1.71	3.18	1.71	0.55	0.14	0.25	0.43	2.34
−1.22	2.10	3.05	−2.16	0.55	2.18	0.15	1.88

TABLE A8.2: A realization of a bivariate linear process with delay

$$x_{1t} = 0.6x_{1t-1} + z_{1t}$$

$$x_{2t} = 0.5x_{2t-1} + 2x_{1t-10} + y_{2t},$$
$$y_{2t} = 0.5y_{2t-1} + z_{2t}$$

$t = 1\text{-}25$	$t = 26\text{-}50$	$t = 51\text{-}75$	$t = 76\text{-}100$	$t = 1\text{-}25$	$t = 26\text{-}50$	$t = 51\text{-}75$	$t = 76\text{-}100$
-2.07	-0.78	0.00	0.20	0.32	-3.65	8.00	4.88
-1.15	0.31	-1.99	-0.42	0.35	-3.38	7.91	3.01
0.69	-0.95	-1.75	1.18	-2.03	-3.04	8.81	6.05
-0.46	-0.90	0.70	0.82	-4.16	-3.03	2.36	5.67
-1.49	-0.30	0.73	1.50	-3.55	-2.64	5.92	7.23
-0.70	-1.02	1.16	2.92	-1.04	-1.01	2.94	2.32
-1.07	-0.53	0.06	1.18	2.60	2.88	2.05	1.27
-0.69	0.15	-0.02	1.23	0.67	-1.18	-1.52	1.26
-0.68	1.40	1.10	3.16	-0.25	-1.91	-4.87	4.86
1.27	1.22	-0.35	0.79	-0.90	-3.75	-2.96	4.75
-1.05	0.59	-1.67	0.68	-4.69	-3.61	-2.26	3.55
-0.05	0.70	-1.57	1.14	-3.50	-3.08	-4.23	1.50
-0.84	1.70	1.16	1.02	1.62	-4.18	-5.26	3.37
0.62	2.78	1.84	1.02	0.81	-4.75	-0.96	5.69
-0.49	1.98	3.35	-0.71	-0.95	-2.62	0.37	7.52
-1.29	1.39	0.40	-0.17	-2.24	-2.15	3.58	10.32
-0.49	1.85	0.45	-1.50	-4.50	-1.61	1.63	8.41
-1.06	2.60	1.30	-0.26	-4.55	-1.28	1.05	7.55
-0.38	0.51	0.93	-0.38	-3.85	1.14	3.77	10.38
-0.52	2.77	1.17	0.93	0.78	2.89	1.60	9.14
-0.13	1.16	-1.74	-0.33	-0.02	4.68	-3.67	6.93
1.30	1.07	-1.28	-1.12	-0.72	4.94	-6.24	6.54
-1.51	-0.48	-0.07	-2.95	-1.84	6.41	-1.82	4.13
-0.43	-0.52	1.50	-2.09	-1.78	10.54	2.11	3.49
-1.33	0.37	0.53	-1.11	-2.77	9.06	7.51	0.40

9

Estimation of
Cross Spectra

It is shown in Section 9.1 that the sample cross spectrum has the same undesirable property as the sample spectrum, namely that its variance is independent of record length. However, it can be used to construct a frequency-domain test for cross correlation between time series based on the sample integrated cospectrum and the sample phase spectrum. In Section 9.2 expressions are derived for the variances and covariances of the smoothed co- and quadrature spectra and the smoothed coherency and phase spectra. It is shown that these depend on the uncontrollable influence of the theoretical coherency as well as the controllable influence of the smoothing procedure.

Some numerical examples of the estimation of cross spectra are given in Section 9.3, where it is shown that very large biases occur if the cross correlation function does not have a maximum at zero lag. Theoretical analysis of the bias shows that it can be minimized by displacing or aligning the series so that the cross correlation function of the aligned series has a maximum at zero lag. Section 9.4 includes a practical procedure for estimating cross spectra and a practical example.

9.1 PROPERTIES OF THE SAMPLE CROSS SPECTRUM

9.1.1 Moments of the sample cross spectrum for two uncorrelated white noise processes

In this section the means, variances and covariances of the sample co- and quadrature spectral estimators and the sample phase and cross amplitude spectral estimators are derived, under the assumption that the two processes are uncorrelated white noise processes. These results will be useful in two contexts. In Section 9.1.2 they will be used for deriving a test for correlation between two time series, and in Sections 9.1.3 and 9.2.1 they will be used for deriving

363

the moments of the sample and smoothed cross spectral estimators under fairly general assumptions about the stochastic processes $X_1(t)$ and $X_2(t)$.

As in previous work, the two white noise processes are denoted by $Z_1(t)$, $Z_2(t)$ and are assumed to have zero means. The sample Fourier transforms are denoted by

$$Z_i(f) = \int_{-T/2}^{T/2} Z_i(t)\, e^{-j2\pi ft}\, dt$$

$$= A_i(f) - jB_i(f),$$

where $A_i(f)$, $B_i(f)$ are the cosine and sine transforms of $Z_i(t)$. On dropping the dependence on f in the cosine and sine transforms, the sample auto- and cross spectra are

$$C_{ii}(f) = \frac{|Z_i(f)|^2}{T} = \frac{A_i^2 + B_i^2}{T}, \quad i = 1, 2,$$

$$C_{12}(f) = \frac{|Z_1^*(f)Z_2(f)|}{T} \tag{9.1.1}$$

$$= \frac{1}{T}[(A_1 + jB_1)(A_2 - jB_2)]$$

$$= \frac{1}{T}[(A_1A_2 + B_1B_2) - j(B_2A_1 - B_1A_2)]. \tag{9.1.2}$$

Hence the sample co- and quadrature spectra are

$$L_{12}(f) = \frac{1}{T}(A_1A_2 + B_1B_2), \tag{9.1.3}$$

$$Q_{12}(f) = \frac{1}{T}(B_2A_1 - B_1A_2). \tag{9.1.4}$$

Now it has been shown in Section 6.3.1 that if the $Z_i(t)$ are Normal processes, the A_i and B_i are Normal rv's. It was also shown that if the processes $Z_i(t)$ have zero means,

$$E[A_i] = E[B_i] = 0, \tag{9.1.5}$$

and for the harmonic frequencies $f_m = m/T$,

$$\text{Var}\,[A_i] = \text{Var}\,[B_i] = \frac{T}{2}\,\sigma_i^2,$$

$$\text{Cov}\,[A_i, B_i] = 0, \quad i = 1, 2. \tag{9.1.6}$$

If, in addition, the two processes $Z_1(t)$ and $Z_2(t)$ are uncorrelated,

$$\text{Cov}\,[A_1, A_2] = 0 = \text{Cov}\,[B_1, B_2],$$

$$\text{Cov}\,[A_1, B_2] = 0 = \text{Cov}\,[B_1, A_2]. \tag{9.1.7}$$

Moments of sample co- and quadrature spectra. Using these results it is possible to derive the moments of the sample co- and quadrature spectra. For example, using (9.1.3) and (9.1.7),

$$E[L_{12}(f)] = \frac{1}{T}\{E[A_1 A_2] + E[B_1 B_2]\} = 0,$$

and from (9.1.6)

$$\text{Var }[L_{12}(f)] = \frac{1}{T^2} E[A_1^2 A_2^2 + B_1^2 B_2^2 + 2B_1 B_2 A_1 A_2]$$

$$= \frac{\sigma_1^2}{2}\frac{\sigma_2^2}{2} + \frac{\sigma_1^2}{2}\frac{\sigma_2^2}{2} + 0$$

$$= \frac{\sigma_1^2 \sigma_2^2}{2}.$$

Similarly,

$$E[Q_{12}(f)] = 0,$$

$$\text{Var }[Q_{12}(f)] = \frac{\sigma_1^2 \sigma_2^2}{2},$$

$$\text{Cov }[L_{12}(f), Q_{12}(f)] = 0.$$

It may also be shown that $L_{12}(f)$ and $Q_{12}(f)$ are uncorrelated with $C_{11}(f)$ and $C_{22}(f)$. Hence the joint distribution of the estimators $C_{11}(f)$, $C_{22}(f)$, $L_{12}(f)$ and $Q_{12}(f)$ may be characterized by the *covariance matrix*

$$\begin{pmatrix} \sigma_1^2 & 0 & 0 & 0 \\ 0 & \sigma_2^2 & 0 & 0 \\ 0 & 0 & \frac{1}{2}\sigma_1^2\sigma_2^2 & 0 \\ 0 & 0 & 0 & \frac{1}{2}\sigma_1^2\sigma_2^2 \end{pmatrix}. \tag{9.1.8}$$

Distribution of the sample cross amplitude spectral estimator. The sample cross amplitude spectrum is defined as $A_{12}(f) = |C_{12}(f)|$, so that, using (9.1.1), the square of the cross amplitude spectral estimator is

$$A_{12}^2(f) = |C_{12}(f)|^2$$

$$= L_{12}^2(f) + Q_{12}^2(f)$$

$$= \left(\frac{|Z_1(f)|^2}{T}\right)\left(\frac{|Z_2(f)|^2}{T}\right)$$

$$= C_{11}(f)C_{22}(f).$$

It is convenient now to introduce the rv

$$Y^2(f) = \frac{4A_{12}^2(f)}{\sigma_1^2\sigma_2^2} = \left(\frac{2C_{11}(f)}{\sigma_1^2}\right)\left(\frac{2C_{22}(f)}{\sigma_2^2}\right) = UV.$$

Making use of the chi-squared property of $C_{11}(f)$ discussed in Section 6.3.3 and the independence property of the two processes $Z_1(t)$, $Z_2(t)$, it follows that the rv $Y^2(f)$ is the product of two independent chi-squared rv's U, V, each with two degrees of freedom. Hence

$$E[Y^2(f)] = E[U]E[V] = 4,$$
$$E[Y^4(f)] = E[U^2]E[V^2] = (8)(8) = 64,$$

using (3.3.6). It follows that

$$\text{Var }[Y^2(f)] = 48,$$

$$E[A_{12}^2(f)] = \left(\frac{\sigma_1^2 \sigma_2^2}{4}\right) E[Y^2(f)] = \sigma_1^2 \sigma_2^2, \qquad (9.1.9)$$

and

$$\text{Var }[A_{12}^2(f)] = \left(\frac{\sigma_1^4 \sigma_2^4}{16}\right) \text{Var }[Y^2(f)] = 3\sigma_1^4 \sigma_2^4.$$

Note that whereas the variance of the sample spectrum is equal to the square of its mean, the variance of the sample cross amplitude spectrum is three times the square of its mean. The increase in variance is due to the fact that variability is now being introduced by two processes rather than one.

Distribution of the sample phase spectral estimator. Using (9.1.3) and (9.1.4) the sample phase spectral estimator is

$$F_{12}(f) = \arctan\left\{-\frac{Q_{12}(f)}{L_{12}(f)}\right\}$$

$$= \arctan\left\{-\frac{B_2 A_1 - B_1 A_2}{A_1 A_2 + B_1 B_2}\right\}.$$

Now consider the random variable $L_{12}(f)$. The rv's A_i, B_i are Normally distributed, so that the range of the rv $A_1 A_2 + B_1 B_2$ extends from $-\infty$ to $+\infty$ and hence it is reasonable to approximate its distribution by a Normal distribution. Similar considerations apply for the rv $Q_{12}(f)$. Thus $L_{12}(f)$, $Q_{12}(f)$ are approximately Normally and independently distributed and have the same variance. Hence $F_{12}(f)$ is approximately uniformly distributed in the range $-\pi/2$ to $\pi/2$. These results will be used in the next section to derive a test for correlation between two time series.

9.1.2 A test for correlation between time series

Situations often arise where it is required to test whether two time series are correlated or uncorrelated. For example, it may be necessary to test whether two control variables are correlated, or whether the residuals are correlated after a suitable model has been fitted to two economic time series. The results of Section 8.2.2 show that, provided both time series have been prefiltered to convert them to white noise, the sample ccf of the filtered series can be used to test whether the two series are correlated. However, the ccf is useful only in detecting certain types of correlation. For instance, if neighboring points in two time series are cross correlated, it would be expected that the ccf will be large in the neighborhood of the origin and small at values distant from the origin. On the other hand, if there is a tendency for the ccf to contain periodic components, these may not be detected using the ccf. Hence it is necessary to develop a frequency-domain test for correlation between time series which is a generalization of the test for white noise given in Section 6.3.2. This frequency-domain test should be used in conjunction with the test based on the ccf.

Choice of test criteria. The discussion in Section 8.4.4 suggests that the sample coherency spectrum $K_{12}^2(f)$ and the sample phase spectrum $F_{12}(f)$ could be used as the basis for a frequency-domain test for correlation between time series. However, it is noted that

$$K_{12}^2(f) = \frac{|C_{12}(f)|^2}{C_{11}(f)C_{22}(f)} = \frac{\left|\dfrac{X_1^*(f)X_2(f)}{T}\right|^2}{\dfrac{|X_1(f)|^2}{T}\dfrac{|X_2(f)|^2}{T}} = 1.$$

Thus the sample coherency spectrum is identically equal to unity regardless of the nature of the bivariate stochastic process. Hence an alternative approach is required, based on the integrated sample co-spectrum and the sample phase spectrum. These two criteria focus attention on two different aspects of the cross correlation between the two processes.

(1) The integrated sample co-spectrum. Consider the integrated co-spectrum

$$J_{12}(f) = \int_{-f}^{f} \Lambda_{12}(g)\, dg,$$

which measures the total in-phase covariance between the two processes for all frequencies less than f. Then an estimator of $J_{12}(f)$ is given by the sample integrated co-spectrum

$$\frac{1}{N\Delta} \sum_{i=0}^{k} L_{12}(f_i), \quad f_i = \frac{2i}{N}.$$

However, it is more convenient to use the normalized estimator

$$\hat{J}_{12}(f_k) = \frac{2}{NS_1S_2\Delta} \sum_{i=0}^{k} L_{12}(f_i), \tag{9.1.10}$$

where S_1, S_2 are the estimators of the standard deviations of the two processes. If the two processes are uncorrelated, then $\Lambda_{12}(f)$ is identically zero and hence $J_{12}(f_k)$ is identically zero, but if the two processes are correlated,

$J_{12}(f)$ takes on non-zero values. Using (8.3.16), the normalization in (9.1.10) ensures that $\hat{J}_{12}(f_k) = r_{12}(0)$ when $f_k = 1/2\Delta$ cps.

Figure 9.1 shows the estimate corresponding to (9.1.10) for samples of $N = 100$ from three bivariate Normal processes. These processes were of the form

$$X_{1t} = Z_{1t} + aZ_{2t},$$
$$X_{2t} = aZ_{1t} + Z_{2t},$$

with Z_1, Z_2 random Normal deviates and $a = 0, 0.1$ and 0.3. Thus the cross correlations are zero for all non-zero lags, but $\rho_{12}(0) = 0, 0.20$ and 0.55 respectively for the three cases. Figure 9.1 shows that when $\rho_{12} = 0$ the integrated co-spectrum fluctuates about zero and indicates no correlation between the two processes. When $\rho_{12} = 0.20$, the integrated spectrum rises

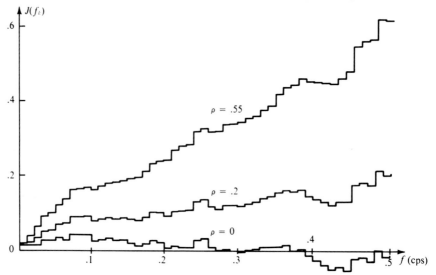

FIG. 9.1: Sample integrated co-spectra for three bivariate correlated series

steadily to the value 0.20 at $f = 0.5$ cps and shows clear evidence of correlation. Since $\hat{J}(1/2\Delta) = \hat{r}_{12}(0)$, the value of 0.20 at $f = 0.5$ cps provides an excellent estimate of $\rho_{12}(0)$, which is known to be 0.20. The curve for $\rho_{12} = 0.55$ shows that there is marked correlation between the two series. Thus the behavior of the three curves in Figure 9.1 confirms that the test is a sensitive indicator of correlation between time series. The value of the sample co- and quadrature spectra when $\rho = 0$ are given in Table 9.1 and could be used by the reader to generate the integrated co-spectrum of Figure 9.1.

(2) *The phase spectrum.* Another indication of the correlation between two time series is provided by the phase spectral estimator $F_{12}(f)$. It was shown in Section 9.1.1 that if the two processes are uncorrelated, the sample

TABLE 9.1: Sample co- and quadrature spectra for two uncorrelated
white noise processes

f_k	$L_{12}(f_k)$	$Q_{12}(f_k)$	$F_{12}(f_k)$	f_k	$L_{12}(f_k)$	$Q_{12}(f_k)$	$F_{12}(f_k)$
0.01	0.08	1.53	1.52	0.26	-1.20	-0.47	0.39
0.02	0.03	-1.44	-1.35	0.27	-0.38	0.08	-0.22
0.03	0.71	-0.67	-0.75	0.28	0.22	1.24	1.40
0.04	-0.10	-0.78	1.44	0.29	-0.21	0.05	-0.22
0.05	-0.39	-1.17	-1.25	0.30	-0.15	-0.45	1.25
0.06	-0.19	0.38	-1.10	0.31	0.26	0.08	0.32
0.07	0.63	0.81	0.91	0.32	0.12	-0.14	-0.89
0.08	0.00	-0.04	1.47	0.33	0.37	-0.52	-0.96
0.09	-0.03	0.28	-1.47	0.34	0.02	-0.48	-1.54
0.10	-0.79	-0.15	0.19	0.35	0.01	1.11	1.56
0.11	0.17	0.43	1.19	0.36	0.16	-0.60	-1.32
0.12	-0.15	-0.35	-1.17	0.37	-0.86	-0.54	0.56
0.13	-0.27	0.18	-0.57	0.38	0.39	0.31	0.67
0.14	0.09	-0.16	-1.09	0.39	-1.05	0.29	-0.27
0.15	-0.40	0.79	-1.10	0.40	-0.63	0.78	-0.89
0.16	-0.42	0.78	-1.08	0.41	-0.50	-0.45	0.73
0.17	0.21	0.31	0.97	0.42	-0.53	0.18	-0.32
0.18	0.49	0.04	0.08	0.43	0.23	0.03	0.11
0.19	-0.15	-0.76	1.38	0.44	-0.41	2.42	-1.40
0.20	-0.79	1.19	-0.98	0.45	1.71	-1.00	-0.53
0.21	0.23	1.49	1.42	0.46	0.04	1.23	1.54
0.22	-0.08	-0.31	1.31	0.47	-0.52	-0.25	0.45
0.23	0.02	0.04	1.06	0.48	1.39	1.36	0.77
0.24	0.90	0.61	0.60	0.49	-0.67	0.08	-0.12
0.25	0.21	0.21	0.78	0.50	0.10	-0.91	0.00

phase spectrum will be approximately uniformly distributed in the range $-\pi/2$, $\pi/2$. Hence the cumulative distribution function of the phase angle will be a straight line in this range.

The numerical values of the phase estimates for the two white noise series with $\rho = 0$ are shown in Table 9.1 alongside the co- and quadrature spectral estimates. The sample cdf of the phase estimates is shown in Figure 9.2, and it is seen that there is good agreement between the actual and theoretical cdf. To guide the eye in deciding whether deviations from linearity are real, 95% confidence limits can be inserted at distances $\pm 1.36/\sqrt{N/2}$ and 75% limits at $\pm 1.02/\sqrt{N/2}$ from the theoretical cdf.

It is seen that the empirical cdf lies well within these limits when $\rho_{12} = 0$. When $\rho_{12} = 0.20$ and 0.55, the cumulative sample phase spectra also lie near the theoretical straight line. Thus when $\rho_{12} = 0$, both the integrated sample co-spectrum and the phase spectrum tests show no evidence of correlation. When $\rho_{12} = 0.20$ and 0.55, the co-spectrum test shows evidence of correlation but the phase spectrum test does not, confirming that the theoretical phase spectrum is zero. In general, of course, a correlated bivariate process would have a non-zero co-spectrum and a non-zero phase spectrum and hence a realization of such a series would be expected to "fail" both the integrated co-spectrum and phase spectrum tests.

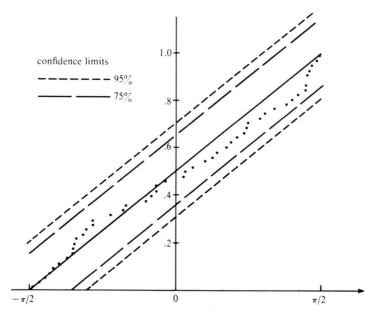

FIG. 9.2: Sample integrated phase spectrum for a bivariate series

9.1.3 General moment properties of sample cross spectral estimators

In this section the results of Section 9.1.1 are generalized to include correlated non-white noise processes. The precise derivation of these results is complicated and is given in Appendix A9.1. The methods used in this section are heuristic and are generalizations of the methods used for univariate spectra in Section 6.4.1.

The computation of the covariance matrix of $C_{11}(f)$, $C_{22}(f)$, $L_{12}(f)$ and $Q_{12}(f)$ for correlated non-Normal processes proceeds in three stages. First, the matrix of covariances between these estimators at two distinct frequencies is evaluated for uncorrelated, non-Normal white noise processes. Then the covariance matrix of $C_{11}(f)$, $C_{22}(f)$, $C_{12}(f)$, $C_{21}(f)$ may be determined. Finally, the values of $C_{11}(f)$, $C_{22}(f)$, $C_{12}(f)$, $C_{21}(f)$ for any bivariate process may be expressed in terms of $C_{11}(f)$, $C_{22}(f)$, $C_{12}(f)$ and $C_{21}(f)$ for uncorrelated white noise processes. Using the covariance matrix derived in the second step, the covariance matrix of the general process may then be calculated.

Generalized covariance matrix of cross spectral estimators for uncorrelated white noises. The results of Section 9.1.1 were derived for the *harmonic frequencies* $f_m = m/T$ for uncorrelated *Normal* white noise processes. In Appendix A9.1 more general results are derived which apply for *all frequencies* and for uncorrelated *non-Normal white* noise processes. These results show that

$$E[L_{12}(f)] = \Lambda_{12}(f) = 0,$$
$$E[Q_{12}(f)] = \Psi_{12}(f) = 0. \tag{9.1.11}$$

Further, the matrix

$$\begin{pmatrix} W_0 K_4^{(1)} + \sigma_1^4 \{ W^2(-) + W^2(+) \} & 0 & 0 & 0 \\ 0 & W_0 K_4^{(2)} + \sigma_2^4 \{ W^2(-) + W^2(+) \} & 0 & 0 \\ 0 & 0 & \frac{\sigma_1^2 \sigma_2^2}{2} \{ W^2(-) + W^2(+) \} & 0 \\ 0 & 0 & 0 & \frac{\sigma_1^2 \sigma_2^2}{2} \{ W^2(-) + W^2(+) \} \end{pmatrix}$$

$$\tag{9.1.12}$$

gives the covariances between the estimators $C_{11}(f)$, $C_{22}(f)$, $L_{12}(f)$, $Q_{12}(f)$ at two adjacent frequencies f_1 and f_2. For example, the element in the first row and the first column is Cov $[C_{11}(f_1), C_{11}(f_2)]$, the element in the first row and second column is Cov $[C_{11}(f_1), C_{22}(f_2)]$ and so on. The matrix (9.1.12) is called the *generalized covariance matrix* of the estimators. When $f_1 = f_2 = f$, this reduces to the ordinary covariance matrix between $C_{11}(f)$, $C_{22}(f)$, $L_{12}(f)$ and $Q_{12}(f)$. In (9.1.12), $W_0 = \Delta^2/N$, and

$$W(-) = \frac{\Delta \sin \pi N \Delta (f_1 - f_2)}{N \sin \pi \Delta (f_1 - f_2)}, \quad W(+) = \frac{\Delta \sin \pi N \Delta (f_1 + f_2)}{N \sin \pi \Delta (f_1 + f_2)} \tag{9.1.13}$$

for discrete processes. Similarly, $W_0 = 1/T$ and

$$W(-) = \frac{\sin \pi T (f_1 - f_2)}{\pi T (f_1 - f_2)}, \quad W(+) = \frac{\sin \pi T (f_1 + f_2)}{\pi T (f_1 + f_2)} \tag{9.1.14}$$

in the continuous case. $K_4^{(1)}$ and $K_4^{(2)}$ are the fourth cumulants of the white noise processes $Z_1(t)$ and $Z_2(t)$ respectively. The fourth cumulants vanish if the $Z_i(t)$ are Normal.

The matrix (9.1.12) shows that the spectral estimators are uncorrelated with the other spectral estimators at the same or adjacent frequencies. Furthermore, they are uncorrelated with themselves for sufficiently wide frequency spacing. Note that when $f_1 = f_2$, the variances of the estimators are constants which do not depend on T, the length of the record. Hence, cross spectral estimators show the same bad behavior as autospectral estimators. Note also that the covariances of the co- and quadrature spectra do not involve fourth cumulant terms, so the covariances of the co- and quadrature spectra are always of order $1/T^2$ for $(f_1 - f_2)$ large.

Generalized covariance matrix of $C_{11}(f)$, $C_{22}(f)$, $C_{12}(f)$, $C_{21}(f)$. Since

$$C_{12}(f) = L_{12}(f) - jQ_{12}(f),$$
$$C_{21}(f) = L_{12}(f) + jQ_{12}(f),$$

the covariance matrix of C_{11}, C_{22}, C_{12} and C_{21} is readily derived from the matrix (9.1.12). For example, using elements of (9.1.12),

$$\begin{aligned}
\text{Cov}\,[C_{12}(f_1), C_{21}(f_2)] &= E[(L_2(f_1) - jQ_{12}(f_1))(L_{12}(f_2) + jQ_{12}(f_2))] \\
&= \text{Cov}\,[L_{12}(f_1), L_{12}(f_2)] + \text{Cov}\,[Q_{12}(f_1), Q_{12}(f_2)] \\
&= \sigma_1^2 \sigma_2^2 W^2(-).
\end{aligned}$$

The final result for the generalized covariance matrix of $C_{11}(f)$, $C_{22}(f)$, $C_{12}(f)$, $C_{21}(f)$ is

$$\begin{pmatrix}
W_0 K_4^{(1)} \\ + \sigma_1^4 \{W^2(-) + W^2(+)\} & 0 & 0 & 0 \\[2mm]
0 & \begin{matrix} W_0 K_4^{(2)} \\ + \sigma_2^4 \{W^2(-) + W^2(+)\} \end{matrix} & 0 & 0 \\[2mm]
0 & 0 & \sigma_1^2 \sigma_2^2 W^2(+) & \sigma_1^2 \sigma_2^2 W^2(-) \\[2mm]
0 & 0 & \sigma_1^2 \sigma_2^2 W^2(-) & \sigma_1^2 \sigma_2^2 W^2(+)
\end{pmatrix}$$

$$(9.1.15)$$

which will now be used to derive the covariance matrix of the cross spectral estimators for non-white noise processes. Note that unless f_1 and f_2 are very close to one another, all the covariances are approximately zero.

Generalized covariance matrix of cross spectral estimators for general processes. Use is now made of the result given in Section 8.1.4 that any bivariate stochastic process with power spectra $\Gamma_{11}(f)$, $\Gamma_{22}(f)$, $\Gamma_{12}(f)$ can be generated by passing two white noise sources through a lattice network of four linear systems. Thus, on taking Fourier transforms of the equations (8.1.14) and using the same approximations as in (6.4.3),

$$X_1(f) \approx H_{11}(f)Z_{1T}(f) + H_{12}(f)Z_{2T}(f),$$
$$X_2(f) \approx H_{21}(f)Z_{1T}(f) + H_{22}(f)Z_{2T}(f),$$

where $Z_{iT}(f)$ is the Fourier transform of $Z_i(t)$ over $-T/2 \leqslant t \leqslant T/2$. Hence

$$\begin{aligned}
C_{11}(f) &\approx |H_{11}(f)|^2 C_{Z_1 Z_1}(f) + |H_{12}(f)|^2 C_{Z_2 Z_2}(f) \\
&\quad + H_{11}^*(f)H_{12}(f)C_{Z_1 Z_2}(f) + H_{11}(f)H_{12}^*(f)C_{Z_2 Z_1}(f), \quad (9.1.16)
\end{aligned}$$

$$\begin{aligned}
C_{22}(f) &\approx |H_{21}(f)|^2 C_{Z_1 Z_1}(f) + |H_{22}(f)|^2 C_{Z_2 Z_2}(f) \\
&\quad + H_{21}^*(f)H_{22}(f)C_{Z_1 Z_2}(f) + H_{21}(f)H_{22}^*(f)C_{Z_2 Z_1}(f), \quad (9.1.17)
\end{aligned}$$

$$\begin{aligned}
C_{12}(f) &\approx H_{11}^*(f)H_{21}(f)C_{Z_1 Z_1}(f) + H_{12}^*(f)H_{22}(f)C_{Z_2 Z_2}(f) \\
&\quad + H_{11}^*(f)H_{22}(f)C_{Z_1 Z_2}(f) + H_{12}^*(f)H_{21}(f)C_{Z_2 Z_1}(f). \quad (9.1.18)
\end{aligned}$$

Hence, from (8.4.17),

$$E[C_{11}(f)] \approx |H_{11}(f)|^2\sigma_1^2 + |H_{12}(f)|^2\sigma_2^2$$
$$= \Gamma_{11}(f), \tag{9.1.19}$$

$$E[C_{22}(f)] \approx |H_{21}(f)|^2\sigma_1^2 + |H_{22}(f)|^2\sigma_2^2$$
$$= \Gamma_{22}(f), \tag{9.1.20}$$

$$E[C_{12}(f)] \approx H_{11}^*(f)H_{21}(f)\sigma_1^2 + H_{12}^*(f)H_{22}(f)\sigma_2^2$$
$$= \Gamma_{12}(f). \tag{9.1.21}$$

The covariance matrix for the $C_{ij}(f)$ is readily obtained from the definitions (9.1.16–18) and the covariance matrix (9.1.15). For example, using (9.1.16) and (9.1.17) and remembering that the covariance matrix is approximately zero unless $f_1 \approx f_2$,

$$\begin{aligned}
\text{Cov}\,[C_{11}(f_1),\,C_{22}(f_2)] \approx\; & |H_{11}(f_1)|^2|H_{21}(f_2)|^2\sigma_1^4\{W^2(-) + W^2(+)\} \\
& + |H_{12}(f_1)|^2|H_{22}(f_2)|^2\sigma_2^4\{W^2(-) + W^2(+)\} \\
& + H_{11}^*(f_1)H_{12}(f_1)H_{21}^*(f_2)H_{22}(f_2)\sigma_1^2\sigma_2^2 W^2(+) \\
& + H_{11}^*(f_1)H_{12}(f_1)H_{21}(f_2)H_{22}^*(f_2)\sigma_1^2\sigma_2^2 W^2(-) \\
& + H_{11}(f_1)H_{12}^*(f_1)H_{21}^*(f_2)H_{22}(f_2)\sigma_1^2\sigma_2^2 W^2(-) \\
& + H_{11}(f_1)H_{12}^*(f_1)H_{21}(f_2)H_{22}^*(f_2)\sigma_1^2\sigma_2^2 W^2(+).
\end{aligned}$$

The $W^2(+)$ terms are small compared to the $W^2(-)$ terms and may be neglected. Thus, making the approximation $H_{ij}(f_2) \approx H_{ij}(f_1)$ for $f_1 \approx f_2$ and writing $H_{ij}(f_1)$ as H_{ij} gives

$$\begin{aligned}
\text{Cov}\,[C_{11}(f_1),\,C_{11}(f_2)] \approx\; & \{|H_{11}|^2|H_{21}|^2\sigma_1^4 + |H_{12}|^2|H_{22}|^2\sigma_2^4 \\
& + (H_{11}^*H_{12}H_{21}H_{22}^* + H_{11}H_{12}^*H_{21}^*H_{22})\sigma_1^2\sigma_2^2\}W^2(-) \\
=\; & |\Gamma_{12}(f_1)|^2 W^2(-).
\end{aligned}$$

Therefore, on dropping the dependence on f, the generalized covariance matrix of C_{11}, C_{22}, L_{12} and Q_{12} at frequencies f_1 and f_2 for a general process is

$$W^2(-)\begin{pmatrix}
\Gamma_{11}^2 & |\Gamma_{12}|^2 & \Gamma_{11}\Lambda_{12} & \Gamma_{11}\Psi_{12} \\
|\Gamma_{12}|^2 & \Gamma_{22}^2 & \Gamma_{22}\Lambda_{12} & \Gamma_{22}\Psi_{12} \\
\Gamma_{11}\Lambda_{12} & \Gamma_{22}\Lambda_{12} & \tfrac{1}{2}\{\Gamma_{11}\Gamma_{22} + \Lambda_{12}^2 - \Psi_{12}^2\} & \Lambda_{12}\Psi_{12} \\
\Gamma_{11}\Psi_{12} & \Gamma_{22}\Psi_{12} & \Lambda_{12}\Psi_{12} & \tfrac{1}{2}\{\Gamma_{11}\Gamma_{22} - \Lambda_{12}^2 + \Psi_{12}^2\}
\end{pmatrix}$$

$$\tag{9.1.22}$$

The matrix (9.1.22) was given in [1] and [2] and is applicable for $||f_1| - |f_2||$ very small. For frequency differences greater than $1/T$ the covariances are approximately zero. A more rigorous derivation of these results is given in Appendix A9.1. Note for future reference that for T very large, $W^2(-)$ tends to $(1/T)\,\delta(f_1 - f_2)$ in the continuous case, and to $(1/N\Delta)\,\delta(f_1 - f_2)$ in the discrete case.

9.2 PROPERTIES OF SMOOTHED CROSS SPECTRAL ESTIMATORS

9.2.1 Smoothed cross spectral estimators

It was shown in Section 9.1.3 that the estimators of the sample cross spectrum have the same undesirable properties as the sample spectrum, namely that their variances are dominated by a constant term which does not tend to zero as the record length increases. Hence cross spectral estimators must be smoothed using a spectral window just as it was necessary to smooth auto-spectral estimators.

The smoothed cross spectral estimator is defined by

$$\bar{C}_{12}(f) = \int_{-T}^{T} w(u) c_{12}(u)\, e^{-j2\pi fu}\, du, \tag{9.2.1}$$

where the lag window $w(u)$ has the usual properties (6.3.29). Writing $c_{12}(u)$ in terms of the even and odd parts (8.3.19, 20) gives

$$\bar{C}_{12}(f) = \int_{-T}^{T} w(u) l_{12}(u) \cos 2\pi fu\, du - j \int_{-T}^{T} w(u) q_{12}(u) \sin 2\pi fu\, du$$

$$= \bar{L}_{12}(f) - j\bar{Q}_{12}(f), \tag{9.2.2}$$

where $\bar{L}_{12}(f)$ and $\bar{Q}_{12}(f)$ are the smoothed co- and quadrature spectral estimators.

Expected value of the smoothed cross spectral estimator. The sample cross spectral estimator $C_{12}(f)$ is defined by

$$C_{12}(f) = \int_{-T}^{T} c_{12}(u)\, e^{-j2\pi fu}\, du.$$

From (8.3.21) this has expected value

$$E[C_{12}(f)] = \int_{-T}^{T} \left(1 - \frac{|u|}{T}\right) \gamma_{12}(u)\, e^{-j2\pi fu}\, du,$$

which may be written

$$E[C_{12}(f)] = \int_{-\infty}^{\infty} T \left(\frac{\sin \pi Tg}{\pi Tg}\right)^2 \Gamma_{12}(f - g)\, dg \approx \Gamma_{12}(f). \tag{9.2.3}$$

Equation (9.2.3) follows from the fact that when T is sufficiently large, the spectral window is very narrow. Thus to a good approximation, $C_{12}(f)$ is approximately an unbiased estimator of $\Gamma_{12}(f)$. On taking expectations in

(9.2.1) and using (8.3.21) and (9.2.3), the mean of the smoothed cross spectral estimator is

$$E[\bar{C}_{12}(f)] = \int_{-T}^{T} w(u)\left(1 - \frac{|u|}{T}\right)\gamma_{12}(u)\, e^{-j2\pi fu}\, du$$

$$\approx \int_{-\infty}^{\infty} W(g)\Gamma_{12}(f - g)\, dg$$

$$= \bar{\Gamma}_{12}(f). \qquad (9.2.4)$$

$\bar{\Gamma}_{12}(f)$ will be called the *mean smoothed cross spectrum*. Since $E[\bar{C}_{12}(f)] = E[\bar{L}_{12}(f)] - jE[\bar{Q}_{12}(f)]$, it follows that the mean smoothed co- and quadrature spectra are

$$E[\bar{L}_{12}(f)] = \int_{-T}^{T} w(u)\left(1 - \frac{|u|}{T}\right)\lambda_{12}(u)\cos 2\pi fu\, du$$

$$\approx \int_{-\infty}^{\infty} W(g)\Lambda_{12}(f - g)\, dg$$

$$= \bar{\Lambda}_{12}(f) \qquad (9.2.5)$$

and

$$E[\bar{Q}_{12}(f)] = \int_{-T}^{T} w(u)\left(1 - \frac{|u|}{T}\right)\psi_{12}(u)\sin 2\pi fu\, du$$

$$\approx \int_{-\infty}^{\infty} W(g)\Psi_{12}(f - g)\, dg$$

$$= \bar{\Psi}_{12}(f). \qquad (9.2.6)$$

In form, (9.2.4–6) are similar to (6.3.35) and (6.3.37) for the expected value of the auto-spectral estimator. However, there is an important difference in that the autocovariance function $\gamma_{11}(u)$ in (6.3.37) is symmetric about the origin. Hence, provided $|\gamma_{11}(u)|$ tends to zero fairly quickly, the bias $B_{11}(f) = \bar{\Gamma}_{11}(f) - \Gamma_{11}(f)$ can be expected to tend to zero quickly as the truncation point M of the lag window is increased. The situation is different for the cross spectral estimator since the cross correlation function is not symmetrical about zero. Thus in an extreme case where one process is an exact copy of the other process but delayed by an amount τ, the cross correlation function will be identical to the autocorrelation function but centered at lag τ instead of zero. The effect on (9.2.4) for the mean value of the cross spectral estimator is that there will be appreciable bias if the truncation point M is less than the delay τ. Furthermore if τ is large, the numerical value of the lag window $w(u)$ will be small when $u = \tau$, and hence very large truncation points may be necessary in order to reduce the bias to a reasonable size. This effect will be demonstrated in Section 9.3, where it will be shown that the trouble can be remedied by *aligning* the two series to ensure that the cross correlation function has a maximum in the neighborhood of zero lag.

Covariance matrix of smoothed cross spectral estimators. Using the convolution property (A2.1.8), the smoothed cross spectral estimator (9.2.1) may be written in the alternative form

$$\bar{C}_{12}(f) = \int_{-\infty}^{\infty} C_{12}(f - g)W(g)\, dg. \tag{9.2.7}$$

Hence

$$\text{Cov}\,[\bar{C}_{ij}(f_1),\, \bar{C}_{kl}(f_2)]$$

$$= \int_{-\infty}^{\infty} \int_{-\infty}^{\infty} \text{Cov}\,[C_{ij}(f_1 - g),\, C_{kl}(f_2 - h)]W(g)W(h)\, dg\, dh. \tag{9.2.8}$$

Using the covariance matrix (9.1.22), the covariance matrix for the smoothed spectral estimators may be derived. For example, when T is large, (9.1.22) shows that

$$\text{Cov}\,[C_{11}(f_1),\, C_{22}(f_2)] \approx |\Gamma_{12}(f_1)|^2 \frac{\delta(f_1 - f_2)}{T}.$$

Hence

$$\text{Cov}\,[\bar{C}_{11}(f_1),\, \bar{C}_{22}(f_2)]$$

$$\approx \int_{-\infty}^{\infty} \int_{-\infty}^{\infty} |\Gamma_{12}(f_1 - g)|^2 \frac{\delta(f_1 - f_2 - g + h)}{T} W(g)W(h)\, dg\, dh$$

$$= \int_{-\infty}^{\infty} \frac{|\Gamma_{12}(f_1 - g)|^2}{T} W(g)W(f_2 + g - f_1)\, dg. \tag{9.2.9}$$

Making the assumption that $\Gamma_{12}(f)$ is approximately constant over the bandwidth of the spectral window and substituting $h = f_1 - g$ in (9.2.9) gives

$$\text{Cov}\,[\bar{C}_{11}(f_1),\, \bar{C}_{22}(f_2)] \approx \frac{|\Gamma_{12}(f_1)|^2}{T} \int_{-\infty}^{\infty} W(f_1 - h)W(f_2 - h)\, dh. \tag{9.2.10}$$

For $f_1 = f_2 = f$, (9.2.10) reduces to

$$\text{Cov}\,[\bar{C}_{11}(f),\, \bar{C}_{22}(f)] \approx \frac{|\Gamma_{12}(f)|^2}{T} \int_{-\infty}^{\infty} W^2(g)\, dg$$

$$= |\Gamma_{12}(f)|^2 \frac{I}{T}, \tag{9.2.11}$$

using (6.4.13). Similar results are obtained for the other spectral estimators.

Thus the effect of smoothing is to reduce the variances and the covariances of the unsmoothed estimators by the factor I/T. Hence the covariance matrix of the smoothed estimators is obtained by multiplying the covariance matrix (9.1.22) of the sample estimators by I/T instead of by $W^2(-)$. A more precise derivation of these results is given in Appendix A9.1.

The above covariance matrix is not of direct interest but is required as an intermediate stage in the computation of the covariance matrix of the smoothed cross amplitude, squared coherency and phase spectral estimators. This matrix is derived in the next section.

9.2.2 Smoothed cross amplitude, squared coherency and phase estimators

As shown in Section 8.4.4, the correlation between two stochastic processes can be described in the frequency domain by their cross amplitude and phase spectra, or more usefully by their squared coherency and phase spectra.

There are several ways in which smoothed estimators of these spectra may be defined. One simple way is to substitute the smoothed estimators of the co- and quadrature spectra into the expressions for the theoretical spectra. Thus, using (8.3.28), the smoothed cross amplitude estimator is defined by

$$\bar{A}_{12}(f) = \sqrt{\bar{L}_{12}^2(f) + \bar{Q}_{12}^2(f)}. \tag{9.2.12}$$

Similarly, using (8.3.29), the smoothed phase spectral estimator is defined by

$$\bar{F}_{12}(f) = \arctan\left(-\frac{\bar{Q}_{12}(f)}{\bar{L}_{12}(f)}\right). \tag{9.2.13}$$

Finally, using (8.4.18), the smoothed squared coherency estimator is defined by

$$\bar{K}_{12}^2(f) = \frac{\bar{L}_{12}^2(f) + \bar{Q}_{12}^2(f)}{\bar{C}_{11}(f)\bar{C}_{22}(f)}. \tag{9.2.14}$$

Note that even if $\bar{L}_{12}(f)$ and $\bar{Q}_{12}(f)$ were unbiased estimators, the estimators (9.2.12–14) would be biased. However, the bias produced in this way will be small compared with the bias produced by truncation of the cross correlation function and by the fact that it is not symmetrical about zero, and hence it is unlikely to inflate the mean square error. Since all the estimators are non-linear functions of the estimators $\bar{L}_{12}(f)$, $\bar{Q}_{12}(f)$, $\bar{C}_{11}(f)$, $\bar{C}_{22}(f)$, their moments can be derived by expanding in the form of a Taylor series as shown in Section 3.2.5 and in [2]. As an example, the mean and variance of the smoothed cross amplitude estimator (9.2.12) are derived.

For convenience, the dependence on frequency is dropped so that (9.2.12) may be written

$$\bar{A}_{12} = \sqrt{\bar{L}_{12}^2 + \bar{Q}_{12}^2}.$$

Now consider small perturbations $\delta\bar{L}_{12}$ and $\delta\bar{Q}_{12}$ about the expected values $E[\bar{L}_{12}] = \Lambda_{12}$, $E[\bar{Q}_{12}] = \psi_{12}$ so that

$$\bar{L}_{12} = \Lambda_{12} + \delta\bar{L}_{12},$$
$$\bar{Q}_{12} = \Psi_{12} + \delta\bar{Q}_{12},$$
$$E[\delta\bar{L}_{12}] = 0 = E[\delta\bar{Q}_{12}].$$

Similarly,

$$E[\delta \bar{L}_{12}^2] = \text{Var}\,[\bar{L}_{12}],$$
$$E[\delta \bar{Q}_{12}^2] = \text{Var}\,[\bar{Q}_{12}],$$
$$E[\overline{\delta L_{12}\, \delta Q_{12}}] = \text{Cov}\,[\bar{L}_{12},\, \bar{Q}_{12}].$$

On expanding (9.2.12) in the form of a Taylor series,

$$\bar{A}_{12} = \sqrt{(\Lambda_{12} + \delta \bar{L}_{12})^2 + (\Psi_{12} + \delta \bar{Q}_{12})^2}$$
$$\approx \alpha_{12}\left(1 + \frac{\Lambda_{12}\,\delta \bar{L}_{12} + \Psi_{12}\,\delta \bar{Q}_{12}}{\alpha_{12}^2}\right).$$

Hence

$$E[\bar{A}_{12}] \approx \alpha_{12}, \tag{9.2.15}$$

$$\text{Var}\,[\bar{A}_{12}] \approx \frac{\Lambda_{12}^2\,\text{Var}\,[\bar{L}_{12}] + \Psi_{12}^2\,\text{Var}\,[\bar{Q}_{12}] + 2\Lambda_{12}\Psi_{12}\,\text{Cov}\,[\bar{L}_{12},\, \bar{Q}_{12}]}{\alpha_{12}^2}. \tag{9.2.16}$$

From the covariance matrix (9.1.22), with $W^2(-)$ replaced by I/T,

$$\text{Var}\,[\bar{L}_{12}] \approx \frac{I}{2T}\{\Gamma_{11}\Gamma_{22} + \Lambda_{12}^2 - \Psi_{12}^2\},$$

$$\text{Var}\,[\bar{Q}_{12}] \approx \frac{I}{2T}\{\Gamma_{11}\Gamma_{22} - \Lambda_{12}^2 + \Psi_{12}^2\},$$

$$\text{Cov}\,[\bar{L}_{12},\, \bar{Q}_{12}] \approx \frac{I}{T}\Lambda_{12}\Psi_{12}.$$

Substituting these results in (9.2.16), the *variance for the smoothed cross amplitude estimator* is

$$\text{Var}\,[\bar{A}_{12}] \approx \frac{I}{2T}\alpha_{12}^2\left(1 + \frac{1}{\kappa_{12}^2}\right). \tag{9.2.17}$$

Note that when the X_1 and X_2 processes are identical, $\bar{A}_{12} = \bar{C}_{11}$, $\alpha_{12} = \Gamma_{11}$ and $\kappa_{12}^2 = 1$. Hence in this case (9.2.17) yields

$$\text{Var}\,[\bar{C}_{11}] \approx \frac{I}{T}\Gamma_{11}^2,$$

which is identical with the result (6.4.13) derived previously. Similar expressions may be derived for the covariances of the estimators $\bar{A}_{12}$, $\bar{F}_{12}$ and $\bar{K}_{12}^2$. These are:

Variance of smoothed coherency and squared coherency estimator

$$\text{Var}\,[|\bar{K}_{12}|] \approx \frac{I}{2T}(1 - \kappa_{12}^2)^2, \tag{9.2.18}$$

$$\text{Var}\,[\bar{K}_{12}^2] \approx \frac{I}{2T}4\kappa_{12}^2(1 - \kappa_{12}^2)^2. \tag{9.2.19}$$

Variance of smoothed phase estimator

$$\text{Var}\,[\bar{F}_{12}] \approx \frac{I}{2T}\left(\frac{1}{\kappa_{12}^2} - 1\right). \tag{9.2.20}$$

Note that this variance is independent of the theoretical phase function.

Covariance properties

$$\text{Cov}\,[\bar{F}_{12},\,\bar{A}_{12}] \approx 0,$$
$$\text{Cov}\,[\bar{F}_{12},\,\bar{K}_{12}^2] \approx 0. \tag{9.2.21}$$

The above results will be used in the next section to derive confidence intervals for the phase and coherency spectrum.

9.2.3 *Confidence intervals for squared coherency and phase spectra*

In this section some practical implications of the results of Section 9.2.2 are discussed and used to construct confidence intervals for coherency and phase spectra.

The results (9.2.17) to (9.2.20) show that the variances of these estimators depend on the *smoothing factor* I/T, which can be controlled by window closing, and the *coherency spectrum* $\kappa_{12}^2(f)$ of the two processes $X_1(t)$, $X_2(t)$.

They also show that in all cases, excluding (9.2.17), the variance of the estimator is zero when the coherency is unity and increases as the coherency tends to zero. In fact, the variances of the cross amplitude spectrum and phase spectrum estimators tend to infinity as the coherency tends to zero. This is to be expected, since a low coherency implies a large noise level and hence an inefficient estimate. Thus it is possible to make the important practical observation that the *sampling properties of the phase and cross amplitude estimators may be dominated by the uncontrollable influence of the coherency spectrum rather than by the controllable influence of the smoothing factor I/T.*

Confidence intervals for the coherency spectrum. The covariance property (9.2.21) shows that the phase and coherency estimators are uncorrelated, and hence it is permissible to derive confidence intervals for these spectra separately. Statisticians will recognize that, apart from the effect of smoothing, the variance (9.2.18) of $|\bar{K}_{12}(f)|$ is identical to the variance of an ordinary correlation coefficient. Hence R. A. Fisher's z-transformation [3] can be applied. Thus, using (3.2.28), the estimator

$$\bar{Y}_{12}(f) = \text{arctanh}\,[|\bar{K}_{12}|] = \frac{1}{2}\ln\frac{1 + |\bar{K}_{12}|}{1 - |\bar{K}_{12}|}$$

has a variance

$$\text{Var}\,[\bar{Y}_{12}(f)] \approx \frac{I}{2T}, \tag{9.2.22}$$

which is independent of frequency and which suggests that the estimate $\bar{Y}_{12}(f)$ should be plotted rather than the coherency itself, since the confidence interval can be represented by a constant interval on the Y scale.

To derive the confidence interval, it is reasonable to assume that the rv $\bar{Y}_{12}(f)$ is approximately Normal. Then an approximate $100(1 - \alpha)\%$ confidence interval for $\bar{Y}_{12}(f) = \text{arctanh } \kappa_{12}(f)$ is

$$\bar{y}_{12}(f) \pm \eta \left(1 - \frac{\alpha}{2}\right) \sqrt{\frac{I}{2T}}. \qquad (9.2.23)$$

For example, suppose that the observed coherency is $\bar{K}_{12}^2(f) = 0.64$ or $|K_{12}(f)| = 0.8$ and that $I/2T = 0.09$. Then $\bar{y}_{12}(f) = 1.099$ and the 95% confidence interval for arctanh $[\bar{\kappa}_{12}(f)]$ is $1.099 \pm 1.96 \sqrt{0.09} = 0.511, 1.687$.

On transforming back to the original scale, the 95% confidence limits for $\kappa_{12}^2(f)$ are $(0.22, 0.87)$. In practice it is better to plot the coherency on the Y scale and then insert the constant confidence interval (9.2.23) on this diagram. Examples of transformed coherencies and their confidence intervals will be given in Section 9.3.

Confidence intervals for the phase spectrum. It is more difficult to obtain an approximation to the distribution of the phase estimator than that of the coherency estimator. In [1] an accurate approximation to the distribution of this estimator is given, but it is unwieldy. However, it is possible to use the result (9.2.20) to obtain crude confidence intervals for the phase spectrum [2]. More precise joint confidence intervals for the gain and phase will be given in Chapter 10.

It was stated in Section 9.1.1 that if the true coherency is zero, the sample phase estimator is uniformly distributed in the range $(-\pi/2, \pi/2)$. Furthermore, (9.2.20) shows that the effect of smoothing is to reduce the variance of the phase estimator. Hence it is to be expected that smoothing will constrain the estimator to be concentrated in a much narrower band than $(-\pi/2, \pi/2)$. For simplicity, it is desirable to find a transformation such that the distribution of the transformed variable is approximately Normal. The transformation $\tan \bar{F}_{12}$ is suggested because the range of the transformed variable extends from $-\infty$ to $+\infty$. Using (9.2.20) and (3.2.26),

$$\text{Var } [\tan \bar{F}_{12}] \approx \sec^4 \phi \, \frac{I}{2T} \left(\frac{1}{\kappa_{12}^2} - 1\right). \qquad (9.2.24)$$

Hence on approximating the distribution of $\tan \bar{F}_{12}$ by a Normal distribution, approximate confidence intervals for $\tan \Phi_{12}$, with confidence coefficient $100(1 - \alpha)\%$, may be obtained from

$$\tan \bar{F}_{12}(f) \pm \eta \left(1 - \frac{\alpha}{2}\right) \sqrt{\sec^4 \phi \, \frac{I}{2T} \left(\frac{1}{\kappa_{12}^2} - 1\right)}. \qquad (9.2.25)$$

Note that since the true coherency is unknown, it must be replaced by its estimate in (9.2.24). Since (9.2.20) shows that the variance of $\bar{F}_{12}$ is independent of ϕ_{12}, it would be expected that the interval (9.2.25), when converted back to a confidence interval for ϕ_{12}, will be approximately independent of ϕ_{12}.

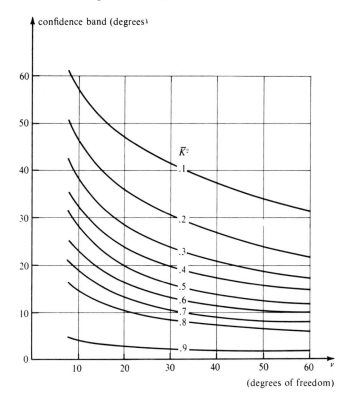

FIG. 9.3: 95% confidence limits for the phase spectrum

Figure 9.3 shows the 95% limits for various degrees of freedom of the spectral estimate. These values are adapted from [4]. For example, if $v = 27$ and $\bar{K}_{12}^2 = 0.5$, the confidence interval is $\bar{F} \pm 17°$.

9.3 CROSS SPECTRAL ANALYSIS USING SIMULATED SERIES

In this section the ideas introduced in the previous section are illustrated by comparing the smoothed phase and coherency spectral estimates of simulated series with their known theoretical phase and coherency spectra. The first section presents the formulae for digital computation of the smoothed estimates. Section 9.3.2 is intended to give the reader some experience in interpreting cross spectral estimates. It will then become clear that the procedures described up to the present require modification in order to produce satisfactory estimates. Section 9.3.3 shows that this can be achieved by *aligning* the two series, that is, moving one of the series relative to the other so that their cross correlation function has its maximum at zero lag.

9.3.1 *Discrete estimation formulae*

The formulae for the estimation of smoothed cross spectra using discrete data are similar to those for autospectra described in Section 7.1.1. As in Section 7.1.1, it is assumed that the data x_{1t}, x_{2t}, $t = 1, \ldots, N$, have been obtained by sampling at an interval of Δ seconds and that the spectral estimates are computed for *positive frequencies* only. For purposes of computation it is convenient to assume $\Delta = 1$ so that $0 \leqslant f \leqslant \frac{1}{2}$ cps. If $\Delta \neq 1$, the correct estimate can be recovered by multiplying the computed estimate by Δ and plotting the computed estimates in the range $0 \leqslant f \leqslant 1/2\Delta$ cps. As in Section 7.1.1, the number of covariance lags used in the spectral calculations is denoted by L. The smoothed spectral estimates are to be computed at the frequencies $0, 1/2F, \ldots, \frac{1}{2}$, where F is of the order of two or three times L. The lag window may be one of the three windows described in Section 7.1.1.

If trends are present, spurious coherencies may occur between the two series. In such cases, it is advisable to difference both series. As shown in Section 8.4.5, the differencing operation will not alter the theoretical coherency and phase spectra. In what follows, it is assumed that the covariances are either of the original or filtered data, as is appropriate in the given situation.

The formulae required and the order in which the computations are performed is as follows:

(1) For the x_{1t} data

(a) *The acvf estimate*

$$c_{11}(k) = \frac{1}{N} \sum_{t=1}^{N-k} (x_{1t} - \bar{x}_1)(x_{1t+k} - \bar{x}_1), \quad 0 \leqslant k \leqslant L - 1, \quad (9.3.1)$$

where $\bar{x}_1 = (1/N) \sum_{t=1}^{N} x_{1t}$.

(b) *The smoothed spectral estimate*

$$\bar{C}_{11}(i) = 2 \left\{ c_{11}(0) + 2 \sum_{k=1}^{L-1} c_{11}(k)w(k) \cos \frac{\pi ki}{F} \right\}, \quad 0 \leqslant i \leqslant F. \quad (9.3.2)$$

(2) For the x_{2t} data

(a) *The acvf estimate*

$$c_{22}(k) = \frac{1}{N} \sum_{t=1}^{N-k} (x_{2t} - \bar{x}_2)(x_{2t+k} - \bar{x}_2), \quad 0 \leqslant k \leqslant L - 1, \quad (9.3.3)$$

where $\bar{x}_2 = (1/N) \sum_{t=1}^{N} x_{2t}$.

(b) *The smoothed spectral estimate*

$$\bar{C}_{22}(i) = 2\left\{c_{22}(0) + 2\sum_{k=1}^{L-1} c_{22}(k)w(k)\cos\frac{\pi ki}{F}\right\}, \quad 0 \leqslant i \leqslant F. \quad (9.3.4)$$

(3) For the x_{1t} and x_{2t} data

(a) *The ccvf estimate*

$$c_{12}(k) = \frac{1}{N}\sum_{t=1}^{N-k}(x_{1t} - \bar{x}_1)(x_{2t+k} - \bar{x}_2), \quad 0 \leqslant k \leqslant L - 1,$$

$$c_{12}(-k) = \frac{1}{N}\sum_{t=1}^{N-k}(x_{1t+k} - \bar{x}_1)(x_{2t} - \bar{x}_2), \quad 0 \leqslant k \leqslant L - 1. \quad (9.3.5)$$

(b) *The even and odd ccvf estimates*

$$l_{12}(k) = \tfrac{1}{2}\{c_{12}(k) + c_{12}(-k)\}, \quad 0 \leqslant k \leqslant L - 1, \quad (9.3.6)$$

$$q_{12}(k) = \tfrac{1}{2}\{c_{12}(k) - c_{12}(-k)\}, \quad 0 \leqslant k \leqslant L - 1. \quad (9.3.7)$$

Note that $q_{12}(0) = 0$.

(c) *The smoothed co- and quadrature spectral estimates*

$$\bar{L}_{12}(i) = 2\left\{l_{12}(0) + 2\sum_{k=1}^{L-1} l_{12}(k)w(k)\cos\frac{\pi ik}{F}\right\}, \quad 0 \leqslant i \leqslant F, \quad (9.3.8)$$

$$\bar{Q}_{12}(i) = 4\sum_{k=1}^{L-1} q_{12}(k)w(k)\sin\frac{\pi ik}{F}, \quad 1 \leqslant i \leqslant F - 1, \quad (9.3.9)$$

$$\bar{Q}_{12}(0) = \bar{Q}_{12}(F) = 0.$$

(d) *The smoothed cross amplitude spectral estimate*

$$\bar{A}_{12}(i) = \sqrt{\bar{L}_{12}^2(i) + \bar{Q}_{12}^2(i)}, \quad 0 \leqslant i \leqslant F. \quad (9.3.10)$$

(e) *The smoothed phase spectral estimate*

$$\bar{F}_{12}(i) = \arctan - \frac{\bar{Q}_{12}(i)}{\bar{L}_{12}(i)}, \quad 0 \leqslant i \leqslant F. \quad (9.3.11)$$

(f) *The smoothed squared coherency spectral estimate*

$$\bar{K}_{12}^2(i) = \frac{\bar{A}_{12}^2(i)}{\bar{C}_{11}(i)\bar{C}_{22}(i)}, \quad 0 \leqslant i \leqslant F. \quad (9.3.12)$$

The factor 2 in equations (9.3.2, 4, 8, 9) is to preserve the Fourier transform relationship between the sample spectra and the sample covariances, as in Section 7.1.1. Appendix A9.2 gives a flow chart for bivariate spectral calculations.

Normalization. It is sometimes useful, when correlating two time series with different scales of measurement, to normalize the above quantities so that *correlation* estimates and spectral *density* estimates are obtained. The formulae are identical to those quoted above, with covariances replaced by correlations. Note, however, that the cross amplitude spectrum no longer has any meaning. The normalized correlation estimates are obtained from the covariance estimates using

$$r_{ii}(k) = \frac{c_{ii}(k)}{c_{ii}(0)}, \quad i = 1, 2, \tag{9.3.13}$$

$$r_{12}(k) = \frac{c_{12}(k)}{\sqrt{c_{11}(0)c_{22}(0)}}. \tag{9.3.14}$$

9.3.2 Some numerical examples of cross spectral estimation

Details of the computations. This section contains numerical examples of cross spectral analysis using simulated bivariate time series whose spectra are known. Comparisons are made between the theoretical spectra and the smoothed coherency and phase estimates (9.3.11) and (9.3.12). The effect of window bandwidth on the variance of the smoothed estimates is investigated by comparing the theoretical spectra with the estimates based on realizations of the bivariate time series. All numerical examples in this section are smoothed using the Tukey window.

Similarly, the bias is investigated by calculating the mean smoothed co- and quadrature spectra

$$\bar{\Lambda}_{12}(f) = 2\left\{ \lambda_{12}(0) + 2 \sum_{k=1}^{L-1} \lambda_{12}(k)w(k) \cos 2\pi f k \right\},$$

$$\bar{\Psi}_{12}(f) = 2\left\{ 0 + 2 \sum_{k=1}^{L-1} \psi_{12}(k)w(k) \sin 2\pi f k \right\}, \quad 0 \leqslant f \leqslant \tfrac{1}{2}, \tag{9.3.15}$$

and the mean smoothed auto spectra $\bar{\Gamma}_{11}(f)$, $\bar{\Gamma}_{22}(f)$. From these, mean smoothed phase and coherency spectra are derived according to

$$\bar{\phi}_{12}(f) = \arctan\left\{ -\frac{\bar{\Psi}_{12}(f)}{\bar{\Lambda}_{12}(f)} \right\},$$

$$\bar{\kappa}_{12}^2(f) = \frac{\bar{\Lambda}_{12}^2(f) + \bar{\Psi}_{12}^2(f)}{\bar{\Gamma}_{11}(f)\bar{\Gamma}_{22}(f)}. \tag{9.3.16}$$

In addition the smoothed cross spectral estimates $\bar{L}_{12}(f)$, $\bar{Q}_{12}(f)$, $\bar{F}_{12}(f)$ and $\bar{K}_{12}^2(f)$ are computed using formulae (9.3.8) to (9.3.12).

Two independent first-order ar processes ($\alpha_1 = -0.9$). The first processes investigated are the two independent first-order ar processes, with $\alpha_1 = -0.9$, $N = 100$, whose cross correlation function was evaluated in Section 8.2.1. For this bivariate process, the theoretical and mean smoothed coherency spectra are identically zero and the theoretical phase spectrum is uniformly distributed in the interval $(-\pi/2, \pi/2)$. Hence no comparison between the theoretical and mean smoothed spectra is made. The main object of this example is to make comparisons between the theoretical coherency, which is zero, and the coherency estimates for realizations of 100 terms of each series. Figure 9.4 shows the smoothed coherency spectral estimates for $L = 4, 8, 16$ and 40.

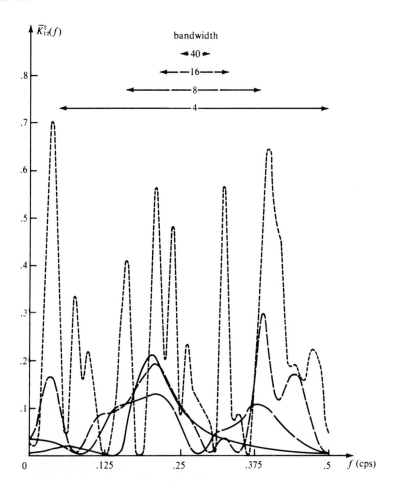

FIG. 9.4: Smoothed coherency estimates for two uncorrelated first-order ar processes

Figure 9.4 demonstrates very clearly the effect of window closing on the smoothed coherency estimate, the theoretical value being zero in this example. For $L = 4$ and 8 the coherencies are reasonably smooth and close to zero, but as L is increased, and hence the bandwidth is decreased, very large coherencies begin to appear. It was shown in Section 9.1.3 that this is partly due to the large variance of the estimator when the bandwidth is small. In addition, as shown in Section 9.1.2, as the bandwidth is made smaller the smoothed coherency tends to unity at all frequencies since the sample coherency estimate for unsmoothed data is identically equal to one at all frequencies.

Figure 9.5 shows the smoothed coherency estimate $\bar{K}_{12}^2$ when $L = 16$ for the original series and the series after the filtering operation described in Section 8.2.2. It is seen that filtering of the two series only marginally improves the coherency estimate. This is to be compared with the conclusion drawn in Section 8.2.2 that filtering can lead to greatly improved estimates of the cross correlation function. This behavior of the coherency estimate is explained in Section 9.3.3.

A bivariate autoregressive process. The second process investigated is the bivariate ar process (8.1.20),

$$X_{1t} - 0.6X_{1t-1} + 0.5X_{2t-1} = Z_{1t},$$
$$X_{2t} - 0.4X_{1t-1} - 0.5X_{2t-1} = Z_{2t},$$

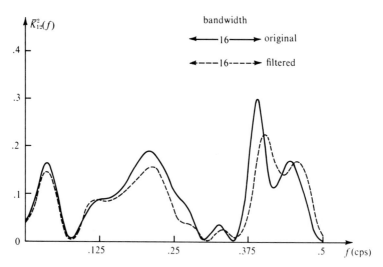

FIG. 9.5: Smoothed coherency estimates for two uncorrelated series: filtered and original series

where Z_{1t}, Z_{2t} are two mutually independent white noise processes.

The theoretical coherency and phase spectra are given by (8.4.19) and (8.4.20) respectively. The theoretical coherency κ_{12}^2 is plotted in Figure 9.6, together with the mean smoothed coherencies $\bar{\kappa}_{12}^2$ for $L = 4$, 8 and 16. It is seen that considerable bias exists for $L = 4$ and 8, the peak of the coherency being displaced by about 0.1 cps for $L = 4$ and 0.05 for $L = 8$. For $L = 16$, good agreement between $\bar{\kappa}_{12}^2$ and κ_{12}^2 is obtained, and for $L = 32$ the theoretical and smoothed spectra are indistinguishable. Hence an estimate of the

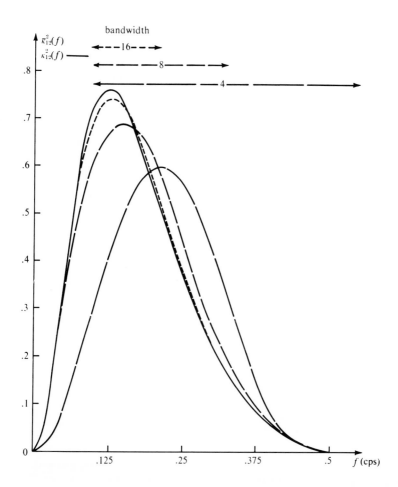

FIG. 9.6: Mean smoothed coherency spectra for the bivariate autoregressive process (8.1.20)

coherency for this process with acceptably small bias should be obtained with $L = 16$.

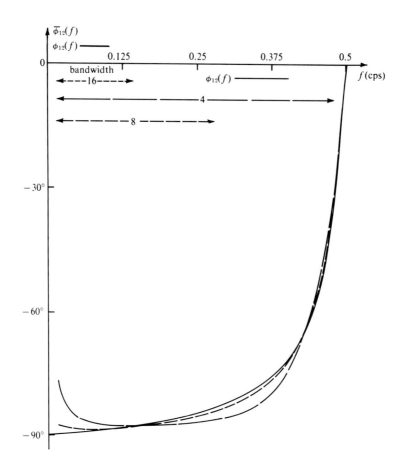

Fig. 9.7: Mean smoothed phase spectra for the bivariate autoregressive process
        (8.1.20)

Figure 9.7 shows the theoretical and mean smoothed phase spectra for the process (8.1.20) when $L = 4$, 8 and 16. Excellent agreement between $\bar{\phi}_{12}$ and ϕ_{12} is obtained for $L = 8$, and for $L = 16$ the mean smoothed phase spectrum is indistinguishable from the theoretical spectrum. Hence the phase spectrum could be estimated with fewer lags than are needed for the coherency spectrum.

Table A9.1 and Figure 9.8 show the sample auto- and cross correlation functions based on a realization of $N = 100$ terms of the process (8.1.20). The original data for these series are given in Table A8.1. Figure 9.9 shows the theoretical coherency and the coherency estimates computed from these correlation functions. The estimate $\bar{K}_{12}^2$ using $L = 4$ is considerably displaced from the theoretical coherency, as is the mean smoothed coherency $\bar{\kappa}_{12}^2$.

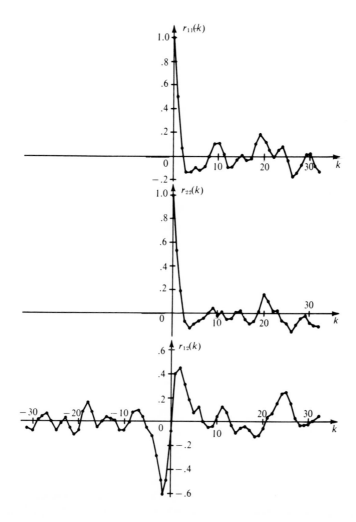

Fig. 9.8: Sample auto- and cross correlations for the bivariate autoregressive process (8.1.20) ($N = 100$)

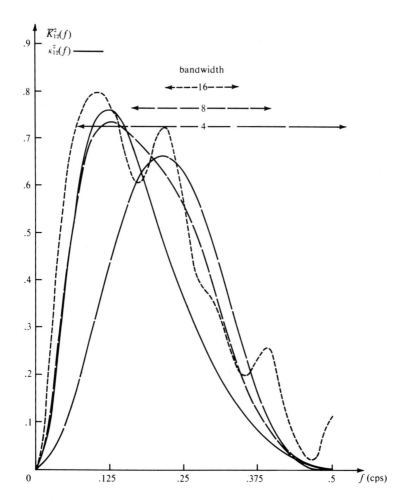

FIG. 9.9: Smoothed coherency estimates for the bivariate autoregressive process (8.1.20) ($N = 100$)

Doubling L to 8 produces a marked change in $\bar{K}_{12}^2$, but increasing L to 16 produces little change. Hence in this case the estimate based on 16 or possibly 12 would be accepted using the window-closing technique of Section 7.2.4. Note that for $L = 16$ there is quite good agreement between $\bar{K}_{12}^2$ and κ_{12}^2. However, increasing L to 32 produces wild oscillations in $\bar{K}_{12}^2$.

The theoretical phase spectrum and the smoothed phase estimates are shown in Figure 9.10 for $L = 4, 8$ and 16. The window-closing procedure suggests that very little change in phase occurs above $L = 8$ and that with $L = 16$, spurious peaks appear in the estimate. Hence the estimate based on

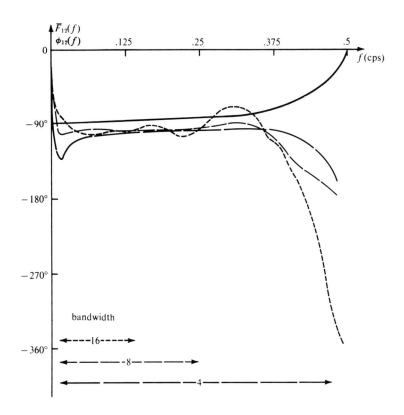

FIG. 9.10: Smoothed phase estimates for the bivariate autoregressive process (8.1.20) ($N = 100$)

$L = 8$ would probably be accepted, and comparison with Figure 9.7 shows that there is good agreement with the theoretical phase spectrum in the range 0 to 0.4 cps. For frequencies above 0.4 cps, the estimates tend to move downward, whereas the theoretical phase shown in Figure 9.7 moves upward. Figure 9.9 shows that $f = 0.4$ cps corresponds to the point where the coherency falls to a small value. Using an average coherency of 0.1 in this region, Figure 9.3 shows that the 95% confidence interval for the phase for $L = 4$ is approximately $\pm 30°$.

Noise through a linear system with delay. The third process investigated is (8.1.22), where X_{2t} is the output from a first-order linear system with a delay of 10 time units

$$X_{2t} = 0.5X_{2t-1} + 2X_{1t-10} + Y_t.$$

The input X_{1t} to the system is a first-order ar process

$$X_{1t} = 0.6X_{1t-1} + Z_{1t}.$$

The noise Y_t is a first-order ar process

$$Y_t = 0.5Y_{t-1} + Z_{2t},$$

and Z_{1t}, Z_{2t} are two mutually independent white noise processes. The theoretical correlation functions of this process are given in Section 8.1.4.

The theoretical coherency and phase spectra, derived using the methods of Section 8.4.3, are

$$\kappa_{12}^2(f) = \frac{5 - 4\cos 2\pi f}{6.36 - 5.2\cos 2\pi f},$$

$$\phi_{12}(f) = \arctan\left\{\frac{-\sin 2\pi f}{2 - \cos 2\pi f}\right\} - 20\pi f.$$

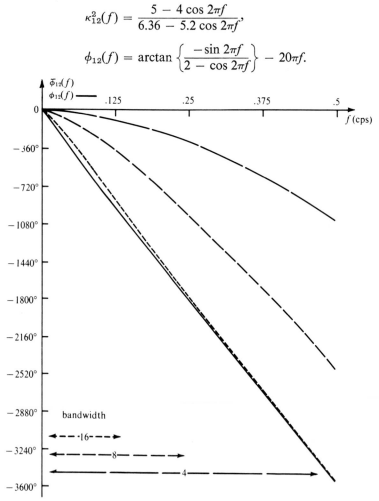

FIG. 9.11: Theoretical and mean smoothed phase spectra for the linear process (8.1.22) (before alignment)

The theoretical and mean smoothed phase spectra for this linear process are shown in Figure 9.11, from which it is seen that good estimates of the phase can be obtained with as few as 12 or 16 lags.

The theoretical coherency spectrum κ_{12}^2 is plotted in Figure 9.12, together with the mean smoothed coherencies $\bar{\kappa}_{12}^2$ for $L = 16$, 24 and 32. It is seen that the mean smoothed coherencies are markedly different from the theoretical coherency even for 32 lags, and that the difference is not attributable to lack of smoothness of the theoretical coherency. The reason is that bias is being introduced because of the large delay between the input and output, as predicted in Section 9.2.1.

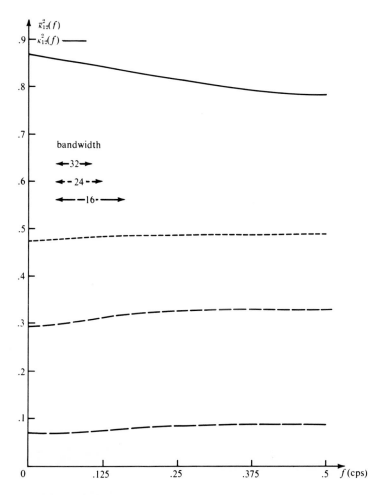

FIG. 9.12: Theoretical and mean smoothed coherency spectra for the linear process (8.1.22) (before alignment)

When $L = 8$, the mean smoothed coherency is approximately zero, as would be expected since the delay between the two series exceeds the number of lags used. Hence in this instance the bias equals the function itself.

It is clear from this theoretical investigation that little would be learned from a spectral analysis of a realization of 100 or so terms of this process unless care is exercised. To demonstrate this conclusion, the auto- and cross correlations of a realization of $N = 100$ terms were computed and are shown in Table A9.2 and Figure 9.13. The original data for this example are given

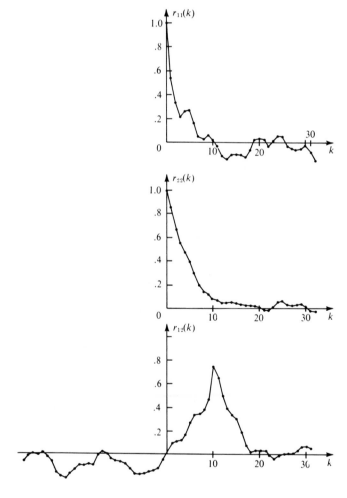

FIG. 9.13: Sample auto- and cross correlations for the linear process (8.1.22)
$(N = 100)$

in Table A8.2. Figure 9.14 shows the coherency spectral estimate based on a realization of $N = 100$ terms when $L = 8$, 16 and 32. It is clear that the estimate is not converging to a stable function, and that for $L = 32$ it tends to "blow up." Hence no satisfactory conclusions can be drawn concerning the coherency estimate. The phase estimates for $L = 4$, 8, 16 and 32 are shown in Figure 9.15. It is seen that the estimates are very poor when the number of lags is less than or comparable to the delay period. Once the number of lags is greater than the delay of 10, the estimate improves rapidly and an excellent estimate is obtained with $L = 32$.

The examples of this section illustrate the general point that good estimates of phase may be obtained in situations where the coherency is badly estimated. In the next section it is shown that it is usually possible to obtain considerable

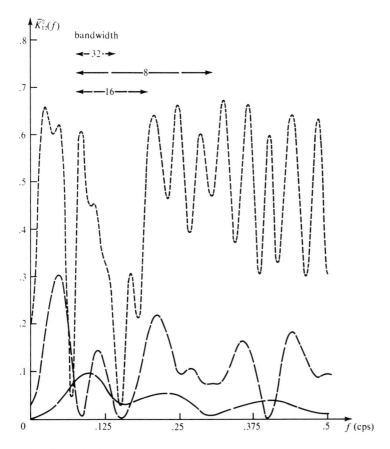

FIG. 9.14: Smoothed coherency estimates for the linear process (8.1.22) ($N = 100$, before alignment)

improvement in the estimates of coherency and phase by aligning the two processes.

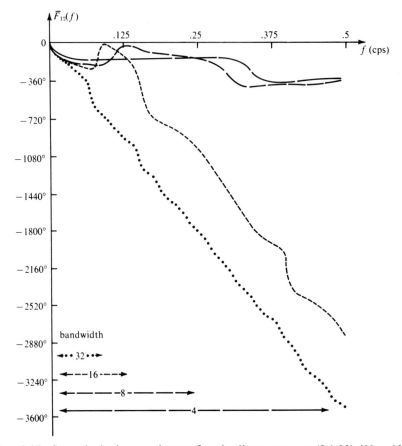

FIG. 9.15: Smoothed phase estimates for the linear process (8.1.22) ($N = 100$, before alignment)

9.3.3 Improvement of cross spectral estimates

It was shown in the last section that large bias can occur in the estimation of coherency spectra, especially when there is large delay. In this section the bias in the phase and coherency spectral estimators are evaluated and it is shown that this bias can be considerably reduced by the process of *alignment*. Alignment consists of centering the ccf so that the largest absolute value of the ccf is at zero lag.

Bias in coherency estimators. Approximate expressions for the bias of the smoothed coherency estimators may be obtained by following a procedure similar to that in Section 6.3.5. For example, the bias in the smoothed coherency estimator is

$$B(f) = E[\bar{K}_{12}^2(f) - \kappa_{12}^2(f)]$$

$$= E\left[\frac{|\bar{C}_{12}(f)|^2}{\bar{C}_{11}(f)\bar{C}_{22}(f)} - \frac{|\Gamma_{12}(f)|^2}{\Gamma_{11}(f)\Gamma_{22}(f)}\right]. \qquad (9.3.17)$$

Using (3.2.23) the bias in the coherency estimator may be approximated by

$$B(f) = \kappa_{12}^2(f)\left[\frac{B_{12}(f)}{\alpha_{12}^2(f)} - \frac{B_{11}(f)}{\Gamma_{11}(f)} - \frac{B_{22}(f)}{\Gamma_{22}(f)}\right], \qquad (9.3.18)$$

where $B_{12}(f)$, $B_{11}(f)$, $B_{22}(f)$ are the biases in $|\bar{C}_{12}(f)|^2$, $\bar{C}_{11}(f)$ and $\bar{C}_{22}(f)$ respectively. For the present it is assumed that the autospectra are sufficiently smooth compared with the spectral windows so that the biases in the autospectral estimators may be ignored. First, the bias $B_{12}(f)$ in the squared cross amplitude spectrum is calculated. That is,

$$B_{12}(f) = E[\bar{A}_{12}^2(f) - \alpha_{12}^2(f)].$$

Now,

$$E[|\bar{C}_{12}(f)|^2] = E\left[\int_{-\infty}^{\infty} C_{12}(g)W(f-g)\,dg \int_{-\infty}^{\infty} C_{12}^*(h)W(f-h)\,dh\right]$$

$$= \int_{-\infty}^{\infty}\int_{-\infty}^{\infty} W(f-g)W(f-h)E[C_{12}(g)C_{12}^*(h)]\,dg\,dh. \qquad (9.3.19)$$

But,

$$E[C_{12}(g)C_{12}^*(h)] = \text{Cov}\,[C_{12}(g), C_{12}^*(h)] + E[C_{12}(g)]E[C_{12}^*(h)],$$

and from (9.1.22) and (9.2.3) this is approximately

$$E[C_{12}(g), C_{12}^*(h)] \approx \frac{1}{T}\Gamma_{11}(g)\Gamma_{22}(g)\,\delta(g-h) + \Gamma_{12}(g)\Gamma_{12}^*(h).$$

Hence

$$E[|\bar{C}_{12}(f)|^2] \approx \int_{-\infty}^{\infty}\frac{W^2(f-g)}{T}\Gamma_{11}(g)\Gamma_{22}(g)\,dg + |\bar{\Gamma}_{12}(f)|^2. \qquad (9.3.20)$$

If $\Gamma_{11}(f)$ and $\Gamma_{22}(f)$ are smooth relative to the width of the spectral window, then (9.3.20) reduces to

$$E[|\bar{C}_{12}(f)|^2] \approx \Gamma_{11}(f)\Gamma_{22}(f)\frac{I}{T} + |\bar{\Gamma}_{12}(f)|^2 \qquad (9.3.21)$$

and

$$B(f) \approx \frac{I}{T} + \frac{|\bar{\Gamma}_{12}(f)|^2 - |\Gamma_{12}(f)|^2}{\Gamma_{11}(f)\Gamma_{22}(f)}, \qquad (9.3.22)$$

using (9.3.18).

Equation (9.3.22) shows that even if the theoretical cross spectrum is zero, the mean smoothed coherency can be large. This explains the large coherency estimates, obtained in Figure 9.5, for the two independent first-order ar processes discussed in Section 8.2. For example, when $L = 40$,

$$\frac{I}{T} = \frac{(0.75)40}{100} = 0.3,$$

which agrees quite well with the average value estimated from the values of Figure 9.4. Note that as L increases (and I/T increases) the average coherency also increases. As indicated in Section 9.1.2, when $M = L\Delta$ tends to T, the coherency tends to one for all values of f.

Also shown by (9.3.22) is that filtering independent series will not produce improved coherency estimates. This is demonstrated in Figure 9.4 for the original and filtered independent processes, where it is seen that the average coherency for both the original and filtered data is about 0.1. This agrees very well with the value $I/T = (0.75)\ 16/100 = 0.12$ predicted by (9.3.22).

To obtain an explicit expression for the bias (9.3.22), it is necessary to evaluate $|\bar{\Gamma}_{12}(f)|^2 - |\Gamma_{12}(f)|^2$. From (9.2.4),

$$\bar{\Gamma}_{12}(f) = \int_{-\infty}^{\infty} w(u)\gamma_{12}(u)\, e^{-j2\pi fu}\, du,$$

so that

$$|\bar{\Gamma}_{12}(f)|^2 = \int_{-\infty}^{\infty}\int_{-\infty}^{\infty} w(u)w(v)\gamma_{12}(u)\gamma_{12}(v)\, e^{-j2\pi f(u-v)}\, du\, dv.$$

Hence

$$|\bar{\Gamma}_{12}(f)|^2 - |\Gamma_{12}(f)|^2 = \int_{-\infty}^{\infty}\int_{-\infty}^{\infty} \gamma_{12}(u)\gamma_{12}(v)\, e^{-j2\pi f(u-v)}\, (w(u)w(v)-1)\, du\, dv.$$

$$(9.3.23)$$

Writing

$$w(u)w(v) - 1 = (w(u) - 1)(w(v) - 1) + (w(u) - 1) + (w(v) - 1)$$

gives

$$
\begin{aligned}
|\bar{\Gamma}_{12}(f)|^2 &- |\Gamma_{12}(f)|^2 \\
&= \int_{-\infty}^{\infty} (w(u)-1)\gamma_{12}(u)\, e^{-j2\pi fu}\, du \int_{-\infty}^{\infty} (w(v)-1)\gamma_{12}(v)\, e^{j2\pi fv}\, dv \\
&+ \int_{-\infty}^{\infty} (w(u)-1)\gamma_{12}(u)\, e^{-j2\pi fu}\, du \int_{-\infty}^{\infty} \gamma_{12}(v)\, e^{j2\pi fv}\, dv \\
&+ \int_{-\infty}^{\infty} \gamma_{12}(u)\, e^{-j2\pi fu}\, du \int_{-\infty}^{\infty} (w(v)-1)\gamma_{12}(v)\, e^{j2\pi fv}\, dv.
\end{aligned}
$$

Using the approximations (6.3.37) for bias gives, for the Tukey window,

$$
|\bar{\Gamma}_{12}(f)|^2 - |\Gamma_{12}(f)|^2 \approx \left(\frac{0.063}{M^2}\right)\Gamma_{12}^{(2)}\left(\frac{0.063}{M^2}\right)\Gamma_{12}^{(2)*}
$$

$$
+ \left(\frac{0.063}{M^2}\right)\{\Gamma_{12}^{(2)}\Gamma_{12}^* + \Gamma_{12}\Gamma_{12}^{(2)*}\}, \qquad (9.3.24)
$$

where $\Gamma_{12}^{(2)}$ is the second derivative of the cross amplitude spectrum at frequency f. Writing $\Gamma_{12}(f) = \alpha_{12}(f)\, e^{j\phi_{12}(f)}$ and taking derivatives with respect to f gives

$$|\bar{\Gamma}_{12}(f)|^2 - |\Gamma_{12}(f)|^2 \approx \frac{0.126}{M^2}\{\alpha_{12}\alpha_{12}^{(2)} - \alpha_{12}^2(\phi_{12}^{(1)})^2\},$$

on neglecting terms of order $1/M^4$. Hence if the biases $B_{11}(f)$, $B_{22}(f)$ in (9.3.18) may be neglected, the bias in the coherency estimator is approximately

$$B(f) \approx \frac{0.75M}{T} + \frac{0.126}{M^2}\left\{\frac{\alpha_{12}\alpha_{12}^{(2)} - \alpha_{12}^2(\phi_{12}^{(1)})^2}{\Gamma_{11}\Gamma_{22}}\right\} \qquad (9.3.25)$$

for the Tukey window. For the Parzen window, 0.75 is replaced by 0.54 and 0.126 by 0.304.

The most important feature of (9.3.25) is that the bias is proportional to the square of the first derivative of the phase spectrum. If the constant term and the term in $\alpha_{12}^{(2)}$ are neglected, (9.3.25) reduces to

$$B(f) \approx \frac{0.126}{M^2}(\kappa_{12}^2)(\phi_{12}^{(1)})^2, \qquad (9.3.26)$$

so that the bias in coherency is directly proportional to the coherency and the rate of change $\phi_{12}^{(1)}$ of the phase spectrum. Hence if there are large delays between two processes, the coherency estimate can be very poor since $\phi_{12}^{(1)}$ will be large. The bias in cross spectral estimators was first pointed out by Akaike [5].

Alignment. The bias in coherency due to phase shift may be reduced appreciably by *alignment* of the two processes. Thus, suppose the cross correlation function has its largest absolute value, or peak, at lag S. Aligning the processes so that the peak occurs at zero, changes $\Gamma_{12}(f)$ from

$$\alpha_{12}(f)\, e^{j\phi_{12}(f)}$$

to

$$\Gamma'_{12}(f) = \alpha'_{12}(f)\, e^{j\phi'_{12}(f)} = \alpha_{12}(f)\, e^{j(\phi_{12}(f) - 2\pi fS)}.$$

Hence

$$\phi'^{(1)}_{12} = \frac{d}{df}(\phi'_{12}(f)) = (\phi_{12}^{(1)} - 2\pi S),$$

and so the bias (9.3.26) may be considerably reduced, as will be demonstrated in the next section.

Use of the phase spectrum to determine the alignment parameter. The choice of the alignment parameter S by locating the peak in the ccf does not always lead to a satisfactory spectral analysis. It may happen that the phase spectrum of the aligned series still has a linear phase component $\phi(f) = 2\pi fd$, showing that a further alignment d is necessary. As a practical procedure, it is recommended that a first guess of the alignment parameters should be made on the basis of the peak in the ccf. In some cases, the resulting phase spectrum will not contain a linear component and the analysis can be terminated. In those cases where a linear component $\phi(f) = 2\pi fd$ still remains, a modified alignment $S + d$ can be chosen and the analysis repeated.

Bias in phase estimators. Approximate expressions for the bias in phase estimators may be derived using an approach similar to that used above. The final result for the Tukey window is

$$B(f) \approx \frac{0.063}{M^2}\left[\frac{1}{\alpha_{12}^2}\frac{d}{df}(\alpha_{12}^2\phi_{12}^{(1)})\right]$$

$$= \frac{0.063}{M^2}\left[\phi_{12}^{(2)} + \phi_{12}^{(1)}\frac{d}{df}\ln\alpha_{12}^2\right]. \tag{9.3.27}$$

For the Parzen window, (9.3.27) holds with 0.063 replaced by 0.152.

From (9.3.27) it is seen that the bias is proportional to the second derivative of the phase spectrum and is also proportional to the product of the first derivative of the phase spectrum times the first derivative of the logarithm of the cross amplitude spectrum. For bivariate processes involving large delays the quantity $\phi_{12}^{(1)}$ will probably dominate $\phi_{12}^{(2)}$. Since $\phi_{12}^{(1)}$ is multiplied by $d(\ln\alpha^2)/df$, however, the net bias may be quite small. Such a situation obtains in the linear filter example, shown in Figure 9.11, which gives the theoretical and mean smoothed phase spectra. It is seen that the smoothed and theoretical spectra agree very well, even for 16 lags.

9.3.4 *Discrete estimation formulae for aligned processes*

Suppose that the sample ccvf has its peak at lag S, where S could be positive or negative. Then the aligned estimate is based on the ccvf centered so that its peak is at zero lag. Thus the aligned ccvf estimate is

$$c_{12}''(k) = c_{12}(S + k). \tag{9.3.28}$$

If a lag window of length L is to be used with the aligned estimate, then

$$-L \leqslant k + S \leqslant L,$$

and it is necessary to compute $c_{12}(k)$ for

$$-L - S \leqslant k \leqslant L - S.$$

The usual formulae given in Section 9.3.1 may then be applied using the aligned ccvf estimate. The even and odd ccvf estimates (9.3.6) and (9.3.7) become

$$l_{12}''(k) = \tfrac{1}{2}\{c_{12}(S + k) + c_{12}(S - k)\}, \tag{9.3.29}$$

$$q_{12}''(k) = \tfrac{1}{2}\{c_{12}(S + k) - c_{12}(S - k)\}, \tag{9.3.30}$$

and (9.3.8) to (9.3.13) may then be used without alteration.

9.3.5 *Examples of cross spectral estimation with alignment*

Figure 9.16 shows mean smoothed coherency spectra based on $L = 8$, 16 and 32 for the linear filter example, after alignment with $S = 10$ based on the peak of the ccf in Figure 9.13. Comparison of Figure 9.16 with Figure 9.12, which shows the corresponding smoothed spectra before alignment, indicates that alignment results in a considerable reduction in bias, that is, an improvement in fidelity.

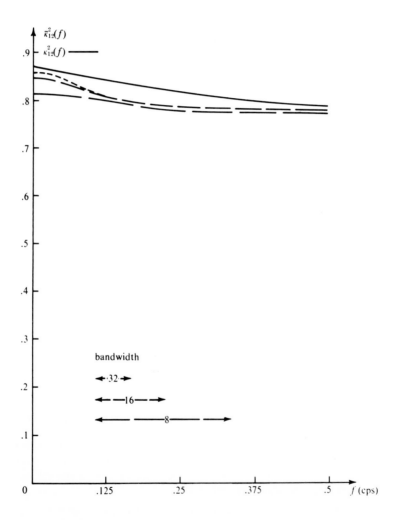

FIG. 9.16: Mean smoothed coherency spectra for the linear process (8.1.22) (after alignment, $S = 10$)

Figure 9.17 shows the mean smoothed phase spectra for $L = 4$ and 32. Comparison with the mean smoothed spectra before alignment, given in Figure 9.11, shows that much more rapid convergence to the true value is obtained with the aligned estimator.

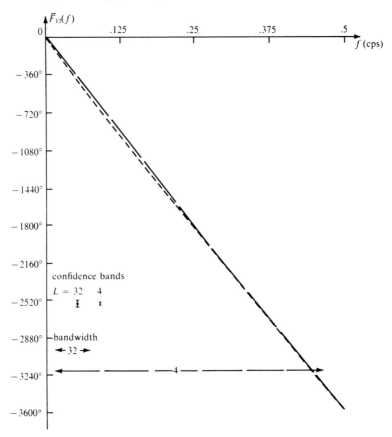

FIG. 9.17: Mean smoothed phase spectra for the linear process (8.1.22) (after alignment, $S = 10$)

Figure 9.18 shows the smoothed coherency estimates after alignment for the linear filter data. Comparison with the unaligned spectra of Figure 9.14 shows the marked improvement in the estimate. Note that oscillations begin to occur in the estimate based on $L = 16$ and hence the estimate based on $L = 8$ or possibly $L = 12$ would be accepted. Note also that the estimate for $L = 8$ is seen to agree very well with the theoretical coherency spectrum. The phase spectra estimates after alignment are not shown, since they agree so closely with the phase spectra shown in Figure 9.17. As noted in Section 9.3.3, the bias in the phase estimator is usually small, and so the difference between

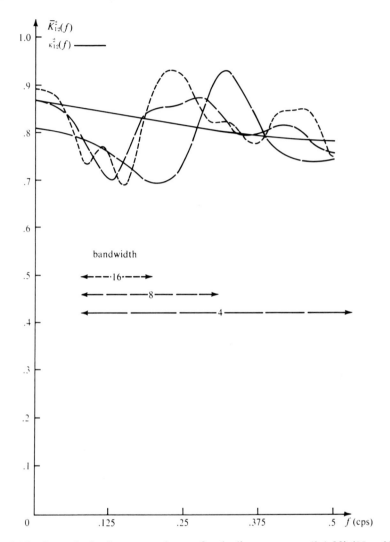

FIG. 9.18: Smoothed coherency estimates for the linear process (8.1.22) ($N = 100$, after alignment, $S = 10$)

the unaligned and aligned phase estimates is not as drastic as the difference between the unaligned and aligned coherency estimates.

Hence it can be concluded from this analysis that the process of alignment has transformed a very bad coherency estimate into a good estimate.

Confidence intervals for coherency and phase. The smoothed coherency estimates of Figure 9.18 have been replotted in Figure 9.19 on the transformed scale $Y_{12} = \text{arctanh} \, |\bar{K}_{12}|$, and the constant confidence limits computed according

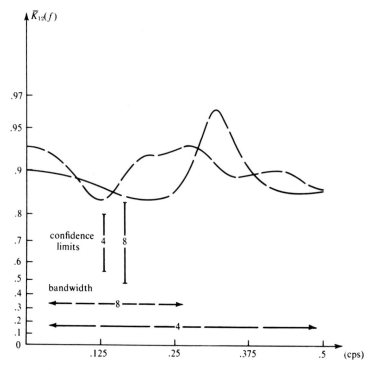

FIG. 9.19: Transformed coherency estimates for the linear process (8.1.22) ($N = 100$, after alignment, $S = 10$)

to (9.2.23) are shown. Since the bias before alignment is so small for the phase estimator, it is justifiable to attach confidence intervals to the unaligned spectra which are shown in Figure 9.17. Taking an average coherency figure of 0.8 over the whole frequency range, the 95% intervals for $L = 4$ and $L = 32$ are 5° and 15° using Figure 9.3.

9.4 PRACTICAL ASPECTS OF CROSS SPECTRAL ESTIMATION

This section contains a discussion of practical problems arising in the estimation of cross spectra. These are analogous to the problems arising in the estimation of autospectra discussed in Section 7.3.

9.4.1 The design of a cross spectral analysis

As in autospectral analysis, it is desirable to consider the choice of record length in advance of collecting the data. In all calculations of this kind, no precise statements can be made, since the best choice of record length depends on knowing the exact spectra. However, if guesses can be made of how the spectra are likely to behave, the problem of data-gathering can be based on semiquantitative grounds rather than on wild guesses.

As discussed in Section 7.3.1, there are four stages in the design procedure for autospectra:

(1) The sampling interval must be at most $1/2f_0$ where f_0 cps is the maximum frequency of interest.

(2) Electronic filtering may be necessary before sampling the record to ensure that there is no power or cross power at frequencies above f_0 in the continuous traces.

(3) A guess must be made of the width a of the finest detail of interest in the coherency spectrum. As shown in Section 9.3, it is usually more difficult to estimate the coherency spectrum than the phase spectrum and hence the design calculations can be based on the coherency spectrum entirely. High fidelity can be achieved in estimating the coherency spectrum if the bandwidth of the spectral window is less than the width a of the finest detail. Hence the formula (7.3.2) for the number of lags L applies, namely,

$$L = \frac{b_1}{a\Delta},$$

where b_1 is the standardized bandwidth of the window. Note that the above calculation assumes that the two series have been aligned. Since the shift S required to align the series will usually be small compared with the total length of the series, this factor can be ignored at the design stage.

(4) To trust the fine detail in the coherency spectrum, it is necessary that the confidence interval be acceptably small. In Section 9.2.3 it was shown that confidence intervals for the coherency could be based on the result

$$\text{Var}\,[\text{arctanh}\,|K_{12}|] \approx \frac{I}{2T} = \frac{1}{\nu} = \frac{L}{2b_1 N},$$

where b_1 is the standardized bandwidth of the window. The 95% confidence limits for $\text{arctanh}\,|\bar{\kappa}_{12}|$ are given by (9.2.23), that is,

$$\pm 1.96 \sqrt{\frac{L}{2b_1 N}} = \pm \frac{1.96}{\sqrt{\nu}}. \tag{9.4.1}$$

Hence, from the desired width of the confidence interval, say $\pm c$, the number of data points required to achieve this width on average is

$$N = \frac{L}{2b_1}\left(\frac{1.96}{c}\right)^2 \tag{9.4.2}$$

or, from (7.3.2),

$$N = \frac{1}{2a\Delta}\left(\frac{1.96}{c}\right)^2. \tag{9.4.3}$$

An example. Suppose that the phase and coherency spectra are needed up to $f_0 = 2$ cps. It is also required to estimate a peak of width $a = 0.20$ cps in the transformed coherency spectrum with a 95% confidence interval of ± 0.2 using the Tukey window.

Then

$$\Delta = \frac{1}{2f_0} = 0.25 \text{ seconds,}$$

$$L = \frac{1.333}{(0.2)(0.25)} = 27,$$

$$N = \frac{1}{2(0.2)(0.25)} \left(\frac{1.96}{0.2}\right)^2 = 960.$$

The number of degrees of freedom with each estimate is approximately 95 and the record length should be at least 240 seconds.

9.4.2 *A practical procedure for estimating cross spectra*

It is suggested that the estimation of cross spectra should be conducted in five stages:

(1) Preliminary decision stage

(a) The series are inspected visually to see if there are any obvious trends. If trends are present they can be eliminated using the covariance estimates based on the first difference of each series or one of the digital filters of Section 7.3.5.

(b) It may be necessary to decide whether to analyze the data over a wide frequency range or whether to filter the data into component series relating to distinct frequency bands. If large variations of power can be expected over the total frequency range, then a separate analysis for the low-frequency and high-frequency components would be a minimum requirement. This decision requires some prior knowledge of the spectra. If this is not available, it may be necessary to conduct a pilot analysis. Alternatively, stages *(1)* through *(4)* should be completed and this analysis used as a basis for filtering, followed by reanalysis.

(c) The maximum number of lags $L_{\max}$ chosen for the calculation of the auto- and cross covariances is decided.

(2) First computation stage

(a) The auto- and cross covariances and correlations for the original and differenced data are computed, then plotted.

(b) Even though trends may not be visible in the data, they may be present. They can be detected by a failure of the auto- and cross covariances to damp out. As indicated in Section 7.3.5, trends produce large power at low frequencies which leaks into the spectrum at other frequencies and causes distortion of the spectrum. In cross spectral analysis it also produces spurious coherencies between the two series.

(3) Intermediate decision stage

(a) A decision is made whether to use the original covariances $c_{ij}(k)$ or the detrended covariances $c'_{ij}(k)$.

(b) The cross covariance or correlation function selected in (a) should be examined and the lag S corresponding to its maximum absolute value noted.

(c) A set of three truncation points $L_1 < L_2 < L_3$ should be chosen based on the way the auto- and cross correlation functions damp out.

(4) Second computation stage

(a) The two autospectra and the phase and coherency spectra based on the aligned cross correlations (9.3.28) are computed.

(b) The four spectra should be plotted for the set of three bandwidths. The two autospectra should be plotted on a logarithmic scale, the phase on a linear scale and the coherency on the transformed scale

$$Y = \operatorname{arctanh} |\bar{K}_{12}(f)|.$$

(5) Interpretation stage

(a) The phase spectrum is examined to see if further alignment is needed. If so, the second computing stage is repeated using the new alignment parameter determined from the phase spectrum.

(b) If no further alignment is necessary, the effects of the window-closing procedure should be appraised and the analysis classified as good, intermediate or poor, as described in Section 7.3.3. Final plots for presentation of the spectra should be prepared based on these decisions.

(c) Vertical lines representing the confidence intervals for phase can be added for each bandwidth, using Figure 9.3, and confidence intervals for coherency, using formula (9.2.23).

(d) Horizontal lines corresponding to the bandwidths of the spectral windows should be added so that the detail in the spectrum can be appraised.

9.4.3 An account of a practical cross spectral estimation

The procedure of Section 9.4.2 was applied to data, a section of which is shown in Figure 8.2. These data have been analyzed in [6] and a more detailed description will be given in Chapter 11. For the present it is sufficient to state that the variables used for cross spectral analysis are the input in-phase and out-of-phase currents $x_1(t)$, $x_2(t)$ to a turbo-alternator. It is necessary to compute the coherency and phase spectra of these two variables since both are input variables arising on an equal footing. This information will be required in Chapter 11 when it will be used in an input–output analysis to determine the frequency response functions of the turbo-alternator. The data consisted of 4000 pairs of data points read at 8 points per second.

(1) Preliminary decision stage

(a) Inspection of the data did not reveal any obvious trends. However, since the data covered such a long time period, it was expected that the analysis would have to be based on the detrended covariances.

(b) Since the data were read at 8 points per second, the Nyquist frequency is 4 cps. It was known *a priori* that there would be little power above 1 cps, and so the data were filtered to remove power above 1 cps using the filter

$$H(\mathcal{Z}) = \left\{ \frac{1}{7} \sum_{k=-3}^{3} \mathcal{Z}^k \right\}^4 .$$

Since there was negligible power above 1 cps in the filtered record, only two points per second were retained. Thus the final data consisted of 1000 pairs of data points. The first 100 values of the filtered current data are given in Table A11.1.

(c) A value of $L_{max} = 80$ was chosen initially.

(2) First computation stage

(a) The auto- and cross correlations of the data described under *(1-b)* were computed and plotted. Figure 9.20 shows the ccf estimates plotted up to $k = \pm 70$ lags. It is seen that the cross correlations damp out very slowly, as do the autocorrelations (not shown).

(b) The differenced cross correlations are also shown in Figure 9.20. It is seen that the cross correlation function drops to zero very quickly and

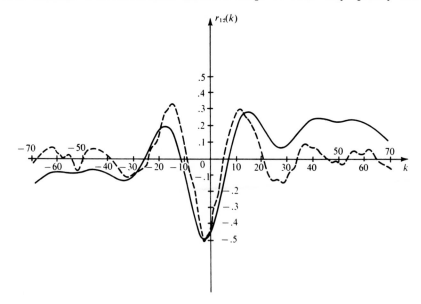

Fig. 9.20: Sample ccf's for original and differenced current data ($N = 1000$)

oscillates about zero with a well-defined period. The main characteristics of the cross correlation function are the delta-function type behavior near the origin and the subsequent periodic behavior. It is seen from Figure 9.20 that the low-frequency trend masks a great deal of detail in the ccf of the original data.

(3) Intermediate decision stage

(a) The above considerations indicate clearly that the differenced cross correlations should be used for spectral analysis.

(b) The ccf is almost symmetric about the origin. The peak occurs at lag -2, and so the shift parameter S was taken to be -2.

(c) Values of $L = 32$, 48 and 64 were chosen initially for the calculation of the spectra.

(4) Second computation stage

(a) The autospectra, the transformed coherency and phase spectra based on $S = -2$ were computed using the Tukey window.

(b) The autospectra are plotted in Figure 9.21 for $L = 64$. The transformed coherency spectra and the phase spectra are shown for $L = 32$ and 64 in Figures 9.22 and 9.23 respectively.

(5) Interpretation stage

(a) The phase spectrum of the aligned series shows no linear trend, and hence further alignment is not considered necessary.

(b) The window-closing procedure suggests that a lag of at least 32 is required for reasonable estimates of all four spectra. For example, Figure 9.22

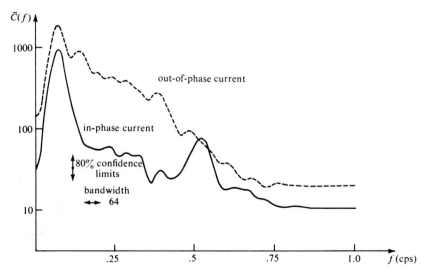

Fig. 9.21: Sample autospectra of differenced current data ($N = 1000$)

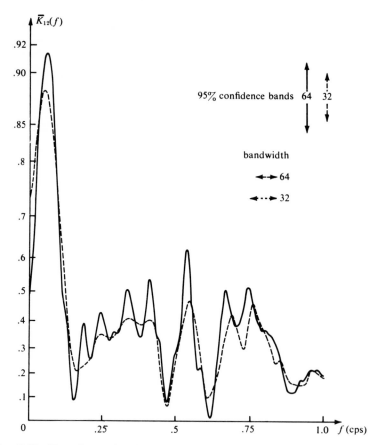

Fᴵɢ. 9.22: Transformed coherency spectrum for differenced current data
        $(N = 1000)$

shows that halving the bandwidth by extending the lag from $L = 32$ to $L = 64$
does not change the broad features of the coherency spectrum. With $L = 64$,
however, oscillations begin to appear due to instability. Hence a final value
of $L = 48$ (not shown on Figure 9.22) is considered adequate. Similar considerations apply to the phase estimates shown in Figure 9.23.

(c) Confidence intervals for phase and transformed coherency were read
off from Figure 9.3 and formula (9.2.23) using

$$\nu = \frac{2(1.33)1000}{L},$$

with $L = 32, 64$. The 95% confidence intervals for the transformed coherency
can be converted into confidence intervals for $\kappa_{12}^2(f)$, since the coherency
scale is marked on Figure 9.22. Since there are 1000 observations in the series,
the confidence intervals are quite narrow.

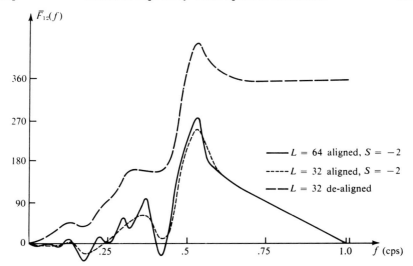

FIG. 9.23: Phase spectrum for differenced current data ($N = 1000$)

(d) Bandwidths are calculated from

$$b = \frac{1.33}{L\Delta}$$

and marked on the figures.

Conclusions. The main features of the cross spectral analysis are the presence of a large peak in the coherency spectrum in the neighborhood of 0.07 cps and a flat region with an average value of approximately $\bar{K}_{12}^2(f) = 0.18$ stretching over the whole frequency range. The large peak near 0.07 cps is associated with the facts that the spectra of both currents have peaks near this frequency and that the band 0 to 0.1 cps contains most of the power. Hence it would be expected that the in-phase and out-of-phase currents are highly correlated in this band. The phase spectra of Figure 9.23 show that the out-of-phase current leads the in-phase current by about 2 seconds. Figure 9.23 also shows the phase spectrum for $L = 32$ aligned and dealigned, that is, corrected by subtracting $2\pi f S\Delta$ from the aligned phase. It is seen that $S = -2$ very effectively removed the linear phase shift between the two currents.

REFERENCES

[1] N. R. Goodman, "On the joint estimation of the spectra, co-spectrum and quadrature spectrum of a two-dimensional stationary Gaussian process." Scientific Paper 10, Engineering Statistics Laboratory, New York University (1957).

[2] G. M. Jenkins, "Cross-spectral analysis and the estimation of linear open loop transfer functions." Chapter 18 of *Time Series*, M. Rosenblatt, ed. John Wiley, New York, 1963.

[3] A. Hald, *Statistical Theory with Engineering Applications*. John Wiley, New York, 1952, p. 609.

[4] C. W. J. Granger, *Spectral Analysis of Economic Time Series*. Princeton University Press, Princeton, 1964.

[5] H. Akaike and Y. Yamamouchi, "On the statistical estimation of frequency response functions." *Ann. Inst. Stat. Math.* **14**, 1 (1962).

[6] K. N. Stanton, "Measurement of turboalternator transfer functions using normal operating data." *Proc. Inst. Electr. Engrs.* **110**, 11 (1963).

APPENDIX A9.1 COVARIANCE OF COVARIANCE FUNCTION ESTIMATORS

In this appendix, a derivation is given of the covariance between the covariance function estimators (8.2.3). The covariance function estimators may be rewritten in the symmetric form

$$c_{ij}(u) = \begin{cases} \dfrac{1}{T} \displaystyle\int_{-(T-|u|)/2}^{(T-|u|)/2} X_i\left(t - \dfrac{u}{2}\right) X_j\left(t + \dfrac{u}{2}\right) dt, & -T \leqslant u \leqslant T \\ 0 & , \quad |u| > T. \end{cases} \quad \text{(A9.1.1)}$$

It is assumed that the stochastic processes $X_i(t)$, $i = 1, 2, 3, 4$, have the properties

$$E[X_i(t)] = 0, \qquad\qquad i = 1, 2, 3, 4, \qquad\qquad \text{(A9.1.2)}$$

$$\text{Cov}\,[X_i(t), X_j(t + u)] = \gamma_{ij}(u), \quad j = 1, 2, 3, 4, \quad -\infty \leqslant u \leqslant \infty \qquad \text{(A9.1.3)}$$

and

$$\begin{aligned} \text{Cov}\,[X_i(t)X_j(t + u_1), X_k(v)X_l(v + u_2)] = {}&\gamma_{ik}(v - t)\gamma_{jl}(v - t + u_2 - u_1) \\ &+ \gamma_{il}(v - t + u_2)\gamma_{jk}(v - t - u_1) \\ &+ K(v - t, u_1, u_2), \qquad \text{(A9.1.4)} \end{aligned}$$

where K is the fourth joint cumulant. The cross spectrum between the processes $X_i(t)$ and $X_j(t)$ is defined by

$$\Gamma_{ij}(f) = \int_{-\infty}^{\infty} \gamma_{ij}(u)\, e^{-j2\pi fu}\, du, \qquad\qquad \text{(A9.1.5)}$$

$$\gamma_{ij}(u) = \int_{-\infty}^{\infty} \Gamma_{ij}(f)\, e^{j2\pi fu}\, df. \qquad\qquad \text{(A9.1.6)}$$

Derivation of covariance. From (A9.1.1) and (A9.1.4), the covariance between the estimators $c_{ij}(u_1)$ and $c_{kl}(u_2)$ is

$$\text{Cov}\,[c_{ij}(u_1), c_{kl}(u_2)]$$

$$\begin{aligned} = \dfrac{1}{T^2} \int_{-(T-|u_1|)/2}^{(T-|u_1|)/2} \int_{-(T-|u_2|)/2}^{(T-|u_2|)/2} \Bigg\{ &\gamma_{ik}\left(v - t - \dfrac{u_2 - u_1}{2}\right) \gamma_{jl}\left(v - t + \dfrac{u_2 - u_1}{2}\right) \\ + \gamma_{il}\left(v - t + \dfrac{u_2 + u_1}{2}\right) &\gamma_{jk}\left(v - t - \dfrac{u_2 + u_1}{2}\right) + K(v - t, u_1, u_2) \Bigg\}\, dv\, dt. \end{aligned}$$

$$\text{(A9.1.7)}$$

Substituting $v - t = r$, $t = s$ transforms the region of integration from a rectangle to a parallelogram, as shown in Figure 5.11. This gives three regions of integration, designated (1), (2) and (3). Hence, for the case $|u_2| > |u_1|$, (A9.1.7) becomes

$$\text{Cov}\,[c_{ij}(u_1),\, c_{kl}(u_2)] = \frac{1}{T^2} \int_{(|u_2|-|u_1|)/2}^{(T-|u_1|+|u_2|)/2} \gamma(r)\,dr \int_{-(T-|u_1|)/2}^{(T-|u_2|)/2} ds \qquad \text{[region (1)]}$$

$$+ \frac{1}{T^2} \int_{-(|u_2|-|u_1|)/2}^{(|u_2|-|u_1|)/2} \gamma(r)\,dr \int_{-[(T-|u_2|)/2]-r}^{[(T-|u_2|)/2]-r} ds \qquad \text{[region (2)]}$$

$$+ \frac{1}{T^2} \int_{-[T-(|u_1|+|u_2|)/2]}^{-(|u_2|-|u_1|)/2} \gamma(r)\,dr \int_{-(T-|u_2|)/2}^{(T-|u_1|)/2} ds \qquad \text{[region (3)]}$$

$$\text{(A9.1.8)}$$

where

$$\gamma(r) = \gamma_{ik}\left(r - \frac{u_2 - u_1}{2}\right)\gamma_{jl}\left(r + \frac{u_2 - u_1}{2}\right) + \gamma_{il}\left(r + \frac{u_2 + u_1}{2}\right)\gamma_{jk}\left(r - \frac{u_2 + u_1}{2}\right)$$

$$+ K(r, u_1, u_2).$$

Integrating (A9.1.8) with respect to s and combining terms gives

$$\text{Cov}\,[c_{ij}(u_1),\, c_{kl}(u_2)] = \frac{1}{T^2}\left\{T' \int_{-T'}^{T'} \gamma(r)\left(1 - \frac{|r|}{T'}\right) dr - T'' \int_{-T''}^{T''} \gamma(r)\left(1 - \frac{|r|}{T''}\right) dr\right\}$$

$$\text{(A9.1.9)}$$

where

$$T' = T - \frac{|u_1| + |u_2|}{2}, \qquad T'' = \frac{|u_2| - |u_1|}{2}.$$

When $|u_1| > |u_2|$, the result is (A9.1.9) with $T'' = (|u_1| - |u_2|)/2$.

Simplification of result. Consider now the contribution due to the fourth cumulant term $K(r, u_1, u_2)$. For X_i Normal, $K = 0$, and so the following results are exact for Normal processes. For non-Normal stochastic processes which are linear processes of the form (5.2.6,7), the contribution due to $K(r, u_1, u_2)$ from an integral of the form

$$\int_{-T'}^{T'} K(r, u_1, u_2)\left(1 - \frac{|r|}{T'}\right) dr$$

is of the order $\gamma_{ij}(u_1)\gamma_{kl}(u_2)$, using (5.2.15). Hence the contribution from the fourth cumulant term may be neglected in (A9.1.9).

For T large, the terms of order $1/T^2$ may also be neglected, and (A9.1.9) reduces to

$$\text{Cov}\,[c_{ij}(u_1),\, c_{kl}(u_2)] \approx \frac{1}{T} \int_{-\infty}^{\infty} \gamma(r)\,dr$$

$$= \frac{1}{T} \int_{-\infty}^{\infty} \left\{\gamma_{ik}\left(r - \frac{u_2 - u_1}{2}\right)\gamma_{jl}\left(r + \frac{u_2 - u_1}{2}\right)\right.$$

$$\left. + \gamma_{il}\left(r + \frac{u_2 + u_1}{2}\right)\gamma_{jk}\left(r - \frac{u_2 + u_1}{2}\right)\right\} dr. \qquad \text{(A9.1.10)}$$

Setting $i = j = k = l = 1$ in (A9.1.10) and making the transformation $r = s - (u_2 - u_1)/2$ gives the Bartlett formula (5.3.22). In particular, for $u_2 = u_1$,

$$\text{Var } [c_{11}(u)] \approx \frac{1}{T} \int_{-\infty}^{\infty} \gamma_{11}^2(r)\, dr. \tag{A9.1.11}$$

Covariance of spectral estimators. The covariance between spectral estimators $C_{ij}(f_1)$ and $C_{kl}(f_2)$ may be derived from the results of the preceding section as follows:

$$\text{Cov } [C_{ij}(f_1), C_{kl}(f_2)] = \text{Cov } \left[\int_{-T}^{T} c_{ij}(u_1)\, e^{-j2\pi f_1 u_1}\, du_1, \int_{-T}^{T} c_{kl}(u_2)\, e^{-j2\pi f_2 u_2}\, du_2 \right]$$

$$= \int_{-T}^{T} \int_{-T}^{T} \text{Cov } [c_{ij}(u_1), c_{kl}(u_2)]\, e^{-j2\pi(f_1 u_1 + f_2 u_2)}\, du_1\, du_2. \tag{A9.1.12}$$

To simplify (A9.1.12), an alternative form of (A9.1.10) is derived.

Alternative form for Cov $[c_{ij}(u_1), c_{kl}(u_2)]$. From (A9.1.9) and (A9.1.6)

$$\text{Cov } [c_{ij}(u_1), c_{kl}(u_2)] = \frac{1}{T^2} \left\{ T' \int_{-T'}^{T'} \gamma(r) \left(1 - \frac{|r|}{T'} \right) dr - T'' \int_{-T''}^{T''} \gamma(r) \left(1 - \frac{|r|}{T''} \right) dr \right\}$$

$$= \frac{1}{T^2} \int_{-\infty}^{\infty} \int_{-\infty}^{\infty} \{ \Gamma_{ik}(g_1) \Gamma_{jl}(g_2)\, e^{j\pi u_1(g_1 - g_2)}\, e^{-j\pi u_2(g_1 - g_2)}$$

$$+ \Gamma_{il}(g_1) \Gamma_{jk}(g_2)\, e^{j\pi u_1(g_1 - g_2)}\, e^{j\pi u_2(g_1 - g_2)} \}$$

$$\times \left[T' \int_{-T'}^{T'} e^{j2\pi r(g_1 + g_2)} \left(1 - \frac{|r|}{T'} \right) dr \right.$$

$$\left. - T'' \int_{-T''}^{T''} e^{j2\pi r(g_1 + g_2)} \left(1 - \frac{|r|}{T''} \right) dr \right] dg_1\, dg_2.$$

This reduces to

$$\frac{1}{T^2} \int_{-\infty}^{\infty} \int_{-\infty}^{\infty} \{\Gamma\} \frac{\sin^2 \pi(g_1 + g_2)T' - \sin^2 \pi(g_1 + g_2)T''}{\pi^2(g_1^2 + g_2^2)}\, dg_1\, dg_2,$$

where $\{\Gamma\}$ stands for the quantity in braces above. But

$$\sin^2 aT' - \sin^2 aT'' = \sin a(T - |u_1|) \sin a(T - |u_2|),$$

and hence, substituting $g_1 = f + g$, $g_2 = f - g$ so that $dg_1\, dg_2 = 2\, df\, dg$,

$$\text{Cov } [c_{ij}(u_1), c_{kl}(u_2)] = \frac{2}{T^2} \int_{-\infty}^{\infty} \int_{-\infty}^{\infty} \frac{\sin 2\pi f(T - |u_1|)}{2\pi f} \frac{\sin 2\pi f(T - |u_2|)}{2\pi f}$$

$$\times \{ \Gamma_{ik}(f + g) \Gamma_{jl}(f - g)\, e^{j2\pi g(u_1 - u_2)} + \Gamma_{il}(f + g) \Gamma_{jk}(f - g)\, e^{j2\pi g(u_1 + u_2)} \}\, df\, dg, \tag{A9.1.13}$$

which provides an alternative form for (A9.1.9) and is exact if the X_i are Normal. For $|u_1|$ and $|u_2|$ small and T large, integrating (A9.2.2) over f gives

$$\text{Cov } [c_{ij}(u_1), c_{kl}(u_2)]$$

$$= \frac{1}{T} \int_{-\infty}^{\infty} \{ \Gamma_{ik}(g) \Gamma_{jl}(-g)\, e^{j2\pi g(u_1 - u_2)} + \Gamma_{il}(g) \Gamma_{jk}(-g)\, e^{j2\pi g(u_1 + u_2)} \}\, dg, \tag{A9.1.14}$$

since $[(\sin 2\pi fT)/2\pi fT]^2$ tends to $(1/2T)\, \delta(f)$ when T is large.

Substituting (A9.1.13) in (A9.1.12),

Cov $[C_{ij}(f_1), C_{kl}(f_2)]$

$$= \int_{-T}^{T} \int e^{-j2\pi(f_1 u_1 + f_2 u_2)} \frac{2}{T^2} \int_{-\infty}^{\infty} \int \frac{\sin 2\pi f(T - |u_1|)}{2\pi f} \frac{\sin 2\pi f(T - |u_2|)}{2\pi f}$$
$$\times \{\Gamma_{ik}(f + g)\Gamma_{jl}(f - g) e^{j2\pi g(u_1 - u_2)} + \Gamma_{il}(f + g)\Gamma_{jk}(f - g) e^{j2\pi g(u_1 + u_2)}\}$$
$$\times df\, dg\, du_1\, du_2.$$

Interchanging orders of integration, collecting terms and simplifying

Cov $[C_{ij}(f_1), C_{kl}(f_2)]$

$$= \frac{1}{T^2} \int_{-\infty}^{\infty} \Gamma_{ik}(x) \frac{\sin \pi T(f_1 - x)}{\pi(f_1 - x)} \frac{\sin \pi T(f_2 + x)}{\pi(f_2 + x)} dx \int_{-\infty}^{\infty} \Gamma_{jl}(-y)$$
$$\times \frac{\sin \pi T(f_1 + y)}{\pi(f_1 + y)} \frac{\sin \pi T(f_2 - y)}{\pi(f_2 - y)} dy + \frac{1}{T^2} \int_{-\infty}^{\infty} \Gamma_{il}(x) \frac{\sin \pi T(f_1 - x)}{\pi(f_1 - x)}$$
$$\times \frac{\sin \pi T(f_2 - x)}{\pi(f_2 - x)} \int_{-\infty}^{\infty} \Gamma_{jk}(-y) \frac{\sin \pi T(f_1 + y)}{\pi(f_1 + y)} \frac{\sin \pi T(f_2 + y)}{\pi(f_2 + y)} dy.$$
$$\text{(A9.1.15)}$$

Simplification of result. The result (A9.1.15) is exact for Normal rv's. It may be simplified for random processes whose spectra are approximately constant over the range f_1 to f_2, since then the terms $\Gamma_{ik}(f_1)$ may be taken outside the integral. Hence for noise which is approximately white in the frequency range f_1 to f_2,

$$\text{Cov } [C_{ij}(f_1), C_{kl}(f_2)] \approx \Gamma_{ik}(f_1)\Gamma_{jl}(-f_1) \left\{\frac{\sin \pi T(f_1 + f_2)}{\pi T(f_1 + f_2)}\right\}^2$$
$$+ \Gamma_{il}(f_1)\Gamma_{jk}(-f_1) \left\{\frac{\sin \pi T(f_1 - f_2)}{\pi T(f_1 - f_2)}\right\}^2.$$
$$\text{(A9.1.16)}$$

Equation (A9.1.16) is exact for Normal white noise processes. For non-white and/or non-Normal processes, the result is only approximate.

All the above results apply in the discrete case, except that the terms in $\Gamma(f)$ are multiplied by Δ, and the frequency range is $-1/2\Delta \leqslant f < 1/2\Delta$. Thus for the discrete case, (A9.1.16) becomes

$$\text{Cov } [C_{ij}(f_1), C_{kl}(f_2)] \approx \Delta^2\Gamma_{ik}(f_1)\Gamma_{jl}(-f_1) \left\{\frac{\sin \pi N \Delta(f_1 + f_2)}{N \sin \pi \Delta(f_1 + f_2)}\right\}^2$$
$$+ \Delta^2\Gamma_{il}(f_1)\Gamma_{jk}(-f_1) \left\{\frac{\sin \pi N \Delta(f_1 - f_2)}{N \sin \pi \Delta(f_1 - f_2)}\right\}^2.$$
$$\text{(A9.1.17)}$$

Setting $X_i = X_j = X_k = X_l = Z$ in (A9.1.16) and (A9.1.17) gives the results (6.3.17) and (6.3.15) for white noise, and more generally (6.4.9) for non-white noise.

The results (A9.1.16) and (A9.1.17) show that for T large, the covariance between two spectral estimators is of order $1/T^2$ except when $f_1 = f_2$. Hence to a good degree of approximation, spectral estimators at spacing greater than $1/T$ may be regarded as uncorrelated.

Generalized covariance matrix. The general results (A9.1.16) and (A9.1.17) may be used to derive the generalized covariance matrix (9.1.22). For example, the term Cov $[L_{12}(f), Q_{12}(f)]$ may be derived as follows:

$$L_{12}(f) = \tfrac{1}{2}\{C_{12}(f) + C_{12}(-f)\} = \tfrac{1}{2}\{C_{12}(f) + C_{21}(f)\},$$

$$Q_{12}(f) = \frac{1}{2j}\{C_{12}(f) - C_{12}(-f)\} = \frac{1}{2j}\{C_{12}(f) - C_{21}(f)\}.$$

Hence,

$$\text{Cov } [L_{12}(f), Q_{12}(f)] = \text{Cov } \left[\frac{C_{12}(f) + C_{21}(f)}{2}, \frac{C_{12}(f) - C_{21}(f)}{2j}\right]$$

$$= \frac{1}{4j} \{\text{Cov } [C_{12}(f), C_{12}(f)] - \text{Cov } [C_{12}(f), C_{21}(f)]$$

$$+ \text{Cov } [C_{21}(f), C_{12}(f)] - \text{Cov } [C_{21}(f), C_{21}(f)]\}.$$

Substituting for Cov $[C_{ij}(f), C_{kl}(f)]$ from (9.1.15) yields

$$\text{Cov } [L_{12}(f), Q_{12}(f)] = \frac{1}{4j}\{\Gamma_{11}(f)\Gamma_{22}(-f)W^2(+) + \Gamma_{12}(f)\Gamma_{21}(-f)W^2(-)$$

$$- \Gamma_{12}(f)\Gamma_{21}(-f)W^2(+) - \Gamma_{11}(f)\Gamma_{22}(-f)W^2(-)$$

$$+ \Gamma_{21}(f)\Gamma_{12}(-f)W^2(+) + \Gamma_{22}(f)\Gamma_{11}(-f)W^2(-)$$

$$- \Gamma_{22}(f)\Gamma_{11}(-f)W^2(+) - \Gamma_{21}(f)\Gamma_{12}(-f)W^2(-)\},$$

using the notation of (9.1.13) and (9.1.14). This reduces to

$$\text{Cov } [L_{12}(f), Q_{12}(f)]$$

$$= \frac{1}{4j}\{W^2(+)(-\Gamma_{12}^2(f) + \Gamma_{12}^2(-f)) + W^2(-)(\Gamma_{12}^2(f) - \Gamma_{12}^2(-f))\}.$$

Since

$$\Gamma_{12}^2(f) - \Gamma_{12}^2(-f)$$

$$= \Lambda_{12}^2(f) + 2j\Lambda_{12}(f)\Psi_{12}(f) - \Psi_{12}^2(f) - \{\Lambda_{12}^2(f) - 2j\Lambda_{12}(f)\Psi_{12}(f) - \Psi_{12}^2(f)\}$$

$$= 4j\Lambda_{12}(f)\Psi_{12}(f),$$

on neglecting the terms in $W^2(+)$,

$$\text{Cov } [L_{12}(f), Q_{12}(f)] \approx \Lambda_{12}(f)\Psi_{12}(f)W^2(-).$$

Chi-squared properties of autospectral estimators. Consider the stochastic process $X_1(t)$, where $X_1(t)$ is Normal with mean zero and variance σ_1^2. The spectral estimator $C_{11}(f)$ is

$$C_{11}(f) = \frac{1}{T}\left|\int_{-T/2}^{T/2} X_1(t)\, e^{-j2\pi ft}\, dt\right|^2$$

$$= \frac{1}{T}\left[\left\{\int_{-T/2}^{T/2} X_1(t)\cos 2\pi ft\, dt\right\}^2 + \left\{\int_{-T/2}^{T/2} X_1(t)\sin 2\pi ft\, dt\right\}^2\right]$$

$$= \frac{1}{T}\{X_c^2(f) + X_s^2(f)\},\qquad\qquad (A9.1.18)$$

where $X_c(f)$ and $X_s(f)$ are the Fourier cosine and sine transforms of $X_1(t)$ respectively. Since the Fourier transform is a linear operation and $X_1(f)$ is a Normal process, it follows that $X_c(f)$ and $X_s(f)$ are Normal. But from (A9.1.18),

$C_{11}(f)$ is a sum of two squared Normal rv's and hence $C_{11}(f)$ is distributed as a chi-squared rv with two degrees of freedom. The results of Section 6.3.3 follow immediately.

For non-Normal processes, the Fourier transforms $X_c(f)$ and $X_s(f)$ are weighted sums over time t of the random variables X_t. Hence the above results will be approximately true for non-Normal processes.

Covariance of smoothed spectral estimators. The smoothed spectral estimator $\bar{C}_{ij}(f)$ is related to $C_{ij}(f)$ by

$$\bar{C}_{ij}(f) = \int_{-\infty}^{\infty} C_{ij}(g) W(f - g)\, dg, \qquad (A9.1.19)$$

where $W(f)$ is the spectral window corresponding to the lag window $w(t)$. Hence

$$\bar{C}_{ij}(f) = \int_{-T}^{T} c_{ij}(u) w(u)\, e^{-j2\pi f u}\, du. \qquad (A9.1.20)$$

The covariance between smoothed spectral estimators may be derived as follows. Since

$$\bar{c}_{ij}(u) = c_{ij}(u) w(u), \qquad (A9.1.21)$$

$$\text{Cov}\,[\bar{c}_{ij}(u_1),\, \bar{c}_{kl}(u_2)] = w(u_1) w(u_2)\, \text{Cov}\,[c_{ij}(u_1),\, c_{kl}(u_2)]. \qquad (A9.1.22)$$

Hence, from (A9.1.12) and (A9.1.22),

$$\text{Cov}\,[\bar{C}_{ij}(f_1),\, \bar{C}_{kl}(f_2)]$$

$$= \int_{-T}^{T} \int_{-T}^{T} w(u_1) w(u_2)\, \text{Cov}\,[c_{ij}(u_1),\, c_{kl}(u_2)]\, e^{-j2\pi(f_1 u_1 + f_2 u_2)}\, du_1\, du_2. \qquad (A9.1.23)$$

Now $w(u)$ is zero for $|u| > M$, where $M \ll T$. Hence the approximation (A9.1.14) may be used for $\text{Cov}\,[c_{ij}(u_1),\, c_{kl}(u_2)]$ in (A9.1.23).

Thus,

$$\text{Cov}\,[\bar{C}_{ij}(f_1),\, \bar{C}_{kl}(f_2)] \approx \int_{-T}^{T} \int \frac{w(u_1) w(u_2)}{T}\, e^{-j2\pi(f_1 u_1 + f_2 u_2)}$$

$$\times \int_{-\infty}^{\infty} \{ \Gamma_{ik}(g) \Gamma_{jl}(-g)\, e^{j2\pi g(u_1 - u_2)}$$

$$+\ \Gamma_{il}(g) \Gamma_{jk}(-g)\, e^{j2\pi g(u_1 + u_2)} \}\, dg\, du_1\, du_2. \qquad (A9.1.24)$$

Interchanging orders of integration gives

$$\text{Cov}\,[\bar{C}_{ij}(f_1),\, \bar{C}_{kl}(f_2)]$$

$$\approx \frac{1}{T} \int_{-\infty}^{\infty} W(f_1 - g) \{ \Gamma_{ik}(g) \Gamma_{jl}(-g) W(f_2 + g) + \Gamma_{il}(g) \Gamma_{jk}(-g) W(f_2 - g) \}\, dg. \qquad (A9.1.25)$$

Making the assumption that the Γ's are smooth over the width of the spectral window allows us to remove the Γ's from the integration, and hence (A9.1.25) becomes

$$\text{Cov}\,[\bar{C}_{ij}(f_1),\, \bar{C}_{kl}(f_2)] \approx \frac{\Gamma_{ik}(f_1) \Gamma_{jl}(-f_1)}{T} \int_{-\infty}^{\infty} W(f_1 - g) W(f_2 + g)\, dg$$

$$+ \frac{\Gamma_{il}(f_1) \Gamma_{jk}(-f_1)}{T} \int_{-\infty}^{\infty} W(f_1 - g) W(f_2 - g)\, dg. \qquad (A9.1.26)$$

Hence, provided the spectral windows are narrow and do not overlap very much, the covariance between smoothed spectral estimators will be very small.

For $f_1 = f_2$, (A9.1.26) becomes

$$\text{Cov}\,[\bar{C}_{ij}(f_1),\,\bar{C}_{kl}(f_1)] \approx \frac{\Gamma_{ik}(f_1)\Gamma_{jl}(-f_1)}{T} \int_{-\infty}^{\infty} W(f_1 - g)W(f_1 + g)\,dg$$

$$+ \frac{\Gamma_{il}(f_1)\Gamma_{jk}(-f_1)}{T} \int_{-\infty}^{\infty} W^2(f_1 - g)\,dg. \qquad (A9.1.27)$$

Neglecting the first term on the right-hand side of (A9.1.27), since it represents only a small amount of overlapping,

$$\text{Cov}\,[\bar{C}_{ij}(f_1),\,\bar{C}_{kl}(f_1)] \approx \frac{\Gamma_{il}(f_1)\Gamma_{jk}(-f_1)}{T} \int_{-\infty}^{\infty} W^2(g)\,dg$$

$$= \frac{\Gamma_{il}(f_1)\Gamma_{jk}(-f_1)}{T} \int_{-\infty}^{\infty} w^2(u)\,du, \qquad (A.9.1.28)$$

by Parseval's theorem. The result (A9.1.27) may be used to derive the generalized covariance matrix between smoothed spectral estimators. As stated in Section 9.2.1, this matrix is the same as the matrix (9.1.22) except that the multiplier $W^2(-)$ is replaced by I/T, where

$$I = \int_{-M}^{M} w^2(u)\,du.$$

APPENDIX A9.2   FLOW CHART FOR BIVARIATE SPECTRAL CALCULATIONS

The following is a flow chart for a computer program CROSSPEC which accepts auto- and cross covariance estimates COV(K,I,J) or DCOV(K,I,J), K$=0$, MAXM, I$=1,2$, J$=1,2$ from program MULTICOR described in Appendix A5.3. Additional inputs are DELTA, NF, M$\leqslant$MAXM$-|S|$, and S, the number of lags necessary to align the two processes so that the largest cross covariance is centered at zero. Output consists of printout of the covariances (echo check), the smoothed autospectra for each truncation point M, and the phase and squared coherency spectra, and plots of the logarithm of the autospectra, the squared coherency, and the phase spectrum with overlays for additional truncation points.

Program CROSSPEC

1) *Input* parameters N, MAXM, DELTA, NF, S.

2) *Read* IDENT(1), COV(K,1,1), K$=0$, MAXM

       IDENT(2), COV(K,2,2), K$=0$, MAXM

           COV(K,1,2), K$=0$, MAXM

           COV(K,2,1), K$=0$, MAXM.

3) *Read* M, *set* COV(K)$=$COV(K,1,1), K$=0$, MAXM.

4) *Call* subroutine AUTOSPEC [Appendix A7.1].

5) *Store* SPEC(K,1) = SPEC(K), K = 0, NF.

6) *Set* COV(K) = COV(K,2,2), K = 0, MAXM.

7) *Call* subroutine AUTOSPEC.

8) *Store* SPEC(K,2) = SPEC(K), K = 0, NF.

9) *Call* subroutine EVOD.

Subroutine EVOD

Calculate EV(K) = COV(K + S,1,2) + COV(K − S,2,1), K = 0, M

OD(K) = COV(K + S,1,2) − COV(K − S,2,1), K = 0, M

(NOTE   COV(K,1,2) = COV(−K,2,1)).

10) *Call* subroutine CROSPEC.

Subroutine CROSPEC

Calculate smoothed co- and quadrature spectra and the squared cross amplitude,

$$\text{COSPEC(I)} = 2.*\text{DELTA}*\left\{\text{EV(0)} + 2.* \sum_{K=1}^{M-1} \text{EV(K)W(K) COS } \frac{\pi KI}{NF}\right\}$$

$$\text{QSPEC(I)} = 4.*\text{DELTA}* \sum_{K=1}^{M-1} \text{OD(K)W(K) SIN } \frac{\pi KI}{NF}$$

$$\text{SQ(I)} = \text{COSPEC(I)}*\text{COSPEC(I)} + \text{QSPEC(I)}*\text{QSPEC(I)}.$$

As in subroutine AUTOSPEC, the Fourier transform can be performed very rapidly using either the fast Fourier transform or the algorithm listed below.

11) *Calculate* PHASE(K) = ARCTAN(−QSPEC(K)/COSPEC(K))

COHSQ(K) = SQ(K)/(SPEC(K,1)*SPEC(K,2)).

12) *Calculate* LOGSPEC(K,1) = LOG10(SPEC(K,1))

LOGSPEC(K,2) = LOG10(SPEC(K,2))

observing the cautionary notes in (5) of AUTOSPEC subroutine.

13) *Print* the smoothed autospectra SPEC(K,1), SPEC(K,2), the phase PHASE(K), the squared coherency COHSQ(K), the bandwidth B and the degrees of freedom D.

14) *Plot* and *overlay*: the LOGSPEC(K,1) for all values of M used
the LOGSPEC(K,2) for all values of M used
the PHASE(K)
the COHSQ(K).

Algorithm

To find COSPEC(I), QSPEC(I),

set $C = COS \dfrac{\pi I}{NF}$, V0 = 0., V1 = 0.

       $SN = SIN \dfrac{\pi I}{NF}$, Z0 = 0., Z1 = 0.

Do 1, K = M − 1, 1

     V2 = 2.*C*V1 − V0 + W(K)*EV(K)

     Z2 = 2.*C*Z1 − Z0 + W(K)*OD(K)

     V0 = V1

     V1 = V2

     Z0 = Z1

1   Z1 = Z2

COSPEC(I) = 2.*DELTA*{EV(0) + 2.*(V1*C − V0)}

QSPEC(I) = 4.*DELTA*Z1*SN.

APPENDIX A9.3   SAMPLE CORRELATIONS FOR DATA OF APPENDIX A8.1

Table A9.1: Sample correlations for the data of Table A8.1

k								
0–7	1.000	0.505	0.071	−0.139	−0.137	−0.092	−0.124	−0.092
8–15	0.009	0.103	0.110	0.028	−0.097	−0.096	−0.025	0.011
16–23	−0.031	−0.019	0.116	0.195	0.138	0.049	−0.010	0.058
24–31	0.083	−0.031	−0.167	−0.140	−0.069	0.025	0.026	−0.080
				Autocorrelations $r_{11}(k)$				
0–7	−0.075	0.409	0.452	0.320	0.195	0.080	0.123	−0.004
8–15	−0.050	−0.035	0.056	0.133	0.082	−0.033	−0.098	−0.048
16–23	−0.039	−0.071	−0.121	−0.110	−0.059	0.044	0.072	0.156
24–31	0.234	0.245	0.153	0.026	−0.037	−0.027	−0.020	0.004
				Cross correlations $r_{12}(k)$				
0–7	−0.075	−0.498	−0.485	−0.278	−0.114	−0.050	0.042	0.109
8–15	0.087	−0.005	−0.066	−0.067	0.017	0.040	0.043	0.001
16–23	−0.049	0.085	0.175	0.101	−0.077	−0.102	−0.042	0.043
24–31	−0.014	−0.064	0.001	0.081	0.063	0.027	−0.064	−0.049
				Cross correlations $r_{21}(k)$				
0–7	1.000	0.536	0.186	−0.056	−0.121	−0.080	−0.066	−0.048
8–15	0.006	0.054	−0.020	0.005	−0.060	−0.042	0.018	0.025
16–23	−0.051	−0.084	−0.063	0.014	0.166	0.107	0.019	0.032
24–31	−0.063	−0.081	−0.155	−0.045	−0.049	−0.011	−0.080	−0.096
				Autocorrelations $r_{22}(k)$				

TABLE A9.2: Sample correlations for the data of Table A8.2

k								
0–7	1.000	0.540	0.335	0.219	0.262	0.274	0.151	0.056
8–15	0.030	0.058	0.017	−0.035	−0.113	−0.139	−0.101	−0.101
16–23	−0.107	−0.123	−0.066	0.026	0.037	0.024	−0.027	0.016
24–31	0.059	0.052	−0.030	−0.043	−0.062	−0.055	−0.028	−0.091
			Autocorrelations $r_{11}(k)$					
0–7	0.013	0.098	0.114	0.116	0.176	0.264	0.338	0.336
8–15	0.369	0.460	0.752	0.661	0.505	0.385	0.328	0.307
16–23	0.195	0.081	0.017	0.038	0.031	0.033	−0.012	−0.040
24–31	−0.016	0.003	0.012	0.008	0.034	0.062	0.074	0.059
			Cross correlations $r_{12}(k)$					
0–7	0.013	−0.057	−0.131	−0.147	−0.152	−0.172	−0.171	−0.163
8–15	−0.120	−0.089	−0.074	−0.071	−0.042	0.003	0.018	−0.012
16–23	−0.101	−0.095	−0.105	−0.109	−0.143	−0.185	−0.209	−0.191
24–31	−0.163	−0.079	−0.026	0.003	−0.013	−0.009	−0.007	0.073
			Cross correlations $r_{21}(k)$					
0–7	1.000	0.848	0.678	0.546	0.473	0.400	0.299	0.200
8–15	0.145	0.124	0.084	0.071	0.043	0.044	0.051	0.041
16–23	0.028	0.024	0.026	0.020	0.010	−0.012	−0.018	0.012
24–31	0.045	0.058	0.029	0.023	0.030	0.037	0.002	−0.026
			Autocorrelations $r_{22}(k)$					

10

Estimation of
Frequency Response Functions

In this chapter, the problem of estimating the frequency response function of a linear system is considered, when records of the input and corresponding output of the system are available.

By way of introduction, the estimation of an impulse response function is discussed. It is concluded that this approach is unsatisfactory, both because it involves the estimation of too many parameters and also because the estimates have bad statistical properties, stemming from the fact that neighboring estimates of the impulse response function are highly correlated. These difficulties can be removed by estimating the frequency response function using cross spectral analysis. It is shown how to obtain good estimates of the gain and phase using the window-closing procedure, and confidence intervals for these functions are derived. It is concluded that, whereas cross spectral analysis is sometimes a useful exploratory tool for estimating the characteristics of a linear system, the ultimate objective in this work should be to estimate the parameters in a model using least squares methods, suitably modified to account for autocorrelation in the residuals.

10.1 INTRODUCTION

This chapter deals with the second problem relating to bivariate time series, discussed at the beginning of Chapter 8, namely where the stochastic processes $X_1(t)$, $X_2(t)$ are *known* to be the input and output of some physical system. Given records $x_1(t)$, $x_2(t)$ from the system during the interval $0 \leqslant t \leqslant T$, it is required to estimate the system characteristics. For example, $x_1(t)$ might be the input gas rate and $x_2(t)$ the output yield from a gas furnace as shown in Figure 8.3.

Problems of this kind arise frequently on industrial processes. Two situations can be distinguished: where $x_1(t)$ and $x_2(t)$ represent normal operating records, and where deliberate changes are made in the input $x_1(t)$, and $x_2(t)$ is the corresponding output. The dangers associated with analyzing data of the first type are well known. The most important of these is that any relation connecting $x_1(t)$ and $x_2(t)$ which is fitted to the data may be quite worthless in predicting the effect of deliberate changes in $x_1(t)$ on $x_2(t)$. This could occur, for example, if $x_1(t)$ had no direct influence on $x_2(t)$, but was correlated with a third variable $x_3(t)$ which directly influenced $x_2(t)$. Hence the second type of data is preferable for estimation purposes, but it may not always be possible to collect data of this kind, since experiments on the system may be ruled out. Note also that classical methods of estimating the system characteristics using step and sinusoidal changes may be unsuccessful in process situations because of large disturbances generated within the system. Hence it is necessary to resort to statistical methods which make due allowance for noise generated in the system.

Estimation of impulse response functions. To estimate the system characteristics, the simplifying assumption that the system is *linear* is made initially. That is, the input and output may be described accurately by the dynamic stochastic model

$$X_2(t) - \mu_2 = \int_0^\infty h(u)(X_1(t-u) - \mu_1)\, du + Z(t), \qquad (10.1.1)$$

where $h(u)$ is the impulse response function of the system and $Z(t)$ is a noise or error term which is *assumed* to be uncorrelated with the input $X_1(t)$. The model (10.1.1) is likely to be inadequate in some circumstances, due to non-linearities in the input–output relationship, feedback from the output to the input by a controller, as described in [1], and the effect of other input variables on the output, as described in Chapter 11. For the present, it is assumed that the model (10.1.1) adequately represents the real situation. This is so when changes in $X_1(t)$ are sufficiently small and no feedback occurs.

The model (10.1.1) in the discrete form,

$$X_{2t} - \mu_2 = \sum_{m=0}^\infty h_m(X_{1t-m} - \mu_1) + Z_t, \qquad (10.1.2)$$

is frequently used to estimate weights h_m from process input–output records. The approach can be criticized for two reasons. First, the number of weights h_m required to characterize the system may be large. Since physical systems can usually be described by differential equations of the form (2.3.18) involving few parameters, it is more sensible to parameterize the problem by fitting a model

$$X_{2t} - \mu_2 - \alpha_1(X_{2t-1} - \mu_2) - \cdots - \alpha_m(X_{2t-m} - \mu_2)$$
$$= \beta_0(X_{1t} - \mu_1) + \beta_1(X_{1t-1} - \mu_1) + \cdots + \beta_l(X_{1t-l} - \mu_1) + Z_t.$$
$$(10.1.3)$$

In this way the number of parameters which has to be estimated is kept to a small and manageable number. The second criticism is that the least squares estimators of h_m obtained from (10.1.2) are highly correlated in the same way that the estimators of the auto- and cross correlation functions are highly correlated. An example of this behavior will be given in Section 10.2.

Estimation of frequency response functions. The system characteristics may also be estimated in the frequency domain using spectral analysis. The main advantage of this approach is that it removes the difficulties associated with the second criticism given above. It will be shown in Section 10.3 that cross spectral analysis may be used to estimate the frequency response function

$$H(f) = \int_0^\infty h(u)\, e^{-j2\pi f u}\, du, \tag{10.1.4}$$

using the estimation equation

$$\hat{H}(f) = \frac{\overline{C}_{12}(f)}{\overline{C}_{11}(f)}. \tag{10.1.5}$$

In (10.1.5) $\overline{C}_{12}(f)$ is the smoothed estimator of the cross spectrum between input and output and $\overline{C}_{11}(f)$ is the smoothed estimator of the input spectrum. The estimators (10.1.5) are uncorrelated at neighboring frequencies and hence the estimator of $h(u)$ obtained by taking the inverse transform of (10.1.5) will be much smoother than that obtained by estimating $h(u)$ directly.

Since the window-closing procedure used in spectral analysis will adjust itself to the local smoothness properties of the frequency response function, it is to be expected that fewer parameters will be needed in the frequency domain than in the time domain. However, spectral analysis still requires the estimation of more parameters than a suitably chosen parametric model. Hence parametric estimation should be regarded as the ultimate objective in this kind of work. The main value of spectral analysis in the area of system identification is as an exploratory tool which can be used to suggest possible models. However, it has several advantages when compared with a parametric approach. First, it is easily generalized to deal with multivariate systems as will be shown in Chapter 11. Second, in many practical problems engineers are interested only in describing the gain and phase over a *very limited* frequency range, whereas a parametric model provides a model of much wider applicability. And finally, because of the flexibility of the spectral approach the time series can be filtered into frequency bands which may then be analyzed separately. This is necessary in some applications because it may be unreasonable to suppose that the same parametric model holds over wide frequency ranges.

10.2 ESTIMATION OF IMPULSE RESPONSE FUNCTIONS

10.2.1 Direct estimation of impulse response functions

It was stated in Section 10.1 that direct estimation of the impulse response function $h(u)$ is not a sensible approach. To illustrate the pitfalls associated with the method, artificial data were constructed using the linear model

$$X_{2t} = X_t + Z_t,$$
$$X_t = 0.25X_{t-1} - 0.5X_{t-2} + X_{1t}, \qquad (10.2.1)$$

where Z_t is white noise and X_{1t} is the system input. The system output X_{2t} is composed of white noise Z_t added to the response X_t of a linear second-order system whose input is X_{1t}. The data used for analysis consisted of pairs of values of x_{1t} and x_{2t}, and are listed in Appendix A10.1.

The model

$$(X_{2t} - \mu_2) = \sum_{m=0}^{M} h_m(X_{1t-m} - \bar{X}_1) + Z_t, \qquad (10.2.2)$$

where $\bar{X}_1$ is the mean level of the input process, was then fitted to the data. Since the point M beyond which h_m is negligible will not be known, it is necessary to try a series of values of M and stop when the estimate of h_m has become small compared with the noise level. For fixed M the weights h_m may be estimated by least squares, that is, by minimizing

$$S = \sum_{t=M+1}^{N} \{(x_{2t} - \mu_2) - \sum_{m=0}^{M} h_m(x_{1t-m} - \bar{x}_1)\}^2 \qquad (10.2.3)$$

with respect to μ_2 and h_m, $m = 0, 1, \ldots, M$, under the assumption that the noise is white. This leads to the normal equations

$$\sum_{t=M+1}^{N} (x_{2t} - \bar{x}_2)(x_{1t-k} - \bar{x}_1)$$

$$= \hat{h}_0 \sum_{t=M+1}^{N} (x_{1t} - \bar{x}_1)(x_{1t-k} - \bar{x}_1) + \cdots + \hat{h}_M \sum_{t=1}^{N} (x_{1t-M} - \bar{x}_1)(x_{1t-k} - \bar{x}_1),$$

$$k = 0, 1, 2, \ldots, M. \qquad (10.2.4)$$

Note that the equations (10.2.4) are appropriate only if the noise Z_t is white. Initially the correlation structure of the noise will not be known, so the estimation has to proceed in two stages. First, the estimates (10.2.4) are obtained and then the autocorrelation function of the residuals calculated. On the basis of these, a more efficient estimation procedure can be designed to allow for the correlation structure of the noise. An example of this approach is given in Section 10.2.2.

Since the noise Z_t was known to be white in this example, the normal equations (10.2.4) were used to estimate the parameters from a series of 100 terms generated from the model (10.2.1). Table 10.1 shows the estimates $\hat{h}_m$ for values of $M = 10, 12, 16$. Comparison of the estimates with the theoretical impulse response values shows that the estimates are poor. This is because the estimators have large variances and also because neighboring estimators are correlated, as evidenced by the oscillatory behavior of $\hat{h}_m$ for m large.

10.2.2 Parametric estimation of impulse response functions

A correct parametric analysis in the time domain involves the estimation of parameters in the model (10.1.3), as described in [1]. The number of parameters which need to be included in the model may be determined by introducing more terms on both sides of (10.1.3) and at each stage calculating the variance and the acf of the residuals. The model is adequate when there is no evidence of autocorrelation in the residuals, which should be subjected to one of the two tests for white noise discussed in Sections 5.3.5 and 6.3.2.

A model of the form

$$X_{2t} - \mu_2 = \alpha_1(X_{2t-1} - \mu_2) + \alpha_2(X_{2t-2} - \mu_2) + \beta_0(X_{1t} - \bar{X}_1) + Z_t \qquad (10.2.5)$$

was tried first for the data generated from (10.2.1). Under the assumption that the noise Z_t is white, the normal equations may then be obtained by minimizing the sum of squares

$$\sum_{t=3}^{N} \{x_{2t} - \mu_2 - \alpha_1(x_{2t-1} - \mu_2) - \alpha_2(x_{2t-2} - \mu_2) - \beta_0(x_{1t} - \bar{x}_1)\}^2,$$

with respect to μ_2, α_1, α_2 and β_0.

Provided the input and output time series are stationary, the normal equations may be approximated, using the method described in Section 5.4.1, to give the approximate estimation equations

$$c_{22}(1) \approx \hat{\alpha}_1 c_{22}(0) + \hat{\alpha}_2 c_{22}(1) + \hat{\beta}_0 c_{12}(-1),$$
$$c_{22}(2) \approx \hat{\alpha}_1 c_{22}(1) + \hat{\alpha}_2 c_{22}(0) + \hat{\beta}_0 c_{12}(-2), \qquad (10.2.6)$$
$$c_{12}(0) \approx \hat{\alpha}_1 c_{12}(-1) + \hat{\alpha}_2 c_{12}(-2) + \hat{\beta}_0 c_{11}(0).$$

TABLE 10.1: Estimation of impulse response functions using three truncation points

m	0	1	2	3	4	5	6	7
Theoretical	1.000	0.250	−0.438	−0.234	0.154	0.055	−0.066	−0.044
$M = 10$	1.056	0.342	−0.572	0.037	−0.141	0.373	−0.249	0.107
$M = 12$	1.018	0.427	−0.716	0.210	−0.320	0.561	−0.443	0.313
$M = 16$	1.029	0.424	−0.692	0.198	−0.307	0.527	−0.438	0.284

m	8	9	10	11	12	13	14	15	16
Theoretical	0.022	0.028	−0.004	−0.014	−0.001	0.006	0.002	−0.002	0.000
$M = 10$	−0.289	0.220	−0.163	0.201	−0.112	−0.031	0.089	0.074	−0.010
$M = 12$	−0.518	0.471	−0.417	0.181	−0.062				
$M = 16$	−0.504	0.452	−0.412						

Solution of (10.2.6) using the covariance estimates of Table A10.2 yielded estimates $\hat{\alpha}_1 = 0.072$, $\hat{\alpha}_2 = -0.276$, $\hat{\beta}_0 = 1.182$. The estimated residuals

$$\hat{z}_t = x_{2t} - \bar{x}_2 - \hat{\alpha}_1(x_{2t-1} - \bar{x}_2) - \hat{\alpha}_2(x_{2t-2} - \bar{x}_2) - \hat{\beta}_0(x_{1t} - \bar{x}_1)$$

$$= (x_{2t} - .21) - 0.072(x_{2t-1} - .21) + 0.276(x_{2t-2} - .21) - 1.182(x_{1t} - .17)$$

resulting from this fit were then obtained and their autocorrelations calculated. The first 10 values of the acf of the residuals are shown in Table 10.2.

TABLE 10.2:   Autocorrelations of residuals from fitted dynamic model

k	1	2	3	4	5	6	7	8	9	10
$r_{zz}(k)$	-0.14	0.31	-0.02	0.08	0.05	0.05	-0.07	-0.08	0.00	-0.12

The autocorrelations of Table 10.2 are not in agreement with the hypothesis that the residuals z_t are white noise. They suggest, instead, that the model (10.2.5) should be modified to

$$X_{2t} - \mu_2 = \alpha_1(X_{2t-1} - \mu_2) + \alpha_2(X_{2t-2} - \mu_2) + \beta_0(X_{1t} - \bar{X}_1)$$
$$+ Z_t + \delta_1 Z_{t-1} + \delta_2 Z_{t-2}$$

to account for the ma nature of the acf of the residuals.

In fitting an ar model to a pair of input–output time series when measurement noise is known to be present in the output, it is easily seen that the residuals will behave as an ma process of order equal to the order of the system relating the two series. Hence in this case, two ma parameters δ_1 and δ_2 are required to whiten the residuals.

A grid of values of (δ_1, δ_2) was chosen and the input and output series filtered according to

$$y_{2t} - \delta_1 y_{2t-1} - \delta_2 y_{2t-2} = x_{2t},$$
$$y_{1t} - \delta_1 y_{1t-1} - \delta_2 y_{1t-2} = x_{1t}.$$

The model (10.2.5) was then refitted to the filtered series y_{2t}, y_{1t} for each pair of values (δ_1, δ_2), and the estimates (10.2.6) calculated for the parameters α_1, α_2 and β_0. The final estimates chosen were those which minimized the residual sum of squares. For the above example, the best values of δ_1 and δ_2 are $\hat{\delta}_1 = -0.3$, $\hat{\delta}_2 = +0.8$, and the revised system parameter estimates are $\hat{\alpha}_1 = 0.251$, $\hat{\alpha}_2 = -0.479$, $\hat{\beta}_0 = 1.10$. The acf of the residuals from this model is small, which confirms the adequacy of the model.

The impulse response function corresponding to the revised model (10.2.5) is given in Table 10.3, and it is seen that the values agree much better with their theoretical values than those obtained by direct estimation of the impulse response.

TABLE 10.3: Estimates of the impulse response function using parametric estimation

m		0	1	2	3	4	5
theoretical	h_m	1.00	0.250	−0.438	−0.234	0.154	0.055
parametric estimation	$\hat{h}_m$	1.10	0.276	−0.458	−0.235	0.160	0.153
		6	7	8	9	10	
theoretical	h_m	−0.066	−0.044	0.022	0.028	−0.004	
parametric estimation	$\hat{h}_m$	−0.038	−0.083	−0.003	0.039	0.011	

10.3 ESTIMATION OF FREQUENCY RESPONSE FUNCTIONS

10.3.1 Gain and phase estimators

To apply spectral methods to the estimation of frequency response functions, it is necessary to relax the physical realizability condition $h(u) = 0$, $u < 0$, and assume a model

$$X_2(t) - u_2 = \int_{-\infty}^{\infty} h(u)(X_1(t - u) - \bar{X}_1)\, du + Z(t).$$

If the noise $Z(t)$ is white, an argument similar to that used in Appendix A5.1 shows that the least squares estimate $\hat{h}(u)$ of $h(u)$ satisfies the integral equation

$$c_{12}(u) = \int_{-\infty}^{\infty} \hat{h}(v)c_{11}(u - v)\, dv, \quad -T \leqslant u \leqslant T. \qquad (10.3.1)$$

If the data comes from a linear physical system, the condition $h(u) = 0$, $u \leqslant 0$, will be automatically realized apart from the sampling errors introduced by the finite length of record. In fact, if infinite lengths of record were available, the equations (10.3.1) would hold with $h(u)$ identically zero when $u \leqslant 0$.

The solution to the integral equation (10.3.1) may be considerably simplified by using Fourier transforms. Thus, transforming (10.3.1) gives

$$C_{12}(f) = \hat{H}(f)C_{11}(f), \qquad (10.3.2)$$

where

$$\hat{H}(f) = \int_0^{\infty} \hat{h}(u)\, e^{-j2\pi fu}\, du.$$

Hence the frequency response function estimator is

$$\hat{H}(f) = \frac{C_{12}(f)}{C_{11}(f)},\tag{10.3.3}$$

that is, the ratio of the cross spectral estimator to the input spectral estimator. The estimator (10.3.3) may be rewritten

$$\hat{G}(f)\, e^{j\hat{F}(f)} = \frac{A_{12}(f)}{C_{11}(f)}\, e^{jF_{12}(f)},\tag{10.3.4}$$

where $\hat{H}(f) = \hat{G}(f)\, e^{j\hat{F}(f)}$. Thus the estimators of gain and phase are

$$\hat{G}(f) = \frac{A_{12}(f)}{C_{11}(f)}\tag{10.3.5}$$

and

$$\hat{F}(f) = F_{12}(f).\tag{10.3.6}$$

It was shown in Section 9.1.1 that the variance of the phase estimator is approximately independent of the record length T. Since the variances of $A_{12}(f)$ and $C_{11}(f)$ are approximately independent of T, it follows that the variance of $\hat{G}(f)$ is independent of T. Hence the estimators (10.3.5) and (10.3.6) need to be smoothed to reduce their variances.

One way of deriving smoothed gain and phase estimators is to use smoothed estimators in place of the sample spectra in (10.3.5) and (10.3.6). This leads to the smoothed gain and phase estimators

$$\bar{G}(f) = \frac{\bar{A}_{12}(f)}{\bar{C}_{11}(f)},\tag{10.3.7}$$

$$\bar{F}(f) = \arctan\left(-\frac{\bar{Q}_{12}(f)}{\bar{L}_{12}(f)}\right).\tag{10.3.8}$$

The bias and variance properties of these estimators may be derived using the methods of Section 9.2. An alternative approach, considered in the next section, is to treat the problem of frequency response function estimation as one of *least squares analysis in the frequency domain*. This approach has the advantage that it yields approximate confidence intervals based on the distribution theory associated with least squares, rather than confidence intervals based on the first two moments of the spectral estimators, as in the previous treatment.

10.3.2 Least squares analysis in the frequency domain

In this section it is shown that the problem of estimating a frequency response function is formally equivalent to a least squares regression analysis conducted at each frequency. It is also shown that many of the least squares formulae developed in Section 4.3 carry over directly into the frequency domain.

It was shown in Section 6.4.1 that (10.1.1) is approximately true for a finite segment of the $X_1(t)$ and $X_2(t)$ processes, provided the impulse response $h(u)$ tends to zero in a time which is short compared with T. Hence, defining

$$X_i(f) = \int_0^T X_i(t)\, e^{-j2\pi ft}\, dt,$$

the Fourier transform of (10.1.1) is

$$X_2(f) \approx H(f)X_1(f) + Z(f). \tag{10.3.9}$$

Now (10.3.9) may also be written

$$Z(f) \approx \{X_2(f) - X_1(f)\hat{H}(f)\} + X_1(f)\{\hat{H}(f) - H(f)\},$$

and hence

$$|Z(f)|^2 \approx |X_2(f) - X_1(f)\hat{H}(f)|^2 + |X_1(f)|^2|\hat{H}(f) - H(f)|^2. \tag{10.3.10}$$

The cross-product terms vanish since

$$X_1^*(f)X_2(f) = \hat{H}(f)\,|X_1(f)|^2,$$

using (10.3.2).

Note that the decomposition (10.3.10) is formally equivalent to the decomposition (4.3.10) for the residual sum of squares in an ordinary least squares regression analysis. From (10.3.9), the best estimate of the noise at frequency f is

$$\hat{Z}(f) = X_2(f) - \hat{H}(f)X_1(f).$$

On dividing (10.3.10) by T,

$$C_{ZZ}(f) \approx C_{\hat{Z}\hat{Z}}(f) + C_{11}(f)|\hat{H}(f) - H(f)|^2. \tag{10.3.11}$$

The sample spectrum of the residual process which appears in (10.3.11) may be calculated using (10.3.9). Thus

$$C_{\hat{Z}\hat{Z}}(f) = \frac{1}{T}|\hat{Z}(f)|^2$$

$$= \frac{1}{T}|X_2(f) - X_1(f)\hat{H}(f)|^2$$

$$= \frac{1}{T}\left\{|X_2(f)|^2 - \frac{|X_1(f)X_2(f)|^2}{|X_1(f)|^2}\right\}$$

$$= \frac{|X_2(f)|^2}{T}\{1 - K_{12}^2(f)\}, \tag{10.3.12}$$

where $K_{12}^2(f)$ is the sample squared coherency spectrum. However, $K_{12}^2(f)$ is identically unity, as shown in Section 9.1.2, so that

$$C_{\hat{Z}\hat{Z}}(f) = 0.$$

Equation (10.3.11) implies that the two degrees of freedom associated with $C_{zz}(f)$ are taken up entirely by the regression term $|X_1(f)|^2|\hat{H}(f) - H(f)|^2$. Thus a consequence of the narrow bandwidth associated with the sample spectrum and cross spectrum is that the information at a given frequency f is absorbed entirely in estimating the gain and phase and gives *no information* about the noise spectrum. It is now shown that this can be rectified by smoothing.

10.3.3 *Smoothed least squares analysis in the frequency domain*

In this section it is shown that the least squares analysis of the previous section can be modified to give efficient smoothed estimators of the gain and phase of the linear system and also of the noise spectrum $\Gamma_{zz}(f)$. It is then shown how to use these estimators to derive an approximate test of significance for whether the true coherency is zero, as well as approximate confidence intervals for the gain and phase of the linear system.

Suppose that smoothed estimators of the gain and phase have been computed according to (10.3.7) and (10.3.8). Then (10.3.11) may be replaced by the corresponding smoothed formula

$$\bar{C}_{zz}(f) \approx \bar{C}_{\hat{z}\hat{z}}(f) + \bar{C}_{11}(f)|\bar{H}(f) - H(f)|^2. \tag{10.3.13}$$

In applying a smoothing operation to (10.3.11), it is assumed that the true frequency response function $H(f)$ remains approximately constant over the bandwidth of the spectral window.

As indicated in Section 9.2, this assumption will not be valid unless the two series have been aligned so that the ccf has its peak at zero lag. To derive the approximate distribution properties of the estimators it will now be assumed that the two series have been aligned.

Suppose that the smoothing procedure applied to the auto- and cross spectra produces ν degrees of freedom per estimate. Then

$$\frac{\nu\bar{C}_{zz}(f)}{\Gamma_{zz}(f)}$$

is distributed as a χ_ν^2 rv, and (10.3.13) may be written

$$\frac{\nu\bar{C}_{zz}(f)}{\Gamma_{zz}(f)} \approx \frac{\nu\bar{C}_{\hat{z}\hat{z}}(f)}{\Gamma_{zz}(f)} + \frac{\nu\bar{C}_{11}(f)}{\Gamma_{zz}(f)}|\bar{H}(f) - H(f)|^2. \tag{10.3.14}$$

The decomposition (10.3.14) shows that the chi-squared rv with ν degrees of freedom on the left-hand side is decomposed into two component chi-squared rv's. The first component is distributed as $\chi_{\nu-2}^2$ and can be used to estimate the noise spectrum. The second component is distributed as χ_2^2 and can be used to estimate the gain and phase. This result follows from the fact that the right-hand term in (10.3.13) can be shown to have two degrees of freedom, regardless of the amount of smoothing, using the statistical differential technique of Section 3.2.5.

It may be further shown that the two components on the right-hand side of (10.3.14) are statistically independent. Hence, using the additive property for chi-squared rv's given in Section 3.3.5, the other component has $(v - 2)$ degrees of freedom.

Finally, using the smoothed version of (10.3.12), the smoothed noise spectral estimator may be calculated from

$$\bar{C}_{\hat{z}\hat{z}}(f) = \bar{C}_{22}(f)(1 - \bar{K}_{12}^2(f)). \tag{10.3.15}$$

The above results are now used to solve the following problem.

A test of significance for non-zero coherency. Suppose that $H(f)$ is identically zero for all f, that is, the input and output process are completely uncorrelated and hence the theoretical coherency is identically zero.

For $H(f) = 0$, the second term on the right-hand side of (10.3.14) is

$$\frac{v\bar{C}_{11}(f)\bar{G}^2(f)}{\Gamma_{zz}(f)} = \frac{v\bar{C}_{22}(f)\bar{K}_{12}^2(f)}{\Gamma_{zz}(f)}, \tag{10.3.16}$$

using (9.3.12) and (10.3.7).

The decomposition (10.3.14) shows that the rv (10.3.16) is approximately distributed as χ_2^2 and

$$\frac{v\bar{C}_{\hat{z}\hat{z}}(f)}{\Gamma_{zz}(f)} = \frac{v\bar{C}_{22}(f)(1 - \bar{K}_{12}^2(f))}{\Gamma_{zz}(f)}$$

is approximately distributed as χ_{v-2}^2. Hence the rv

$$\frac{(v - 2)\bar{K}_{12}^2(f)}{2(1 - \bar{K}_{12}^2(f))} \tag{10.3.17}$$

is approximately distributed as $F_{2,v-2}$ if $H(f) = 0$.

As an example, suppose that an estimate of $\bar{K}_{12}^2(f) = 0.3$ has been obtained using a Tukey window with $\Delta = 1$, $L = 20$, $N = 100$. Then

$$v = \frac{8}{3} \frac{(100)}{20} = 13$$

and

$$\frac{(v - 2)\bar{K}_{12}^2}{2(1 - \bar{K}_{12}^2)} = 2.36.$$

The upper 95% point $f_{2,11}(0.95)$ is 4.0, using Figure 3.12. Since the observed value of the criterion (10.3.17) is less than 4.0, it could be concluded that there is no evidence that the true coherency is different from zero.

It is only in rare situations that it will be necessary to apply a test of significance of the above type. For example, it could be used as a rough test for cross correlation between time series which involves less computation than the test based on the integrated sample co-spectrum described in Section 9.1.2. It happens much more frequently that the object of the investigation is to *estimate* the gain and phase, and to give approximate *confidence intervals* for these functions. This is discussed in the following section.

10.3.4 Confidence intervals for gain and phase functions

The results of the preceding section may be used to derive approximate confidence intervals for gain and phase. From (10.3.14), it is seen that if $H(f)$ is known,

$$\Pr\left\{\frac{\nu - 2}{2} \frac{\bar{C}_{11}(f)|\bar{H}(f) - H(f)|^2}{\bar{C}_{\hat{z}\hat{z}}(f)} \leqslant f_{2,\nu-2}(1 - \alpha)\right\} = 1 - \alpha.$$

Hence, if $H(f)$ is unknown, a confidence region for $H(f)$ with confidence coefficient $1 - \alpha$ is given by

$$|\bar{H}(f) - H(f)|^2 \leqslant \frac{2}{\nu - 2} \frac{\bar{C}_{\hat{z}\hat{z}}(f)}{\bar{C}_{11}(f)} f_{2,\nu-2}(1 - \alpha). \qquad (10.3.18)$$

In terms of the gain and phase (10.3.18) may be written

$$(G \cos \phi - \bar{G} \cos \bar{F}_{12})^2 + (G \sin \phi - \bar{G} \sin \bar{F}_{12})^2$$

$$\leqslant \frac{2}{\nu - 2} \frac{\bar{C}_{\hat{z}\hat{z}}}{C_{11}} f_{2,\nu-2}(1 - \alpha), \qquad (10.3.19)$$

on dropping the dependence on frequency f. In terms of the parameters $G \cos \phi$, $G \sin \phi$, (10.3.19) defines a circle of radius k as shown in Figure 10.1(a). When mapped into the (G, ϕ) plane, this becomes the region shown in Figure 10.1(b). As a rough approximation, this region can be enclosed by a rectangle. Thus the confidence interval for the gain is $OT \pm TR$ and the confidence interval for the phase is the angle between the tangents OP and OQ to the circle. This is the region

$$|G - \bar{G}| \leqslant k, \qquad \sin |\phi - \bar{\phi}| \leqslant \frac{k}{\bar{G}}.$$

Noting that

$$\frac{k^2}{\bar{G}^2} = \frac{2}{\nu - 2} \frac{1 - \bar{K}_{12}^2}{\bar{K}_{12}^2} f_{2,\nu-2}(1 - \alpha),$$

the $100(1 - \alpha)\%$ confidence intervals for G may be written in the alternative form

$$\bar{G}(f)\left\{1 \pm \sqrt{\frac{2}{\nu - 2} f_{2,\nu-2}(1 - \alpha)\left(\frac{1 - \bar{K}_{12}^2(f)}{\bar{K}_{12}^2(f)}\right)}\right\}, \qquad (10.3.20)$$

and similarly, for ϕ,

$$\bar{F}_{12}(f) \pm \arcsin \sqrt{\frac{2}{\nu - 2} f_{2,\nu-2}(1 - \alpha) \left(\frac{1 - \bar{K}_{12}^2(f)}{\bar{K}_{12}^2(f)} \right)}. \quad (10.3.21)$$

Note that the confidence intervals are small when the number of degrees of freedom ν is large and when the coherency $\bar{K}_{12}^2(f)$ is large.

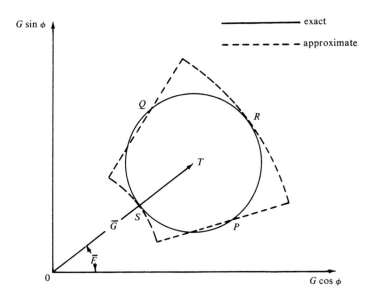

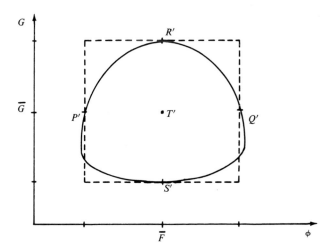

FIG. 10.1: Confidence regions for gain and phase

An example. Suppose that the estimated coherency is $\bar{K}_{12}^2 = 0.8$ and the gain and phase estimates are $\bar{G} = 10$, $\bar{F}_{12} = 70°$, based on $\nu = 17$. Then the 95% confidence intervals (10.3.20) and (10.3.21) are

$$10 \left\{ 1 - \sqrt{\frac{2}{17}(3.68)\left(\frac{0.2}{0.8}\right)} \right\} \leqslant G \leqslant 10 \left\{ 1 + \sqrt{\frac{2}{17}(3.68)\left(\frac{0.2}{0.8}\right)} \right\},$$

$$70 - \arcsin\sqrt{\frac{2}{17}(3.68)\left(\frac{0.2}{0.8}\right)} \leqslant \phi \leqslant 70 + \arcsin\sqrt{\frac{2}{17}(3.68)\left(\frac{0.2}{0.8}\right)},$$

that is,

$$6.7 \leqslant G \leqslant 13.3, \qquad 51° \leqslant \phi \leqslant 89°.$$

Bias in gain estimators. The confidence intervals (10.3.20) and (10.3.21) for the gain and phase were derived under the assumption that the estimators $\bar{G}(f)$ and $\bar{F}(f)$ are unbiased. As shown in Section 9.3.3, the bias in phase and coherency estimators can be minimized by aligning the two series. It is now shown that the bias in the gain estimator can also be reduced by aligning the series. A method of derivation similar to that in Section 9.3.3 is followed.

By definition, the bias in gain is

$$\begin{aligned} B(f) &= E[\bar{G}(f) - G(f)] \\ &= E\left[\frac{\bar{A}_{12}(f)}{\bar{C}_{11}(f)}\right] - \frac{\alpha_{12}(f)}{\Gamma_{11}(f)}. \end{aligned} \tag{10.3.22}$$

Assuming that the bias in the input spectrum is negligible, (10.3.22) becomes

$$B(f) \approx \frac{E[\bar{A}_{12}(f)] - \alpha_{12}(f)}{\Gamma_{11}(f)},$$

so that it is only necessary to determine the bias $E[\bar{A}_{12}(f)] - \alpha_{12}(f)$. Proceeding as in Section 9.3.3, the bias in the gain estimator is

$$B(f) \approx \frac{0.063}{M^2}\frac{1}{\Gamma_{11}}\{\alpha_{12}^{(2)} - \alpha_{12}(\phi_{12}^{(1)})^2 + 2\alpha_{12}^{(1)}\phi_{12}^{(1)}\sin 2\phi_{12}\}, \tag{10.3.23}$$

using the Tukey window.

Note that the term $\alpha_{12}(\phi_{12}^{(1)})^2$ occurs in the expression for the bias in gain, just as it did in the expression (9.3.26) for the bias in coherency. Hence the bias in gain is reduced by alignment for the same reasons as were stated in Section 9.3.

10.4 EXAMPLES OF FREQUENCY RESPONSE ESTIMATION

In this section the methods developed in Section 10.3 are used to estimate frequency response functions of simulated and real physical systems. First the stages in the estimation of frequency response functions are summarized.

10.4.1 A practical procedure for estimating frequency response functions

Discrete estimation formulae. The computations required in the estimation of frequency response functions are almost identical to those described for cross spectra in Section 9.3.1. The only additional calculations required are:

(1) The gain estimate

$$\bar{G}(f) = \frac{\bar{A}_{12}(f)}{\bar{C}_{11}(f)}. \tag{10.4.1}$$

(2) The residual or noise spectrum estimate

$$\bar{C}_{zz}(f) = \bar{C}_{22}(f)(1 - \bar{K}_{12}^2(f)). \tag{10.4.2}$$

(3) Approximate $100(1 - \alpha)\%$ *confidence intervals for gain*

$$\bar{G}(f) \pm \bar{G}(f) \sqrt{\frac{2}{\nu - 2} f_{2,\nu-2}(1 - \alpha) \left(\frac{1 - \bar{K}_{12}^2(f)}{\bar{K}_{12}^2(f)} \right)}, \tag{10.4.3}$$

where ν is the number of degrees of freedom associated with the smoothing of the output spectrum and $f_{2,\nu-2}(1 - \alpha)$ is the upper $100(1 - \alpha)\%$ point of the $F_{2,\nu-2}$ distribution.

(4) Approximate $100(1 - \alpha)\%$ *confidence intervals for phase*

$$\bar{F}_{12}(f) \pm \arcsin \sqrt{\frac{2}{\nu - 2} f_{2,\nu-2}(1 - \alpha) \left(\frac{1 - \bar{K}_{12}^2(f)}{\bar{K}_{12}^2(f)} \right)}. \tag{10.4.4}$$

Stages in the estimation of gain and phase. The five stages suggested in Section 9.4.2 for the estimation of cross spectra apply equally well to the estimation of gain and phase. The only major changes are to the second computation stage which should now read:

(4) Second computation stage
(a) The two autospectra, the noise spectrum and the phase and gain spectra based on the aligned cross correlations (9.3.28) are computed.
(b) The above spectra are plotted for a range of truncation points. The two autospectra and the noise spectrum should be plotted on logarithmic scales. Bode plots should be made for gain and phase, that is, the logarithm of gain should be plotted against the logarithm of frequency, and phase plotted against the logarithm of frequency.
(c) In some cases it may be necessary to plot the transformed coherency. The only other change is that in stage 5.2 the confidence intervals are obtained from (10.4.3) for gain, from (10.4.4) for phase and from (9.2.23) for coherency. A flow chart for frequency response calculations is given in Appendix A10.2.

10.4.2 *Analysis of a simulated system*

A linear second-order system was simulated in this experiment. The output data x_{2t} was generated according to the model (10.2.1), namely,

$$X_{2t} = X_t + Z_t$$

and

$$X_t = 0.25X_{t-1} - 0.5X_{t-2} + X_{1t}, \tag{10.4.5}$$

where Z_t is white noise and X_{1t} is the input.

The input data x_{1t} used was a realization of the second-order process (7.1.9), that is,

$$X_{1t} = X_{1t-1} - 0.5X_{1t-2} + Z'_t.$$

The input and output data are listed in Appendix A10.1.

The input process has the theoretical spectrum

$$\Gamma_{11}(f) = \frac{2}{2.25 - 3 \cos 2\pi f + \cos 4\pi f}, \quad 0 \leqslant f \leqslant 0.5 \text{ cps}, \tag{10.4.6}$$

which is shown in Figure 7.7 as the solid curve. Since the noise spectrum is white,

$$\Gamma_{zz}(f) = 2, \quad 0 \leqslant f \leqslant 0.5. \tag{10.4.7}$$

The theoretical frequency response function of the linear system (10.4.5) is

$$H(f) = \frac{1}{1 - 0.25e^{-j2\pi f} + 0.5e^{-j4\pi f}}, \quad -\tfrac{1}{2} \leqslant f < \tfrac{1}{2}. \tag{10.4.8}$$

Hence the theoretical gain and phase functions are

$$G(f) = \frac{1}{\sqrt{1.3125 - 0.75 \cos 2\pi f + \cos 4\pi f}}, \tag{10.4.9}$$

and

$$\phi(f) = \arctan \frac{\sin 2\pi f(4 \cos 2\pi f - 1)}{2 + \cos 2\pi f(4 \cos 2\pi f - 1)}. \tag{10.4.10}$$

The gain function (10.4.9) is shown as a solid curve in Figure 10.3, and the phase function (10.4.10) appears as a solid curve in Figure 10.4. The theoretical coherency is

$$\kappa_{12}^2 = \frac{1}{1 + (1.3125 - 0.75 \cos 2\pi f + \cos 4\pi f)(2.25 - 3 \cos 2\pi f + \cos 4\pi f)}.$$

This function is shown as the solid line in Figure 10.5. It is seen that the coherency is fairly high over the range 0 to 0.25 cps, where the input spectra and gain are high. However, the coherency is extremely small over the range

0.3 to 0.5 cps, where both the input spectrum and system gain are small. Hence it is to be expected that good estimates of gain, phase and coherency could be obtained for the frequency range 0 to 0.25 cps and poor estimates for the range 0.3 to 0.5 cps.

Since the data are simulated, many of the decisions required in the five-stage procedure of Sections 9.4.2 and 10.4.1 are not necessary. Nevertheless it is instructive to follow these stages through as if the data were obtained from a real process.

(1) Preliminary decision stage

(a) The data showed no trends, as would be expected since both the input and output were generated from stationary models. Hence no digital filtering to remove trends was needed.

(b) No filtering into distinct frequency bands was needed.

(c) Since the input and output series contained $N = 100$ terms, the auto- and cross correlations were evaluated initially up to 30 lags.

(2) First computation stage

The auto- and cross correlations were computed for the original and differenced data. The correlations of the original data are shown in Figure 10.2, and the covariances are given in Appendix A10.2.

(3) Intermediate decision stage

(a) The original correlations were used for the spectral analysis.

(b) Since the cross correlation function had its maximum value at zero lag, no alignment was required.

(c) Based on the way the correlation functions damp out, truncation points of $L = 8$, 12 and 16 were used for the subsequent analysis.

(4) Second computation stage

(a) The autospectra, gain, phase, coherency and noise spectra based on the Tukey window were calculated from the non-aligned correlations.

(b) The gain, phase, squared coherency and noise spectra are plotted in Figures 10.3, 10.4, 10.5 and 10.6 respectively for $L = 8$, 12 and 16.

(5) Interpretation stage

(a) The window-closing procedure shows that there is some change in all spectra when L is increased from 8 to 12 but little change when L is increased to 16. Hence the final spectra accepted were those based on $L = 16$. Note that the gain, phase and squared coherency estimates agree very well with the theoretical values in the range 0 to 0.35 cps but that large discrepancies appear above this frequency because the coherency drops sharply. The residual spectrum of Figure 10.6 shows excellent agreement with the theoretical value over the whole range 0 to 0.5 cps.

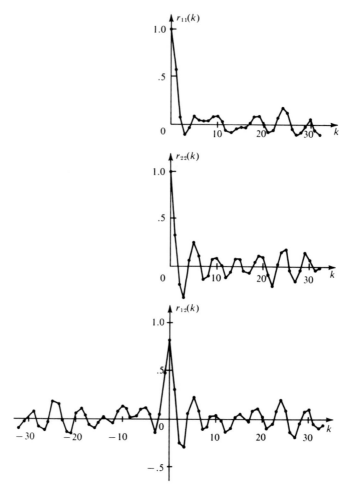

FIG. 10.2: Sample auto- and cross correlations for simulated linear system
(*N* = 100)

(b) Confidence intervals for gain and phase based on (10.4.3) and (10.4.4)
are shown in Figures 10.3 and 10.4. It is seen that these intervals diverge
rapidly above 0.35 cps because of the drop in coherency. Hence the confidence
intervals provide valuable guides in the interpretation of the gain and phase
plots.

Calculation of the impulse response function. To make direct comparisons
with the time-domain estimation procedures used in Section 10.2, the impulse-
response function corresponding to the cross spectra based on *L* = 16 was
evaluated from

$$h_m = \int_0^{1/2} \frac{\bar{L}_{12}(f)}{\bar{C}_{11}(f)} \cos 2\pi fm \, df + \int_0^{1/2} \frac{\bar{Q}_{12}(f)}{\bar{C}_{11}(f)} \sin 2\pi fm \, df. \quad (10.4.12)$$

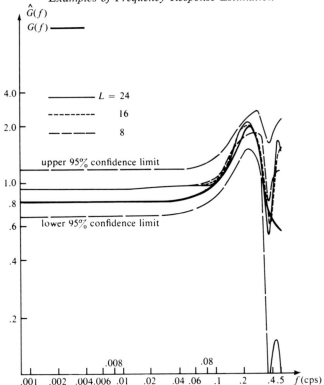

FIG. 10.3: Theoretical and estimated gain functions for a simulated linear system ($N = 100$)

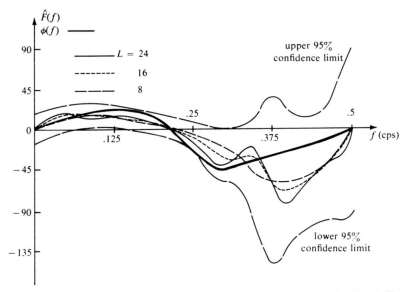

FIG. 10.4: Theoretical and estimated phase functions for a simulated linear system ($N = 100$)

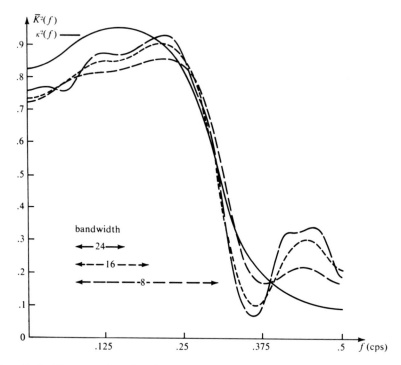

FIG. 10.5: Theoretical and estimated coherency spectra for a simulated linear
system ($N = 100$)

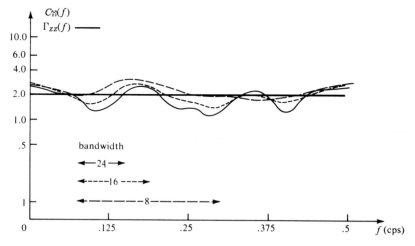

FIG. 10.6: Theoretical and estimated residual spectra for a simulated linear
system ($N = 100$)

TABLE 10.4: Comparison of three methods of estimating impulse response functions

m	0	1	2	3	4	5	6	7	8	9	10
theoretical	1.000	0.250	−0.438	−0.234	0.154	0.055	−0.066	−0.044	0.022	0.028	−0.004
parametric est.	1.100	0.276	−0.458	−0.235	0.160	0.153	−0.038	−0.083	−0.003	0.039	0.011
spectral est.	0.978	0.359	−0.550	−0.124	0.171	0.006	−0.055	−0.022	0.105	0.000	−0.046
direct ($M = 10$)	1.056	0.324	−0.572	0.037	−0.141	0.373	−0.249	0.107	−0.289	0.220	−0.163

This impulse response is compared with the direct and parametric impulse response estimates in Table 10.4. It is seen that it is smoother than the direct estimate and agrees reasonably well with the theoretical impulse response. However, it is not as good as the parametric estimate.

Following a suggestion in [4], values of h_m were also computed for m negative, to determine whether the physical realizability condition was satisfied. The largest value was $h_{-1} = 0.11$, all other values being less in magnitude than 0.1, and so it was concluded that the gain and phase estimates approximately describe a physically realizable system.

10.4.3 Analysis of gas furnace data

Description of the data. The data of Figure 8.3 were obtained from a gas furnace producing carbon dioxide. The output variable is the concentration of carbon dioxide measured as a percentage of the outlet gas from the furnace. The concentration is affected by two input variables, the air rate and the gas rate. In the experiment described here, the input air rate was fixed so that the frequency response function between the input gas rate and the output concentration could be determined.

Continuous measurements were available of both the input and output. Examination of the continuous records revealed that no discernible changes occurred at intervals of less than about 9 to 10 seconds and so the records were read at intervals of 9 seconds, yielding 296 pairs of data points, which are given in Appendix A10.1.

Estimation of gain and phase. A description of the estimation procedure will be given using the basic stages described in Sections 9.4.2 and 10.4.1.

(1) Preliminary decision stage

(a) Inspection of the data (Figure 8.3) did not reveal any obvious trends. However, the auto- and cross correlations of the original and differenced data were computed according to (9.3.13, 14).

(b) The Nyquist frequency corresponding to $\Delta = 9$ seconds is 1/18 cps.

(c) As a preliminary step, it was decided to compute the correlations up to a maximum lag of $L_{max} = 80$.

(2) First computation stage

The auto- and cross correlations were computed and examined. The cross correlations of the original data are shown in Figure 10.7, together with the differenced cross correlations. The approximate covariances for the differenced data are given in Appendix A10.1.

(3) Intermediate decision stage

(a) The presence of trends can be seen in the original ccf, so it was decided to use the differenced correlations.

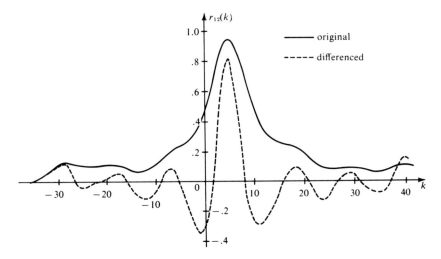

FIG. 10.7: Sample ccf's for original and differenced gas furnace data
($N = 296$)

(b) The ccf of the differenced data has a maximum at $S = 5$.

(c) On the basis of the damping of this ccf, truncation points of $L = 20, 30$ and 40 were chosen for evaluation of the spectra.

(4) Second computation stage

The autospectra, gain, phase and noise spectra were computed for the above truncation points using a shift $S = 5$. The gain function is plotted in Figure 10.8, the phase function in Figure 10.9 and the noise spectrum in Figure 10.10.

(5) Interpretation stage

The window-closing procedure suggests that very little change occurs in these spectra for values of L above 30. The values shown in all figures refer to $L = 30$ and $L = 40$, and it is seen that increasing the bandwidth has little effect on frequencies less than 0.02 cps but produces unstable oscillations above this frequency.

Interpretation of gain estimate. The Bode plot of Figure 10.8 shows that the system is second-order. The estimate of the time constants, obtained by fitting various second-order systems until a good visual fit was obtained, are $T_1 = 6.7$ seconds and $T_2 = 13$ seconds. Note that the 95% confidence intervals diverge rapidly above 0.025 cps because of the falling off in coherency. The gain estimate at zero frequency is 3.1, and hence the dc gain of the system is 3.1.

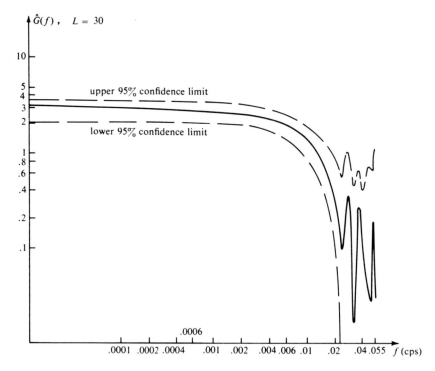

FIG. 10.8: Gain estimate for gas furnace data ($N = 296$)

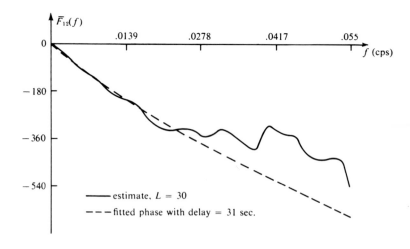

FIG. 10.9: Phase estimate for gas furnace data ($N = 296$)

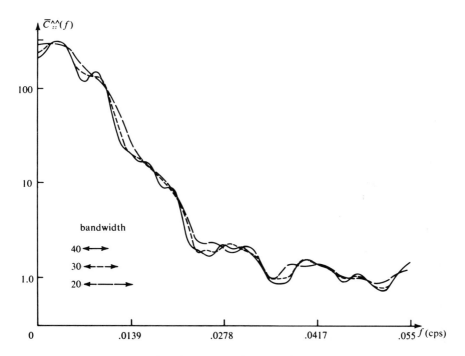

Fig. 10.10: Residual spectrum from gas furnace data ($N = 296$)

Interpretation of phase estimate. A discrete second-order system with $T_1 = 6.7$ seconds and $T_2 = 13$ seconds has the phase function

$$\phi_{12}(f) = \arctan \frac{0.13 \sin 2\pi f - 0.76 \sin 4\pi f}{1 - 0.76 \cos 2\pi f + 0.13 \cos 4\pi f}, \quad 0 \leqslant f \leqslant \tfrac{1}{2}. \quad (10.4.13)$$

The phase estimate for $L = 30$ in Figure 10.9 is much larger than this, suggesting that there is dead time or delay. The difference between the phase estimate and the phase (10.4.13) was plotted, and a straight line approximation to this curve was drawn. The approximating line intersected the line $f = 0.055$ at $\phi = -11$, and hence the delay $d = 11/[2\pi(0.055)] = 31$ seconds. The resulting phase function $F(f) = \bar{F}_{12}(f) - 62\pi f$ is shown in Figure 10.9 as a dashed line.

It can be concluded that the furnace behaves like a second-order system with dc gain of 3.1 units, time constants of 6.7 and 13 seconds and a delay of 31 seconds.

Interpretation of noise spectrum. Since the data have been filtered by differencing, it follows that the noise z_t' actually measured is related to the original noise by $z'_t = z_t - z_{t-1}$. Hence, using (6.2.17), the noise spectrum estimate $\bar{C}_{\hat{z}\hat{z}}(f)$ can be recovered from the filtered noise estimate $\bar{C}_{\hat{z}'\hat{z}'}(f)$ by using

$$\bar{C}_{\hat{z}\hat{z}}(f) = \frac{\bar{C}_{\hat{z}'\hat{z}'}(f)}{4 \sin^2 \pi f \Delta}.$$

The spectrum $\bar{C}_{\hat{z}\hat{z}}(f)$ is shown in Figure 10.10, which indicates that approximately white noise has been passed through the dynamics of the system.

Further examples of frequency response estimation. An example of the application of cross spectral techniques to the estimation of the frequency response function of a heat exchanger is given in [2]. A wide variety of interesting applications is also given in the collection of papers [3].

As a general conclusion, spectral methods are often very useful in suggesting dynamic models for physical systems, as in the gas furnace example. However, since spectral methods involve estimating a parameter at each frequency, the efficiency of these methods is not high. More positive results may usually be obtained by parameterizing the problem, using models such as (10.1.3).

REFERENCES

[1] G. E. P. Box and G. M. Jenkins, *Statistical Models for Forecasting and Control.* Holden-Day, San Francisco (to be published).

[2] G. M. Jenkins, "An example of the estimation of a linear open-loop transfer function." *Technometrics* **5**, 227 (1963).

[3] K. Matusita (ed.), "Studies of the statistical estimation of frequency response functions." Reprinted from *Ann. Inst. Stat. Math.*, Supplement III (1964).

[4] H. Akaike, "Some problems in the application of the cross-spectral method." Seminar on Spectral Analysis of Time Series, Madison, Wisconsin, 1966. Published by John Wiley, New York, 1967, as *Proceedings of an Advanced Seminar on Spectral Analysis of Time Series*, B. Harris, editor.

APPENDIX A10.1   DATA AND COVARIANCES FOR TWO FREQUENCY RESPONSE ESTIMATIONS

TABLE A10.1: Input and output to a simulated linear system, $N = 100$

1–10	-0.88	-0.12	-0.89	-1.38	-0.08	1.04	2.14	0.36	-1.11	-1.78
11–20	-2.76	-1.78	0.98	1.00	-0.71	-1.01	-1.31	-0.85	-0.47	1.64
21–30	0.06	-0.18	-1.02	-1.05	-0.66	-1.13	-0.52	-0.71	-0.21	-0.14
31–40	0.14	1.59	-0.77	-1.09	-1.77	-1.21	0.46	-0.08	-0.64	-0.36
41–50	-0.88	-0.62	0.29	1.91	2.15	1.05	0.32	1.07	2.67	2.45
51–60	1.31	1.11	1.94	0.34	1.83	1.16	0.62	-1.09	-1.62	-0.40
61–70	0.19	-1.60	-2.26	0.30	1.73	2.31	0.81	-0.40	0.30	-0.51
71–80	-2.12	-2.43	0.73	3.09	4.97	1.81	-0.46	-0.34	0.04	0.82
81–90	-1.64	-2.29	-0.77	1.92	1.93	0.85	-0.65	0.35	0.79	1.62
91–100	3.25	1.87	0.76	2.25	0.77	-0.16	0.19	0.61	0.92	-0.70

Input: $X_{1t} = X_{1t-1} - 0.5X_{1t-2} + Z_{1t}$

1–10	-1.03	-1.09	-0.47	-2.07	-1.52	2.27	3.14	0.26	-1.78	-1.82
11–20	-2.81	0.11	3.22	1.92	0.06	-3.48	-2.37	-0.34	0.43	1.97
21–30	2.01	-2.39	-0.94	-0.67	-1.25	0.05	-1.32	0.52	-1.15	0.40
31–40	0.80	2.09	-0.46	-2.66	-1.95	-0.84	-0.51	0.82	-1.62	-0.16
41–50	0.48	-0.36	-0.55	1.54	2.83	2.68	-0.57	0.54	4.70	1.90
51–60	1.23	-0.40	1.20	-2.02	1.97	-0.93	-0.12	-2.34	-4.42	0.10
61–70	1.06	0.06	-3.25	0.21	2.59	4.48	-0.92	-1.55	0.77	0.34
71–80	-3.27	-3.84	0.53	4.73	5.84	1.24	-3.62	0.59	1.04	3.56
81–90	-0.63	-2.09	-1.38	4.42	3.86	0.03	-2.11	-0.18	4.13	2.67
91–100	2.73	2.02	0.15	1.28	3.49	-0.73	-0.28	-0.84	1.37	-0.34

Output: $X_{2t} = X_t + Z_t, \quad X_t = 0.25X_{t-1} - 0.5X_{t-2} + X_{1t}$

TABLE A10.2: Covariance estimates for the data of Table A10.1

k	$c_{11}(k)$	k	$c_{11}(k)$	k	$c_{11}(k)$	k	$c_{11}(k)$
0	1.948	10	0.219	20	0.070	30	0.119
1	1.153	11	0.082	21	−0.136	31	−0.051
2	0.180	12	−0.138	22	−0.136		
3	−0.257	13	−0.174	23	0.142		
4	−0.105	14	−0.095	24	0.391		
5	0.164	15	−0.067	25	0.297		
6	0.123	16	−0.063	26	−0.056		
7	0.049	17	0.000	27	−0.233		
8	0.081	18	0.168	28	−0.173		
9	0.206	19	0.210	29	0.034		

Input autocovariances

k	$c_{12}(k)$	k	$c_{12}(k)$	k	$c_{12}(k)$	k	$c_{12}(k)$
0	2.374	10	0.184	20	0.155	30	0.283
1	1.185	11	−0.007	21	−0.195	31	0.039
2	−0.645	12	−0.349	22	−0.397		
3	−0.972	13	−0.205	23	0.081		
4	−0.064	14	0.107	24	0.526		
5	0.615	15	0.195	25	0.501		
6	0.234	16	0.042	26	−0.064		
7	−0.283	17	−0.019	27	−0.447		
8	−0.244	18	0.126	28	−0.073		
9	0.150	19	0.284	29	0.304		

Input–output cross covariances

TABLE A10.2—*continued*

k	$c_{21}(k)$	k	$c_{21}(k)$	k	$c_{21}(k)$	k	$c_{21}(k)$
0	2.374	10	0.415	20	0.082	30	0.158
1	1.376	11	0.158	21	−0.471	31	−0.109
2	0.095	12	−0.152	22	−0.460		
3	−0.472	13	−0.095	23	0.080		
4	0.101	14	0.040	24	0.608		
5	0.371	15	−0.124	25	0.596		
6	0.331	16	−0.310	26	−0.040		
7	0.044	17	−0.193	27	−0.405		
8	0.030	18	0.155	28	−0.212		
9	0.389	19	0.322	29	0.250		

Output–input cross covariances

k	$c_{22}(k)$	k	$c_{22}(k)$	k	$c_{22}(k)$	k	$c_{22}(k)$
0	4.400	10	0.412	20	0.449	30	0.280
1	1.522	11	0.142	21	−0.564	31	−0.203
2	−0.991	12	−0.605	22	−1.021		
3	−1.521	13	−0.256	23	0.044		
4	0.302	14	0.333	24	0.724		
5	1.220	15	0.349	25	0.903		
6	0.573	16	−0.272	26	−0.338		
7	−0.530	17	−0.233	27	−0.769		
8	−0.499	18	0.073	28	−0.257		
9	0.366	19	0.526	29	0.688		

Output autocovariances

TABLE A10.3: Coded input to gas furnace

1–9	-1.09	0.00	1.78	3.39	3.73	4.41	4.61	3.48	1.27
10–18	-1.80	-5.88	-10.55	-14.21	-15.20	-13.02	-8.14	-4.75	-1.93
19–27	0.88	4.35	7.71	8.66	8.75	8.91	9.87	12.63	17.75
28–36	19.76	19.34	18.66	18.32	17.67	16.08	12.65	7.90	3.60
37–45	1.15	0.88	3.31	6.45	9.60	14.09	26.70	28.34	28.12
46–54	24.83	19.29	14.85	12.14	12.39	16.08	19.05	20.23	18.15
55–63	5.35	1.22	0.09	1.64	6.71	10.19	11.46	11.55	11.12
64–72	11.21	12.23	12.57	11.57	9.13	6.20	2.55	-2.80	-10.80
73–81	-15.51	-17.99	-18.25	-14.56	-9.44	-5.70	-4.31	-5.77	-9.60
82–90	-16.16	-18.75	-18.91	-17.46	-14.74	-12.01	-9.27	-5.24	0.40
91–99	7.88	9.43	9.30	10.06	11.37	11.98	10.54	5.95	-0.80
100–108	-3.14	-2.88	-1.53	-1.09	-1.87	-2.55	-2.29	-0.07	2.54
109–117	3.30	1.02	-4.23	-11.39	-22.75	-25.94	-27.16	-25.10	-17.90
118–126	-13.46	-10.81	-9.10	-8.76	-8.85	-8.00	-5.44	-4.16	-2.71
127–135	0.00	4.03	8.41	12.85	16.07	17.46	16.83	14.85	9.93
136–144	6.48	5.77	5.77	6.32	7.47	9.00	9.93	9.68	7.90
145–153	3.99	-1.61	-5.53	-6.03	-4.24	-1.94	-0.49	0.60	1.61
154–162	3.01	5.17	5.66	5.60	5.73	5.92	6.71	9.33	13.37
163–171	14.60	13.53	7.72	2.18	-2.37	-7.14	-10.99	-12.69	-11.75
172–180	-6.76	0.33	5.56	6.43	4.84	1.09	-3.10	-6.97	-10.47
181–189	-12.18	-11.83	-8.73	-3.36	0.63	0.84	0.00	0.01	2.09
190–198	5.56	7.82	8.58	9.18	8.62	4.16	-3.36	-9.59	-18.13
199–207	-23.78	-24.99	-24.73	-23.30	-20.53	-17.39	-12.61	-5.69	-1.37
208–216	-0.24	-0.50	-1.35	-2.76	-5.34	-8.71	-12.43	-14.39	-14.22
217–225	-11.75	-8.13	-6.34	-5.82	-6.25	-7.13	-8.48	-10.39	-13.46
226–234	-16.28	-16.19	-11.49	-4.88	-1.60	-0.07	-0.92	-6.20	-10.86
235–243	-15.25	-18.58	-20.29	-20.24	-19.61	-19.52	-17.94	-13.02	-10.30
244–252	-9.18	-7.98	-8.67	-10.47	-11.23	-8.76	-3.95	1.85	6.62
253–261	7.09	6.05	5.01	6.03	9.43	12.23	12.49	8.24	1.02
262–270	0.25	3.82	9.22	10.32	8.66	5.27	0.93	-4.58	-7.48
271–279	-9.47	-10.29	-9.28	-6.45	-4.24	-2.76	-1.58	-0.33	1.02
280–288	2.51	2.80	0.00	-4.93	-7.59	-8.24	-7.40	-5.28	-2.04
289–296	0.34	2.04	2.53	1.95	1.31	0.17	-1.82	-2.62	

[actual gas rate (cu. ft. per min.) = 0.600 − 0.004 × (coded value)]

TABLE A10.4: Output CO_2 concentration (%) from gas furnace

1–9	53.8	53.6	53.5	53.5	53.4	53.1	52.7	52.4	52.2
10–18	52.0	52.0	52.4	53.0	54.0	54.9	56.0	56.8	56.8
19–27	56.4	55.7	55.0	54.3	53.2	52.3	51.6	51.2	50.8
28–36	50.5	50.0	49.2	48.4	47.9	47.6	47.5	47.5	47.6
37–45	48.1	49.0	50.0	51.1	51.8	51.9	51.7	51.2	50.0
46–54	48.3	47.0	45.8	45.6	46.0	46.9	47.8	48.2	48.3
55–63	47.9	47.2	47.2	48.1	49.4	50.6	51.5	51.6	51.2
64–72	50.5	50.1	49.8	49.6	49.4	49.3	49.2	49.3	49.7
73–81	50.3	51.3	52.8	54.4	56.0	56.9	57.5	57.3	56.6
82–90	56.0	55.4	55.4	56.4	57.2	58.0	58.4	58.4	58.1
91–99	57.7	57.0	56.0	54.7	53.2	52.1	51.6	51.0	50.5
100–108	50.4	51.0	51.8	52.4	53.0	53.4	53.6	53.7	53.8
109–117	53.8	53.8	53.3	53.0	52.9	53.4	54.6	56.4	58.0
118–126	59.4	60.2	60.0	59.4	58.4	57.6	56.9	56.4	56.0
127–135	55.7	55.3	55.0	54.4	53.7	52.8	51.6	50.6	49.4
136–144	48.8	48.5	48.7	49.2	49.8	50.4	50.7	50.9	50.7
145–153	50.5	50.4	50.2	50.4	51.2	52.3	53.2	53.9	54.1
154–162	54.0	53.6	53.2	53.0	52.8	52.3	51.9	51.6	51.6
163–171	51.4	51.2	50.7	50.0	49.4	49.3	49.7	50.6	51.8
172–180	53.0	54.0	55.3	55.9	55.9	54.6	53.5	52.4	52.1
181–189	52.3	53.0	53.8	54.6	55.4	55.9	55.9	55.2	54.4
190–198	53.7	53.6	53.6	53.2	52.5	52.0	51.4	51.0	50.9
199–207	52.4	53.5	55.6	58.0	59.5	60.0	60.4	60.5	60.2
208–216	59.7	59.0	57.6	56.4	55.2	54.5	54.1	54.1	54.4
217–225	55.5	56.2	57.0	57.3	57.4	57.0	56.4	55.9	55.5
226–234	55.3	55.2	55.4	56.0	56.5	57.1	57.3	56.8	55.6
235–243	55.0	54.1	54.3	55.3	56.4	57.2	57.8	58.3	58.6
244–252	58.8	58.8	58.6	58.0	57.4	57.0	56.4	56.3	56.4
253–261	56.4	56.0	55.2	54.0	53.0	52.0	51.6	51.6	51.1
262–270	50.4	50.0	50.0	52.0	54.0	55.1	54.5	52.8	51.4
271–279	50.8	51.2	52.0	52.8	53.8	54.5	54.9	54.9	54.8
280–288	54.4	53.7	53.3	52.8	52.6	52.6	53.0	54.3	56.0
289–296	57.0	58.0	58.6	58.5	58.3	57.8	57.3	57.0	

TABLE A10.5: Covariance estimates for differenced gas furnace data

k	$c_{11}(k)$	k	$c_{11}(k)$	k	$c_{11}(k)$	k	$c_{11}(k)$
0	10.9	10	0.8	20	−0.6	30	−0.8
1	8.1	11	0.9	21	0.1	31	0.0
2	3.9	12	1.0	22	0.7	32	−0.9
3	−0.2	13	0.9	23	0.9	33	1.7
4	−3.1	14	0.3	24	0.6	34	1.8
5	−3.9	15	−0.4	25	0.3	35	1.4
6	−3.6	16	−0.6	26	−0.1	36	0.6
7	−2.9	17	−1.0	27	−0.5	37	0.0
8	−2.1	18	−1.4	28	−1.1	38	−0.5
9	−1.1	19	−1.3	29	−1.3	39	−1.0

Input autocovariances

k	$c_{12}(k)$	k	$c_{12}(k)$	k	$c_{12}(k)$	k	$c_{12}(k)$
0	0.79	10	0.69	20	−0.12	30	−0.13
1	0.43	11	0.74	21	0.01	31	0.00
2	−0.30	12	0.68	22	0.17	32	0.10
3	−1.23	13	0.55	23	0.30	33	0.15
4	−1.92	14	0.42	24	0.32	34	0.20
5	−2.10	15	0.22	25	0.25	35	0.20
6	−1.70	16	0.00	26	0.10	36	0.17
7	−0.94	17	−0.15	27	−0.06	37	−0.01
8	−0.14	18	−0.23	28	−0.10	38	−0.20
9	0.42	19	−0.23	29	−0.14	39	−0.36

Input–output cross covariances

TABLE A.10.5—*continued*

k	$c_{21}(k)$	k	$c_{21}(k)$	k	$c_{21}(k)$	k	$c_{21}(k)$
0	0.79	10	0.17	20	−0.05	30	−0.27
1	0.89	11	0.26	21	−0.01	31	−0.15
2	0.79	12	0.30	22	0.01	32	0.02
3	0.55	13	0.29	23	0.04	33	0.09
4	0.29	14	0.24	24	0.09	34	0.12
5	0.05	15	0.13	25	0.12	35	0.15
6	−0.15	16	−0.02	26	0.06	36	0.11
7	−0.20	17	−0.12	27	−0.10	37	0.02
8	−0.15	18	−0.13	28	−0.28	38	−0.13
9	0.02	19	−0.08	29	−0.33	39	−0.20

Output–input cross covariances

k	$c_{22}(k)$	k	$c_{22}(k)$	k	$c_{22}(k)$	k	$c_{22}(k)$
0	0.598	10	−0.054	20	−0.060	30	−0.056
1	0.465	11	0.002	21	−0.027	31	−0.054
2	0.294	12	0.034	22	0.004	32	−0.025
3	0.093	13	0.038	23	0.025	33	0.037
4	−0.073	14	0.028	24	0.032	34	0.064
5	−0.168	15	−0.004	25	0.036	35	0.075
6	−0.201	16	−0.030	26	0.033	36	0.061
7	−0.193	17	−0.065	27	0.024	37	0.026
8	−0.156	18	−0.083	28	0.004	38	−0.002
9	−0.116	19	−0.083	29	−0.035	39	−0.020

Output autocovariances

APPENDIX A10.2   FLOW CHART FOR FREQUENCY RESPONSE
CALCULATIONS

The following is a flow chart for a computer program FRQRSP which accepts the same inputs as a program CROSSPEC (Appendix A9.2). Printer output from FRQRSP consists of the covariances (echo check), the smoothed autospectra for each truncation point M, and the gain, phase, squared coherency and residual spectra, together with approximate upper and lower 95% confidence intervals, for the gain and phase functions. Plotter output consists of the input, output and residual logspectra, the log gain versus log frequency plot, with upper and lower confidence intervals, plus the phase versus frequency plot, all with overlays for each additional truncation point used.

Program FRQRSP

1) through 11) as in program CROSSPEC, so that at this point in the program the following quantities are available, for $K = 0$, NF

$$\text{SPEC}(K,1), \text{SPEC}(K,2), \text{SQ}(K)$$

$$\text{Phase}(K), \text{COHSQ}(K).$$

12) *Calculate* $\text{GAIN}(K) = \text{SQRT}(\text{SQ}(K))/\text{SPEC}(K,1)$

$$\text{RESID}(K) = \text{SPEC}(K,2)(1. - \text{COHSQ}(K)).$$

13) *Calculate* approximate $f_{2,D-2}$ probability point as

$$D = 8*N/(3*M)$$

$$E = D - 2$$

$$A = 2.*(2.93 + 11.7/E)/E.$$

14) *Calculate* upper and lower 95% gain and phase confidence intervals as

$$G(K) = \text{SQRT}(A*\text{RESID}(K)/\text{SPEC}(K,1))$$

$$P(K) = \text{ARCSIN}(G(K)/\text{GAIN}(K))$$

$$GU(K) = \text{GAIN}(K) + G(K)$$

$$GL(K) = \text{GAIN}(K) - G(K)$$

$$PU(K) = \text{PHASE}(K) + P(K)$$

$$PL(K) = \text{PHASE}(K) - P(K).$$

15) *Calculate* logarithms to give

$$\text{LOGSPEC}(K,1) = \text{LOG10}(\text{SPEC}(K,1))$$

$$\text{LOGSPEC}(K,2) = \text{LOG10}(\text{SPEC}(K,2))$$

$$\text{LOGRESID}(K) = \text{LOG10}(\text{RESID}(K))$$

$$\text{LOGGAIN}(K) = \text{LOG10}(\text{GAIN}(K))$$

$$\text{LOGGU}(K) = \text{LOG10}(GU(K))$$

$$\text{LOGGL}(K) = \text{LOG10}(GL(K)).$$

16) *Print* autospectra (input, output, residual), squared coherency, phase, gain, plus upper and lower 95% confidence limits for phase and gain.

17) *Plot* and *overlay* logspectra (input, output, residual) versus frequency, phase plus upper and lower 95% confidence limits versus frequency, log gain plus upper and lower 95% confidence limits versus log frequency.

NOTE: Because the phase can change abruptly from $+90°$ to $-90°$, phase plots can become rather difficult to decipher when overlays are made, and when a logfrequency scale is used. For these reasons, it is suggested that each phase spectrum be plotted on a single graph, and as a function of frequency, not logfrequency.

11

Multivariate Spectral Analysis

In this chapter, the methods of Chapters 8, 9 and 10 are generalized to deal with any number of time series. In particular, it is shown how to describe in the frequency domain q time series arising on an equal footing and how to estimate the multivariate frequency response function of a system having q inputs and r outputs. Up to now matrix theory has been avoided in order to minimize the amount of mathematical technique required to understand the basic ideas in spectral analysis. However, further progress is impossible without the introduction of matrix theory.

In Section 11.1 some of the concepts used in the analysis of univariate and bivariate time series are recast in terms of matrix theory. In particular, the covariance matrix of a time series is defined, and it is shown that the spectrum is intimately connected with the latent roots of this covariance matrix. In Section 11.2 a multivariate linear system is introduced. A linear multivariate process is defined as the output from such a system when the inputs are a set of uncorrelated white noise processes. Important special cases of a multivariate linear process are the bivariate ar and ma processes.

In Section 11.4 the basic ideas in multivariate spectral analysis and frequency response function estimation are developed. To introduce these concepts, the important ideas in multiple regression and multivariate analysis are reviewed in Section 11.3. Finally, in Section 11.5, the more practical aspects of multivariate frequency response estimation are discussed and an example is given based on two inputs and two outputs from a turbo-alternator.

It is conventional to use lower-case letters for vectors and capital letters for matrices. Since this notation has been used to distinguish between time-domain and frequency-domain quantities, it cannot always be used here to distinguish between vectors and matrices. In this book matrices and vectors are denoted by bold-face type. Where possible, upper-case bold letters will refer to matrices, but occasionally they may refer to vectors, the exact meaning being made clear in each case.

11.1 PROPERTIES OF THE COVARIANCE MATRIX

11.1.1 The covariance matrix of a real stochastic process

It was shown in Section 3.1.5 that the second-moment properties of a set of rv's can be summarized by their covariance matrix (3.1.20). A stochastic process can be characterized by an infinite set of rv's, and the second-moment properties of the process can be described by the covariance matrix of the rv's at any subset of times $t_1, t_2, \ldots, t_N$. For a discrete process, these times will be equidistant and so, if the process is stationary,

$$\text{Cov}\,[X(t_i),\, X(t_j)] = \sigma^2 \rho(i - j), \qquad (11.1.1)$$

where $\rho(k)$ is the acf at lag k. The covariance matrix associated with these N times is the array of numbers such that the element in the ith row and the jth column is $\text{Cov}\,[X(t_i),\, X(t_j)]$. Thus, using (11.1.1), the covariance matrix is

$$\mathbf{V}_N = \sigma^2 \begin{pmatrix} 1 & \rho(1) & \rho(2) & \cdots & \rho(N-1) \\ \rho(1) & 1 & \rho(1) & \cdots & \rho(N-2) \\ \rho(2) & \rho(1) & 1 & \cdots & \rho(N-3) \\ \vdots & \vdots & \vdots & & \vdots \\ \rho(N-1) & \rho(N-2) & \rho(N-3) & \cdots & 1 \end{pmatrix}.$$

$$(11.1.2)$$

A matrix of the form (11.1.2), which possesses the property that the elements on symmetric diagonals are identical, is called a *Toeplitz* matrix.

Positive semi-definite property. As indicated in Section 3.1.5, the covariance matrix of a set of rv's is positive semi-definite. For a stationary stochastic process, it follows that the matrices $\mathbf{V}_N$ for $N = 2, 3, \ldots, \infty$ are positive semi-definite, that is, all principal minors of the determinant of $\mathbf{V}_N$ are positive or zero. This implies that the autocorrelations of a stationary time series satisfy a wide range of conditions. For example, if $N = 2$, $|\mathbf{V}_2| \geqslant 0$ implies that

$$|\rho(1)| \leqslant 1.$$

Similarly, by considering the rv's $X(t)$, $X(t + s)$,

$$|\rho(s)| \leqslant 1$$

for any s.

A more interesting example occurs when $N = 3$, in which case

$$|\mathbf{V}_3| = \begin{vmatrix} 1 & \rho(1) & \rho(2) \\ \rho(1) & 1 & \rho(1) \\ \rho(2) & \rho(1) & 1 \end{vmatrix} \geqslant 0. \qquad (11.1.3)$$

It may be verified that (11.1.3) implies

$$|\rho(2)| \leqslant 1,$$

$$\left| \frac{\rho(2) - \rho^2(1)}{1 - \rho^2(1)} \right| \leqslant 1. \tag{11.1.4}$$

The first of the conditions (11.1.4) does not introduce anything new, but the second defines a constraint which must be satisfied by $\rho(1)$ and $\rho(2)$. To illustrate this constraint, consider the first-order ar process for which $\rho(2) = \rho^2(1)$, $\rho(3) = \rho^3(1)$, and so on. The function

$$\pi(2) = \frac{\rho(2) - \rho^2(1)}{1 - \rho^2(1)} \tag{11.1.5}$$

is zero if the process is first-order ar. Hence, when $\pi(2)$ is non-zero it measures the *excess correlation* over and above that expected if the process were first-order ar. Thus $\pi(2)$ can be used to check whether an empirical time series can be adequately fitted by a first-order process, as described in Section 5.4.3.

More generally, by considering $|\mathbf{V}_k|$, it may be shown that

$$\pi(k - 1) = \frac{\|\mathbf{V}_k\|}{|\mathbf{V}_{k-1}|} \tag{11.1.6}$$

lies between -1 and $+1$, where $\|\mathbf{V}_k\|$ is the determinant of the cofactor of the element in the first column and kth row of $\mathbf{V}_k$. The plot of $\pi(k)$ versus k is called the *partial autocorrelation function*. It has the property that if the process is ar of order m,

$$\pi(k) \neq 0, \quad k \leqslant m$$
$$\pi(k) = 0, \quad k > m,$$

and hence it can be used to check whether an empirical time series can be fitted by an ar process of a given order.

11.1.2 Latent roots and the spectrum

In this section it is shown that the latent roots of the covariance matrix $\mathbf{V}_N$ are approximately equal to the power spectrum ordinates at the frequencies i/N. The reader is referred to Appendix A11.1 for some elementary properties of latent roots and vectors which are necessary for this section.

Transformation of correlated random variables to obtain independence. Suppose that the rv's $\mathbf{X}' = (X_1, X_2, \ldots, X_N)$ have covariance matrix $\mathbf{V}$. Now consider linear functions $\mathbf{l}_i'\mathbf{X}$, $\mathbf{l}_j'\mathbf{X}$ of these rv's where $\mathbf{l}_i$, $\mathbf{l}_j$ are left-hand latent vectors of $\mathbf{V}$. Then using (A11.1.7),

$$\text{Cov } [\mathbf{l}_i'\mathbf{X}, \mathbf{l}_j'\mathbf{X}] = \mathbf{l}_i'\mathbf{V}\mathbf{l}_j = \begin{cases} \lambda_i, & i = j \\ 0, & i \neq j \end{cases}. \tag{11.1.7}$$

Hence the transformations

$$\mathbf{Y}_i = \mathbf{l}_i'\mathbf{X}, \quad i = 1, 2, \ldots, N, \qquad (11.1.8)$$

convert the correlated rv's X_i into uncorrelated rv's Y_i. Further, the variance of the rv Y_i is equal to λ_i, the latent root associated with the latent vector $\mathbf{l}_i$. For example, if $N = 2$, the latent roots are obtained from

$$\begin{vmatrix} 1 - \lambda & \rho \\ \rho & 1 - \lambda \end{vmatrix} = 0, \qquad (11.1.9)$$

so that $\lambda_1 = 1 + \rho$, $\lambda_2 = 1 - \rho$. Similarly the latent vectors are

$$\mathbf{l}_1' = \left(\frac{1}{\sqrt{2}}, \frac{1}{\sqrt{2}} \right),$$

$$\mathbf{l}_2' = \left(\frac{1}{\sqrt{2}}, -\frac{1}{\sqrt{2}} \right). \qquad (11.1.10)$$

Hence

$$Y_1 = \frac{1}{\sqrt{2}} (X_1 + X_2),$$

$$Y_2 = \frac{1}{\sqrt{2}} (X_1 - X_2) \qquad (11.1.11)$$

are uncorrelated and $\text{Var}\,[Y_1] = 1 + \rho$, $\text{Var}\,[Y_2] = 1 - \rho$, as may be verified directly. The inverse transformation to (11.1.8), namely,

$$\mathbf{X}_i = \mathbf{l}_i'\mathbf{Y} = l_{1i}Y_1 + l_{2i}Y_2 + \cdots + l_{Ni}Y_N \qquad (11.1.12)$$

shows that the rv X_i may be written as a linear function of the uncorrelated rv's Y_i. Finally, using (3.2.18), the variance of X_i may be decomposed according to

$$\text{Var}\,[X_i] = \sum_{j=1}^{N} l_{ji}^2 \lambda_j. \qquad (11.1.13)$$

Latent roots of circular stochastic processes. The latent vectors of the covariance matrix (11.1.2) of a stochastic process are, in general, complicated functions of the autocorrelations. However, there is considerable simplification if it is assumed that the process is *periodic* or *circular* with period N. This means that

$$X(t) = X(t + N),$$

and hence the autocorrelation satisfies the further condition

$$\rho(k) = \rho(N - k). \qquad (11.1.14)$$

As N tends to infinity, the circular process tends to the actual process. Hence for finite N, the properties of the circular process provide approximations to the properties of the actual process.

With the assumption (11.1.14), the covariance matrix of the circular process is

$$
\mathbf{W}_N = \sigma^2
\begin{pmatrix}
1 & \rho(1) & \rho(2) & \cdots & \rho(N-1) \\
\rho(N-1) & 1 & \rho(1) & \cdots & \rho(N-2) \\
\vdots & \vdots & \vdots & & \vdots \\
\rho(1) & \rho(2) & \cdots & \rho(N-1) & 1
\end{pmatrix}.
$$

(11.1.15)

The latent roots of $\mathbf{W}_N$ satisfy

$$
|\mathbf{W}_N - \lambda\mathbf{I}| =
\begin{vmatrix}
a_1 & a_2 & \cdots & a_N \\
a_N & a_1 & \cdots & a_{N-1} \\
\vdots & \vdots & & \vdots \\
a_2 & a_3 & \cdots & a_1
\end{vmatrix}
= 0,
$$

(11.1.16)

where $a_1 = 1 - \lambda$, $a_2 = \rho(1), \ldots, a_N = \rho(N-1)$. The determinant (11.1.16) is called a *circulant*, and when expanded it gives

$$
|\mathbf{W}_N - \lambda\mathbf{I}| = \prod_{k=1}^{N} \sum_{i=1}^{N} a_i \omega_k^{i-1},
$$

(11.1.17)

where $\omega_k = e^{j(2\pi k/N)}$ is one of the Nth roots of unity. Substituting for the a_i in (11.1.17) and assuming that $N = 2n$, the latent roots of $\mathbf{W}_N$ may be expressed in the form

$$
\lambda_k = 1 + 2 \sum_{i=1}^{n-1} \rho(i) \cos \frac{2\pi i k}{N} + \rho\left(\frac{N}{2}\right) \cos \pi k.
$$

(11.1.18)

Thus the latent roots corresponding to $k = N$, $k = N/2$ are distinct, but the remaining roots occur in pairs with $\lambda_k = \lambda_{N-k}$. The latent vectors corresponding to λ_k, λ_{N-k} are

$$
\mathbf{l}_k' = \left(\cos \frac{2\pi k}{N}, \cos \frac{4\pi k}{N}, \ldots, \cos 2\pi k \right)
$$

$$
\mathbf{l}_{N-k}' = \left(\sin \frac{2\pi k}{N}, \sin \frac{4\pi k}{N}, \ldots, \sin 2\pi k \right),
$$

that is, sine and cosine waves at frequencies $f_k = k/N$, $k = 0, 1, \ldots, n$.
Hence, using (11.1.18), the rv's

$$
U(i) = \sum_{t=1}^{N} X_t \cos \frac{2\pi t i}{N}, \quad i = 0, 1, \ldots, n
$$

$$
V(i) = \sum_{t=1}^{N} X_t \sin \frac{2\pi t i}{N}, \quad i = 1, 2, \ldots, n-1
$$

(11.1.19)

are mutually uncorrelated. Further, using (11.1.12),

$$X_t = \sum_{i=0}^{n} U(i) \cos \frac{2\pi t i}{N} + \sum_{i=1}^{n-1} V(i) \sin \frac{2\pi t i}{N}, \qquad (11.1.20)$$

and using (11.1.13),

$$\mathrm{Var}\,[X_t] = \lambda_0 + 2 \sum_{j=1}^{n-1} \lambda_j + \lambda_n. \qquad (11.1.21)$$

Equation (11.1.18) shows that as N tends to infinity, λ_k tends to $2\Gamma(k/N)$, that is, the latent roots map out the spectral curve. Similarly, as N tends to infinity (11.1.19) and (11.1.20) become

$$U(f) = \sum_{t=1}^{\infty} X_t \cos 2\pi f t,$$

$$V(f) = \sum_{t=1}^{\infty} X_t \sin 2\pi f t, \qquad (11.1.22)$$

and

$$X_t = \int_0^{1/2} U(f) \cos 2\pi f t \, df + \int_0^{1/2} V(f) \sin 2\pi f t \, df. \qquad (11.1.23)$$

Equation (11.1.23) shows that the process X_t can be represented as a mixture of sine and cosine waves at a continuous range of frequencies. The amplitudes (11.1.22) of these sine waves form an orthogonal (independent) process or a process of orthogonal increments, as discussed in Section 5.2.2.

11.1.3 *The covariance matrix of a complex stochastic process*

It was shown in Section 8.2.1 that the spectral analysis of more than one time series leads to the consideration of complex rv's, for example, the sample cross spectrum of two processes. While it is possible to work with the in-phase and out-of-phase components separately, greater mathematical elegance is achieved if they are combined and regarded as the real and imaginary parts of a complex rv. In this section, a calculus appropriate to complex rv's is developed.

Mean and covariance matrix of complex rv's. A complex rv is defined by

$$X_1 = U_1 + jV_1$$

where U_1, V_1 are real rv's. Using (3.2.15), its mean is

$$E[X_1] = E[U_1] + jE[V_1].$$

The covariance between two complex rv's is defined by

$$\text{Cov}\,[X_1, X_2^*] = E[(X_1 - E[X_1])(X_2^* - E[X_2^*])]$$
$$= \text{Cov}\,[(U_1 + jV_1), (U_2 - jV_2)]$$
$$= \text{Cov}\,[U_1, U_2] + \text{Cov}\,[V_1, V_2]$$
$$+ j\{\text{Cov}\,[V_1, U_2] - \text{Cov}\,[U_1, V_2]\}, \quad (11.1.24)$$

where an asterisk denotes a complex conjugate. In general it is seen that the covariance between two complex rv's is complex but that the variance is real, since

$$\text{Var}\,[X_1] = \text{Cov}\,[X_1, X_1^*] = \text{Var}\,[U_1] + \text{Var}\,[V_1]. \quad (11.1.25)$$

The covariance between two real rv's is symmetric, but the covariance of a complex rv satisfies

$$\text{Cov}\,[X_1, X_2^*] = \{\text{Cov}\,[X_2, X_1^*]\}^*, \quad (11.1.26)$$

which follows directly from the definition (11.1.24).

Covariance matrix of complex rv's. Suppose that $\mathbf{X}' = (X_1, X_2, \ldots, X_N)$ is a row vector of N complex rv's. Then the covariance matrix is defined by

$$\mathbf{V}_N = E[(\mathbf{X} - E[\mathbf{X}])(\mathbf{X}^* - E[\mathbf{X}^*])']$$

$$= \begin{pmatrix}
\text{Var}\,[X_1] & \text{Cov}\,[X_1, X_2^*] & \cdots & \text{Cov}\,[X_1, X_N^*] \\
\text{Cov}\,[X_2, X_1^*] & \text{Var}\,[X_2] & \cdots & \text{Cov}\,[X_2, X_N^*] \\
\vdots & \vdots & & \vdots \\
\text{Cov}\,[X_N, X_1^*] & \text{Cov}\,[X_N, X_2^*] & \cdots & \text{Var}\,[X_N]
\end{pmatrix}.$$

From (11.1.26) it follows that the matrix $\mathbf{V}_N$ is Hermitian, that is, all minors of $\mathbf{V}_N$ are positive. For example, if $N = 2$,

$$\begin{vmatrix}
\text{Var}\,[X_1] & \text{Cov}\,[X_1, X_2^*] \\
\text{Cov}\,[X_2, X_1^*] & \text{Var}\,[X_2]
\end{vmatrix} \geqslant 0,$$

that is,

$$\kappa_{12}^2 = \frac{|\text{Cov}\,[X_1, X_2^*]|^2}{\text{Var}\,[X_1]\,\text{Var}\,[X_2]} \leqslant 1. \quad (11.1.27)$$

Thus κ_{12}^2 behaves like the square of a correlation coefficient and is called the *squared coherency* between the two complex rv's.

Auto- and cross covariance functions of complex processes. Suppose that two complex stochastic processes $X_1(t)$, $X_2(t)$ have means μ_1, μ_2. Then the auto-covariance functions of the two processes are defined by

$$\gamma_{ii}(u) = E[(X_i(t) - \mu_i)(X_i^*(t + u) - \mu_i^*)], \quad i = 1, 2, \quad (11.1.28)$$

and their cross covariance function by

$$\gamma_{12}(u) = E[(X_1(t) - \mu_1)(X_2^*(t + u) - \mu_2^*)]. \quad (11.1.29)$$

Using (11.1.26),

$$\gamma_{ii}(u) = \gamma_{ii}^*(-u),$$
$$\gamma_{12}(u) = \gamma_{21}^*(-u). \quad (11.1.30)$$

For real processes, (11.1.30) reduces to

$$\gamma_{ii}(u) = \gamma_{ii}(-u),$$
$$\gamma_{12}(u) = \gamma_{21}(-u), \qquad (11.1.31)$$

which are the results (8.1.2) and (8.1.3) given previously.

Using (11.1.24), the auto- and cross covariances of the complex processes can be written in terms of their component real processes. Thus

$$\gamma_{X_1 X_2}(u) = \gamma_{U_1 U_2}(u) + \gamma_{V_1 V_2}(u) + j\{\gamma_{V_1 U_2}(u) - \gamma_{U_1 V_2}(u)\}.$$

The spectra and cross spectra of complex processes. The arguments given in Sections 6.2.1 and 8.3.3 for real processes apply equally well for complex processes. Thus the cross spectrum of a complex process is given by

$$\Gamma_{il}(f) = \int_{-\infty}^{\infty} \gamma_{il}(u)\, e^{-j2\pi f u}\, du.$$

The autospectrum of a complex process is real and positive, but cannot be written as a one-sided transform since the autocovariance function satisfies (11.1.30). For real processes, the autocovariance function satisfies (11.1.31) and hence can be written as a cosine transform (7.1.3).

The cross spectrum between two complex processes has the same properties as the cross spectrum between two real processes given in Section 8.3.3.

11.2 MULTIVARIATE STOCHASTIC PROCESSES

In this section some basic properties of multivariate stochastic processes are derived using matrix theory. The concepts introduced in Chapters 8, 9 and 10 are thus presented in greater generality. It will be seen that inclusion of more than two processes introduces some new and interesting features.

11.2.1 The lagged covariance matrix

Real processes. It was shown in Section 8.1.2 that two stationary stochastic processes are usefully described in the time domain by their auto- and cross covariance functions. Suppose that it is now required to describe a *real* multivariate stochastic process which consists of a vector

$$\mathbf{X}'(t) = (X_1(t), X_2(t), \ldots, X_q(t))$$

of univariate processes. If attention is focused on second-moment properties, the multivariate process can be characterized by a matrix defined for each value of the lag u by

$$\mathbf{V}(u) = E[(\mathbf{X}(t) - \boldsymbol{\mu})(\mathbf{X}(t + u) - \boldsymbol{\mu})']$$
$$= \begin{pmatrix} \gamma_{11}(u) & \gamma_{12}(u) & \cdots & \gamma_{1q}(u) \\ \gamma_{21}(u) & \gamma_{22}(u) & \cdots & \gamma_{2q}(u) \\ \vdots & \vdots & & \vdots \\ \gamma_{q1}(u) & \gamma_{q2}(u) & \cdots & \gamma_{qq}(u) \end{pmatrix}.$$

$$(11.2.1)$$

The matrix $V(u)$, $-\infty \leqslant u \leqslant \infty$, is called the *lagged covariance matrix* of the multivariate stochastic process. Since $\gamma_{ij}(u)$ is not equal to $\gamma_{ji}(u)$, the matrix $V(u)$ is not symmetric. However, it satisfies the relation

$$V'(u) = V(-u), \tag{11.2.2}$$

since

$$V'(u) = E[(X(t + u) - \mu)(X(t) - \mu)'] = V(-u).$$

Complex processes. The lagged covariance matrix of a complex multivariate stochastic process is defined by

$$V(u) = E[(X(t) - \mu)(X(t + u) - \mu)^{*'}].$$

Its elements are the same as those of (11.2.1), with the complex covariances defined by

$$\gamma_{ij}(u) = E[(X_i(t) - \mu_i)(X_j(t + u) - \mu_j)^*].$$

An alternative way of presenting the properties of a multivariate process is to give tables of the individual auto- and cross covariances as a function of the lag u. For graphical representation, plots of the individual auto- and cross covariance functions are preferable.

Lagged correlation matrix. For many practical purposes, especially when the stochastic processes have different scales, it is more convenient to work with the lagged correlation matrix based on the correlations $\rho_{ij}(u)$.

11.2.2 The spectral matrix

From now on it is assumed that each individual process in the multivariate process is complex. As shown in Section 11.1.3, each pair of processes can be described by a cross spectrum defined by

$$\Gamma_{il}(f) = \int_{-\infty}^{\infty} \gamma_{il}(u)\, e^{-j2\pi f u}\, du \tag{11.2.3}$$

and conversely

$$\gamma_{il}(u) = \int_{-\infty}^{\infty} \Gamma_{il}(f)\, e^{j2\pi f u}\, df. \tag{11.2.4}$$

The matrix of auto- and cross spectra

$$\Gamma(f) = \begin{pmatrix} \Gamma_{11}(f) & \Gamma_{12}(f) & \cdots & \Gamma_{1q}(f) \\ \Gamma_{21}(f) & \Gamma_{22}(f) & \cdots & \Gamma_{2q}(f) \\ \vdots & \vdots & & \vdots \\ \Gamma_{q1}(f) & \Gamma_{q2}(f) & \cdots & \Gamma_{qq}(f) \end{pmatrix} \tag{11.2.5}$$

is called the *spectral matrix* of the stochastic process.

Hermitian semi-definite property. A very important property of the spectral matrix is that the auto- and cross spectra must jointly satisfy certain conditions, as follows.

Proceeding as in the definition of the auto-spectrum in Section 6.2.1, it is necessary to define a complex stochastic process $Y(t)$ which is a linear combination of the q individual stochastic processes, namely,

$$Y(t) = \boldsymbol{\lambda}^{*\prime}\mathbf{X}(t) = \lambda_1^* X_1(t) + \lambda_2^* X_2(t) + \cdots + \lambda_q^* X_q(t),$$

where the λ_i are arbitrary complex constants. Then the acvf of the $Y(t)$ process is

$$
\begin{aligned}
\gamma_{YY}(u) &= E[(Y(t) - \mu_Y)(Y(t+u) - \mu_Y)^*] \\
&= E[\boldsymbol{\lambda}^{*\prime}(\mathbf{X}(t) - \boldsymbol{\mu})(\mathbf{X}(t+u) - \boldsymbol{\mu})^*\boldsymbol{\lambda}] \\
&= \boldsymbol{\lambda}^{*\prime}\mathbf{V}(u)\boldsymbol{\lambda}.
\end{aligned}
\tag{11.2.6}
$$

On taking Fourier transforms of (11.2.6) and making use of (11.2.4), the autospectrum of the $Y(t)$ process may be written in terms of the spectral matrix of the multivariate process. Thus

$$\Gamma_{YY}(f) = \boldsymbol{\lambda}^{*\prime}\boldsymbol{\Gamma}(f)\boldsymbol{\lambda}. \tag{11.2.7}$$

Since $\Gamma_{YY}(f)$ is a real scalar, $\Gamma_{YY}(f) = \Gamma_{YY}^*(f) = \Gamma_{YY}^{*\prime}(f)$.

Hence, using (11.2.7),

$$
\begin{aligned}
\Gamma_{YY}^{*\prime}(f) &= (\boldsymbol{\lambda}^{*\prime}\boldsymbol{\Gamma}(f)\boldsymbol{\lambda})^{*\prime} \\
&= (\boldsymbol{\lambda}^{\prime}\boldsymbol{\Gamma}^*(f)\boldsymbol{\lambda}^*)^{\prime} \\
&= \boldsymbol{\lambda}^{*\prime}\boldsymbol{\Gamma}^{*\prime}(f)\boldsymbol{\lambda} = \Gamma_{YY}(f) = \boldsymbol{\lambda}^{*\prime}\boldsymbol{\Gamma}(f)\boldsymbol{\lambda}.
\end{aligned}
$$

Thus

$$\boldsymbol{\Gamma}(f) = \boldsymbol{\Gamma}^{*\prime}(f), \tag{11.2.8}$$

and so the spectral matrix is Hermitian. This implies that

$$\Gamma_{il}(f) = \Gamma_{li}^*(f).$$

Furthermore, since the quadratic form (11.2.7) is non-negative for all values of f, it follows that $\boldsymbol{\Gamma}(f)$ is a *positive semi-definite Hermitian matrix*. This means that every principal minor of $\boldsymbol{\Gamma}(f)$ is non-negative. For example, if $q = 2$,

$$\begin{vmatrix} \Gamma_{11}(f) & \Gamma_{12}(f) \\ \Gamma_{21}(f), & \Gamma_{22}(f) \end{vmatrix} \geqslant 0,$$

which implies that the coherency satisfies

$$0 \leqslant \kappa_{12}^2(f) = \frac{|\Gamma_{12}(f)|^2}{\Gamma_{11}(f)\Gamma_{22}(f)} \leqslant 1.$$

Similarly, for $q = 3$,

$$\begin{vmatrix} \Gamma_{11}(f) & \Gamma_{12}(f) & \Gamma_{13}(f) \\ \Gamma_{21}(f) & \Gamma_{22}(f) & \Gamma_{23}(f) \\ \Gamma_{31}(f) & \Gamma_{32}(f) & \Gamma_{33}(f) \end{vmatrix} \geqslant 0. \tag{11.2.9}$$

It will be shown in Section 11.3 that (11.2.9) implies the existence of a multiple coherency $\kappa_{123}^2(f)$ such that

$$0 \leqslant \kappa_{123}^2(f) \leqslant 1.$$

11.2.3 Multivariate linear systems

In Section 10.3 it was shown how to estimate the frequency response function of a system which has a single input and a single output. In general, a physical system may have several inputs and several outputs. For example, Figure 11.1

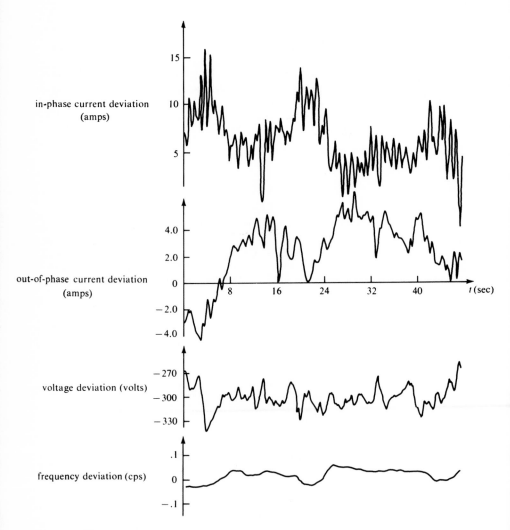

FIG. 11.1: Inputs and outputs from a 50 megawatt turbo-alternator

shows part of some continuous records corresponding to two inputs and two outputs to a turbo-alternator. It is now shown that a multivariate linear system may be described in the time domain by its impulse response matrix and in the frequency domain by its frequency response matrix.

Impulse response matrix. If a multivariate system is linear, then a typical output can be obtained by adding up the contributions from each of the q input variables. Thus, for the ith output

$$X_i(t) - \mu_{X_i} = \int_0^\infty h_{i1}(u)(Z_1(t - u) - \mu_{Z_1})\, du$$

$$+ \cdots + \int_0^\infty h_{iq}(u)(Z_q(t - u) - \mu_{Z_q})\, du.$$

The response of the whole system which consists of r outputs, $i = q + 1, \ldots, q + r$, may then be written symbolically as

$$\mathbf{X}(t) - \mathbf{\mu}_X = \int_0^\infty \mathbf{h}(u)(\mathbf{Z}(t - u) - \mathbf{\mu}_Z)\, du, \qquad (11.2.10)$$

where the *impulse response matrix* $\mathbf{h}(u)$ is given by

$$\mathbf{h}(u) = \begin{pmatrix} h_{(q+1)1}(u) & h_{(q+1)2}(u) & \cdots & h_{(q+1)q}(u) \\ h_{(q+2)1}(u) & h_{(q+2)2}(u) & \cdots & h_{(q+2)q}(u) \\ \vdots & \vdots & & \vdots \\ h_{(q+r)1}(u) & h_{(q+r)2}(u) & \cdots & h_{(q+r)q}(u) \end{pmatrix}. \qquad (11.2.11)$$

An example. Consider the general multivariate system corresponding to the bivariate case (8.1.17), namely,

$$\frac{d\mathbf{X}(t)}{dt} + \mathbf{A}\mathbf{X}(t) = \mathbf{Z}(t).$$

This has the impulse response matrix

$$\mathbf{h}(u) = \mathbf{B}'\, e^{-u\mathbf{S}}.$$

As an example, for the bivariate case

$$\frac{dX_1}{dt} + 2X_1 + \tfrac{1}{2}X_2 = Z_1,$$

$$\frac{dX_2}{dt} + 2X_1 + 2X_2 = Z_2,$$

the impulse response matrix is

$$\mathbf{h}(u) = \begin{pmatrix} \tfrac{1}{2}(e^{-u} + e^{-3u}) & -(e^{-u} - e^{-3u}) \\ -\tfrac{1}{4}(e^{-u} - e^{-3u}) & \tfrac{1}{2}(e^{-u} + e^{-3u}) \end{pmatrix}. \qquad (11.2.12)$$

Frequency response matrix. An alternative method of describing the multivariate system is by its frequency response matrix $H(f)$. This is a matrix whose elements are the Fourier transforms of the elements of the impulse response matrix, namely,

$$H_{il}(f) = \int_0^\infty h_{il}(u) \, e^{-j2\pi fu} \, du.$$

Thus the frequency response matrix may be written

$$\mathbf{H}(f) = \int_0^\infty \mathbf{h}(u) \, e^{-j2\pi fu} \, du. \tag{11.2.13}$$

On taking the Fourier transform of (11.2.10), it is seen that the amplitudes of the outputs at frequency f can be calculated from

$$\mathbf{X}(f) = \mathbf{H}(f)\mathbf{Z}(f), \tag{11.2.14}$$

which is the matrix analog of (2.3.23). For example, for two outputs and three inputs, (11.2.14) gives

$$X_4(f) = H_{41}(f)Z_1(f) + H_{42}(f)Z_2(f) + H_{43}(f)Z_3(f)$$
$$X_5(f) = H_{51}(f)Z_1(f) + H_{52}(f)Z_2(f) + H_{53}(f)Z_3(f).$$

In the special case where the inputs are complex signals $e^{j2\pi ft}$, the response of the ith output is

$$X_i(t) = (H_{i1}(f) + H_{i2}(f) + \cdots + H_{iq}(f)) \, e^{j2\pi ft}. \tag{11.2.15}$$

For the whole system, the equations (11.2.15) may be written

$$\mathbf{X}(t) = \mathbf{H}(f)\mathbf{1} \, e^{j2\pi ft}, \tag{11.2.16}$$

where $\mathbf{1}$ is a column vector consisting entirely of ones.

Equation (11.2.14) may be used to calculate the overall response of the system at a particular frequency. Thus the overall gains are

$$G_i(f) = (G_{i1}^2(f) + \cdots + G_{iq}^2(f))^{1/2},$$

and the overall phase shifts are

$$\phi_i(f) = \phi_{i1}(f) + \phi_{i2}(f) + \cdots + \phi_{iq}(f).$$

An example. Consider the multivariate system

$$\frac{d\mathbf{X}}{dt} + \mathbf{A}\mathbf{X} = \mathbf{Z}.$$

This has the frequency response matrix

$$\mathbf{H}(f) = (j2\pi f\mathbf{I} + \mathbf{A})^{-1}, \tag{11.2.17}$$

where $\mathbf{I}$ is the identity matrix with ones on the diagonal and zeros elsewhere.

For the second-order system

$$\frac{dX_1}{dt} + 2X_1 + \tfrac{1}{2}X_2 = Z_1$$

$$\frac{dX_2}{dt} + 2X_1 + 2X_2 = Z_2$$

discussed previously,

$$\mathbf{H}(f) = \begin{pmatrix} j2\pi f + 2 & \tfrac{1}{2} \\ 2 & j2\pi f + 2 \end{pmatrix}^{-1}$$

$$= \frac{1}{(j2\pi f + 2)^2 - 1}\begin{pmatrix} j2\pi f + 2 & -2 \\ -\tfrac{1}{2} & j2\pi f + 2 \end{pmatrix}$$

$$= \begin{pmatrix} \dfrac{j2\pi f + 2}{(j2\pi f + 3)(j2\pi f + 1)} & \dfrac{-2}{(j2\pi f + 3)(j2\pi f + 1)} \\ \dfrac{-\tfrac{1}{2}}{(j2\pi f + 3)(j2\pi f + 1)} & \dfrac{j2\pi f + 2}{(j2\pi f + 3)(j2\pi f + 1)} \end{pmatrix}$$

$$= \begin{pmatrix} \dfrac{\tfrac{1}{2}}{j2\pi f + 1} + \dfrac{\tfrac{1}{2}}{j2\pi f + 3} & \dfrac{-1}{j2\pi f + 1} + \dfrac{1}{j2\pi f + 3} \\ \dfrac{-\tfrac{1}{4}}{j2\pi f + 1} + \dfrac{\tfrac{1}{4}}{j2\pi f + 3} & \dfrac{\tfrac{1}{2}}{j2\pi f + 1} + \dfrac{\tfrac{1}{2}}{j2\pi f + 3} \end{pmatrix}.$$

The inverse transform of this is

$$\mathbf{h}(u) = \begin{pmatrix} \tfrac{1}{2}(e^{-u} + e^{-3u}) & -(e^{-u} - e^{-3u}) \\ -\tfrac{1}{4}(e^{-u} - e^{-3u}) & \tfrac{1}{2}(e^{-u} + e^{-3u}) \end{pmatrix},$$

the result (11.2.12) stated previously.

11.2.4 Multivariate linear processes

Stationarity. When the inputs $Z_i(t)$ in (11.2.10) are a set of white noise processes, the model (11.2.10) defines a multivariate linear process. For complete generality it is assumed that the white noise processes are correlated at simultaneous times but are otherwise uncorrelated. Specifically

$$\text{Cov}\,[Z_i(t), Z_k(t')] = w_{ik}\delta(t - t').$$

Hence the lagged covariance matrix is

$$\mathbf{V}_Z(u) = \mathbf{W}\delta(u). \tag{11.2.18}$$

Using (11.2.10), it follows that the lagged covariance matrix of the linear process $\mathbf{X}(t)$ is

$$\mathbf{V}_X(u) = \text{Cov}\,[\mathbf{X}(t), \mathbf{X}^{*\prime}(t + u)]$$

$$= \int_0^\infty \int_0^\infty \mathbf{h}(v)\,\text{Cov}\,[\mathbf{Z}(t - v), \mathbf{Z}^{*\prime}(t + u - s)]\mathbf{h}^{*\prime}(s)\,dv\,ds. \tag{11.2.19}$$

When the lagged covariance matrix of $Z(t)$ is of the form (11.2.18), (11.2.19) reduces to

$$\mathbf{V}_X(u) = \int_0^\infty \mathbf{h}(v)\mathbf{W}\mathbf{h}^{*\prime}(v + u)\, dv. \qquad (11.2.20)$$

Hence the multivariate process is stationary to second order since the lagged covariance matrix depends on u only. However, since

$$\mathbf{V}_X(u) \leqslant \mathbf{V}_X(0),$$

where the inequality refers to every element in the matrix, it is necessary to impose the further condition that $\mathbf{V}_X(0)$ is finite, that is,

$$\int_0^\infty \mathbf{h}(v)\mathbf{W}\mathbf{h}^{*\prime}(v)\, dv < \mathbf{M}.$$

Spectral matrix of a linear process. On taking the Fourier transform of (11.2.19), it follows that the spectral matrix associated with the linear process (11.2.10) is

$$\mathbf{\Gamma}_X(f) = \mathbf{H}(-f)\mathbf{\Gamma}_Z(f)\mathbf{H}^{*\prime}(-f), \qquad (11.2.21)$$

where $\mathbf{H}^*(f) = \int_0^\infty \mathbf{h}^*(u)\, e^{j2\pi f u}\, du$.

In the special case where the lagged covariance matrix is of the form (11.2.18), (11.2.21) becomes

$$\mathbf{\Gamma}_X(f) = \mathbf{H}(-f)\mathbf{W}\mathbf{H}^{*\prime}(-f). \qquad (11.2.22)$$

An example. Suppose

$$\mathbf{H}(f) = (j2\pi f\mathbf{I} + \mathbf{A})^{-1}$$

and hence

$$\mathbf{\Gamma}_X(f) = (-j2\pi f\mathbf{I} + \mathbf{A})^{-1}\mathbf{W}(j2\pi f\mathbf{I} + \mathbf{A}')^{-1},$$

since $\mathbf{H}^*(-f) = \mathbf{H}(f)$ when $\mathbf{h}(u)$ is real. For the two-input, two-output case

$$\frac{dX_1}{dt} + 2X_1 + \tfrac{1}{2}X_2 = Z_1,$$

$$\frac{dX_2}{dt} + 2X_1 + X_2 = Z_2$$

discussed previously,

$$\mathbf{H}(f) = (j2\pi f\,\mathbf{I} + \mathbf{A})^{-1}$$

$$= \frac{1}{(j2\pi f + 1)(j2\pi f + 3)}\begin{pmatrix} j2\pi f + 2 & -2 \\ -\tfrac{1}{2} & j2\pi f + 2 \end{pmatrix},$$

and hence

$$\mathbf{\Gamma}_x(f) = \frac{1}{(-j2\pi f + 1)(-j2\pi f + 3)} \begin{pmatrix} -j2\pi f + 2 & -2 \\ -\frac{1}{2} & -j2\pi f + 2 \end{pmatrix}$$

$$\times \mathbf{W} \times \begin{pmatrix} j2\pi f + 2 & -\frac{1}{2} \\ -2 & j2\pi f + 2 \end{pmatrix} \frac{1}{(j2\pi f + 1)(j2\pi f + 3)}$$

$$= \frac{1}{\{1 + (2\pi f)^2\}\{9 + (2\pi f)^2\}} \begin{pmatrix} -j2\pi f + 2 & -2 \\ -\frac{1}{2} & -j2\pi f + 2 \end{pmatrix}$$

$$\times \mathbf{W} \times \begin{pmatrix} j2\pi f + 2 & -\frac{1}{2} \\ -2 & j2\pi f + 2 \end{pmatrix}.$$

When

$$\mathbf{W} = \begin{pmatrix} 1 & 0 \\ 0 & 1 \end{pmatrix},$$

this reduces to

$$\mathbf{\Gamma}_x(f) = \frac{1}{\{1 + (2\pi f)^2\}\{9 + (2\pi f)^2\}} \begin{pmatrix} 8 + (2\pi f)^2 & -5 - j3\pi f \\ -5 + j3\pi f & \frac{17}{4} + (2\pi f)^2 \end{pmatrix}.$$

11.2.5 *Multivariate autoregressive and moving average processes*

Multivariate ar and ma processes arise when the impulse response matrix (11.2.11) in the general linear process takes on special forms. These processes may be written down by replacing the parameters occurring in the univariate forms by a matrix of parameters. For example, the discrete first-order multivariate ar process is obtained by rewriting (5.2.26) as

$$\mathbf{X}_t - \boldsymbol{\mu} = \boldsymbol{\alpha}(\mathbf{X}_{t-1} - \boldsymbol{\mu}) + \mathbf{Z}_t. \qquad (11.2.23)$$

For example, when there are two variables, (11.2.23) is

$$X_{1t} - \mu_1 = \alpha_{1,11}(X_{1t-1} - \mu_1) + \alpha_{1,12}(X_{2t-1} - \mu_2) + Z_{1t}$$
$$X_{2t} - \mu_2 = \alpha_{1,21}(X_{1t-1} - \mu_1) + \alpha_{1,22}(X_{2t-1} - \mu_2) + Z_{2t}.$$

Similarly, the discrete first-order ma process is

$$\mathbf{X}_t - \boldsymbol{\mu} = \mathbf{Z}_t + \boldsymbol{\beta}_1 \mathbf{Z}_{t-1},$$

and for two variables it is

$$X_{1t} - \mu_1 = Z_{1t} + \beta_{1,11}Z_{1t-1} + \beta_{1,12}Z_{2t-1},$$
$$X_{2t} - \mu_2 = Z_{2t} + \beta_{1,21}Z_{1t-1} + \beta_{1,22}Z_{2t-1}.$$

Moving average processes. The general ma process may be written

$$\mathbf{X}_t - \boldsymbol{\mu} = \mathbf{Z}_t + \boldsymbol{\beta}_1 \mathbf{Z}_{t-1} + \cdots + \boldsymbol{\beta}_l \mathbf{Z}_{t-l}. \qquad (11.2.24)$$

The corresponding lagged covariance matrix may be evaluated, using the definition (11.2.1), and is

$$\mathbf{V}_X(k) = \begin{cases} \boldsymbol{\beta}_1 \mathbf{V}_Z \boldsymbol{\beta}'_{1+k} + \boldsymbol{\beta}_2 \mathbf{V}_Z \boldsymbol{\beta}'_{2+k} + \cdots + \boldsymbol{\beta}_{l-k} \mathbf{V}_Z \boldsymbol{\beta}'_l, & k \leqslant l \\ 0, & k > l. \end{cases}$$
(11.2.25)

The process (11.2.24) has the frequency response function

$$\mathbf{H}(f) = \mathbf{I} + \boldsymbol{\beta}_1 \, e^{-j2\pi f} + \cdots + \boldsymbol{\beta}_l \, e^{-j2\pi l f},$$

and hence the spectral matrix is

$$\boldsymbol{\Gamma}_X(f) = (\mathbf{I} + \boldsymbol{\beta}_1 \, e^{j2\pi f} + \cdots + \boldsymbol{\beta}_l \, e^{j2\pi l f})\mathbf{W}(\mathbf{I} + \boldsymbol{\beta}'_1 \, e^{-j2\pi f} + \cdots + \boldsymbol{\beta}'_l \, e^{-j2\pi l f}).$$
(11.2.26)

Autoregressive processes. The general discrete ar process may be written

$$\mathbf{X}_t - \boldsymbol{\mu} = \boldsymbol{\alpha}_1(\mathbf{X}_{t-1} - \boldsymbol{\mu}) + \cdots + \boldsymbol{\alpha}_m(\mathbf{X}_{t-m} - \boldsymbol{\mu}) + \mathbf{Z}_t, \quad (11.2.27)$$

and the lagged covariance matrix satisfies the matrix difference equation

$$\mathbf{V}_X(k) = \boldsymbol{\alpha}_1 \mathbf{V}_X(k-1) + \cdots + \boldsymbol{\alpha}_m \mathbf{V}_X(k-m), \quad k > 0.$$

In the special case $m = 1$, this has the solution

$$\mathbf{V}_X(k) = \boldsymbol{\alpha}_1^k \mathbf{V}_X(0),$$

so that the lagged covariance matrix is easily obtained by taking powers of the $\boldsymbol{\alpha}_1$ matrix. However, it is necessary to evaluate $\mathbf{V}_X(0)$ by direct methods, as illustrated in the example of Section 8.1.5. Regarding (11.2.27) as a linear system with frequency response matrix

$$\mathbf{H}(f) = [\mathbf{I} - \boldsymbol{\alpha}_1 \, e^{-j2\pi f} - \cdots - \boldsymbol{\alpha}_m \, e^{-j2\pi m f}]^{-1},$$

then using (11.2.21), the spectral matrix is

$$\boldsymbol{\Gamma}_X(f) = [\mathbf{I} - \boldsymbol{\alpha}_1 \, e^{j2\pi f} - \cdots - \boldsymbol{\alpha}_m \, e^{j2\pi m f}]^{-1}$$
$$\times \, \mathbf{W} \times [\mathbf{I} - \boldsymbol{\alpha}'_1 \, e^{-j2\pi f} - \cdots - \boldsymbol{\alpha}'_m \, e^{-j2\pi m f}]^{-1}. \quad (11.2.28)$$

Similarly, the lagged covariance matrix of the continuous ar process

$$\mathbf{a}_m \frac{d^m \mathbf{X}(t)}{dt^m} + \cdots + \mathbf{a}_0 \mathbf{X}(t) = \mathbf{Z}(t)$$
(11.2.29)

satisfies the differential equation

$$\mathbf{a}_m \frac{d^m \mathbf{V}(u)}{du^m} + \cdots + \mathbf{a}_0 \mathbf{V}(u) = 0.$$

For example, suppose $m = 1$ and $\mathbf{a}_m = \mathbf{I}$. Then

$$\mathbf{V}(u) = e^{-\mathbf{a}_0 u} \mathbf{V}(0).$$

The spectral matrix corresponding to (11.2.29) may be obtained by regarding it as a linear system with frequency response matrix

$$\mathbf{H}(f) = [\mathbf{a}_m (j2\pi f)^m + \cdots + \mathbf{a}_0 \mathbf{I}]^{-1}.$$

Mixed processes. More generally still, it is possible to define a multivariate mixed ar–ma process

$$\mathbf{X}_t - \boldsymbol{\mu} = \boldsymbol{\alpha}_1(\mathbf{X}_{t-1} - \boldsymbol{\mu}) + \cdots + \boldsymbol{\alpha}_m(\mathbf{X}_{t-m} - \boldsymbol{\mu}) + \mathbf{Z}_t + \boldsymbol{\beta}_1\mathbf{Z}_{t-1} + \cdots + \boldsymbol{\beta}_l\mathbf{Z}_{t-l}.$$
$$(11.2.30)$$

The model (11.2.30) gives rise to a wide class of lagged covariance matrices and hence provides a very powerful model for the fitting of multivariate time series.

11.3 TIME-DOMAIN MULTIVARIATE ANALYSIS

It was shown in Chapters 9 and 10 that cross spectral analysis and frequency response estimation represent extensions to the frequency domain of ordinary correlation and regression analysis. Similarly, multivariate spectral analysis and multivariate frequency response estimation represent extensions of the ideas of multiple correlation analysis and multivariate analysis to the frequency domain. In this section, the basic ideas in multiple correlation and regression analysis and multivariate analysis are reviewed. Complete understanding of the least squares theory of Appendix A4.1 is now assumed.

11.3.1 Multiple regression analysis, single output

The model. Consider a special case of the multivariate dynamic model (11.2.10) in which there is only one output, and assume that the system responds so quickly that it can be effectively described by its steady-state behavior. Then with an appropriate change of notation, (11.2.10) may be written

$$X_{t(q+1)} - \mu_{q+1} = h_1(X_{t1} - \bar{X}_1) + h_2(X_{t2} - \bar{X}_2) + \cdots + h_q(X_{tq} - \bar{X}_q) + Z_t,$$
$$(11.3.1)$$

where Z_t is a noise term. As noted in Section 4.3.4, it is useful to subtract the means from the regression variables in a least squares model to make the parameters orthogonal to the constant term μ_{q+1}.

Normal equations. Assuming that the noise Z_t is white and that observations are made at times $t = 1, 2, \ldots, N$, the normal equations (A4.1.7) are

$$(\mathbf{X}'\mathbf{X})\hat{\mathbf{h}} = \mathbf{X}'\mathbf{x},$$
$$\hat{\mu}_{q+1} = \bar{x}_{q+1},$$
$$(11.3.2)$$

where

$$\mathbf{X} = \begin{pmatrix} x_{11} - \bar{x}_1 & x_{12} - \bar{x}_2 & \cdots & x_{1q} - \bar{x}_q \\ x_{21} - \bar{x}_1 & x_{22} - \bar{x}_2 & \cdots & x_{2q} - \bar{x}_q \\ \vdots & \vdots & & \vdots \\ x_{N1} - \bar{x}_1 & x_{N2} - \bar{x}_2 & \cdots & x_{Nq} - \bar{x}_q \end{pmatrix},$$

$$\mathbf{h}' = (h_1, h_2, \ldots, h_q),$$
$$(11.3.3)$$
$$\mathbf{x}' = (x_{1q+1} - \bar{x}_{q+1}, x_{2q+1} - \bar{x}_{q+1}, \ldots, x_{Nq+1} - \bar{x}_{q+1}).$$

Equations (11.3.2) can be written in terms of covariance estimates

$$c_{ij} = \frac{1}{N} \sum_{t=1}^{N} (x_{ti} - \bar{x}_i)(x_{tj} - \bar{x}_j), \qquad (11.3.4)$$

as

$$\mathbf{C}_{qq}\hat{\mathbf{h}} = \mathbf{c}_{q+1},$$
$$\hat{\mu}_{q+1} = \bar{x}_{q+1}, \qquad (11.3.5)$$

where $\mathbf{C}_{qq}$ is the covariance matrix of the inputs, and $\mathbf{c}_{q+1}$ is the vector of cross covariances between the inputs and the output.

An example. For $q = 2$, the model (11.3.1) is

$$X_{t3} - \mu_3 = h_1(X_{t1} - \bar{X}_1) + h_2(X_{t2} - \bar{X}_2) + Z_t, \quad t = 1, 2, \ldots, N,$$

and the estimation equations (11.3.5) are

$$\hat{h}_1 c_{11} + \hat{h}_2 c_{12} = c_{13},$$
$$\hat{h}_1 c_{21} + \hat{h}_2 c_{22} = c_{23},$$
$$\hat{\mu}_3 = \bar{x}_3.$$

11.3.2 Multiple correlation

The expression (A4.1.11) for the residual sum of squares from the fitted regression is

$$\sum z_t^2 = \mathbf{x'x} - \hat{\mathbf{h}}'(\mathbf{X'X})\hat{\mathbf{h}}, \qquad (11.3.6)$$

or, using (11.3.4) and (11.3.5),

$$\sum z_t^2 = N c_{(q+1)(q+1)} - \hat{\mathbf{h}}'\mathbf{c}_{q+1}. \qquad (11.3.7)$$

Equation (11.3.6) shows that the residual sum of squares can be written as the difference between the total or output sum of squares and a positive quantity called the *regression sum of squares*. If the regression sum of squares is expressed as a proportion $r_{(q+1)12\ldots q}^2$ of the total sum of squares, then (11.3.7) may be written

$$\sum_{t=1}^{N} z_t^2 = N c_{(q+1)(q+1)}(1 - r_{(q+1)12\ldots q}^2), \qquad (11.3.8)$$

and $r_{(q+1)12\ldots q}^2$ is the square of the *multiple correlation coefficient* between the output x_{q+1} and the q inputs. Alternatively, the output variance may be written

$$c_{(q+1)(q+1)} = r_{(q+1)12\ldots q}^2 c_{(q+1)(q+1)} + (1 - r_{(q+1)12\ldots q}^2)c_{(q+1)(q+1)}. \qquad (11.3.9)$$

Equation (11.3.9) shows that the output variance can be decomposed into the regression sum of squares, which represents that part of the output which can be "accounted for" or predicted from the inputs, plus a residual sum of squares which is due to noise and cannot be predicted from the inputs. Hence the square of the multiple correlation coefficient represents that proportion of the output variance which can be accounted for by the inputs.

Equating (11.3.7) with (11.3.8) shows that the multiple correlation coefficient may be estimated from

$$r^2_{(q+1)12\ldots q}c_{(q+1)(q+1)} = \hat{\mathbf{h}}'\mathbf{c}_{(q+1)}. \tag{11.3.10}$$

Substituting for the estimates $\hat{\mathbf{h}}$ as given by (11.3.5) gives an alternative form for the multiple correlation coefficient,

$$r^2_{(q+1)12\ldots q} = 1 - \frac{|\mathbf{C}_{(q+1)(q+1)}|}{c_{(q+1)(q+1)}|\mathbf{C}_{qq}|}, \tag{11.3.11}$$

where $\mathbf{C}_{(q+1)(q+1)}$ is the covariance matrix of all the $q+1$ variables and $\mathbf{C}_{qq}$ the covariance matrix of the inputs only. Equation (11.3.11) may also be written in terms of the corresponding correlation matrices. Thus

$$r^2_{(q+1)12\ldots q} = 1 - \frac{|\mathbf{R}_{(q+1)(q+1)}|}{|\mathbf{R}_{qq}|}. \tag{11.3.12}$$

An example. For $q = 2$, (11.3.10) becomes

$$r^2_{312}c_{33} = (\hat{h}_1, \hat{h}_2)\begin{pmatrix} c_{13} \\ c_{23} \end{pmatrix} = \hat{h}_1 c_{13} + \hat{h}_2 c_{23}. \tag{11.3.13}$$

Using the alternative form (11.3.12),

$$r^2_{312} = 1 - \frac{\begin{vmatrix} 1 & r_{12} & r_{13} \\ r_{21} & 1 & r_{23} \\ r_{31} & r_{32} & 1 \end{vmatrix}}{\begin{vmatrix} 1 & r_{12} \\ r_{21} & 1 \end{vmatrix}} \tag{11.3.14}$$

$$= \frac{r^2_{13} + r^2_{23} - 2r_{12}r_{13}r_{23}}{1 - r^2_{12}}.$$

Distribution theory of multiple correlation coefficients. To develop a distribution theory, the sample quantities in the above formulae are replaced by the corresponding rv's. Note that these rv's are assumed to be Normal, as are the residuals Z_t in (11.3.1). Then (11.3.9) corresponds to the decomposition of a χ^2_{N-1} into a χ^2_q and χ^2_{N-q-1}. Thus, under the null hypothesis that all the parameters h_i in the model (11.3.1) are zero, the rv corresponding to

$$\frac{r^2_{(q+1)12\ldots q}}{1 - r^2_{(q+1)12\ldots q}} \cdot \frac{N-1-q}{q} \tag{11.3.15}$$

will be distributed as $F_{q,N-1-q}$.

Confidence intervals. More generally, if the parameters in the model are non-zero, their joint confidence region is given by (A4.1.14), which in the present notation becomes

$$(\mathbf{h} - \hat{\mathbf{h}})' \mathbf{C}_{qq} (\mathbf{h} - \hat{\mathbf{h}}) \leqslant \frac{q}{N} f_{q,N-1-q} (1 - \alpha) s^2, \tag{11.3.16}$$

where s^2 is the estimate of the residual variance. For example, if $q = 2$, the confidence region for (h_1, h_2) is

$$(h_1 - \hat{h}_1)^2 c_{11} + (h_2 - \hat{h}_2)^2 c_{22} + 2(h_1 - \hat{h}_1)(h_2 - \hat{h}_2) c_{12}$$

$$\leqslant \frac{2}{N} f_{2,N-3} (1 - \alpha) s^2. \tag{11.3.17}$$

Formulae for theoretical quantities. The above formulae were derived using sample functions. By suitable interpretation, they apply equally well to the population or theoretical quantities. For example, (11.3.8) becomes

$$\sigma_Z^2 = \sigma_{q+1}^2 (1 - \rho_{(q+1)12\ldots q}^2), \tag{11.3.18}$$

where $\rho_{(q+1)12\ldots q}^2$ is the theoretical multiple correlation coefficient.

11.3.3 Partial correlation

The multiple correlation coefficient measures the correlation between the output and the best prediction of the output using *all* the inputs. It is also useful to be able to measure the correlation between the output and a single input. This leads to the notion of a partial correlation coefficient.

To illustrate the basic idea, suppose $q = 2$ so that the model (11.3.1) is

$$X_{t3} - \mu_3 = h_1 (X_{t1} - \bar{X}_1) + h_2 (X_{t2} - \bar{X}_2) + Z_t.$$

Clearly, if both h_1 and h_2 are non-zero, the rv X_3 will be correlated with both X_1 and X_2. However, the correlation coefficients ρ_{31} and ρ_{32} which describe the separate correlations between (X_3, X_1) and (X_3, X_2) are not very meaningful, since X_1 and X_2 may be correlated. As an extreme example, it might happen that X_3 and X_1 are highly correlated with X_2. When allowance is made for ρ_{32} and ρ_{12}, the actual "direct" correlation between X_3 and X_1 may be very small.

Thus it is necessary to remove the influence of the variable X_2 before computing the correlation between X_3 and X_1. This is achieved by conducting a least squares regression of X_3 on X_2 and of X_1 on X_2. The partial correlation coefficient is then defined to be the correlation between the residuals from these two regressions. With the residuals may be associated rv's

$$E_1 = X_1 - \mu_1 - \frac{\gamma_{12}}{\gamma_{22}} (X_2 - \mu_2),$$

$$E_3 = X_3 - \mu_3 - \frac{\gamma_{23}}{\gamma_{22}} (X_2 - \mu_2),$$

where γ_{ik} is the covariance between X_i and X_k. Then

$$\text{Cov}\,[E_1, E_3] = \gamma_{13} - \frac{\gamma_{12}\gamma_{23}}{\gamma_{22}}, \tag{11.3.19}$$

$$\text{Var}\,[E_1] = \gamma_{11}(1 - \rho_{12}^2),$$

$$\text{Var}\,[E_3] = \gamma_{33}(1 - \rho_{23}^2).$$

Hence the correlation between E_3 and E_1 is

$$\rho_{31|2} = \frac{\rho_{13} - \rho_{23}\rho_{12}}{\sqrt{(1 - \rho_{12}^2)(1 - \rho_{23}^2)}}, \tag{11.3.20}$$

which is called the *partial correlation* between X_3 and X_1, allowing for X_2. The corresponding sample partial correlation coefficient is obtained by replacing the population correlations ρ_{ij} by their estimates r_{ij}. The partial correlation coefficient $\rho_{32|1}$ is obtained by interchanging the suffixes 1 and 2 in (11.3.20).

Note that in the special case where the rv's X_3, X_1 and X_2 refer to three consecutive times of a stationary time series, $\rho_{13} = \rho(2)$, $\rho_{12} = \rho_{23} = \rho(1)$, where $\rho(k)$ is the acf at lag k. In this case (11.3.20) reduces to

$$\frac{\rho(2) - \rho^2(1)}{1 - \rho^2(1)},$$

which is the partial autocorrelation coefficient discussed in Sections 5.4.3 and 11.1.1.

In general, for q input variables the partial correlation coefficient between the output X_{q+1} and any input X_k is defined as the ordinary correlation coefficient between $(X_{q+1} - \hat{X}_{q+1})$ and $(X_k - \hat{X}_k)$, where $\hat{X}_{q+1}$, $\hat{X}_k$ are the least squares predictors of X_{q+1}, X_k obtained from the other variables excluding X_k. These have indices $1, 2, \ldots, k - 1, k + 1, \ldots, q$ and are denoted by K. It may be shown [1] that the general form for the partial correlation coefficient is

$$\rho_{(q+1)k|K} = \frac{\pi_{(q+1)k}}{\sqrt{\pi_{(q+1)(q+1)}\pi_{kk}}}, \tag{11.3.21}$$

where π_{lm} is the minor of the element ρ_{lm} in the correlation matrix $\mathbf{R}_{(q+1)(q+1)}$ of all $q + 1$ variables.

An example. Equation (11.3.20) may be obtained using (11.3.21) as follows.

$$\mathbf{R}_{33} = \begin{pmatrix} 1 & \rho_{12} & \rho_{13} \\ \rho_{21} & 1 & \rho_{23} \\ \rho_{31} & \rho_{32} & 1 \end{pmatrix},$$

and so

$$\pi_{31} = \rho_{13} - \rho_{12}\rho_{23},$$

$$\pi_{33} = 1 - \rho_{12}^2,$$

$$\pi_{11} = 1 - \rho_{23}^2,$$

which yields (11.3.20).

Analysis of variance. Using (11.3.14) and (11.3.20), with the theoretical correlations replaced by their sample values, it may be shown that

$$(1 - r_{312}^2) = (1 - r_{32}^2)(1 - r_{31\,|\,2}^2). \qquad (11.3.22)$$

The significance of (11.3.22) may be seen by referring to (11.3.8), which shows that the residual sum of squares after fitting x_1 and x_2 is a proportion $1 - r_{312}^2$ of the total sum of squares. Equation (11.3.22) then shows that the reduction in the sum of squares as a result of fitting x_2 is proportional to $(1 - r_{32}^2)$ and that the *further reduction* as a result of fitting x_1 is $(1 - r_{31\,|\,2}^2)$. Note, however, that x_1 could be fitted first so that (11.3.22) has the alternative form

$$(1 - r_{312}^2) = (1 - r_{31}^2)(1 - r_{32\,|\,1}^2).$$

Thus the decomposition (11.3.9) may be set out in the form of two analysis of variance tables, as shown in Table 11.1.

TABLE 11.1: Analysis of variance table for a multiple regression analysis

	Fitting x_1 first	
Source	Sum of squares	Degrees of freedom
fitting x_1	$r_{31}^2 \sum (x_{t3} - \bar{x}_3)^2$	1
fitting x_2, given x_1	$(r_{312}^2 - r_{31}^2) \sum (x_{t3} - \bar{x}_3)^2$	1
residual	$(1 - r_{312}^2) \sum (x_{t3} - \bar{x}_3)^2$	$N - 3$
total	$\sum (x_{t3} - \bar{x}_3)^2$	$N - 1$

	Fitting x_2 first	
Source	Sum of squares	Degrees of freedom
fitting x_2	$r_{32}^2 \sum (x_{t3} - \bar{x}_3)^2$	1
fitting x_1, given x_2	$(r_{312}^2 - r_{32}^2) \sum (x_{t3} - \bar{x}_3)^2$	1
residual	$(1 - r_{312}^2) \sum (x_{t3} - \bar{x}_3)^2$	$N - 3$
total	$\sum (x_{t3} - \bar{x}_3)^2$	$N - 1$

Assuming that x_1 does not contribute to the prediction of x_3, the ratio

$$\frac{(N - 3)r_{31}^2}{1 - r_{312}^2}$$

may be compared with the $F_{1, N-3}$ distribution.

Similarly, under the assumption that x_2 does not contribute to the prediction of x_3 after x_1 has been fitted,

$$(N - 3)\left\{\frac{r_{312}^2 - r_{31}^2}{1 - r_{312}^2}\right\}$$

may be compared with the $F_{1,N-3}$ distribution.

An example. To illustrate the above ideas, the power station data of Figure 11.1 were filtered using the low-pass filter

$$H(Z) = \{\tfrac{1}{49}(Z^{24} + \cdots + Z + 1 + Z^{-1} + \cdots + Z^{-24})\}^4.$$

The output variable was the alternator frequency F and the input variables were the in-phase current i_d and the out-of-phase current i_q. Since the filter rejects most of the power above $f = 0.04$ cps, only every twentieth value of the filtered series was retained, giving $N = 41$ values.

The model

$$X_{3t} - \mu_3 = h_1(X_{1t} - \bar{X}_1) + h_2(X_{2t} - \bar{X}_2) + Z_t$$

thus involves the steady-state gains h_1 from i_d to F, and h_2 from i_q to F. The normal equations (11.3.5) are

$$100\hat{\mu}_3 = 82.558,$$
$$5.879\hat{h}_1 + 2.907\hat{h}_2 = 1.145,$$
$$2.907\hat{h}_1 + 43.488\hat{h}_2 = 2.033,$$

yielding estimates $\hat{\mu}_3 = 0.8256$, $\hat{h}_1 = -0.2253$ and $\hat{h}_2 = 0.06181$. The multiple correlation coefficient, calculated from (11.3.14), is 0.977 and the partial correlations, calculated from (11.3.20), are $r_{31|2} = -0.98$ and $r_{32|1} = 0.97$. The analysis of variance for this data is given in Table 11.2.

TABLE 11.2: Analysis of variance table for current-frequency data

Source	Sum of squares	Degrees of freedom	Source	Sum of squares	Degrees of freedom
fitting in-phase current	9.1265	1	fitting out-of-phase current	3.8958	1
fitting out-of-phase, given in-phase	6.5825	1	fitting in-phase, given reactive	11.8132	1
residual	0.3655	38	residual	0.3655	38
total	16.0745	40	total	16.0745	40

The F ratios from Table 11.2 are all very large, and hence it may be concluded that both currents contribute strongly to the prediction of frequency. This is apparent from the large values of the partial autocorrelations. Table 11.2 also shows that the in-phase current is the more important single variable, since it accounts for a greater proportion of the total sum of squares. This is because $r_{13} = 0.75$, whereas $r_{23} = 0.49$. However, the large value of the partial correlation $r_{32|1} = 0.97$ shows that the out-of-phase current also makes an important contribution to the prediction of frequency.

11.3.4 Multivariate analysis, multiple outputs

The model. In the preceding sections, it has been assumed that there is one output variable and several input variables. In general there will be several output variables, so that the regression model may be written

$$
\begin{aligned}
X_{t(q+1)} - \mu_{q+1} &= h_{(q+1)1}(X_{t1} - \bar{X}_1) + \cdots + h_{(q+1)q}(X_{tq} - \bar{X}_q) + Z_{(q+1)t} \\
X_{t(q+2)} - \mu_{q+2} &= h_{(q+2)1}(X_{t1} - \bar{X}_1) + \cdots + h_{(q+2)q}(X_{tq} - \bar{X}_q) + Z_{(q+2)t} \\
\vdots \qquad &\qquad \vdots \qquad\qquad\qquad \vdots \qquad\qquad\qquad \vdots \\
X_{t(q+r)} - \mu_{q+r} &= h_{(q+r)1}(X_{t1} - \bar{X}_1) + \cdots + h_{(q+r)q}(X_{tq} - \bar{X}_q) + Z_{(q+r)t}.
\end{aligned}
$$
$$(11.3.23)$$

The branch of statistics which deals with models of the form (11.3.23) is called multivariate analysis, an account of which is given in [1].

Normal equations. It may be shown [1] that the estimates of the parameters which minimize the determinant of the covariance matrix of the estimates are those which separately minimize the residual sum of squares

$$
\sum_{t=1}^{N} z_{kt}^2, \quad k = q + 1, q + 2, \ldots, q + r.
$$

This means that, as far as the estimation equations are concerned, multivariate analysis can be reduced to q separate multiple regression analyses. Hence, using (11.3.5), the normal equations are

$$
\mathbf{C}_{qq}\hat{\mathbf{h}}_k = \mathbf{c}_{q+k}, \quad k = 1, 2, \ldots, r. \tag{11.3.24}
$$

The equations (11.3.24) can be assembled, after transposition, into a single matrix equation

$$
\hat{\mathbf{H}}\mathbf{C}_{qq}' = \mathbf{C}_{qr}', \tag{11.3.25}
$$

where $\mathbf{C}_{qq}$ is the $q \times q$ matrix of covariances of the inputs and $\mathbf{C}_{qr}$ is the $q \times r$ matrix of cross covariances between inputs and outputs.

An example. Consider the two-input, two-output system for which

$$X_{t3} - \mu_3 = h_{31}(X_{t1} - \bar{X}_1) + h_{32}(X_{t2} - \bar{X}_2) + Z_{3t},$$
$$X_{t4} - \mu_4 = h_{41}(X_{t1} - \bar{X}_1) + h_{42}(X_{t2} - \bar{X}_2) + Z_{4t}.$$

The estimates $\hat{\mu}_3$ and $\hat{\mu}_4$ are

$$\hat{\mu}_3 = \bar{x}_3,$$
$$\hat{\mu}_4 = \bar{x}_4,$$

and the normal equations (11.3.24) are

$$\begin{pmatrix} c_{11} & c_{12} \\ c_{21} & c_{22} \end{pmatrix}\begin{pmatrix} \hat{h}_{31} \\ \hat{h}_{32} \end{pmatrix} = \begin{pmatrix} c_{13} \\ c_{23} \end{pmatrix}, \quad \begin{pmatrix} c_{11} & c_{12} \\ c_{21} & c_{22} \end{pmatrix}\begin{pmatrix} \hat{h}_{41} \\ \hat{h}_{42} \end{pmatrix} = \begin{pmatrix} c_{14} \\ c_{24} \end{pmatrix}.$$

The single matrix equation (11.3.25) becomes

$$\begin{pmatrix} \hat{h}_{31} & \hat{h}_{32} \\ \hat{h}_{41} & \hat{h}_{42} \end{pmatrix}\begin{pmatrix} c_{11} & c_{21} \\ c_{12} & c_{22} \end{pmatrix} = \begin{pmatrix} c_{13} & c_{23} \\ c_{14} & c_{24} \end{pmatrix}.$$

Residual covariance matrix. Since the model (11.3.23) represents an interconnected system, the rv's $Z_{(q+k)t}, Z_{(q+l)t}$ are usually correlated at simultaneous times, so they possess a covariance matrix with elements σ_{kl}^2. The estimated covariance matrix $\mathbf{V}_z$ has elements

$$s_{(q+k)(q+l)}^2 = \frac{1}{N} \sum_{t=1}^{N} \hat{z}_{(q+k)t}\hat{z}_{(q+l)t}$$

$$= \frac{1}{N} \sum_{t=1}^{N} \{x_{t(q+k)} - \hat{h}_{(q+k)1}x_{t1} - \cdots - \hat{h}_{(q+k)q}x_{tq}\}$$

$$\times \{x_{t(q+l)} - \hat{h}_{(q+l)1}x_{t1} - \cdots - \hat{h}_{(q+l)q}x_{tq}\}. \tag{11.3.26}$$

Using the normal equation (11.3.24), (11.3.26) simplifies to

$$s_{(q+k)(q+l)}^2 = c_{(q+k)(q+l)} - \hat{h}_{(q+k)1}c_{1(q+l)} - \hat{h}_{(q+k)2}c_{2(q+l)} - \cdots - \hat{h}_{(q+k)q}c_{q(q+l)}. \tag{11.3.27}$$

Covariance matrix of estimators. Since the normal equations are obtained by treating each regression in (11.3.23) separately, it follows from (A4.1.9) that the covariance matrices of the estimators associated with the individual equations are

$$\mathbf{V}[\mathbf{h}_{q+k}] = (\mathbf{X'X})^{-1}\sigma_{(q+k)(q+k)}^2$$
$$= \mathbf{C}_{qq}^{-1}\sigma_{(q+k)(q+k)}^2.$$

Using (11.3.24), the remaining covariances in the covariance matrix of the estimators of all parameters are derived from

$$E[\hat{\mathbf{h}}_{q+k}, \hat{\mathbf{h}}'_{q+l}] = E[(\mathbf{X'X})^{-1}\mathbf{X'x}_{q+k}\mathbf{x}'_{q+l}\mathbf{X}(\mathbf{X'X})^{-1}]$$
$$= (\mathbf{X'X})^{-1}\sigma_{(q+k)(q+l)}. \tag{11.3.28}$$

Hence the $qr \times qr$ covariance matrix of the estimators of all parameters may be written

$$
\mathbf{V}(\hat{\mathbf{h}}) = \begin{pmatrix}
\mathbf{C}_{qq}\sigma^2_{(q+1)(q+1)} & \mathbf{C}_{qq}\sigma^2_{(q+1)(q+2)} & \cdots & \mathbf{C}_{qq}\sigma^2_{(q+1)(q+r)} \\
\mathbf{C}_{qq}\sigma^2_{(q+2)(q+1)} & \mathbf{C}_{qq}\sigma^2_{(q+2)(q+2)} & \cdots & \mathbf{C}_{qq}\sigma^2_{(q+2)(q+r)} \\
\vdots & \vdots & & \vdots \\
\mathbf{C}_{qq}\sigma^2_{(q+r)(q+1)} & \mathbf{C}_{qq}\sigma^2_{(q+r)(q+2)} & \cdots & \mathbf{C}_{qq}\sigma^2_{(q+r)(q+r)}
\end{pmatrix},
$$

$$(11.3.29)$$

where $\hat{\mathbf{h}}' = (\hat{\mathbf{h}}_{q+1}, \hat{\mathbf{h}}_{q+2}, \ldots, \hat{\mathbf{h}}_{q+r})$. The matrix (11.3.29) may be written more concisely as the *direct product matrix*

$$
\mathbf{V}(\hat{\mathbf{h}}) = \mathbf{C}_{qq} \otimes \mathbf{C}_{ZZ} \tag{11.3.30}
$$

of the input covariance matrix $\mathbf{C}_{qq}$ and the residual covariance matrix $\mathbf{C}_{ZZ}$. The matrix (11.3.30) can therefore be estimated by substituting the estimates (11.3.27) for the σ^2_{kl} in (11.3.29).

Using (11.3.30), confidence intervals for the extended vector of parameters $\mathbf{h}'$ may be obtained from

$$
(\mathbf{h} - \hat{\mathbf{h}})'\mathbf{V}(\hat{\mathbf{h}})(\mathbf{h} - \hat{\mathbf{h}}) \leqslant \frac{qr}{N} s^2 f_{qr,\,q(N-1-r)}(1-\alpha). \tag{11.3.31}
$$

An example. For the two-input, two-output system discussed above, the estimated covariance matrix of the residuals is, using (11.3.27),

$$
\mathbf{V}_{zz} = \begin{pmatrix} s^2_{33} & s^2_{34} \\ s^2_{43} & s^2_{44} \end{pmatrix} = \begin{pmatrix} c_{33} - \hat{h}_{31}c_{13} - \hat{h}_{32}c_{23} & c_{34} - \hat{h}_{31}c_{14} - \hat{h}_{32}c_{24} \\ c_{43} - \hat{h}_{41}c_{13} - \hat{h}_{42}c_{23} & c_{44} - \hat{h}_{41}c_{14} - \hat{h}_{42}c_{24} \end{pmatrix}.
$$

The covariance matrices of the estimates associated with the individual equations are

$$
\mathbf{V}[\hat{\mathbf{h}}_3] = \frac{\begin{pmatrix} c_{11} & c_{21} \\ c_{12} & c_{22} \end{pmatrix}}{D} \sigma^2_{33}, \quad \mathbf{V}[\hat{\mathbf{h}}_4] = \frac{\begin{pmatrix} c_{11} & c_{21} \\ c_{12} & c_{22} \end{pmatrix}}{D} \sigma^2_{44},
$$

where $D = c_{11}c_{22} - c^2_{12}$.

Hence

$$
\text{Var}\,[\hat{h}_{31}] = \frac{c_{11}}{D}\sigma^2_{33}, \qquad \text{Var}\,[\hat{h}_{41}] = \frac{c_{11}}{D}\sigma^2_{44},
$$

$$
\text{Cov}\,[\hat{h}_{31}, \hat{h}_{32}] = \frac{c_{21}}{D}\sigma^2_{33}, \qquad \text{Cov}\,[\hat{h}_{41}, \hat{h}_{42}] = \frac{c_{21}}{D}\sigma^2_{44},
$$

$$
\text{Cov}\,[\hat{h}_{32}, \hat{h}_{31}] = \frac{c_{12}}{D}\sigma^2_{33}, \qquad \text{Cov}\,[\hat{h}_{42}, \hat{h}_{41}] = \frac{c_{12}}{D}\sigma^2_{44},
$$

$$
\text{Var}\,[\hat{h}_{32}] = \frac{c_{22}}{D}\sigma^2_{33}, \qquad \text{Var}\,[\hat{h}_{42}] = \frac{c_{22}}{D}\sigma^2_{44}.
$$

The covariance matrix (11.3.29) of the estimates of all the parameters is then

$$
\mathbf{V}(\hat{\mathbf{h}}) = \begin{pmatrix} \text{Cov}\,[\hat{h}_{31}, \hat{h}_{31}] & \text{Cov}\,[\hat{h}_{31}, \hat{h}_{32}] & \text{Cov}\,[\hat{h}_{31}, \hat{h}_{41}] & \text{Cov}\,[\hat{h}_{31}, \hat{h}_{42}] \\ \text{Cov}\,[\hat{h}_{32}, \hat{h}_{31}] & \text{Cov}\,[\hat{h}_{32}, \hat{h}_{32}] & \text{Cov}\,[\hat{h}_{32}, \hat{h}_{41}] & \text{Cov}\,[\hat{h}_{32}, \hat{h}_{42}] \\ \text{Cov}\,[\hat{h}_{41}, \hat{h}_{31}] & \text{Cov}\,[\hat{h}_{41}, \hat{h}_{32}] & \text{Cov}\,[\hat{h}_{41}, \hat{h}_{41}] & \text{Cov}\,[\hat{h}_{41}, \hat{h}_{42}] \\ \text{Cov}\,[\hat{h}_{42}, \hat{h}_{31}] & \text{Cov}\,[\hat{h}_{42}, \hat{h}_{32}] & \text{Cov}\,[\hat{h}_{42}, \hat{h}_{41}] & \text{Cov}\,[\hat{h}_{42}, \hat{h}_{42}] \end{pmatrix}.
$$

Finally, the estimate of $\mathbf{V}(\hat{\mathbf{h}})$ is given by

$$
\mathbf{V}(\hat{\mathbf{h}}) = \mathbf{C}_{qq} \otimes \mathbf{V}_{zz}
$$

or

$$
\mathbf{V}(\hat{\mathbf{h}}) = \frac{1}{D} \begin{pmatrix} c_{11}s_{33}^2 & c_{11}s_{34}^2 & c_{12}s_{33}^2 & c_{12}s_{34}^2 \\ c_{11}s_{43}^2 & c_{11}s_{44}^2 & c_{12}s_{43}^2 & c_{12}s_{44}^2 \\ c_{21}s_{33}^2 & c_{21}s_{34}^2 & c_{22}s_{33}^2 & c_{22}s_{34}^2 \\ c_{21}s_{43}^2 & c_{21}s_{44}^2 & c_{22}s_{43}^2 & c_{22}s_{44}^2 \end{pmatrix}.
$$

11.4 FREQUENCY DOMAIN MULTIVARIATE ANALYSIS

In this section the methods of Section 11.3 are generalized so that they can be applied in the frequency domain. There are two main points of difference between the models used in this section and those in Section 11.3. First, the models in Section 11.3 described regressions and correlations between processes at simultaneous times and so they describe only the steady-state behavior of systems. The models considered in this section are the dynamic generalizations of these models. Second, the noise, or residuals, in the models of Section 11.3 were assumed to be white. In this section, the noises can be quite general stationary time series.

11.4.1 Multiple frequency response analysis, single output

In this section it is shown how to estimate the frequency response functions associated with the model

$$
X_{(q+1)}(t) - \mu_{(q+1)} = \int_{-\infty}^{\infty} h_{(q+1)1}(u)(X_1(t-u) - \bar{X}_1)\, du + \cdots
$$

$$
+ \int_{-\infty}^{\infty} h_{(q+1)q}(u)(X_q(t-u) - \bar{X}_q)\, du + Z(t), \quad (11.4.1)
$$

which is the dynamic generalization of the steady-state model (11.3.1). To clarify ideas, it is assumed that infinite lengths of record are available for the single output $X_{(q+1)}(t)$ and the q inputs. To simplify the problem still further, consider the special case of $q = 2$ inputs.

Proceeding as in Appendix A5.1, it may be shown that the minimum mse estimates of the impulse response functions $h_{31}(u)$ and $h_{32}(u)$ are obtained by solving the simultaneous Wiener–Hopf equations

$$\gamma_{13}(u) = \int_{-\infty}^{\infty} h_{31}(v)\gamma_{11}(u - v) \, dv + \int_{-\infty}^{\infty} h_{32}(v)\gamma_{12}(u - v) \, dv,$$

$$\gamma_{23}(u) = \int_{-\infty}^{\infty} h_{31}(v)\gamma_{21}(u - v) \, dv + \int_{-\infty}^{\infty} h_{32}(v)\gamma_{22}(u - v) \, dv. \qquad (11.4.2)$$

Note that the equations (11.4.2) can also be obtained by multiplying throughout in (11.4.1), first by $(X_1(t - u) - \bar{X}_1)$ and then by $(X_2(t - u) - \bar{X}_2)$, and taking expectations.

Taking Fourier transforms of (11.4.2) gives the frequency domain equations

$$\Gamma_{13}(f) = H_{31}(f)\Gamma_{11}(f) + H_{32}(f)\Gamma_{12}(f)$$

$$\Gamma_{23}(f) = H_{31}(f)\Gamma_{21}(f) + H_{32}(f)\Gamma_{22}(f). \qquad (11.4.3)$$

Solving for $H_{31}(f)$ and $H_{32}(f)$ gives the following expressions for the frequency response functions, in terms of the auto- and cross spectra:

$$H_{31}(f) = \frac{\Gamma_{13}(f)\Gamma_{22}(f) - \Gamma_{23}(f)\Gamma_{12}(f)}{\Gamma_{11}(f)\Gamma_{22}(f) - |\Gamma_{12}(f)|^2},$$

$$H_{32}(f) = \frac{\Gamma_{23}(f)\Gamma_{11}(f) - \Gamma_{13}(f)\Gamma_{21}(f)}{\Gamma_{11}(f)\Gamma_{22}(f) - |\Gamma_{12}(f)|^2}. \qquad (11.4.4)$$

To obtain expressions for the gains and phases, it is necessary to take the modulus and argument of (11.4.4). For example,

$$G_{31} = \sqrt{A_{31}^2 + B_{31}^2}, \qquad \phi_{31} = \arctan -\frac{B_{31}}{A_{31}}, \qquad (11.4.5)$$

where

$$A_{31} = \frac{(\Lambda_{13}\Gamma_{22} + \Psi_{23}\Psi_{12} - \Lambda_{23}\Lambda_{12})}{(\Gamma_{11}\Gamma_{22} - |\Gamma_{12}|^2)},$$

$$B_{31} = \frac{(\Psi_{13}\Gamma_{22} - \Psi_{23}\Lambda_{12} - \Lambda_{23}\Psi_{12})}{(\Gamma_{11}\Gamma_{22} - |\Gamma_{12}|^2)}. \qquad (11.4.6)$$

For q inputs, (11.4.2) may be written

$$\gamma_{(q+1)}(u) = \int_{-\infty}^{\infty} \gamma_{qq}(u - v)\mathbf{h}_{(q+1)}(v) \, dv, \qquad (11.4.7)$$

where $\gamma_{(q+1)}(u)$ is the lagged vector of cross covariances between the output $q + 1$ and all the inputs, $\mathbf{h}'_{(q+1)} = (h_{(q+1)1}, h_{(q+1)2}, \ldots, h_{(q+1)q})$ and $\gamma_{qq}(u)$ is the lagged covariance matrix of the inputs. Transforming (11.4.7) gives

$$\Gamma_{(q+1)}(f) = \Gamma_{qq}(f)\mathbf{H}_{(q+1)}(f), \qquad (11.4.8)$$

where $\Gamma_{(q+1)}(f)$ is the vector of cross spectra between the output $X_{(q+1)}(t)$ and the inputs, $\Gamma_{qq}(f)$ is the spectral matrix of the inputs and $\mathbf{H}'_{(q+1)}(f) =$

$(H_{(q+1)1}(f), H_{(q+1)2}(f), \ldots, H_{(q+1)q}(f))$. The gain and phase functions may be obtained by solving these equations and taking their modulus and argument as described above.

11.4.2 The multiple coherency spectrum

In this section the multiple coherency spectrum is defined. This is a generalization to the frequency domain of the multiple correlation coefficient introduced in Section 11.3.2. First it is necessary to derive an expression for the residual or noise spectrum, which is one of the basic quantities of interest, apart from the estimates of gain and phase.

The residual spectrum. To evaluate the residual spectrum $\Gamma_{zz}(f)$ corresponding to the model (11.4.1), it is first necessary to compute the autocovariance function of the residual process. Proceeding as in Section 11.3.2, the autocovariance function of $Z(t)$ is

$$\gamma_{zz}(u) = \gamma_{(q+1)(q+1)}(u) - \int_0^\infty h_{(q+1)1}(v)\gamma_{(q+1)1}(u-v)\,dv -$$

$$\cdots - \int_0^\infty h_{(q+1)q}(v)\gamma_{(q+1)q}(u-v)\,dv.$$

Taking Fourier transforms gives the residual spectrum

$$\Gamma_{zz}(f) = \Gamma_{(q+1)(q+1)}(f) - H_{(q+1)1}(f)\Gamma_{(q+1)1}(f) - \cdots - H_{(q+1)q}(f)\Gamma_{(q+1)q}(f),$$
$$(11.4.9)$$

which is the frequency domain analog of (11.3.7).

The squared multiple coherency spectrum. Proceeding as in Section 11.3.2, (11.4.9) may be written

$$\Gamma_{zz}(f) = \Gamma_{(q+1)(q+1)}(f)[1 - \kappa^2_{(q+1)12\ldots q}(f)], \qquad (11.4.10)$$

where

$$\kappa^2_{(q+1)12\ldots q}(f) = H_{(q+1)1}(f)\Gamma_{(q+1)1}(f) + \cdots + H_{(q+1)q}(f)\Gamma_{(q+1)q}(f)$$

is called the *squared multiple coherency spectrum* of the output process and the q input processes. The multiple coherency spectrum measures the proportion of the output spectrum which can be predicted from the inputs. As shown by (11.4.10), the remaining proportion $[1 - \kappa^2_{(q+1)12\ldots q}(f)]$ of the output spectrum is noise.

On substituting in (11.4.9) the expressions (11.4.8) for the frequency response functions, an alternative form for the squared multiple coherency spectrum is obtained which is analogous to (11.3.11), namely,

$$\kappa^2_{(q+1)12\ldots q}(f) = 1 - \frac{|\boldsymbol{\Gamma}_{(q+1)(q+1)}(f)|}{\Gamma_{(q+1)(q+1)}(f)\,|\boldsymbol{\Gamma}_{qq}(f)|}. \qquad (11.4.11)$$

In (11.4.11), $\Gamma_{(q+1)(q+1)}(f)$ is the spectral matrix of all $q + 1$ variables, and $\Gamma_{qq}(f)$ is the spectral matrix of the q input variables. When $q = 2$, (11.4.11) becomes, on dropping the dependence on f,

$$\kappa_{312}^2 = 1 - \frac{\begin{vmatrix} \Gamma_{11} & \Gamma_{12} & \Gamma_{13} \\ \Gamma_{21} & \Gamma_{22} & \Gamma_{23} \\ \Gamma_{31} & \Gamma_{32} & \Gamma_{33} \end{vmatrix}}{\Gamma_{33} \begin{vmatrix} \Gamma_{11} & \Gamma_{12} \\ \Gamma_{21} & \Gamma_{22} \end{vmatrix}}, \tag{11.4.12}$$

which corresponds to (11.3.14). When expanded, (11.4.12) becomes

$$\kappa_{312}^2 = \frac{\Gamma_{22} |\Gamma_{31}|^2 + \Gamma_{11} |\Gamma_{32}|^2 - 2 \operatorname{Re} [\Gamma_{12}\Gamma_{23}\Gamma_{31}]}{\Gamma_{33}(\Gamma_{11}\Gamma_{22} - |\Gamma_{12}|^2)} \tag{11.4.13}$$

where

$$\operatorname{Re} [\Gamma_{12}\Gamma_{23}\Gamma_{31}] = \Lambda_{12}\Lambda_{23}\Lambda_{13} + \Lambda_{12}\Psi_{23}\Psi_{13} - \Psi_{12}\Psi_{23}\Lambda_{13} + \Psi_{12}\Psi_{13}\Lambda_{23} \tag{11.4.14}$$

may be expressed in terms of the co- and quadrature spectra of the three processes.

11.4.3 Partial cross, squared coherency and phase spectra

As in multiple regression analysis, it is useful to be able to measure the cross spectrum between the output and one of the input processes after allowance is made for the effect of the other input processes. This leads to the partial cross spectrum, which is the frequency domain analog of the partial correlation coefficient (11.3.21).

To illustrate the basic idea, it is assumed that there are just two input variables. Generalizing the approach of Section 11.3.3, the output $X_3(t)$ is first predicted from past values of the $X_2(t)$ process only, leading to residuals

$$\varepsilon_3(t) = (X_3(t) - \mu_3) - \int_0^\infty \hat{g}_{32}(u)(X_2(t - u) - \mu_2) \, du$$

where $\hat{g}_{32}(u)$ is given by the solution of the appropriate Wiener–Hopf integral equation. Similarly, the input $X_1(t)$ is predicted from $X_2(t)$ only, leading to residuals

$$\varepsilon_1(t) = (X_1(t) - \mu_1) - \int_0^\infty \hat{g}_{12}(u)(X_2(t - u) - \mu_2) \, du.$$

The partial cross covariance function. The partial cross covariance function between $X_1(t)$ and $X_3(t + u)$, after allowing for $X_2(t)$, is then defined by

$$\gamma_{13|2}(u) = \operatorname{Cov} [\varepsilon_1(t), \varepsilon_3(t + u)]$$

$$= \gamma_{13}(u) - \int_0^\infty \hat{g}_{32}(v)\gamma_{12}(u - v) \, dv - \int_0^\infty \hat{g}_{12}(v)\gamma_{23}(u + v) \, dv$$

$$+ \int_0^\infty \int_0^\infty \hat{g}_{12}(v)\hat{g}_{32}(w)\gamma_{22}(u + v - w) \, dv \, dw. \tag{11.4.15}$$

The partial cross spectrum. The partial cross spectrum is derived by taking the Fourier transform of (11.4.15), and substituting $\hat{G}_{12} = \Gamma_{12}/\Gamma_{22}$, $\hat{G}_{32} = \Gamma_{23}/\Gamma_{22}$, namely,

$$\Gamma_{13|2}(f) = \Gamma_{13}(f) - \frac{\Gamma_{23}(f)\Gamma_{12}(f)}{\Gamma_{22}(f)}. \tag{11.4.16}$$

The *partial cross spectral density function*

$$\kappa_{13|2}(f) = \frac{\Gamma_{13|2}(f)}{\sqrt{\Gamma_{11}(f)(1 - \kappa_{12}^2(f))\Gamma_{33}(f)(1 - \kappa_{23}^2(f))}} \tag{11.4.17}$$

is obtained by normalizing the partial cross spectrum.

Partial coherency spectrum. The squared partial coherency spectrum is the squared modulus of $\kappa_{13|2}(f)$. It is most simply calculated using the spectral analog of (11.3.22), namely,

$$1 - \kappa_{13|2}^2(f) = \frac{1 - \kappa_{312}^2(f)}{1 - \kappa_{23}^2(f)}. \tag{11.4.18}$$

The partial coherency $\kappa_{13|2}^2(f)$ measures the squared covariance "at frequency f" between the processes $X_3(t)$ and $X_1(t)$ when allowance is made for the influence of $X_2(t)$.

Partial phase spectrum. The partial phase spectrum $\phi_{13|2}(f)$ is the argument of (11.4.16) or (11.4.17) and is given by

$$\phi_{13|2}(f) = \arctan\left\{ \frac{\Lambda_{12}\Psi_{23} - \Psi_{12}\Lambda_{23} - \Psi_{13}\Gamma_{22}}{\Lambda_{12}\Lambda_{23} + \Psi_{12}\Psi_{23} - \Lambda_{13}\Gamma_{22}} \right\}. \tag{11.4.19}$$

Similar expressions for the partial squared coherency $\kappa_{23|1}^2(f)$ and the partial phase $\phi_{23|1}(f)$ may be obtained by interchanging the indices 1 and 2 in (11.4.18) and (11.4.19).

The difference between the partial phase $\phi_{13|2}(f)$ and the phases $\phi_{31}(f)$, $\phi_{32}(f)$, obtained from the frequency response model (11.4.1), should be noted. The phase $\phi_{31}(f)$ measures the phase difference between $X_3(t)$ and $X_1(t)$ when a sinusoidal change is made in $X_1(t)$ but there is no change in $X_2(t)$. However, the partial phase $\phi_{13|2}(f)$ measures the "direct" phase difference between $X_1(t)$ and $X_3(t)$ after allowing for the phase differences between $X_2(t)$ and $X_3(t)$ and between $X_2(t)$ and $X_1(t)$. When there is just one input variable, the partial phase angle is equivalent to the ordinary phase angle.

For q inputs, the partial cross spectrum is given by the spectral analog of (11.3.21), namely,

$$\kappa_{(q+1)k|K}(f) = \frac{\pi_{(q+1)k}(f)}{\sqrt{\pi_{(q+1)(q+1)}(f)\pi_{kk}(f)}}, \tag{11.4.20}$$

where π_{lm} is the minor of the element Γ_{lm} in the spectral matrix of all $(q + 1)$ variables.

The partial coherency and phase spectra may then be calculated from (11.4.20).

Summary. As in the analysis of bivariate time series, interest is focused on different types of spectral estimates, depending on whether all the series in a multiple time series arise on an equal footing or whether some are inputs and some outputs to a physical system. If all the series arise on an equal footing, then the main spectrum of interest is the multiple coherency. This is usually supplemented by information about the partial coherency and partial phase spectra between selected pairs of the variables. If the series represent inputs and corresponding outputs to some physical system, the most important part of the analysis is concerned with the estimation of the frequency response functions of the system. The other important estimate is the residual spectrum which describes the noise in the system. In this case, the multiple coherency is only of interest insofar as it affects the confidence intervals for the gain and phase matrix. The estimation of the multiple coherency spectrum is discussed in Section 11.4.5. Confidence intervals for gain and phase functions are derived in Section 11.4.6.

11.4.4 *Multivariate frequency response analysis, multiple outputs*

The model. In this section the time-domain multivariate analysis discussed in Section 11.3.4 is extended to the frequency domain. The steady-state model (11.3.23) is generalized to the dynamic model

$$\mathbf{x}_{(q+r)}(t) - \boldsymbol{\mu}_{(q+r)} = \int_{-\infty}^{\infty} \mathbf{h}(u)(\mathbf{x}_q(t - u) - \bar{\mathbf{x}}_q)\, du + \mathbf{z}_{(q+r)}(t), \quad (11.4.21)$$

where $\mathbf{x}_{(q+r)}(t)$ is the vector of output variables, $\mathbf{x}_q(t)$ is a vector of input variables and $\mathbf{z}_{(q+r)}(t)$ is a vector of noise variables. For example, when there are $q = 2$ inputs and $r = 2$ outputs (11.4.21) is

$$X_3(t) - \mu_3 = \int_{-\infty}^{\infty} h_{31}(u)(X_1(t - u) - \bar{X}_1)\, du +$$
$$\int_{-\infty}^{\infty} h_{32}(u)\,(X_2(t - u) - \bar{X}_2)\, du + Z_3(t),$$

$$X_4(t) - \mu_4 = \int_{-\infty}^{\infty} h_{41}(u)(X_1(t - u) - \bar{X}_1)\, du +$$
$$\int_{-\infty}^{\infty} h_{42}(u)(X_2(t - u) - \bar{X}_2)\, du + Z_4(t).$$

$$(11.4.22)$$

As in the preceding sections, it is assumed initially that infinite lengths of record are available for all the inputs and outputs.

Estimation equations. As in Section 11.3.4, the minimum mse estimates of the impulse response functions $h_{ij}(u)$ are obtained by separately minimizing the mean square errors

$$E\left[\int_{-\infty}^{\infty} Z_i^2(t)\, dt\right].$$

This procedure leads to a set of equations of the form (11.4.7), namely,

$$\gamma_{(q+k)}(u) = \int_{-\infty}^{\infty} \gamma_{qq}(u - v)\mathbf{h}_{(q+k)}(v)\, dv, \quad k = 1, 2, \ldots, r.$$
$$(11.4.23)$$

These may be assembled into a single matrix equation

$$\gamma_{qr}(u) = \int_{-\infty}^{\infty} \gamma_{qq}(u - v)\mathbf{h}'(v)\, dv, \qquad (11.4.24)$$

where $\gamma_{qr}(u)$ is the lagged cross covariance matrix between the q inputs and r outputs, $\mathbf{h}(u)$ is the impulse response matrix and $\gamma_{qq}(u)$ is the lagged covariance matrix of the inputs.

On taking Fourier transforms of (11.4.23), the estimation equations for the frequency response functions may be written

$$\Gamma_{(q+k)}(f) = \Gamma_{qq}(f)\mathbf{H}_{(q+k)}(f), \quad k = 1, 2, \ldots, r. \qquad (11.4.25)$$

As in (11.4.24), the equations (11.4.25) may be assembled into the single matrix equation

$$\Gamma_{qr}(f) = \Gamma_{qq}(f)\mathbf{H}'(f). \qquad (11.4.26)$$

The residual spectral matrix. In addition to estimating the frequency response matrix, it is necessary to characterize the properties of the noise. This is done by calculating the residual or noise spectral matrix $\Gamma_{ZZ}(f)$ whose elements are the cross spectra $\Gamma_{kl}(f)$ between the processes $Z_k(t)$ and $Z_l(t)$. Proceeding as in Section 11.3.4, the cross covariance function between the processes is

$$\gamma_{Z_k Z_l}(u) = \gamma_{(q+k)(q+l)}(u) - \int_{-\infty}^{\infty} h_{(q+k)1}(v)\gamma_{(q+l)1}(u - v)\, dv - $$

$$\cdots - \int_{-\infty}^{\infty} h_{(q+k)q}(v)\gamma_{(q+l)q}(u - v)\, dv. \qquad (11.4.27)$$

On transforming (11.4.27), the cross spectrum is given by

$$\Gamma_{Z_k Z_l}(f) = \Gamma_{(q+k)(q+l)}(f) - H_{(q+k)1}(f)\Gamma_{(q+l)1}(f) - \cdots - H_{(q+k)q}(f)\Gamma_{(q+l)q}(f).$$
$$(11.4.28)$$

Assembling a matrix whose elements are (11.4.28) gives

$$\Gamma'_{ZZ}(f) = \Gamma'_{(q+r)(q+r)}(f) - \mathbf{H}(f)\Gamma'_{qr}(f). \qquad (11.4.29)$$

Note that (11.4.29) enables the residual spectral matrix to be calculated when the frequency response matrix $\mathbf{H}(f)$ and the theoretical values of the output spectral matrix $\mathbf{\Gamma}_{(q+r)(q+r)}(f)$ and input–output cross spectral matrix $\mathbf{\Gamma}_{qr}(f)$ are known. The corresponding estimation problem is considered in Section 11.4.6.

11.4.5 Estimation of multivariate spectra

It was shown in Sections 11.4.2 and 11.4.3 how to compute multiple and partial coherency spectra in terms of the input and output spectra and cross spectra. In this section the problem of estimating these spectra is considered when finite lengths of record are available. The analysis is a straightforward extension of that given in Section 9.3.1 and hence the details are omitted.

Estimation of multiple coherency. The definition (11.4.11) expresses the square of the multiple coherency in terms of auto- and cross spectra. The sample estimator of the multiple coherency is obtained by replacing the theoretical spectra by their smoothed estimators. For example, when $q = 2$, the smoothed multiple coherency estimator is

$$\bar{K}^2_{3 \cdot 12}(f) = \frac{\bar{C}_{22}\,|\bar{C}_{13}|^2 + \bar{C}_{11}\,|\bar{C}_{23}|^2 - 2\text{Re}\,[\bar{C}_{12}\bar{C}_{23}\bar{C}_{31}]}{\bar{C}_{33}(\bar{C}_{11}\bar{C}_{22} - |\bar{C}_{12}|^2)}, \qquad (11.4.30)$$

where

$$\text{Re}\,[\bar{C}_{12}\bar{C}_{23}\bar{C}_{31}] = \bar{L}_{12}\bar{L}_{23}\bar{L}_{13} + \bar{L}_{12}\bar{Q}_{23}\bar{Q}_{13} - \bar{Q}_{12}\bar{Q}_{23}\bar{L}_{13} + \bar{Q}_{12}\bar{Q}_{13}\bar{L}_{23}.$$

Since the estimator (11.4.30) is a function of spectra and cross spectra, its variance can be evaluated using the statistical differential technique of Section 3.2.5 and the result (A9.1.28), namely,

$$\text{Cov}\,[\bar{C}_{ij}(f_1),\ \bar{C}_{kl}(f_1)] \approx \Gamma_{il}(f_1)\Gamma_{jk}(f_1)\,\frac{I}{T}. \qquad (11.4.31)$$

Proceeding as in Section 9.2.2, the final result is

$$\text{Var}\,[\bar{K}^2_{3 \cdot 12}] \approx \frac{1}{2T} \cdot 4\kappa^2_{3 \cdot 12}(1 - \kappa^2_{3 \cdot 12})^2,$$

which is the same as the variance (9.2.19) for the ordinary coherency estimator $\bar{K}^2_{12}$. In Section 11.4.6, an appropriate distribution for $\bar{K}^2_{3 \cdot 12}$ will be derived by regarding the problem as one of multiple regression analysis in the frequency domain.

Estimation of partial coherency and phase. The smoothed partial cross spectrum estimators are obtained by substituting smoothed estimators for the cross spectra in (11.4.19). The smoothed partial coherency spectra and partial phase spectra can then be obtained by taking the modulus squared and argument of the smoothed cross spectrum estimators. For example, when $q = 2$,

the two partial coherencies may be estimated from the smoothed multiple
coherency $\bar{K}_{312}^2$ using the relations

$$1 - \bar{K}_{23|1}^2 = \frac{1 - \bar{K}_{312}^2}{1 - \bar{K}_{13}^2},$$

$$1 - \bar{K}_{13|2}^2 = \frac{1 - \bar{K}_{312}^2}{1 - \bar{K}_{23}^2}. \qquad (11.4.32)$$

Similarly, the smoothed partial phase spectra are

$$\bar{F}_{13|2} = \arctan\left[\frac{\bar{L}_{12}\bar{Q}_{23} - \bar{Q}_{12}\bar{L}_{23} - \bar{Q}_{13}\bar{C}_{22}}{\bar{L}_{12}\bar{L}_{23} + \bar{Q}_{12}\bar{Q}_{23} - \bar{L}_{13}\bar{C}_{22}}\right], \qquad (11.4.33)$$

$$\bar{F}_{23|1} = \arctan\left[\frac{\bar{L}_{12}\bar{Q}_{13} + \bar{Q}_{12}\bar{L}_{13} - \bar{Q}_{23}\bar{C}_{11}}{\bar{L}_{12}\bar{L}_{13} - \bar{Q}_{12}\bar{Q}_{13} - \bar{L}_{23}\bar{C}_{11}}\right]. \qquad (11.4.34)$$

11.4.6 Estimation of multiple frequency response functions

In this section it is shown how to estimate the frequency response functions
corresponding to the model (11.4.1) and to derive confidence intervals for the
gains and phases. The results are obtained by a simple extension of those
derived in Section 10.3.3.

Estimates based on sample spectra. As in previous work, rv's are associated
with the transforms of the data, namely,

$$X_i(f) = \int_0^T X_i(t)\, e^{-j2\pi ft}\, dt.$$

On transforming the model (11.4.1), and making the usual assumptions that
the impulse response functions $h_{(q+1)i}(u)$ tend to zero quickly compared with
the record length, the output transform is

$$X_{(q+1)}(f) \approx H_{(q+1)1}(f)X_1(f) + \cdots + H_{(q+1)q}(f)X_q(f) + Z_{(q+1)}(f). \qquad (11.4.35)$$

Proceeding as in Section 10.3.1, the least squares estimators of the impulse
response functions are obtained by replacing the theoretical auto- and cross
correlations in (11.4.7) by sample values. Thus

$$\mathbf{c}_{(q+1)}(u) = \int_{-\infty}^{\infty} \mathbf{C}_{qq}(u - v)\, \hat{\mathbf{h}}_{(q+1)}(v)\, dv, \quad -T \leqslant u \leqslant T. \qquad (11.4.36)$$

On taking Fourier transforms of (11.4.36), the frequency domain estimation
equations are

$$\mathbf{C}_{(q+1)}(f) = \mathbf{C}_{qq}(f)\hat{\mathbf{H}}_{(q+1)}(f), \qquad (11.4.37)$$

which are the same as the equations (11.4.8) but with theoretical spectra
replaced by the corresponding sample spectra.

Residual sample spectrum. Proceeding as in Section 10.3.2, the residual sample spectrum is

$$C_{zz}(f) \approx C_{\hat{z}\hat{z}}(f) + \frac{1}{T}|X_1(f)\{H_{(q+1)1}(f) - \hat{H}_{(q+1)1}(f)\} +$$
$$\cdots + X_q(f)\{H_{(q+1)q}(f) - \hat{H}_{(q+1)q}(f)\}|^2. \quad (11.4.38)$$

Similarly, the estimated residual spectrum is given by the expressions

$$C_{\hat{z}\hat{z}}(f) = C_{(q+1)(q+1)}(f) - \hat{H}_{(q+1)1}(f)C_{(q+1)1}(f) - \cdots - \hat{H}_{(q+1)q}(f)C_{(q+1)q}(f) \quad (11.4.39)$$

or

$$C_{\hat{z}\hat{z}}(f) = C_{(q+1)(q+1)}(f)[1 - K_{(q+1)12...q}^2(f)], \quad (11.4.40)$$

which are analogous to (11.4.9) and (11.4.10) respectively. However, as noted in Section 10.3.2, $C_{\hat{z}\hat{z}}(f)$ is identically zero since the sample coherency is identically equal to unity. In view of this and the associated bad variance properties of these estimators, smoothing of the estimators is necessary.

Smoothed least squares analysis. The smoothed estimation equations are obtained by replacing the sample spectral estimators in (11.4.37) by the corresponding smoothed estimators. Similarly, the smoothed residual spectral estimators are obtained from (11.4.39) or (11.4.40).

A test for non-zero multiple coherency. Suppose $H_{(q+1)k} = 0$, $k = 1, 2, \ldots, q$, in (11.4.38). Then the output and noise processes are identical. Using (11.4.40), the decomposition (11.4.38) may be written in smoothed form as

$$\frac{\nu \overline{C}_{(q+1)(q+1)}(f)}{\Gamma_{(q+1)(q+1)}(f)} = \frac{\nu \overline{C}_{(q+1)(q+1)}(f)}{\Gamma_{(q+1)(q+1)}(f)}(1 - \overline{K}_{(q+1)12...q}^2(f)) +$$
$$\frac{\nu \overline{C}_{(q+1)(q+1)}(f)}{\Gamma_{(q+1)(q+1)}(f)}\overline{K}_{(q+1)12...q}^2(f). \quad (11.4.41)$$

Equation (11.4.41) shows that the chi-squared rv with ν degrees of freedom on the left-hand side is decomposed into chi-squared rv's with $\nu - 2q$ and $2q$ degrees of freedom respectively. Hence

$$\frac{\overline{K}_{(q+1)12...q}^2(f)}{1 - \overline{K}_{(q+1)12...q}^2(f)}\left(\frac{\nu - 2q}{2q}\right) \quad (11.4.42)$$

is distributed as $F_{2q,\nu-2q}$. As shown for $q = 2$ in Section 10.3.2, (11.4.42) can be used to test whether the multiple coherency function is different from zero.

Confidence intervals for the gains and phases. To illustrate the general method, consider the case of $q = 2$ inputs. Then the smoothed version of (11.4.38) becomes, on dropping the dependence on f,

$$\overline{C}_{zz} = \overline{C}_{\hat{z}\hat{z}} + \overline{C}_{11}|H_{31} - \hat{H}_{31}|^2 + \overline{C}_{22}|H_{32} - \hat{H}_{32}|^2$$
$$+ 2|\overline{C}_{12}||(H_{31} - \hat{H}_{31})(H_{32} - \hat{H}_{32})|. \quad (11.4.43)$$

Proceeding as in Section 10.3.4, the decomposition (11.4.43) leads to a joint confidence region

$$\bar{C}_{11}|H_{31} - \hat{H}_{31}|^2 + \bar{C}_{22}|H_{32} - \hat{H}_{32}|^2 + 2|\bar{C}_{12}||(H_{31} - \hat{H}_{31})(H_{32} - \hat{H}_{32})| \over \bar{C}_{\hat{z}\hat{z}}$$

$$\leqslant \frac{4}{\nu - 4} f_{4,\nu-4}(1 - \alpha), \qquad (11.4.44)$$

for G_{31}, G_{32}, ϕ_{31} and ϕ_{32}. There does not seem to be a simple way of expressing this region in terms of the gain and phase spectra. However, a rough approximation which is sometimes useful is to replace the left-hand side of (11.4.44) by its lower bound

$$\frac{\bar{C}_{11}|H_{31} - \hat{H}_{31}|^2 + \bar{C}_{22}|H_{32} - \hat{H}_{32}|^2}{\bar{C}_{\hat{z}\hat{z}}}.$$

This is equivalent to ignoring the covariance between the terms making up $H_{31}(f)$ and $H_{32}(f)$, and hence the confidence region for G_{31} and ϕ_{31} is independent of that for G_{32} and ϕ_{32}. Applying the further approximation used in Section 10.3.4, the confidence intervals become

$$|G_{31} - \hat{G}_{31}| \leqslant k_1$$
$$\sin|\phi_{31} - \hat{\phi}_{31}| \leqslant \frac{k_1}{G_{31}}$$

$$k_1^2 = \frac{4}{\nu - 4} \frac{\bar{C}_{\hat{z}\hat{z}}}{\bar{C}_{11}} f_{4,\nu-4}(1 - \alpha),$$

$$|G_{32} - \hat{G}_{32}| \leqslant k_2$$
$$\sin|\phi_{32} - \hat{\phi}_{32}| \leqslant \frac{k_2}{G_{32}}$$

$$k_2^2 = \frac{4}{\nu - 4} \frac{C_{\hat{z}\hat{z}}}{\bar{C}_{22}} f_{4,\nu-4}(1 - \alpha).$$

$$(11.4.45)$$

Note that at best these intervals serve only as rough guides and may be badly in error if significant correlation occurs between the two frequency response function estimators.

Bias and alignment. As shown in Chapters 9 and 10, if the series are not aligned, serious bias occurs in the estimation of cross spectra, and the bias is transmitted to the estimation of the gains. The bias is minimized if all the input series are aligned with the output in the model (11.4.1). This above approximate distribution properties apply only when alignment has been made.

11.4.7 *Estimation of multivariate frequency response functions*

A brief discussion is given in this section of the estimation of the frequency response matrix corresponding to the model (11.4.21).

Estimation equations. Estimation equations may be obtained by replacing the spectra in (11.4.26) by their smoothed estimators. Thus

$$\bar{\mathbf{C}}_{qr}(f) = \bar{\mathbf{C}}_{qq}(f)\hat{\mathbf{H}}'(f).$$
(11.4.46)

For example, if $q = 2$, there are two pairs of estimation equations

$$\bar{C}_{13}(f) = \hat{H}_{31}(f)\bar{C}_{11}(f) + \hat{H}_{32}(f)\bar{C}_{12}(f),$$
$$\bar{C}_{23}(f) = \hat{H}_{31}(f)\bar{C}_{21}(f) + \hat{H}_{32}(f)\bar{C}_{22}(f)$$
(11.4.47)

and

$$\bar{C}_{14}(f) = \hat{H}_{41}(f)\bar{C}_{11}(f) + \hat{H}_{42}(f)\bar{C}_{12}(f),$$
$$\bar{C}_{24}(f) = \hat{H}_{41}(f)\bar{C}_{21}(f) + \hat{H}_{42}(f)\bar{C}_{22}(f).$$
(11.4.48)

Estimation of residual spectral matrix. The elements of the residual spectral matrix are obtained by substituting smoothed estimators in (11.4.28). Thus the cross spectrum between $Z_k(t)$ and $Z_l(t)$ is estimated by

$$\bar{C}_{Z_kZ_l}(f) = \bar{C}_{(q+k)(q+l)}(f) - \hat{H}_{(q+k)1}(f)\bar{C}_{(q+l)1}(f) - \cdots - \hat{H}_{(q+k)q}(f)\bar{C}_{(q+l)q}(f),$$
(11.4.49)

which is the frequency domain analog of (11.3.27).

Confidence intervals. Extension of (11.3.31) to give confidence intervals for the gains and phases of the frequency response matrix is not readily achieved. For most practical purposes it is sufficient to treat separately each relation in the model (11.4.21) and to derive approximate confidence intervals, as shown in Section 11.4.6.

11.5 PRACTICAL ASPECTS OF MULTIVARIATE SPECTRAL ANALYSIS

This section begins with a summary of the formulae required for the estimation of bivariate frequency response functions. Section 11.5.2 contains a summary of the stages which should be followed in a practical procedure for estimating these functions. Finally, Section 11.5.3 describes the estimation of the frequency response functions of a two-input, two-output system consisting of an operational turbo-alternator.

11.5.1 Discrete estimation formulae

The discrete system equations are

$$X_{3t} = \sum_{j=0}^{\infty} h_{31j}X_{1t-j} + \sum_{j=0}^{\infty} h_{32j}X_{2t-j} + Z_{3t},$$

$$X_{4t} = \sum_{j=0}^{\infty} h_{41j}X_{1t-j} + \sum_{j=0}^{\infty} h_{42j}X_{2t-j} + Z_{4t}.$$

These lead to the discrete estimation equations

$$\bar{C}_{1k}(f) = \hat{H}_{k1}(f)\bar{C}_{11}(f) + \hat{H}_{k2}(f)\bar{C}_{12}(f),$$
$$\bar{C}_{2k}(f) = \hat{H}_{k1}(f)\bar{C}_{21}(f) + \hat{H}_{k2}(f)\bar{C}_{22}(f),$$

where $k = 3, 4$ and

$$\hat{H}_{kl}(f) = G_{kl}(f)\, e^{j\bar{\phi}_{kl}(f)}, \quad l = 1, 2.$$

On dropping the dependence on f, the estimates may be written as follows:

Gain and phase estimates

$$\left.\begin{array}{l} \bar{G}_{kl} = \sqrt{\bar{A}_{kl}^2 + \bar{B}_{kl}^2}, \\[2mm] \bar{\phi}_{kl} = \arctan\left(-\dfrac{\bar{B}_{kl}}{\bar{A}_{kl}}\right) \end{array}\right\} \quad \begin{array}{l} k = 3, 4, \\[2mm] l = 1, 2, \end{array}$$

where

$$\bar{A}_{k1} = (\bar{L}_{1k}\bar{C}_{22} + \bar{Q}_{2k}\bar{Q}_{12} - \bar{L}_{2k}\bar{L}_{12})/D,$$
$$\bar{B}_{k1} = (\bar{Q}_{1k}\bar{C}_{22} - \bar{Q}_{2k}\bar{L}_{12} - \bar{L}_{2k}\bar{Q}_{12})/D,$$
$$\bar{A}_{k2} = (\bar{L}_{2k}\bar{C}_{11} - \bar{Q}_{1k}\bar{Q}_{12} - \bar{L}_{1k}\bar{L}_{12})/D,$$
$$\bar{B}_{k2} = (\bar{Q}_{2k}\bar{C}_{11} - \bar{Q}_{1k}\bar{L}_{12} + \bar{L}_{1k}\bar{Q}_{12})/D,$$
$$D = \bar{C}_{11}\bar{C}_{22} - |\bar{C}_{12}|^2.$$

Squared coherency estimates

Squared coherency spectra

$$\bar{K}_{lk}^2 = \frac{(\bar{L}_{lk}^2 + \bar{Q}_{lk}^2)}{\bar{C}_{kk}\bar{C}_{ll}}, \quad l = 1, 2, \quad k = 3, 4.$$

Multiple squared coherency spectra

$$\bar{K}_{k12}^2 = \frac{\{\bar{C}_{22}(\bar{L}_{1k}^2 + \bar{Q}_{1k}^2) + \bar{C}_{11}(\bar{L}_{2k}^2 + \bar{Q}_{2k}^2) - 2R\}}{\bar{C}_{kk}D},$$

where

$$R = \bar{L}_{12}\bar{L}_{2k}\bar{L}_{1k} + \bar{L}_{12}\bar{Q}_{2k}\bar{Q}_{1k} - \bar{Q}_{12}\bar{Q}_{2k}\bar{L}_{1k} + \bar{Q}_{12}\bar{L}_{2k}\bar{Q}_{1k}.$$

Partial squared coherency spectra

$$\bar{K}_{kl|m}^2 = 1 - \frac{(1 - \bar{K}_{klm}^2)}{(1 - \bar{K}_{km}^2)}, \quad \begin{array}{l} l = 1, 2, \\ m = 1, 2 \neq l, \\ k = 3, 4. \end{array}$$

Residual spectra

$$\bar{R}_{kk} = \bar{C}_{kk}(1 - \bar{K}_{k12}^2), \quad k = 3, 4.$$

The flow chart for program MULTSPEC which performs the required computations is given in Appendix A11.2.

11.5.2 A practical procedure for estimating multivariate spectra

The stages in the procedure for multivariate frequency response estimation are very similar to those given for the estimation of cross spectra in Section 9.4.2 and for the single-input, single-output frequency response estimation in Section 10.4.1. Hence only a brief summary of the steps is presented here.

(1) Preliminary decision stage. As in Section 9.4.2, plots of the data are inspected for obvious trends, for possible filtering into different frequency bands and for deciding on the maximum number of lags for the computation of the acvf's and ccvf's.

(2) First computation stage. The auto- and cross correlations of the original and differenced data are computed and the correlations plotted. The correlation plots are inspected for failure to damp out, in which case the need for detrending is indicated, and for delays indicated by the peaks in the ccf.

(3) Intermediate decision stage. A decision is made whether to use the original or differenced covariances. The shift values for alignment are determined and three truncation points for future spectral calculations are selected.

(4) Second computation stage. The spectral calculations are performed and corresponding spectra overlayed for the three truncation values used.

(5) Interpretation stage. The plots are analyzed and interpreted, or additional spectral analyses are performed using the information gleaned from the present analysis.

11.5.3 Analysis of turbo-alternator data

These data have been analyzed previously in [3] and consist of normal operating data collected from a 50 megawatt turbo-alternator operating in parallel with an interconnected system having a capacity of approximately 5000 megawatts. A turbo-alternator may be regarded as a two-input, two-output system as shown in Figure 8.1. The input variables are the in-phase (or active) power and the out-of-phase (or reactive) power which measure the load on the system from the grid. The output variables are the amplitude and frequency of the voltage generated at the stator terminals. Knowledge of the transfer functions relating these variables is important in the design of control systems, particularly for load distribution and frequency.

By a change of variables, the in-phase and out-of-phase power can be replaced by the corresponding currents. Hence the variables measured were the deviations from the rated values of the in-phase and out-of phase currents and the corresponding deviations from the rated amplitude and frequency of the voltage. The currents and voltage were sampled 8 times per second, yielding 4808 data values, and the frequency was sampled 2 times per second, yielding 1202 data values.

Linearization of the theoretical system equations [2] showed that the turbo-alternator could be represented approximately as a linear bivariate system with the in-phase and out-of-phase current deviations as inputs to the system and the corresponding voltage and frequency deviations as outputs. In the notation of Section 11.4.4, $x_1(t)$ is the in-phase current, $x_2(t)$ the out-of-phase current, $x_3(t)$ the output voltage and $x_4(t)$ the output frequency.

An analysis given in [2] on similar data from the same system showed that there was little power in the current and voltage signals above 2.5 cps and, for the frequency data, above 0.8 cps. Hence it was decided to filter the current and voltage data using a digital filter with transfer function

$$H(\mathcal{Z}) = \{\tfrac{1}{7}(\mathcal{Z}^3 + \mathcal{Z}^2 + \mathcal{Z} + 1 + \mathcal{Z}^{-1} + \mathcal{Z}^{-2} + \mathcal{Z}^{-3})\}^4,$$

which has the frequency response function

$$H(f) = \left\{\frac{\sin 7\pi f\Delta}{7 \sin \pi f\Delta}\right\}^4, \quad -\frac{1}{2\Delta} \leqslant f < \frac{1}{2\Delta}.$$

This frequency response function is low pass, with negligible transfer of power above 0.75 cps, and so the filtered data was sampled at a rate of 2 points per second.

The first 1000 values of the filtered currents and voltage and the frequency variations were then analyzed, following the stages outlined in Section 11.5.2.

(1) Preliminary decision stage. The plots of the data given in Figure 11.1 were inspected for trends and other conspicuous behavior. No trends were apparent, but it was expected that because of the large number of observations some trend removal might be required. A maximum of 125 lags was selected initially.

(2) First computation stage. Auto- and cross covariances for the original and differenced data were computed, and the correlation functions were plotted.

(3) Intermediate decision stage. The acf's $r_{11}(k)$ and $r_{44}(k)$ for the in-phase current and the frequency showed a fairly strong oscillation with a frequency of approximately 12 to 15 cps and very little trend. By contrast, the acf's $r_{22}(k)$ for the out-of-phase current and $r_{33}(k)$ for the voltage showed considerable trend and very little oscillatory behavior.

The ccf $r_{12}(k)$ is plotted in Figure 11.2, $r_{13}(k)$ and $r_{23}(k)$ in Figure 11.3 and $r_{14}(k)$ and $r_{24}(k)$ in Figure 11.4. These again confirm that trends are present and that the correlations of the differenced data should be used. Truncation points of 32, 48 and 64 lags were chosen initially since it was felt that they would be sufficient to reveal the peaks apparent from some of the correlation functions. On the basis of the peaks in the ccf's, the shift parameters were chosen to be $S_{12} = -2$, $S_{13} = 0$, $S_{23} = 2$, $S_{14} = 3$ and $S_{24} = 5$.

(4) Second computation stage. The spectral calculations described in Section 11.5.1 were performed, using the shifted correlations of the differenced data, and the spectra were plotted.

(5) Interpretation stage. Since there are so many spectral plots in this type of analysis, only the important spectra are presented here for discussion. For all spectra, the window-closing procedure showed very little change in going from $L = 32$ to $L = 64$ lags. Since the analysis was based on 1000 data points, the value $L = 32$ was finally accepted, giving 83 degrees of freedom per estimate for the autospectra.

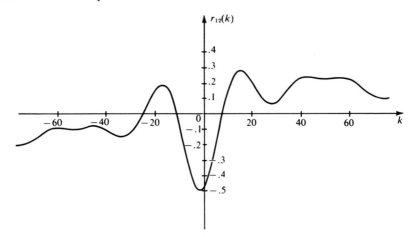

FIG. 11.2: Cross correlation function between input currents

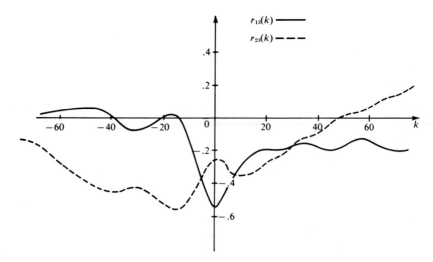

FIG. 11.3: Cross correlation functions between currents and voltage

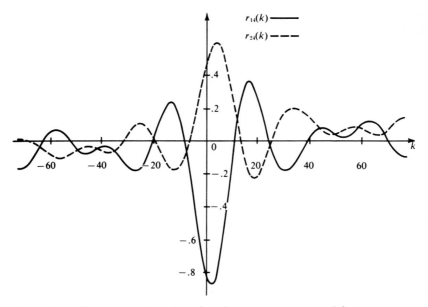

FIG. 11.4: Cross correlation functions between currents and frequency

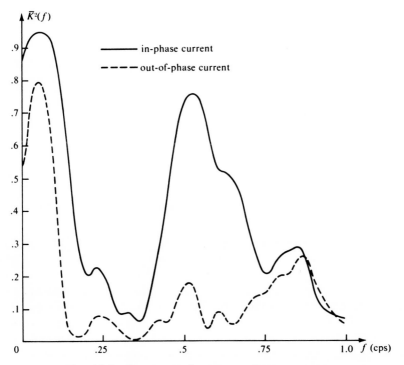

FIG. 11.5: Currents to frequency coherency spectra

Coherency spectra. The squared coherency spectra between the in-phase, out-of-phase currents and frequency are shown in Figure 11.5 and the multiple and partial squared coherency spectra between the two currents and frequency in Figure 11.6.

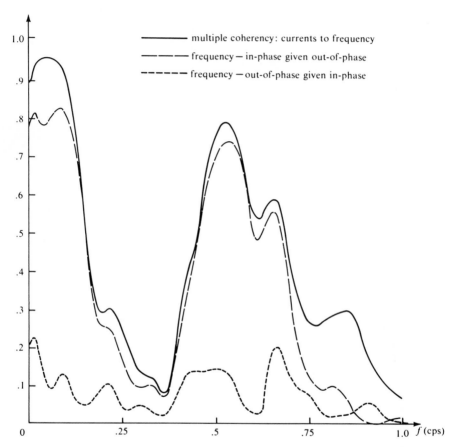

FIG. 11.6: Multiple and partial coherency spectra: currents to frequency

These figures show that the in-phase current and frequency deviations have high coherency over much of the frequency range. Figure 11.5 also suggests that there is a high coherency between the out-of-phase current and frequency. However, the very low partial coherency spectrum between frequency and out-of-phase current given the in-phase current, which is shown in Figure 11.6, indicates that this high coherency is due to the very high coherency between the currents and not to any direct relationship between frequency and out-of-phase current. Hence uninformative gain and phase estimates between the out-of-phase current and frequency variables are to be expected.

The squared coherency, multiple coherency and partial coherency spectra between the two currents and the voltages are shown in Figures 11.7 and 11.8. The in-phase to voltage coherencies are relatively high and uniform to 0.5 cps, where they drop and then begin to rise again at 0.7 cps. The extremely high coherencies above 0.75 cps are probably spurious and are discounted because of the extremely low power levels at these high frequencies. The out-of-phase to voltage coherencies are generally lower, with high coherencies near zero and in the range 0.25 to 0.5 cps. Again, the extremely high coherencies above 0.75 cps are probably spurious.

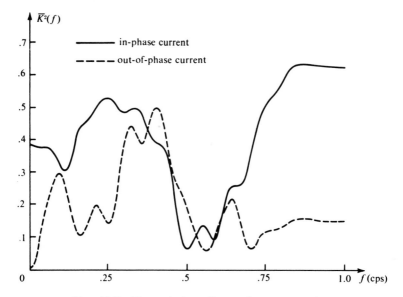

FIG. 11.7: Currents to voltage coherency spectra

Gain functions. The four gain functions are shown in Figures 11.9 to 11.12. The in-phase current to frequency gain function shown in Figure 11.9 has a peak at approximately 0.12 cps with a slope of 2 decades per decade, suggesting a second-order system. The damping factor for the system, obtained using the ratio of peak gain to dc gain, is about 0.2. The out-of-phase to frequency gain function shown in Figure 11.10 is extremely erratic, as expected from the partial squared coherency function. It is concluded that the out-of-phase current and frequency are probably not linearly related.

The gain functions from the two currents to voltage are similar, but the peaks are much less clearly defined. Thus the in-phase current to voltage gain function shown in Figure 11.11 has a low flat peak at about 0.025 cps and a slope of 2 decades per decade, suggesting a slightly oscillatory system with a break point of 0.05 cps and a damping factor of 0.6. The out-of-phase to

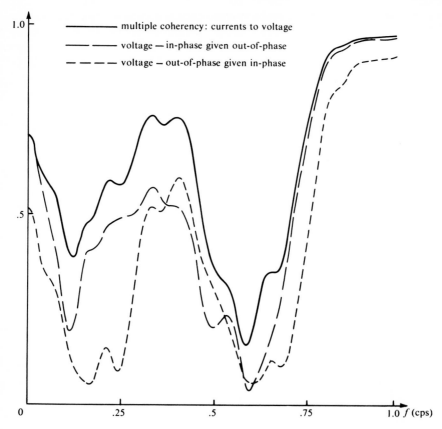

FIG. 11.8: Multiple and partial coherency spectra: currents to voltage

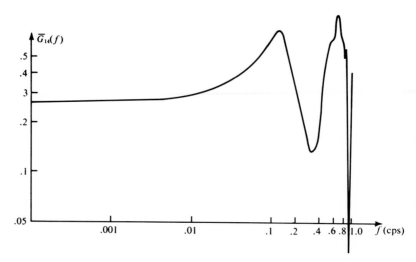

FIG. 11.9: In-phase current to frequency gain function

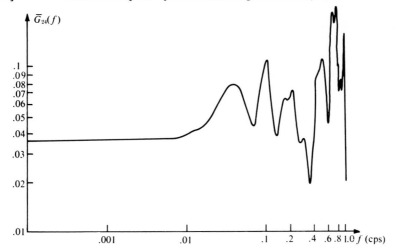

FIG. 11.10: Out-of-phase current to frequency gain function

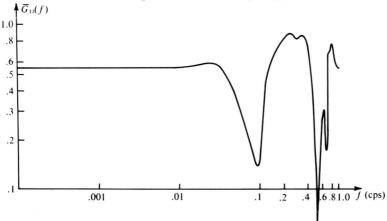

FIG. 11.11: In-phase current to voltage gain function

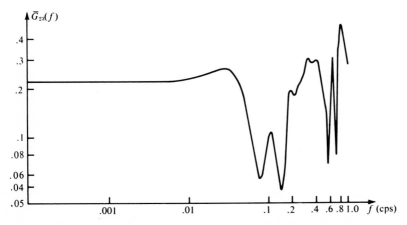

FIG. 11.12: Out-of-phase current to voltage gain function

voltage gain plot suggests a third-order system consisting of a single time constant of 20 seconds and a second-order system with break point at 0.04 cps and damping factor of 0.5. In this analysis, the gain information above 0.1 cps has been discounted because of the low power levels in the input currents above 0.1 cps.

Phase spectra. A difficulty arises in the interpretation of the phase spectra obtained from the shifted correlations in that cross spectra calculated with different shifts enter into the calculation of the phases. To avoid this difficulty, the phase functions shown in Figures 11.13 to 11.16 were based on the unaligned correlation functions. Since the phase spectra are less sensitive to bias due to non-alignment of the time series, this was not considered to be serious.

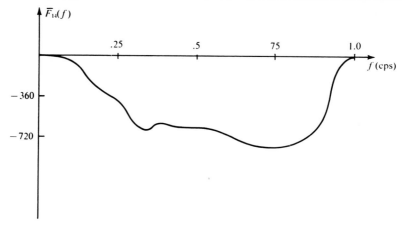

FIG. 11.13: In-phase current to frequency phase function

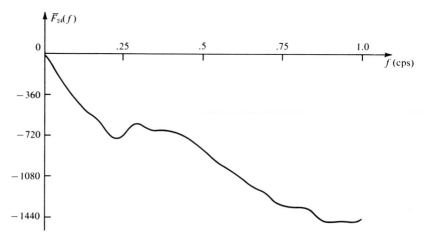

FIG. 11.14: Out-of-phase current to frequency phase function

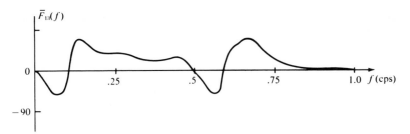

FIG. 11.15: In-phase current to voltage phase function

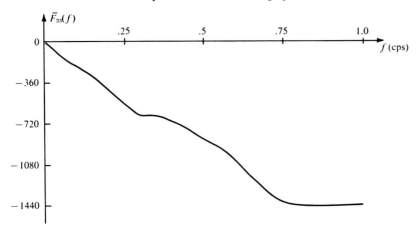

FIG. 11.16: Out-of-phase current to voltage phase function

11.5.4 Summary

The spectral analysis of the power station data may be conveniently summarized in terms of frequency response functions derived from the gain and phase plots.

In-phase current to voltage frequency response function. Using Figures 11.11 and 11.15, the frequency response function $H_{31}(f)$ is estimated to be

$$\hat{H}_{31}(f) = \frac{0.55}{1 + j48f - 1600f^2},$$

that is, a second-order system with damping factor 0.6, resonance frequency 0.025 cps, dc gain 0.55 and delay 0.

In-phase current to frequency frequency response function. From Figures 11.9 and 11.13,

$$\hat{H}_{41}(f) = \frac{0.26\, e^{-j4\pi f}}{1 + j3.3f - 70f^2},$$

that is, a second-order system with damping factor 0.2, resonance frequency 0.12 cps, dc gain 0.26 and delay 2 sampling intervals, equal to 1 sec.

Out-of-phase current to voltage frequency response function. From Figures 11.12 and 11.16

$$\hat{H}_{32}(f) = \frac{0.22\, e^{-j6\pi f}}{(1 + j125f)(1 + j25f - 625f^2)},$$

that is, a second-order system with damping factor 0.5, resonance frequency 0.04 cps, dc gain 0.22, delay 1.5 sec and a first-order system with time constant 20 sec.

It should be emphasized that the graphical estimation procedures used for the estimation of the parameters in these models are not very efficient. Therefore, they should be regarded as tentative models which should now be fitted, if necessary, by parametric methods like those illustrated in Chapter 5. However, for many control purposes, knowledge of the gain and phase plots given by Figures 11.9 to 11.16 would be sufficient.

REFERENCES

[1] T. W. Anderson, *Introduction to Multivariate Statistical Analysis.* John Wiley, New York, 1958.

[2] K. N. Stanton, "Estimation of turbo-alternator transfer functions using normal operating data." *Proc. Inst. Electr. Engrs.* **112**, (9), 1713 (1965).

[3] K. N. Stanton, "Measurement of turbo-alternator transfer functions using normal operating data." *Proc. Inst. Electr. Engrs.* **110**, (11), 2001 (1963).

APPENDIX A11.1   LATENT ROOTS AND VECTORS

The *latent roots* λ_i, $i = 1, \ldots, N$, and corresponding *right-hand latent vectors* $\mathbf{r}_i$ of a matrix $\mathbf{A}$ satisfy

$$\mathbf{A r}_i = \lambda_i \mathbf{r}_i. \tag{A11.1.1}$$

The equations (A11.1.1) written in scalar form imply that

$$a_{11}r_{1i} + a_{12}r_{2i} + \cdots + a_{1N}r_{Ni} = \lambda_i r_{1i}$$
$$a_{21}r_{1i} + a_{22}r_{2i} + \cdots + a_{2N}r_{Ni} = \lambda_i r_{2i}$$
$$\vdots \qquad \vdots \qquad\qquad \vdots \qquad \vdots$$
$$a_{N1}r_{1i} + a_{N2}r_{2i} + \cdots + a_{NN}r_{Ni} = \lambda_i r_{Ni}.$$

Geometrically (A11.1.1) means that in the N-dimensional vector space, the vectors $\mathbf{r}_i$, $i = 1, 2, \ldots, N$, are invariant under the linear transformations $\mathbf{y}_i = \mathbf{A r}_i$. Related to the invariant right-hand vectors $\mathbf{r}_i$ are the *dual* or *adjoint* system of vectors $\mathbf{l}_i$ which satisfy the left-hand equations

$$\mathbf{l}_i' \mathbf{A} = \lambda_i \mathbf{l}_i'. \tag{A11.1.2}$$

It is possible to show that the left-hand vectors are orthogonal, or at right angles, to the right-hand vectors. Thus on postmultiplying (A11.1.2) by $\mathbf{r}_j$,

$$\mathbf{l}_i' \mathbf{A r}_j = \lambda_i \mathbf{l}_i' \mathbf{r}_j.$$

Using (A11.1.1), this implies

$$(\lambda_i - \lambda_j)\mathbf{l}_i'\mathbf{r}_j = 0.$$

Hence, assuming that the latent roots are distinct,

$$\mathbf{l}_i'\mathbf{r}_j = 0 \quad \text{if} \quad i \neq j,$$
$$\mathbf{l}_i'\mathbf{r}_j \neq 0 \quad \text{if} \quad i = j.$$

By suitable normalization,

$$\mathbf{l}_i'\mathbf{r}_i = 1,$$

that is, the right-hand and left-hand vectors are orthonormal. If the latent vectors are assembled into matrices

$$\mathbf{L} = (\mathbf{l}_1, \mathbf{l}_2, \ldots, \mathbf{l}_N) \quad \text{and} \quad \mathbf{R} = (\mathbf{r}_1, \ldots, \mathbf{r}_N)$$

so that the columns of $\mathbf{L}(\mathbf{R})$ are the left- (right-) hand latent vectors of $\mathbf{A}$, then the above conditions imply

$$\mathbf{LR} = \mathbf{I}, \tag{A11.1.3}$$

where $\mathbf{I}$ is the identity matrix consisting of ones on the diagonal and zeros elsewhere.

Symmetric matrices. The covariance matrix of a set of real rv's is real and symmetric. Hence the latent roots and vectors have the properties that the latent roots are real, the latent vectors are orthogonal and the matrices $\mathbf{L}$ and $\mathbf{R}$ are orthogonal. The second property implies that the vectors, which are invariant under transformation, are orthogonal. To demonstrate, it is convenient to assemble the equations (A11.1.1) and (A11.1.2) in matrix form

$$\mathbf{AR} = \mathbf{R}\mathbf{\Lambda}, \tag{A11.1.4}$$

where $\mathbf{\Lambda}$ is the diagonal matrix of latent roots. Similarly,

$$\mathbf{L}'\mathbf{A} = \mathbf{\Lambda}\mathbf{L}'. \tag{A11.1.5}$$

On transposing (A11.1.5), using the fact that $\mathbf{A}' = \mathbf{A}$, $\mathbf{L}' = \mathbf{L}$,

$$\mathbf{AL}' = \mathbf{L}'\mathbf{\Lambda}.$$

Hence on comparing with (A11.1.4)

$$\mathbf{R} = \mathbf{L}'$$

and (A11.1.3) becomes

$$\mathbf{LL}' = \mathbf{I} = \mathbf{R}'\mathbf{R}, \tag{A11.1.6}$$

that is, the latent vectors are orthogonal. Hence, on premultiplying (A11.1.4) by $\mathbf{R}'$,

$$\mathbf{R}'\mathbf{AR} = \mathbf{R}'\mathbf{R}\mathbf{\Lambda} = \mathbf{\Lambda}. \tag{A11.1.7}$$

The geometrical significance of (A11.1.4) when $\mathbf{A}$ is a symmetric matrix is that the quadratic form

$$\mathbf{y}'\mathbf{A}\mathbf{y} = C \tag{A11.1.8}$$

represents a central conic whose axes intersect at the origin. Under a transformation

$$\mathbf{y} = \mathbf{R}\mathbf{x}, \tag{A11.1.9}$$

(A11.1.8) becomes

$$\mathbf{x}'\mathbf{R}'\mathbf{AR}\mathbf{x} = C,$$

that is,

$$\mathbf{x}' \Lambda \mathbf{x} = C$$

or

$$\lambda_1 x_1^2 + \lambda_2 x_2^2 + \cdots + \lambda_N x_N^2 = C.$$

Hence the conic is transformed to canonical form by the transformation (A11.1.9), and the latent roots give the inverse of the lengths of the principal axes of the conic.

APPENDIX A11.2   FLOW CHART FOR MULTIVARIATE FREQUENCY RESPONSE CALCULATIONS

The following is a flow chart for a computer program MULTSPEC which accepts covariance estimates for two input series $X1(t)$, $X2(t)$ and two output series $X3(t)$, $X4(t)$ and computes the frequency response functions $H31$, $H32$, $H41$, $H42$ relating them. Printer output of important functions is provided, but the most important output is via the plotter. Plotted output includes all autospectra (logspec versus frequency), both residual spectra (logspec versus frequency), all total and partial squared coherencies, and all gain and phase plots, with overlays for additional truncation points.

Program MULTSPEC

1) *Input* N, MAXM, NF, DELTA, M.

2) *Input* COV(K,I,I), K=0, MAXM, I=1,2.

3) *Calculate* autospectra, SPEC(K,I), K=0, NF, I=1,2 using AUTOSPEC subroutine (Appendix A7.1).

4) *Read* COV(K,3,3), K=0, MAXM.

5) *Calculate* SPEC(K,3) using AUTOSPEC subroutine.

6) *Read* COV(K,1,2), COV(K,2,1), K=0, MAXM, shift S12

   COV(K,1,3), COV(K,3,1), K=0, MAXM, shift S13

   COV(K,2,3), COV(K,3,2), K=0, MAXM, shift S23.

7) *Use* EVOD subroutine (Appendix A9.2) to calculate even and odd parts.

8) *Call* CROSSPEC subroutine (Appendix A9.2) to calculate

   COSPEC(K,1,2), QSPEC(K,1,2), SQ(K,1,2)

   COSPEC(K,1,3), QSPEC(K,1,3), SQ(K,1,3)

   COSPEC(K,2,3), QSPEC(K,2,3), SQ(K,2,3).

9) *Calculate* DENOM(K)=SPEC(K,1)*SPEC(K,2)−SQ(K,1,2).

10) *Call* subroutine ENDALL.

11) *Store* all quantities in ENDALL which are marked with a marginal asterisk, for future plotting.

12) *Read* COV(K,4,4), K = 0, MAXM.

13) *Calculate* SPEC(K,4) using AUTOSPEC subroutine

14) *Read* COV(K,1,4), COV(K,4,1), K = 0, MAXM, shift S14

   COV(K,2,4), COV(K,4,2), K = 0, MAXM, shift S24.

Repeat steps 7 through 11. Then read another value of M, and use the stored autocovariances and even and odd parts of cross covariances in the subroutines AUTOSPEC, CROSPEC, and ENDALL to calculate the gains, phases, squared coherencies and residual spectra. When the desired values of M have been used, plot and overlay all logspectra and log residual spectra versus frequency, all phases and squared coherencies versus frequency, and all log gains versus log frequency.

Subroutine ENDALL

This subroutine calculates gain, phase, total and partial squared coherencies, and residual spectra. Dropping the index K, the calculations are as follows:

A31 = COSPEC(1,3)*SPEC(2) + QSPEC(2,3)*QSPEC(1,2) − COSPEC(2,3)*

   COSPEC(1,2)

SQA31 = A31*A31

B31 = QSPEC(1,3)*SPEC(2) − QSPEC(2,3)*COSPEC(1,2) − COSPEC(2,3)*

   QSPEC(1,2)

SQB31 = B31*B31

* PHASE 31 = ARCTAN (− B31/A31)

   GAIN 31 = SQRT (SQA31 + SQB31)/DENOM

* LOGGN31 = LOG10(GAIN 31)

   A32 = COSPEC(2,3)*SPEC(1) − COSPEC(1,2)*COSPEC(1,3) − QSPEC(1,2)*

   QSPEC(1,3)

SQA32 = A32*A32

B32 = QSPEC(2,3)*SPEC(1) − COSPEC(1,2)*QSPEC(1,3) + COSPEC(1,2)*

   QSPEC(1,3)

SQB32 = B32*B32

* PHASE 32 = ARCTAN (− B32/A32)

   GAIN 32 = SQRT (SQA32 + SQB32)/DENOM

* LOGGN32 = LOG10(GAIN 32)

* COHSQ(1,3) = SQ(1,3)/(SPEC(1)*SPEC(3))

* COHSQ(2,3) = SQ(2,3)/(SPEC(2)*SPEC(3))

$R = \text{COSPEC}(1,2) * \text{COSPEC}(2,3) * \text{COSPEC}(1,3)$

$\quad + \text{COSPEC}(1,2) * \text{QSPEC}(2,3) * \text{QSPEC}(1,3)$

$\quad - \text{QSPEC}(1,2) * \text{QSPEC}(2,3) * \text{COSPEC}(1,3)$

$\quad + \text{QSPEC}(1,2) * \text{QSPEC}(1,3) * \text{COSPEC}(2,3)$

* COHSQ

$\quad = (\text{SPEC}(2) * \text{SQ}(1,3) + \text{SPEC}(1) * \text{SQ}(2,3) - 2. * R)/(\text{SPEC}(3) * \text{DENOM})$

$\text{COMP} = 1 - \text{COHSQ}$

$\text{RESID} = \text{COMP} * \text{SPEC}(3)$

* LOGRESID = LOG10(RESID)

* COH 132 = 1 − (COMP/(1 − COHSQ(2,3)))

* COH 231 = 1 − (COMP/(1 − COHSQ(1,3))).

APPENDIX A11.3   DATA FOR POWER STATION EXAMPLE

TABLE A11.1: 100 values of coded power station data

0.92	0.95	0.99	1.07	1.13	1.16	1.15	1.08	0.97
0.89	0.85	0.76	0.65	0.59	0.59	0.58	0.58	0.60
0.60	0.55	0.54	0.60	0.62	0.54	0.50	0.58	0.65
0.65	0.69	0.74	0.76	0.72	0.69	0.71	0.81	0.96
1.09	1.10	1.05	1.04	1.05	1.03	1.00	0.92	0.81
0.73	0.60	0.48	0.45	0.44	0.37	0.30	0.27	0.30
0.33	0.33	0.34	0.36	0.38	0.41	0.46	0.50	0.50
0.47	0.44	0.47	0.52	0.52	0.50	0.50	0.49	0.48
0.47	0.46	0.43	0.42	0.46	0.52	0.58	0.61	0.66
0.72	0.72	0.68	0.70	0.77	0.75	0.64	0.56	0.50
0.40	0.28	0.24	0.26	0.21	0.16	0.18	0.19	0.18
0.19								

In-phase current deviations

−0.75	−0.92	−1.04	−1.01	−0.83	−0.64	−0.55	−0.46	−0.31
−0.14	−0.02	0.12	0.32	0.54	0.68	0.72	0.77	0.82
0.87	0.91	0.98	1.10	1.17	1.09	1.00	1.06	1.17
1.18	0.96	0.64	0.60	0.80	0.84	0.68	0.63	0.74
0.81	0.67	0.38	0.17	0.17	0.29	0.41	0.52	0.67
0.77	0.80	0.86	1.01	1.22	1.40	1.49	1.49	1.47
1.54	1.64	1.60	1.46	1.41	1.41	1.39	1.26	1.04
0.89	0.99	1.21	1.31	1.25	1.13	1.04	0.98	0.93
0.86	0.79	0.80	0.91	1.10	1.26	1.26	1.10	0.92
0.79	0.67	0.53	0.44	0.43	0.39	0.32	0.29	0.34
0.38	0.37	0.33	0.26	0.25	0.31	0.40	0.47	0.45
0.36								

Out-of-phase current deviations

(*continued*)

TABLE A.11.1—*continued*

−2.11	−2.08	−2.10	−2.22	−2.39	−2.50	−2.49	−2.43	−2.37
−2.30	−2.25	−2.21	−2.20	−2.22	−2.21	−2.20	−2.20	−2.22
−2.22	−2.21	−2.22	−2.25	−2.26	−2.20	−2.15	−2.18	−2.21
−2.25	−2.27	−2.28	−2.28	−2.26	−2.19	−2.13	−2.15	−2.25
−2.33	−2.32	−2.25	−2.21	−2.23	−2.28	−2.32	−2.33	−2.34
−2.32	−2.26	−2.22	−2.23	−2.27	−2.30	−2.30	−2.28	−2.26
−2.26	−2.25	−2.23	−2.21	−2.23	−2.25	−2.26	−2.22	−2.14
−2.10	−2.15	−2.23	−2.27	−2.26	−2.22	−2.20	−2.19	−2.17
−2.14	−2.10	−2.09	−2.14	−2.24	−2.32	−2.34	−2.30	−2.28
−2.28	−2.26	−2.22	−2.20	−2.20	−2.17	−2.11	−2.07	−2.05
−1.98	−1.90	−1.83	−1.78	−1.77	−1.78	−1.81	−1.83	−1.82
−1.77								

Voltage deviations

4.75	4.75	4.74	4.75	4.75	4.77	4.78	4.76	4.81
4.81	4.84	4.88	4.94	4.96	4.99	5.05	5.11	5.11
5.10	5.10	5.05	5.00	5.01	5.00	5.00	5.01	5.04
5.09	5.09	5.06	5.06	5.04	5.01	4.99	4.97	4.99
5.00	5.01	4.97	4.88	4.81	4.81	4.79	4.79	4.85
4.88	4.90	5.00	5.11	5.15	5.24	5.20	5.20	5.20
5.20	5.21	5.20	5.15	5.15	5.14	5.10	5.11	5.10
5.10	5.09	5.11	5.08	5.10	5.10	5.15	5.15	5.15
5.10	5.15	5.10	5.10	5.10	5.11	5.11	5.10	5.11
5.11	5.08	5.05	5.01	4.90	4.90	4.95	4.94	4.90
4.96	4.97	4.99	5.08	5.16	5.21	5.19	5.19	5.20
5.16								

Frequency deviations

Index

515

Author Index